GIDEON E. WOOD

The Stagsblood Prince

Book One of the Stagsblood Trilogy

Ex Asperis
PUBLISHING

For the fems

Acknowledgement

Cindy Duffin-Carlson helped me find my own Feighan dirt and taught me why it matters. Ricardo Chàvez Gochicoa helps me keep my feet in it.

If you want to learn how to ask for help, write a damn book. Among my helpers are Marc Alba, Travis Beaudoin, Daisy Cobb, Stephanie Costello, Ash Knight, Jennifer Macia, Tyler Paulsen, Teresa Payne, Courtney Younginger, and the members of my Thursday evening group. Thank you all.

Juan Carlos Silva Morante taught me how to count: *uno, dos, tres, cuatro, five.*

I wrote this book in *N'dakinna*, the ancestral homeland of the Abenaki, Pennacook, and Wabanaki Peoples. I acknowledge with gratitude the land and waterways of *N'dakinna*, which the *alnobak* (people) have stewarded throughout the generations.

One

Last night's wine thundering behind his eyes, Prince Tel lay in bed, pondering the naked athlete's jaw. Like the rest of him, it was muscled yet pretty. He was half girlish comeliness, half feral masculinity. It was a heartbreaking balance seen only in certain males—and only for a short time after they crossed into manhood. Tel's latest conquest was pure roughness straining against the underside of smooth skin.

Even such loveliness could not keep the prince from growing bored for long. He fingered the Doe pendant on his mother's delicate chain, as he had done in anxious moments for half his life. Consciousness still gauzy, he called on the power in his blood, knowing it would relieve his hangover a bit. He did not understand this effect but would gladly accept the reprieve and ponder the connection another day. The magic required to conjure or disappear—a flame, a bit of light, a simple object—came to him with ease and cost only a small amount of strength.

A gold marble of energy appeared and spun over the pad of his right index finger. He coaxed it to rotate faster, then slower. As expected, his headache abated. Over his left index finger, he made a twin. Soon, he had one lazily chasing the other. He felt even better.

The beautiful young man next to Tel seemed to awaken all at once, rolling to face his bedmate. By the time he completed this maneuver and opened his eyes, the balls of light had shivered out of existence. He would not find out today that, impossible as it was, Prince Tel of Feigh was a stagsblood dynast aged forty years.

"Your royal highness," he croaked. An attempt at a smile burst apart into a great yawn. The stretching of limbs was even greater.

"Formal this morning, are we?"

"Mm."

Tel fingered a blue swoop of hair from his companion's face, tucking it behind an ear. Most of the lad's facepaint had worn off. Only the kohl around his orange eyes remained, smudged into smoke and fog. "You are extraordinary. Even hungover, I can see this."

A quick laugh chuffed out of the athlete. "*Me*? You're a future king. Besides, bet you can't even tell me my name."

"Nor mine." Tel looked at him as if in profound contemplation. The gorgeous competitor rolled his eyes. Tel allowed a few more seconds to pass as he pantomimed an agonizing search through his memory. "Of course I remember your name, Turo. Turo the Champion. Turo the Titleholder. Turo, favorite of the Queen of Omela herself. An ordinary farm boy, his family working the land located just a few days outside the capital. At twenty, catching the notice of ladies and lords at the games. By twenty and three, one of the greatest to ever participate. Talented with the spear and the disk. A master of escape on the mat. Speed and strength and grace and stamina to rival centuries of the best. All this and unforgivably attractive."

"Are you teasing me?"

"You are a demigod, Turo. A demigod almost two decades younger than me. Surely I am the one being teased." At this, the younger man twisted his nose. The expression made Tel chortle, which he regretted instantly. By reflex, his hand flew to his temple. He let out a breath in a short, pointed burst.

"You know, there's an old Omelan saying about hangovers." Turo rolled away from Tel, onto his belly. He looked back at the prince, silken blue brushing the perfect mole on his shoulder. "Get your head right with a taste of last night." With a playful lack of speed, he eased the covers down, exposing the robust, symmetrical hillocks of his backside.

"Precious Doe and Stag," swore Tel in whispered appreciation. He shook his head to escape the trance. His whole body twitched and heated. In a single motion, he threw himself out of bed.

"Where're you going?"

"Nowhere," said Tel.

"Mm."

The heir to the throne of Feigh, cock heavy and bobbing in the warm air of the room, stood facing the prizewinner. He felt foolish. Despite this, within seconds, the awakening of his flesh was entire.

"Mm. How's a prince your age built so solid?"

"My age?"

"You know what I mean. By *your age*, most highborns go soft. In Omela, at least."

Tel scoffed, looking down the length of his torso. "I am…not what I used to be."

"You are solid. Solid as some I compete against."

"In Feigh, princes train. Sword work. Archery. Grappling. Sparring. And often. Seems to be an expectation of the role."

"Just pretending to be modest, then? And I already know you can handle that sword of yours."

"Very funny. I am much better with a bow."

"I like the black hair on you," said Turo. "Just the right amount. Not too much. Not too little."

The flattery worked on Tel. His cock jumped.

Turo's gaze settled on the insistent thing pointing at him. "Come here," he growled.

"Today is too important a day, even for—"

"No day's too important for a quick fuck."

"There will be no taste of last night," said Tel. "Neither you nor the wine. I need a clear head."

"No. Day. Too. Important." Turo kicked his feet with each word.

Tel stepped to the bed and threw one knee onto the mattress. He brought his mouth to Turo's right ear and said, spanking him with each word, "Today. Is. Too. Important." He left him pouting in the bed and searched for his clothes. His wine-addled, dodgy memory of the previous night made this quite an ordeal. Swearing under his breath, he found the bottom half of his

3

outfit balled and stuffed between the seat cushion and back of a luxurious chair. His body tipped a bit while stepping into his under-breeches. He prevented himself from falling and cursed again. Sliding the bright green woolen hose up his legs, he looked toward the bed. "I would also prefer not being pursued all the way back to Feigh by a jealous lover of Turo the Terrible. Certainly not if he's the powerful beast I have conjured in my mind's eye. I must not be killed. I am to be king." He chuckled.

"I don't prefer men," Turo said. "And I don't have a woman. There's nobody to kill you."

Tel snapped an eyebrow into a peak. Turo's performance last night had been more than competent. It was skilled, enthusiastic. "Then, why? *Twice.*"

"Feighans have too many rules about it. Black and white. Too strict."

"Point taken, but my own reputation suggests this does not apply to all of us." He tilted his head and allowed a hint of a smirk.

"Mm."

The Feighan prince's appetites were well known, even here in Omela, across an ocean. If anything, he had tended to be more insatiable during his extensive visits over the years. One Omelan or another was always eager to accommodate. "It's one of the things I like best about this place. The sensualism. The openness. The refusal to feel shame about pleasure. Still, why? Did somebody—"

"Nobody paid." Turo rolled to the edge of the enormous bed and swung his legs over, covering his lap with a pillow.

Tel noted the unlikely grace of even this mundane set of movements and pushed out an almost imperceptible moan wrapped in a more noticeable sigh.

Turo appeared to weigh something in his mind. "You never fucked a woman?"

Tel's laugh blasted out of him, but memory turned his amusement into a numb gloominess. He caught himself after a few seconds and willed a lighter expression onto his face. "Once. Only once. And a very long time ago at that. I was a handful of years younger than you."

"And?"

Spotting his shirt on the floor next to the bed, Tel crouched to grab it. "And," he answered, standing up and shouldering himself into the linen, "it was the perfect thing to happen at the time. Not to mention, I was seventeen. I would have japed a pumpkin, then japed another before finding my way out of the patch."

Turo snorted and convulsed with laughter. He quieted and considered his hands as they smoothed the pillow on his thighs. "You needed it. Company, I mean. You weren't looking for it, exactly, even when I was offering. But you needed someone. You were hiding it, but you were…you didn't want to be there. Like me. Like you wanted to escape. So, you talked with me." He shrugged. "I don't have as much to say as the rest of them. Being good at the games makes me like a pet to them. A dog. A horse. I'm easy."

Tel attempted to protest, but Turo silenced him with a small gesture.

"I'm simpler. I know it. You don't have to work as hard with me. None of them do. I'm the horse and they're them. I liked you. You listened to me talk about the farm for an hour. Really listened. And I wanted to give you something. Not what you were looking for, but something. It seemed like you should've been happier. I've given it to men before and wanted to, but not as much as I wanted to give it to you. So, accept it and know it at least made me happy." He appeared surprised the words came out of him, like they had forced their way past the gate of his mouth.

The crown prince of Feigh was, for the first time in a long while, speechless. Still, he couldn't let the moment pass in silence. "Mm."

* * *

Over the next hour and a half, Omelan servants scurried in and out with breakfast and unnecessary offers of assistance. Although they moved across marble, noiseless, their presence worsened Tel's headache. He traveled with as few people as safety and practicality would permit. Both at home and abroad, he seemed to spend as much time dismissing staff with a smile as he did making use of their services. In his younger years, he had tried to speak to his attendants like friends. He realized it made most of them uncomfortable and decided if they did not want to chat with him, and he had no tasks for them, they would be happier elsewhere. *Thank you. You may go.*

Turo ate his breakfast like a forest hog attempting to mind its manners. Tel drank hidybrew and eyed him, utterly charmed. His balls sang until they ached. He daydreamed Turo was a Feighan champion. The proximity would be dangerous, the distraction too great. Taking him twice would not be near enough. He prayed to the Doe that the athlete would not be in his sightline at the ceremony later that night.

Once the boy left, Tel cleaned his teeth and buffed his face with a damp cloth. His headache eased slower than it would have forty or even twenty seasons ago, but it eased. He moved about his guest rooms for a while without any purpose and, not for the first time, noted they were almost as grand as his chambers at home. The tapestries were brighter, in fact, and the windows larger, even if the space itself was not quite as generous as his own. He stepped to one of the windows and inhaled the steaming early autumn air. Although the summer was hot in Feigh, it was never as extreme or long-lasting as it was here in southern Omela. He let the sun heat his cheeks and beard while he considered what he might say that evening, when his land and Omela would formally make peace after two centuries of war.

He should feel elation and relief, but a sharper sadness rose out of his usual dull, secret melancholy. He would miss this place. Over the last dozen years, a sincere and inmost love for it had grown. Peace won, it was time to turn to the next phase of his life. He could not imagine what it was. Stretching before him was only blankness. The thought of it made his stomach fill with sand. His attention to and obsession with these stuttering negotiations had taken much of his time and intellect. He had never found the energy to decide what should come next. *Where will I be in four seasons?* Even a vague idea of the next year eluded him.

Knowing whatever the future held, he should meet it fully dressed, he searched about for a few moments until he found his crumpled doublet near the fireplace. Next to it was the thin, green scarf Turo had made him take off last. He covered his bare neck with a loose twist and buttoned the quilted jacket over his linen shirt, noting the skillful embroidery on the padding, done in both vivid and subtler oranges. The colors brought pumpkins to his mind. Laughing, he thought of Turo again. *My antlered master, he was wonderful.*

Returning to the window, he looked across the rooves of the city below and connected to the magical dynasty again, seeking the drops of stagsblood in his veins. He continued to mull what to include in his remarks before the treaty signing. Another sphere, warm yellow, appeared above his upturned hands, bigger and brighter than the ones he had made in bed. At this height and in the light of midmorning, no one could see, even if they were looking. With his mind as much as his hands, he flicked the ball from left to right, spun it, and made it grow and shrink. Moments passed, and he found himself unable to imagine a single sentence with enough gravity or elegance to mark the occasion.

As an idea began to form, three heavy thuds came from the door. The knocks pleased Tel. Solitude never sat well with him while the sun was up. He could not think when he was alone because he could not *stop* thinking. At night, with a book and a fair supply of ale or cider in his chambers, he had no such difficulty. "Caip," he said, hearing the smile in his own voice. He snapped his open hands into loose fists, and the magical globe was extinguished. "Come in."

Correcting his posture, he turned to see the chief of his personal guard and closest friend cross into the room. As tall and brawny as Tel, her strides were long, her footfalls assertive.

"Your royal highness." She showed him the top of her head.

The formality of the entrance dissolved his smile. No one was present to see them. "Rightmajor," he said, figuring her solemn carriage meant he was in for a lecture of one kind or another. He braced himself for her harangue. Although he did not know the nature of her disappointment, he guessed he deserved it. She raised her inflamed eyes and swollen, spotty face. He had missed the state of her features when she walked in.

"The *Crunadam* has arrived," said Caip.

"What is—Already? But we were supposed to have three weeks of rest after the…" He looked at her face again.

Silence, but within it, an abundance of language—the language of too much history, of shared traumas and achievements. In the total quiet, the beginning of a conversation passed between them. Something terrible had occurred. He thought he knew exactly what. "Father?"

"Started a cough right after we sailed," said Caip. "It wouldn't leave him. Four weeks ago, he went to the black." Collapsing into a chair, she seized and sobbed on the cushion.

Tel felt cold. "You will take a place at Table." He inspected the enormous tapestry opposite his temporary bed. "You will, in effect, be Head, but the title will go to my brother, of course." He squinted. "Lag will gripe I lean so heavily on you, but he possesses neither the ambition nor the intellect to cause you much trouble."

In pained and deliberate croaks, Caip spoke again. "Sit with me. There's more."

"I am thinking. I cannot afford to let sentiment take me now. Goddesses and gods, I will not allow it. It will have to come later. If it comes at all. I would like you to choose your own replacement to lead my guard."

"Tel, *sit*."

He searched the face of the crowned man in the tapestry, who stood in flawless, gleaming armor on a patch of tall grass on a dusty bluff. From his perch, the figure surveyed a distant battle, an orgy of scarlet. "What pile of stones or worthless title or faithless lover did you win or lose that day?" He sat next to his weeping friend.

Tel watched her struggle for composure. Her uncharacteristic lack of control made his gut sick with fear. She seemed to shape her sadness into angry authority. "Stay there. Don't interrupt again." The tone surprised and quieted him. He watched her gather her strength again. "Your brother. Has taken. The throne."

"Imposs—"

"Lag. Is king."

"How?"

"Table are unanimous," said Caip. "Lord Craid wasn't present. You weren't present. But they need only ten for quorum. They've declared you of unsound mind."

"Unsound mind?" He tried to take her eyes, but they dodged, finding the marble floor.

She said, "The drink."

"The drink." He felt a bit dizzy and settled further into the cushions of his chair. "I will not be king."

"You won't." She began wailing.

Tel had never seen her so shattered, even when she lost her own parents. He reached toward her and stroked the middle of her back. She moaned. "Caip. This is a surprise. A shock. I cannot even think. But I know it will be—"

"A *nightmare*, Tel. And you're *relieved*."

"You are upset."

"Your brother's a fool. Dishonest. Even as a child, he never passed up an opportunity to cheat. He's weak. Lazy. Vulgar."

"They could take your head for that, rightmajor." He chuckled.

"Take it."

"I am no fool," said Tel, "but I am weak, lazy, and vulgar by some estimations. Inherited, I think. Skips a generation."

"You joke? You *joke?*" She was on her feet, spitting.

"It is only partially in jest. I will have a life of leisure. Pursuit of my diversions. Good men and good wine."

Caip raised a hand. "Stop it. Lag isn't suited. No ideas of his own."

"He will have advisors."

"Who'll too easily manipulate him."

"We will be two of them," said Tel.

"Cat leavings! You're a leader. He's never made one decision of consequence without your uncle whispering in his ear. You can't see his true nature. Under the wine and the fucking you're wise and decent. Under—"

"Under it is less than you think." He sprang from his chair. "It has felt like a burden, anyway. Since my balls dropped and my observations of my father became more sophisticated than blind hero worship. How much happiness do you think my father had? How much sleep?"

"You think you were put on the world for happiness? That you were born to your parents, that you've had everything you ever wanted brought to you on a pillow, that you were given your station by the Stag and Doe so you could be *happy*? No. No. All you need do is bring your drinking under control and…"

He moved to her, lowering his voice. "Do you not see? You have placed too much faith in me. And it does not matter. There is no altering it. Table have decided. I am surprised, but there is nothing to do."

"There *is* something to do, Tel. Go to Table. Go in sobriety. You can convince people of anything. I've seen it. Convincing them of the truth is nothing. Your brother's no good for Feigh. Backward and prejudiced. Greedy and vain. He'll try to erase the work of the last two generations of your family."

"I would have been the third reformer monarch in a row. This is the nature of history, Caip. Things lurch in one direction for some seasons, then another."

"Not too many seasons ago, prince or not, your head would've been taken just for bringing that Omelan to your bed last night. Is that what you want?"

"No."

"Then you must press your case with Table. If you can't win them over…"

"What?" asked Tel, unable to stop a dark chuckle. "What then?"

"You fight."

"Fight? Silence your tongue. You speak of my brother like he is a monster. He is ignorant, but he is not evil. And he is your king now. It pleases neither of us, but he is. I will not hear this disloyalty again. Silence your tongue."

She obeyed her prince.

A fraction of Tel's new reality settled in his chest. He would never again discuss a poem with his father.

Two

Tel stood in the well of the Omelan palace hall used for only the most momentous days and nights. Queen Cessa herself was married here. On a platform behind him were his empty seat and the most noteworthy of dignitaries. He felt awkward standing with his back to the queen. Such a thing would be scandal in his country. His position was supposed to allow the ordinary people in attendance to hear his remarks. Of course, for the most part, he saw only slightly lesser notables facing him in the rows of padded chairs running to the back of the imposing room.

Long free of his hangover, an array of contradicting feelings stood ready to assault him. He shoved these to the far margins of his inner field of vision so he might focus on the business of his last days in Omela. King Lag had written Cessa to insist his brother complete the peace process as planned, standing in for him as he had long stood in for their father. Emotion would have to wait a bit longer.

Tel looked the part, stately and overdressed in the Feighan fashion from his jet hair to the balls of his feet. His green tunic, modified with the addition of a high collar, fit snugly across his chest but had great loose billows for sleeves, only one of which peeked out from the burnt orange of his sumptuous cloak. The embroidery and embellishments were rich and fastidious. He wore tight buckskin leggings worked to a shine and dyed to match the tunic's shade. Over the form-fitting trousers, waist to knee, were the additional puffs of his trunkhose, same in hue as his cloak. In these, careful slashes were cut to show the green leather underneath. The buckskin disappeared into simple russet boots cut of a different hide. His only weapon was his antler-handled dirk, sheathed at his left hip.

Turo was here, in a seat too prominent even for a champion of his renown. When Tel's eyes rested on him, the boy shifted in his chair and spread the mighty slabs of his thighs under the short, plain shift which passed for men's formalwear in Omela. The garments were unadorned but revealing. Turo invited a smirk onto his arresting face, then closed his legs and smiled politely. Tel could not help but beam back, but shame nipped him. Even in his grief and on this pivotal day, he was distracted by his own libido. Tel pressed his lips together and continued to scan the room. He guessed Turo had not heard the news from Feigh.

Using a trick his father had taught him, he allowed silence to thicken and spread until an intense and expectant kind of attention was on him. An uneasy sensation, intense and muddled, rose in his solar plexus. With a deep but even breath, he tamed it.

"Others here are better suited to speak to the solemnity of this occasion and no doubt will. The meaning of tonight defies my abilities to describe. It eclipses any eloquence I may have been gifted. In place of a clumsy attempt at capturing the importance of this gathering, I would like to share with you a story my father...my late father, King Vith, used to tell me when I was young. It is from our blessed texts." Tel had the book in his hand but did not need it.

"The story is told in the homes of my kingdom. In the castles and in the woods and on the ships. It is the story of how we in Feigh believe we all came to be. It is the reason my father knew the wars must end between us. It is the reason I have come to Omela so many times over the last forty and eight seasons, and the reason I have grown to love it.

"*Before all else, there were only the goddesses and the gods, for they did not need more. Everything was the web-footed goddess and god, the soft-backed goddess and god, the finned goddess and god, the scaled goddess and god, the beaked goddess and god, the antlered goddess and god, and nothing.*

"*The goddesses and gods flew through the skyless black, making love in all possible combinations. After millennia, they tired. Finding nowhere to rest, they made a home and called it the world. They made the sun and the moons and the stars and the circle of the year to contain it all—the four seasons, the five hundred and eighty and five days. Each pair claimed a share of the land. The web-footed took a place with swamps and rivers and named it Andow. The soft-backed wanted the rich soils and tall grasses of Sheruck. The finned preferred the lakes and islands and bays of Kamber. Pleased with the rocks and low shrubs of Hebe, the scaled settled there. The beaked wanted the soaring trees and gentle breezes of Omela. The antlered knew the hills and cliffs of Feigh would make them happy.*

"Having had nothing and then the world, they were pleased, but their contentedness lasted only centuries. The goddesses told the gods they adored the plants and the water and the mountains, but these were not enough to love. The gods understood. They also were filled with too much love. The antlered god knew something must be done, so he called to the other gods.

"Secretly, they formed a plan. They threw their seed onto the world and from the wet earth made the amphibians and the invertebrates and the fishes and the reptiles and the birds and the mammals. Both the goddesses and gods marveled at the creatures of the world, loving them.

"Over time, the goddesses noticed the gods were troubled. They fretted day and night and were brought low by the savagery of the animals, who knew only survival and brutality. The antlered goddess knew something must be done, so she called to the other goddesses.

"Secretly, they formed a plan. They mated with the animals and from those unions made the yellow-haired Andowians and the white-haired Sheruckians and the red-haired Kambs and the hairless Hebites and the blue-haired Omelans and the black-haired Feighans. Both the gods and the goddesses marveled at the people of the world, loving them.

"Again, before too long, the gods became depressed. They saw the humans were capable of both more love and more incredible savagery than the animals. They created, and they destroyed. One day, all the humans on the world prepared for war. Although the goddesses and gods had given them all they could ever need, the people were small and afraid and envious.

"Once more, the antlered goddess knew something must be done. She gathered the other goddesses. They went to the field of battle. They stood between the armies and begged them to stop. In their smallness and fear and envy, the soldiers

13

did not see or hear the goddesses. They warred, and the goddesses were marched upon. They were torn apart and beaten into the ground. Only the antlers of the antlered goddess remained.

"The gods went to the empty field. Filled with grief, five of them decided to leave the world forever. The antlered god could not bear to leave the horns of his favorite. He carried the antlers of the goddess everywhere he went. Blind in his mourning, he forgot about all else. He clutched them to his chest and kissed them. He put his tears on them. When rage took him, he beat them on the dirt.

"Centuries passed, and the antlers wore away in his hands like rocks smoothing in a river. Soon, the god had only a pebble, but his grief had not shrunk. He decided he, too, must go. Before leaving, he added the pebble to the dirt in the place he loved best, the Island of Affas. There, he shed his last tear on the world.

"As he tried to go, a child stood in his path. 'Master,' the child said, 'how can you leave us?' The god ignored the girl, brushing past her. She followed. 'Master, you cannot go. No one can do the things you can do. We are weak. What if we need you? What if we miss you?' Tears clung to her eyes, grew, and fell down her face.

"Turning to look upon the crying girl, the antlered one recognized something of himself in her. He felt love for humanity for the first time since the war had taken his mate. Still, he could not stay. His suffering would not allow it. He saw the girl was good. Before he left, he put a few drops of his blood inside the child. 'People will have all they need to protect or destroy themselves now, to spread my lesson or let it die,' the god told the young human after he had made her the first dynast.

"The stagsblood carried the dynasties of the dirt, of the wind, of the fire, and of the rain. He told the child he must leave and recover in the black. He might be able to find his brother gods. Perhaps they would make a new place, but they would not return here. Not as things were. As long as war scrapes across the dirt of the world, the plants and animals and people would live without their creators."

Tel assessed his audience and decided he had kept their attention. "I began by saying King Vıth would tell me this story when I was young. He would particularly emphasize its themes when I was misbehaving. I must confess to having received this lecture within only the last year." He paused,

14

allowing for laughter. "Little princes and princesses can, on the whole, be prone to selfishness, aggression, envy, jealousy, resentment, and wrath, among other vices. Even when they are not so little." The laughter returned, louder.

"Our faiths are different. I know this. But I have been to your temples. I have shared bread and flesh with your high ones. And at their hearts, both faiths require the same devotions of us. They ask us the questions my father asks me when I need a reminder. *My boy, tell me what you know about how the world and humanity came to be.* When I have finished, he asks, *What does the story require of us?*

"My grandfather had to find the depths of his faith on his own, for his father and his mother before him and her father before her failed to ask this question. Luckily, he was able to ask my father. He, in turn, asked me. Tonight, I give him the best answer I have."

He turned his body to the platform. "Your Majesty, Queen Cessa, wise and generous guardian of Omela, thank you for welcoming me to your land. This evening, I pledge to you and your people, on behalf of my... brother, King Lag of Feigh, that our kind shall not pick up arms against yours. I pledge the end of conflict and the beginning of peace. I pledge to treat you as the antlered ones treated the beaked ones: as siblings. As family."

* * *

Once Tel was seated and Queen Cessa had walked down to the well of the room for her speech, the heat and shadow of the person to his right moved closer. Tel smelled the spice of fine perfume.

"Excellent remarks in light of your terrible news."

It was Lord Gawash, closest advisor to the young Hebite king. Many considered him the second most powerful person in Hebe. Like all his people, he was completely hairless. His strange, close-tailored costume was the color of a vicious storm clinging to the horizon of the Gray Sea.

15

His looks were sleek, his movements tidy.

"Thank you."

An Omelan high one had joined Cessa, offering the proceedings a blessing. The Omelan faith had but a single religious text, precisely four words long. It was not even a complete sentence: *Kindness in the mystery.* The Feighan spiritual system was much more complicated, but they had no priests. Worship consisted of private devotions, rituals, discussion, and even debate. The Omelans' cleric class was a complex, layered hierarchy. Tel thought it was the least Omelan aspect of their society. He knew the high one would speak for a while.

"A relief, I suspect. You were a reluctant king-to-be," said Gawash.

"I am sorry?"

"Weren't you? Reluctant?"

Tel's eyes stung. The lord had spoken the truth. "I am reluctant to do some things and—"

"And eager to do others. Yes. I often feel eager myself. Men make me feel very eager. Powerful men? Still more eager. Reluctant or not. King or not."

"I am sorry?" repeated Tel, pretending to miss the suggestion despite the undeniable shifting and tightening in the front of his own breeches.

Gawash fingered the hem of his tunic. "Yes. Reluctance. But such eagerness as well. All across the world, they say this. Tell me, do you ever put that princely cock in anyone not young enough to be your son?"

Tel faced his dark eyes. Without the rooves of brows, they were unreadable. He hoped his own expression was also blank and returned his attention to the officiant and the queen.

"You seem ill at ease, highness. Other than a signature and a lot of listening to dull nonsense, your work's done. And you've had a terrible day. Wouldn't you like to relax?" He opened his hand under the table and nudged Tel with his thumb. On his palm sat two tight buds. "Wouldn't you like to have a little fun? It's from one of our plants. Chew it once or twice and tuck it between your cheek and gums." Gawash took one of the little things in his fingers and demonstrated. "The effect's quite mildly sedating. Rather like two cups of apple wine."

16

In a swift and compact motion, Tel took the remaining bud and put it in his mouth. After a time, he scoffed. "Reluctant." An amusing numbness spread through first his mouth, then his entire jaw.

A half-hour passed before the priest began to bring his remarks toward a conclusion. Lord Gawash moved his perfumed shadow close again. "These Omelans are as perplexing as they are perverse. The signing of a historic treaty and it's the women who cover up heel to head and the men who paint their faces and wear barely enough fabric to soak up a thimble of water. I've seen flashes of more than one foreskin and several cheeks peeking out from these ludicrous shifts. And I have to wear this foolish scarf."

"You could wear a high collar or—"

"Grow my hair?"

"I apologize," said Prince Tel. "I was not thinking."

"Hair is ridiculous. Omelan hair, twice as ridiculous. You're a killjoy if you decline an invitation to an orgy but a whore if your hair isn't long enough to cover the back of your neck in public. Why the emphasis on the nape, of all things?"

"A nape has its appeal. As does an alien morality. And I will not protest long hair on men. Long, blue hair on men. It is incredibly striking. Perhaps it is all the rest of the races, parading around with our necks hanging out, who are ridiculous. Perhaps we offend the goddesses and gods with the naked wickedness of our necks. Since we cannot be certain, at least while I am here, I shall continue to wear scarves and high collars."

"The strangest race of them all, these bluebells."

Tel's jaw tightened. "Do you know the origin of that slur?"

"What slur?" Gawash asked.

"I will not repeat it."

"Bluebell, you mean? I'm certain you'll enlighten me."

"A Feighan insult that originated because the flower resembles an Omelan in a noose. It is disgusting."

"Well, I didn't know that." Tel narrowed his eyes at him. "I was only saying what *I* find disgusting is Omelan men displaying themselves like hogs competing for a ribbon. There's eagerness, and there's *too much* eagerness,

I'm afraid. I prefer to peel off some layers." With this, he leaned back into his chair and turned his attention forward.

Tel did the same, feeling overheated under all the fabric of his clothing. He probed the wet bit of vegetation with his tongue. The high one withdrew, and the queen centered herself in the falling torchlight. Tel regarded the half meter of cobalt braid spilling over the rear of her narrow, floor-length gown. The front of the outfit was unadorned, but what he could see from the platform was covered in elaborate, stitched feathers.

By the time Cessa was nearly through her speech, a weighted kind of placidity had fallen upon him. He cursed Gawash silently. *Two cups of apple wine.* He thought it more like six, plus something else, now that he had his attention on himself. The feathers on Cessa's dress seemed to breathe. Embroidery shifted, swayed, rippled. The warmth on his skin morphed into stranger sensations, tingling tiny sighs of pleasure out of him. He prayed no one could hear them.

Recognition dawned on him. He had experienced this before, with Feighan dreaming plants. Gawash was the unknowing target of his hexes again. He hoped to contain the strength of the herb, deciding to make sure his attention appeared to be fixated on the activity in front of him. As Cessa continued plodding through her thoughts, he daydreamed. When she returned to his side, he offered a dumb grin and vague congratulations on her remarks. She seemed charmed by him, as ever.

Laich, a Feighan playbard, stood next. He recited a long series of verses that told the same story Tel had shared—but with soppy yet effective sentiment and detail. Tel remembered how much his father had loved Laich's work. He could not bear to listen.

"Looks like he's going to lose his supper," hissed Gawash behind his hand.

With considerable effort, Tel refocused and looked at the Hebite. He was unsure how long he had been in his stupor. "What?"

"The songmaker who's going back with you to Feigh. That bud has you out of your wits." Gawash shot him an exasperated expression. "The fat queen spoke about it at length. He looks ready to throw up."

Tel had forgotten about this aspect of the accord, a nod to an arrangement

18

from centuries ago when Omela and Gawash's land had made peace. The Feighan playbard would remain behind for four seasons as part of the queen's household. Cessa's pet songmaker would spend the same time in Feigh. "Right."

He looked at the well of the chamber and saw the Omelan singer's back before retracting his awareness again. The boy had a marvelous, clear, evocative tenor. It rang off the walls and resonated pleasurably in Tel's addled brain. The tune was gloomy, but Tel was too far inside himself to understand words. His thoughts turned to the voyage home, and he witnessed his mood darken.

Three

Caip waited until late morning to shatter Tel's sleep. She insisted grief was no excuse to deviate from his training routine. For years she had said the same thing about his hangovers and pacifism.

With four of his guard's best soldiers, they made the lope to the east in unusual silence until Tel felt his friend's gaze on his cheek. She would not relent until she had his eyes. "How are you feeling today?"

"I woke feeling every glass, every drop. The fog clears, however. I will live."

Her features twisted into what looked like puzzlement for a pair of beats. She seemed ready to say something but did not. After a moment, she scowled at the sun. "A few more days with high collars in this heat, and I'll leave here, baring this neck to the world. Gods and humans both. I'll cross the Gray Sea and never return."

Half a chuckle escaped his mouth before a more doleful expression took control of his face. "I am not sure I will see this country again."

"You do not miss home?"

Tel shifted his weight backward in the saddle. "I miss home," he said, like an arguing child. He found evenness. "I miss home. I just cannot escape the feeling *something* is here for me. A different life. Less trouble. I could disappear. Plow some land. Put something into the ground. Maybe that is my destiny. To add something to the Omelan dirt."

"You never wanted to be king."

"Who would not want to be king?" He did not look at her. "I wanted to be king. And as the king, I would have dreamed of a simpler life. How else could a king avoid madness? Not dreaming of it would be a *sign* of madness. My subjects would have allowed me my fantasy."

While the land to the west of the Omelan capital's walls was patched with the farms about which Tel daydreamed, the east was forested for a long way to the next significant settlement. The least used but well-laid road from the capital brought them past leaner and leaner signs of humanity to the clearing. They visited it twice each week whenever they conducted diplomacy in Omela over the last decade. Caip had argued for three times weekly.

"You must spar to stay strong, you must stay strong to keep living, and you must keep living to rule," she had said, far too often for Tel's taste.

The pair left the guards and their mounts at the margin of the road. This was their practice because Caip felt it unwise to let the women and men hear how she spoke to him while they swung weapons at one another. Leaving their real smallswords behind, they brought their weighted training wasters.

They strode into the void in the woods. Tossing his doublet and tunic onto the dusty grass, Tel glanced to his left and saw tightness in her face. It signaled more than her usual intensity and focus before a bout. Knowing she would only speak a concern when ready to do so, he decided to ignore it.

Caip fell into the style of fighting she used when sparring with him. Her approach balanced aggression and defense, aiming to drill Tel and maintain his competence with the weapon. He was quite skilled, but she was better. If she moved to her more natural style, direct and overwhelming, she would subdue him speedily with her beefy size and strength.

Tel fought like the intellectual he was. Cautious and watchful, he used his nimbleness and quick mind to escape and exhaust an opponent. He knew an unrushed approach and deep, conscious breaths—like those with which he lowered his mind when he used the stagsblood—would help him avoid betraying his next move. He employed feints, retreats, and brief bursts of offense to his advantage.

Tugging Caip all around the clearing in this way, he walked wide, lazy, smirking arcs around her after quick advances and agile dodges. He waved his mock smallsword about in the showy manner she detested.

"Leavings! Will you fight today or will you walk around jerking your dirk for the next hour?" she asked him, panting. No humor was in the question.

He let his sword drop. "Will *I* fight? The question is, will you? You have not even arrived, let alone fought. You are not even here."

She thundered across the distance between them, eyes and body language betraying her simple beat attack. Slower than he should have had to, Tel allowed his knees to bend, lowering his profile. He steadied himself by placing the fingertips of his left hand on the turf. With his right, he drove the tip of his wooden blade directly at her belly. Even at less than half strength, it forced the air from her lungs. While she recovered, he gained a bit of separation with the neat footwork of a dancer. He chuffed at her.

"Night thrust," he said, delighted, while she choked and sputtered.

"Not your usual kind of night thrust, you—"

His voice winter, Tel said, "No. Please. Complete your thought."

"You cannot stay safe simply by avoiding risk. You cannot escape danger with only cleverness, *friend*," The final word was sodden with bile. Her intensity shocked him.

Tel asked, "What troubles you today?" It was sincere. He lowered his waster and kept it lowered.

"Lift your fucking sword."

"You try to provoke me. I will not be provoked." He tossed his weapon out of reach.

"Your every move is a surrender—a denial. You spit at reality. You're naïve. A pacifist even with a thousand conniving blades pointed at you. You never listen to me."

"I—"

"And you let a common gardener's daughter speak to you like this. All the world knows your station except you. You run from it. You run to Omela. There's no reason this great task of yours, which you long ago won, couldn't be passed to another diplomat. But you run. Still you run. From home. And while you run, dull Lag snatches the throne. Any chance you are given, off you go. Away. From yourself. You have learned diplomacy. More than this makes up statecraft. Your state is *home*." Her eyes were red berries, her jaw frozen by two knots, one under each ear. She growled her breaths.

"Caip."

She bolted at him, knocking him flat with a blow of her right forearm to his chest. On top of him, she cried, "What day is today? What day is it? Tell me."

All thought fled his mind. Her eyes were too big. He could not bear to look at his friend.

"What day is it?" She was shrieking now.

Tel thought of the rest of his party at the road. "It is the day after my father died. The day after the treaty signing."

She yelped. "Your father died weeks ago."

"No."

"The news had to cross an ocean. What day is it?" He strained, but she pinned him.

"It is the sixteenth day of autumn." Realization animated him. His almond eyes rounded and stung. He launched her body rightward, off his, and crawled to the left. A few blind beats passed. He emptied his stomach onto the dust under his face.

"Did you forget the rite for Fyor and Hod?" she asked.

"No."

"Did you?"

"Yes."

"Will you do it? Losing your father is not an excuse."

"Tonight." He nodded, wiping sick from his lips with the back of a hand. "After the party."

* * *

Queen Cessa's elaborate celebration of the peace pact culminated with the attendees gathering at palace windows to view the new Omelan skycolors. Using spark powder, the cleverest in the capital had devised a way to loft balls to great heights, where they exploded into glittering blooms of color. Tel had never seen anything like it. Two fresh dreaming buds from Gawash enhanced his experience.

He made his onerous escape as early as he could without offending. The giving and receiving of many flatteries and blessings had been trying, as had the endless expressions of sympathy. Normally, Tel could glad-hand and chin-wag without much thought or effort. These types of occasions were where he showed genuine deftness. Tonight, making polite conversation with courtiers required heroic focus. The palace pulsed around him, the building itself seeming to take on life, respiring like Cessa's feathers had the previous evening. He needed to look past the faint wall of infinite geometric patterns dancing and shifting across his field of vision. It took intense concentration. Somehow, he made it out.

With care, he trod the quiet hallways of the palace. He knew the footprint well, but it seemed foreign tonight. In the relative silence, every bit of noise was both shout and whisper. His boots gliding along the tiles sounded like someone murmuring drivel.

He was relieved to reach the entrance to the enormous courtyard. The silent guard acknowledged him with a nod and left his post, as arranged. Stepping into the open air, he felt like he was breaching the surface of the water after a long dive. This was Cessa's favorite place. Over the years, the pair of royals grew to understand one another in this garden. Here, they met privately and spoke in broad strokes while their people worked on details. Here, he came to know her warmth and sincerity. Here, he had borne her jokes about his layers of Feighan clothes.

No one was allowed among the flowering shrubs, soft paths, and sculptures without her permission. When he had told her what he had to do and that it must be done on the dirt and under the sky, she had agreed to let him use the space. "My friend is superstitious. Feigh is superstitious. You may use my gardens," she had said with affection.

The silvery light from the twin pregnant moons showed the heavy stone bench sitting at the edge of a manicured rectangle of grass. The ritual items were arrayed across the dark gleam of the bench. On the other side of the grassy patch stood a statue. Ancient King Dito looked toward but beyond the fountain at the center of the courtyard. One of the statue's hands clutched a mask of the type a panto might wear on stage. With his other hand, he brandished a short dagger.

He tried to ignore the way the dreaming bud made Dito's face move. A breeze looped into the open space from above, disturbing branches and leaves. The fountain rushed and bubbled. These noises married one another and muttered at him, insistent but nonsensical. Under his beard, he felt sweat surface on his tingling skin. *Let us begin, then.*

He shed his clothes, draping them over the end of the bench. Naked but for his mother's necklace, he took his place in the middle of the green patch and kneeled, setting the sacred tools within reach. The unsheathed blade of his dirk was in his right hand.

"Stag and Doe, witness my remembering."

The sound of rustling branches was a constant, unnerving *shhhh* in his ears. The fountain blathered endlessly, the words just outside his ability to understand.

"I remember Fyor and Hod, who died one hundred seasons ago this day." Hearing the quaver in his voice, he paused for a beat, swallowing. "Fyor was my mother. She gave me life. Hod was my love. He gave me happiness. I remember them both for this and for all those they remembered."

Shhhh Fyor and Hod Fyor and Hod shhhh.

"This grief will cut me." With this, he snatched the handle of the knife with his left hand, pulling it from his right, slicing his palm. "This grief will heal me."

He dragged his bloody cut across the hair and skin just below his navel.

"This rite will wound me." Switching hands, he repeated the exercise with the dirk, painting his lower abdomen with the blood from his left palm. "This rite will mend me."

Tel Tel Tel Tel Tel shhhh shhhh shhhh shhhh gone gone gone gone.

He knew he was only hearing an effect of Gawash's buds but could not help feeling cold to his core. Pressing on, he looked around and above himself, making certain he had the directions right. He stabbed the blade of his knife deep into the Omelan sod and spread his arms perpendicular to his trunk, bleeding palms turned to the moons, fingers separated and curled toward the sky. The blades of grass massaged the skin of his knees in a way he knew was unreal.

He threw his head back. "Eyes of the Stag, cleanse me and cleanse your symbols." One by one, he held the objects up, allowing the moonlight to fall on them. He raised each item—a pitcher of wine, a ceramic jar of spiced oil, a tiny bell on a loop of string, and a cup of Feighan soil scooped from a leather pouch that traveled with him for ritual purposes—and said, "Eyes of the Stag."

The Stag saw the Doe saw the Stag the Doe saw nothing shhhh shhhh.

"Goddess and god, from the north, I ask for a fruitful life, despite my loss."

Nothing only dirt nothing only dirt dirt dirt Fyor and Hod nothing nothing dirt dirt.

He emptied the dirt onto the grass near his knees and squeezed his eyes shut against the garden's whispers. "A fruitful life. I ask the antlered ones." He ground his kneecaps into the Feighan dirt.

"Goddess and god, from the east, I ask for a clear mind, despite my memories." His mind was anything but clear. He tried and failed to blink past the pulsing scrim of shapes and colors rippling across his vision.

Hanging the bell on his right index finger, he said, "A clear mind. I ask the antlered ones."

Fyor and Hod Fyor Hod up to the wind up to the wind up.

Unsure how much longer he could hold his mind, he wanted to scream at the courtyard—to order it to shut up. Deciding to place his focus on one thing, his eyes found King Dito's face.

"Goddess and god, from the south, I ask for passion, despite my gloom." He poured some of the spiced oil onto a few fingers of his right hand and touched his forehead. A trickle made its way to his left eye while another found the wound in his palm. He grimaced against the burning. "Passion. I ask the antlered ones."

Tel hates Tel hates Tel hates Tel hates Tel hates Tel hates shhhh shhhh.

"Goddess and god, from the west, I ask for joy, despite my grief." He emptied a splash of wine onto his left hand. "Joy. I ask the antlered ones." The words came out of him pinched. He heard the miniature clapper of the bell on his finger striking its thin skirt as his hand began to tremble. It sounded to him like a repeated scream. The constant breeze thickened into a gust, causing the plants to sing in harsh whispers. The fountain taunted.

Water for breathing water for breathing water water breathe breath the water the water.

Now was the time for him to meditate, but he found it impossible to lower his mind. Gathering his will, he refocused on the statue's face. He clamped his jaw closed, whole body vibrating.

Fyor Hod Fyor Hod in the water in the water in the water breathing water dying and dying and dying dying again Fyor Hod Fyor Hod Tel Tel Tel Tel watching and watching and watching and watching again.

In the moving shadows and shifting moonslight, the statue was alive. The lines and shapes changed and shifted, darkened and lightened. Tel's mouth opened of its own volition. His scream was silent. Looking down on him from where Dito had been was his mother.

Son son son son son son son son son son son.

Her ghostly, hollow chanting ceased, but there was no silence. The courtyard hissed wickedness. His heart threatened to escape from his chest, to shatter his ribcage. He gave his eyes to the statue again, afraid of what he might see but more afraid to look elsewhere. The throbbing, slithering features became Hod, the first and only boy he loved.

Telly Telly Telly Telly Telly Telly Telly Telly Telly Telly.

He kept his eyes on the statue but softened his gaze. He tried to tame his breathing.

Someone said, "I'm sorry." It was neither the fountain nor the breeze.

Startled, Tel searched the ink of the garden, hyperventilating. Five meters away, on a skinny path, a figure stood frozen. After a moment, he made out the silhouette of a shift as it flapped in the abating rush of wind—an

Omelan male. The slight man held something in his hand.

"Your highness—"

"Who are you and what are you doing here?"

"I'm called Vared. We met last night."

Tel remembered only a gray smudge from the small, informal gathering immediately after the signing. The hours after that darkened to a black void. "Vared."

"I am the songmaker. I'm to return to Feigh with—"

"Ah."

"I was just going to play my terquin." He showed Tel his instrument. "Helps me to sleep. I have the queen's permission."

"Not tonight, balladeer." His answer was meant to be conclusive.

"We talked—Of course. Apologies." He skittered away after a quick, awkward bow of his head.

Shhhh shhhh shhhh shhhh shhhh shhhh shhhh.

Tel took the cup and the pitcher of wine to the bench. He lowered his naked buttocks until they met the cool stone. With his bloody right hand, he wiped as much dirt from inside the little cup as he could. He tipped it at an angle and tried to remove more with his breath. He poured himself a cup of wine. One swallow drained it. He poured again. He drank, refusing to look at the statue in front of him.

* * *

Time and over-honeyed Omelan wine diluted the effects of the Hebite drug. The sounds of the courtyard took on a musical—rather than lingual—quality. Shadows stopped fooling his eyes. No longer did they morph and shift into other, senseless things. A soft, agreeable kind of glisten coated everything. He decided he could face anyone he might encounter while making his way back to his rooms without screaming and running in the opposite direction. Standing, he found himself a bit wobbly. It had been far too long since he had eaten.

Once he had his bearings, he realized how good he felt. The rite was behind him, and hallucinations of Fyor and Hod along with it. The signing of the treaty was also in the past. Work on the trade pact would now continue in the background. He would be needed little, if at all.

A deep laugh rumbled its way out of him as he realized the strangeness of the timing of it all. *The anniversary of two deaths, learning of another, and the agreement signed—all within two days.* He kept forgetting and remembering and re-forgetting his father was gone and that he was no longer to be king. *Some other night. Not now. Grieve later. Enjoy the drink and the drug.*

He dressed. Pouring himself another cup of wine, he focused on the delicious warmth trailing from his cheekbones to his balls. His thoughts came at a reasonable pace, one after the other. He loved to be free of the need to make decisions or change anything. Having made up his mind to delay processing all he had lost, mental and emotional equilibrium was his—at least for this night.

The guard had retaken his post. Tel wondered how late it was. Unrushed, he strolled the hallways to his room, drinking wine and looking at every painting, tapestry, and furnishing he passed. He noted with admiration the Omelans' unabashed love of color. His tour was slow, uninterrupted bliss. Not a single person stood between the soldier watching the courtyard and the one guarding the entry to his suite.

As soon as he was behind the door, he removed his boots and stripped to the waist. He longed for a bath but did not long for the trouble of a retinue of anxious servants parading through his rooms. He would wait for morning. Pitcher and cup in hand, he stopped in the center of the well-appointed cabinet located just off his bedroom. He asked himself what was different. Dismissing it, he backed up to the door, using his weight to push it open.

A half-turn of his body revealed someone in his bed. Tel focused past the fuzz of wine and shimmer of dreaming bud. It was Gawash, atop the covers, nude. His hand dragged lazy strokes over his squat cock.

"Your royal highness, you're a bit of a mess this evening."

"How did you get in here?"

Lord Gawash laughed. "I assumed I wouldn't be the first man sent to your rooms to await you. Noble or common. I assumed correctly. The guard didn't even raise a brow."

Tel narrowed his eyes at the Hebite.

"You sneaked out of the throng so quickly. I didn't have a chance to ask you how you enjoyed my little treat. Two buds is quite a lot for your second time."

Tel poured another little cup of wine and took a sip.

"I also didn't have the chance to ask if you wanted to take me tonight. I decided to gamble." His strokes were less lazy. "My bet is you've never given a Hebite your seed." His grin was a blade across his face. "If it will help you perform, we can always send for a twenty-year-old with a void in his head."

Tel drained his cup and chucked it aside. He did not like this man. Hot-faced and silent, he marched over to the bed and glared down at him.

Gawash moved to the edge of the mattress. "Please."

The Hebite was revolting. Tel's practiced thumb undid the buttons on his leggings with one hand and cupped the back of Gawash's sleek head with the other. As soon as he was free, he was in his throat.

Four

A short time after falling asleep the night before he sailed for Feigh, Tel woke from a nightmare he could not remember. Uneasy, he sought to soothe his head by reminding himself he would soon return to Affas, where he could spend time with his father. Cursing his mind for his forgetting, the full weight of his losses fell upon him at last. He tried to return to sleep, but his exhaustion was so infused with anxiety and grief, he found it impossible to rest.

Naked, he sat on his fine covers and tried to bring his mind low, to empty it so he might hear the goddesses and gods. He had been neglecting his meditation. Weaving a thread of magic fire between the fingers of his healing right hand, he could only hear his own dark, incessant chatter.

Stillness of mind and body eluded him. Restless even in times of pleasure and ease, he could not force himself to stop thinking and moving. He dressed and marched the palace halls. He craned his neck at the canopy of stars over the queen's garden. He read—or tried to read. His eyes aimed themselves at black markings on ivory paper, but in his distress, they conveyed no more meaning than the scratches left by a housecat on the leg of a table. When he forced himself to stay in bed, he spun the covers into damp knots.

The thirst haunted him, stalking his every racing thought. It chased. It seduced and insulted. Now it was both too late and too early to begin drinking. He knew he must remain coherent for his last meeting with the queen before boarding the *Crunadam* and had no faith he would be able to stop once a single warming, relieving, quenching drop met his tongue. A quest for peace in liquid form would take him beyond sleep. Rest was what he needed but not what he craved. Once he was on the ship, he would be free to drink for three weeks if the wind was kind, longer if it was hostile. *Or the other way around.*

His swift mind had always served him well. He was gifted with the ability to retain information, to see problems from many vantages, to sense without effort what situations required of him, to charm and seduce. His mother—and when she was gone, his father—had called him in tender moments *my brightest boy.* He knew, however, the nature of light is to cast shadow. This interior gloom had appeared along the fringes of his consciousness when he was halfway between boy and man. When the water took Fyor and Hod, certain corners of his brain and heart were permanent dusk.

Inside Feigh's bright prince, less luminous was the constant, concealed nervousness. Darker was the tendency of his busy mind to wander from him, to relive and reexamine moments triumphant and tragic, to fret without end about what had not yet occurred. Blacker was the urgent, ever-present drive to escape his own echoing skull. King Vith had—for a time after the loss of his queen—taken to drinking in the afternoons and evenings. It helped him to sleep through his most acute grief. Tel had joined him often in those months and found that mead and ale and apple wine chased the shadows back to the margins for a while.

In recent years, much of his mental energy was consumed with a tense choreography. His mind danced with its own echo. One dancer stepped toward the drink, the other shuffled back. The second performer, of course, could only keep up the sequence for so long. He would tire. He was only an echo—a reflection. The first would lead them both across the floor to relief. The curtain would fall. The curtain would rise again.

Agitated, tremulous, and slick with perspiration, Tel ignored the guard's knowing expression and sent for Turo long after midnight. The boy rushed across the palace to him. Youth's elasticity prevented the fact that he had been asleep from showing on his features. His wild hair betrayed it. He had pulled on some leggings and a slim tunic in a yellow that, in its paleness, was more Feighan than Omelan. There could be no mistaking the garment's cut for anything other than Omelan, with its massive scoop at the neck, lack of billows at the sleeves, and tight fit. Even in Tel's frazzled state, he could not help but notice Turo's raw maleness threatening to break the seams.

"I am lonely."

"I'm here," said Turo. He looked like he was trying to read the prince's face.

"I mean…" Tel felt foolish. He was close to tears. "I mean, I wanted company."

"Alright."

"Not…"

"Alright."

Tel swallowed. "Would you spend some time w—"

"Of course. I'm happy to see you. We both leave tomorrow."

"You and your comrades are off to compete. Against Hebites and Andowians."

"Yes. At Elium."

"The Omelans will win."

Turo appeared embarrassed. "We'll do our best for Queen Cessa."

"You will win."

"I'm sorry about your father. I didn't hear until after the signing." Turo tamed his long blue hair with his fingers, tucking it behind his ears. "I wouldn't have been so…*flirtatious* if…I'm sorry about your father."

"I would like to listen to you talk about your farm."

"Of course. But you'll lie down. Will you lie down?"

"That is not…I truly only want to listen to you."

"And I only want to talk. Please." Turo swept his big open hand toward the bed.

Tel did as he was asked. For over two hours, Turo described every detail of the land his parents worked. While much of the country was prone to summer drought, the region around the capital seemed to have the perfect amount of rain and warm air needed for growing fat citrus. The soil was rich and free of rocks. His family labored long and hard for the little they had but were blessed—the nobles of the area were not of the greedy type. They were left alone to plant, harvest, trade, and enjoy their rectangles of dirt. Turo knew every tree, each pebble.

He spoke in low, easy tones. A short time after he began, he took Tel's feet in his lap and rubbed them with his strong fingers. While Tel could not find sleep, he quieted. In a lull, Turo's head fell forward. He snapped it back up and continued talking.

"You should sleep, champion." It had been long enough since Tel had spoken that it came out a rasp.

"What about you?"

"I will. Eventually. Not tonight, but eventually," said Tel. They got out of bed and padded to the door. "Thank you. We will not see each other again."

Turo frowned and kissed the tired prince. It was neither chaste nor wanton.

* * *

Rings like bruises circled Tel's eyes. He sat next to Cessa on a shaded bench in her courtyard. The queen slowly picked the petals off a large, carrot-colored bloom. She looked at the flower and shook her head. "Great concern today for our peace. Great concern. We know little of your brother."

He recognized it was difficult to even conjure a clear notion of what Lag's reign might be.

"What are his values, Tel?"

"Lag was raised by my parents, with their boundless faith and empathy." Tel paused, thinking, for too long. "He values the input and advice of others. He makes decisions carefully."

"Hm." The ruler of Omela had shredded the entire blossom. Its anatomy lay scattered between and around her feet. "And Omela has no reason to worry he will not want to honor the peace? To trade? To build alliance?"

"I will be at King's Table for each important deliberation. You know where my mind is. You know I detest war because my mother and father taught me to detest it. You know I believe peace is in the interest of not only Feigh—and not only Omela—but of the other four nations as well."

"But Lag?"

Some bitterness tinged his quick little laugh. He had not intended to communicate the sentiment. "Lag wants more than all else to have ease. He is unambitious." He knew his true feelings were standing naked and harsh and ugly in front of them in the lovely softness of the garden, so he charged on. "He will believe peace to be less work, so we will have peace. But—"

"But more work is what makes peace."

"I will do that work. Lag will let me. He did ask us to finalize the treaty, did he not? My brother will revel in being king. In the pomp and the scraping before him. It should be enough for him."

"Pomp and scraping bring to mind my Belo. Hierarchy is his first love." Her chuckle was warm and round. "He admires you a great deal."

Prince Belo was Cessa's only offspring and heir. He had gravitated toward the army and grown into an honorable and heroic leader of its women and men. His military title was not the result of his gilded bloodline but of a fit body, a sharp mind, and an effortless ability to command and inspire. Perhaps more than Cessa herself, he was adored by his people. The Omelan prince had been responsible for a portion of the more challenging negotiations with his Feighan counterpart over the years. An unwavering respect bridged one prince to the other. While his mother had wanted him present for the signing, he had chosen his martial duties.

"And I admire him a great deal. *The man whose career has shown him blood, if he is wise, is the man who wants to prevent its shedding.* He helped me lower my suspicions with those words. They shall remain unforgotten for as long as my heart drums."

Cessa looked at him with her balled face. "Have you eaten?"

Tel began to answer that he had not, but someone approached. His eyes were bleary, and it took a moment to recognize the dramatist, Laich.

"There he is," said Cessa.

"Your royal majesty, your royal highness." He offered the top of his head with a compact and elegant bow.

Tel felt his first burst of amusement of the day. Laich was already costumed in the cleaner, simpler lines and brighter colors of Omelan dress. "I see you are committed to this venture."

"Oh, I am. I asked for permission to see you, your highness, before you departed for home."

"Of course, Laich."

The playbard clasped his hands. "I hope you will take some measure of comfort in knowing the scale of my sorrow at the loss of your father and my greatest patron. Of our king. I certainly know the scale of the honor he extended by offering me this most unusual post, and I intend to make him, you, and Feigh proud. If what I accomplish eliminates one speck of the mistrust and fear that has characterized the relationship between our peoples, I will consider it my greatest accomplishment." He bowed again before raising his eyes to his prince's. "Health and wisdom to King Lag."

"Health and wisdom to King Lag," said Tel and Cessa in quiet unison.

* * *

It took Tel a moment to remember he was on the ship. Swinging his legs over the side of the bed, he let his eyes adjust. He was surprised he did not need to piss. Flicking his right hand, he lit the nearest oil lamp with the stagsblood. This simple dirt magic tired him all over again. He was relieved to see his quarters had been stocked with a supply of ale, as he had asked. When he had marched to his cabin and collapsed into bed immediately after the blessing at the wharf, he had not noticed.

He drank and slept for almost a day, speaking with no one.

Pounding on his door pulled him out of his stupor. He opened it to find Caip standing in the twilight, bearing food. "Eat." She shoved it toward him.

"Maybe." He placed it on the small desk near his bed and noticed the salted pork. He picked up the plate, spun, and sloshed out the door. Caip had to dodge him. He went below, food spilling off the dish, jaw clamped. She tailed him.

Tel barked at the first man he encountered, demanding to know where to find the captain. She was on the 'tween deck, sitting cramped among a dozen crew members eating and drinking. Vared was perched on a box, sharing with them a bawdy Omelan sailor song.

Tel's dish crashed before the captain's feet, silencing the tenor and his terquin.

"Are you animals?" Tel's eyes bulged. His chest heaved. He sensed Caip standing too close behind him and wheeled on her. His face sent her back a long step.

The captain got to her feet. "Your highness?"

"Are you godsdamned animals? Or are you Feighans?" He looked at each of them, spending less time glaring at the singer. Tel recognized he would not know better. He felt a bit of heat kiss his cheeks because Cessa's emissary was witnessing this display. Though he considered walking away, he waited. Silence was his answer.

"No flesh in your bellies until my father's ashes are joined with the dirt." The crew began muttering. He quieted them with his raised palm. "Do not apologize. Eat tack and meal. Peas. Drink your ale rations." Stomping away, he called, "Play your song." He heard the Omelan's hands find the strings.

For weeks, most of his time was spent alone in his quarters, drinking and sleeping. He accepted a few brief, quiet visits from Caip. Noticing the heat of the glances directed at him by the ship's scribe when he ventured into the open air, he twice pulled the young man into his cabin. He japed the clerk without regard for his pleasure. Still, he beamed dumb, worshipful expressions at the prince.

Both times, Tel noted his own lack of generosity. He offered neither reciprocation nor affection. After the second encounter, he considered walking off the deck into the ocean. The thought stuck to him for days. He was trapped, surrounded, buried. By what, he did not know. Even the alcohol was ineffective.

One sweaty night, half-drunk, he read from a book of ancient verse to bring on sleep. A stanza about flowers called to his mind an image of Queen Cessa, orange petals at her feet. He decided against jumping into the mouth of the Gray Sea.

Five

In a moment of clear thinking, Tel realized the *Crunadam* was two or three days from Feighan shores. Wanting to have his wits in hand when he arrived home, he chose to clear his head by abstaining from the drink. Within hours, the tremors began. He spent time with the others aboard the ship, socializing. Making light chat, he tried to give people his eyes. Hiding his frazzled nerves took a considerable amount of thought and effort. He sought to make sure his hands were always planted on his lap, gripping something steady, or concealed.

Enjoying a few rounds of cards with Caip and some of her people, he squinted against the sun blazing off the waves. He realized too late that the game exposed his condition. Caip eyed his trembling hand as he played. He went below in the evening, taking a meal with the captain and some of her crew. They extended a warm welcome and seemed happy to have some of their prince's time. The quaking of his hands as he scooped peas with his tack did not go unnoticed, but no one commented.

Being with people lifted his spirits. He denied himself alcohol.

After dinner—the first time he had done more than picking at food since he could remember—he returned to his cabin. He opened a book, a gift Belo had left with Cessa. The inscription read: *From one future king to another, the diary of an Omelan general from the early days of the war. A man who saw blood and can inspire us to avoid its shedding. With respect and affection. Belo.*

He ran an appreciative hand over the thick paper before beginning to read. Gripped by its vivid retelling of both the mundane and exceptional aspects of military life, he guessed a full two hours had passed before he shut the book. Too edgy yet for sleep, he thought some salt air and stargazing would do him good.

Tel was disappointed to see a ceiling of clouds obscuring the constellations. Still, he appreciated the suggestion of northern chill in the air as it breezed intermittent puffs across his clammy skin. They were close to home, a fact which inspired in him equal measures of dread and relief. The night watch on deck was minimal. The helmswoman acknowledged him with a nod. He gave a little smile and returned the gesture.

He looked up at his colors, which had been raised over the ship the moment he boarded. In the darkness, he could barely make out the flag, a field of beryl green on which a cross of the elements and directions burst through a ring. The cross and ring were the color of the fat autumn gourds grown in Foghar Valley, an area about a week's ride outside the Feighan capital. There sat Tel's personal estate, gifted by his father. With dull sadness, he thought of the late king. Before wearing the rack crown, Vith had spent as much time as possible at the modest castle.

Tel took his time wandering to the bow. When he reached the fo'c'sle, he was startled by the sight of a figure against the rail. "Goddesses."

The shape turned to him. A skein of cobalt curls danced on a burst of wind, almost black in the low light. He hugged himself with his long arms. "Your highness. Good evening."

"Good evening, Vared."

"I didn't mean to startle you."

"I did not expect you. There is no need for apology."

"You look well."

"I have been under the weather."

"Yes."

The monosyllabic response galled Tel, though he did not know why. "Yes." He drummed the flats of his fingers on the rail, trying to hide the tremors. "Tell me, has your time on the ship inspired you to write a song?"

"I'm too shy to compose unless I have privacy. I freeze and my head empties if I know someone's hearing my fumbling. There's certainly no solitude available onboard. Whether above deck or below, two dozen will know what you've done and who you've done it with before you're even finished." The cross of his arms tightened around his slender chest.

"You are cold."

Vared turned away from the prince and said, "Feigh isn't far ahead of us."

"Tomorrow. I am sure of it. You are breathing your first Feighan air."

"Yes."

"My father's ashes will be waiting. There will be a day of rites. We will add him to the dirt. Either my brother or I will take responsibility to remember him every year until we ourselves die. Then, in the same way, someone will remember us and the people we remember. You saw some of this in the palace garden. I was remembering two people I lost before. I hope you did not find it too strange." He felt a nibble of embarrassment.

"No."

"How do Omelans remember their dead?"

"Simply."

A great, cool gust swept across the deck. Tel had to shift a foot to brace himself when the wind struck. Vared did not so much as blink. He was perfect stillness, save the hair.

The songmaker took a slow breath before turning his big eyes—so orange, even for an Omelan, even in the starless night—to Tel. "The family's part is simple, at any rate. The intricate rituals and blessings and carrying on are done by the high ones. But then they leave us. We don't burn our dead, like you. We put the whole body deep under the dirt, instead of mixing ashes into the top layer of dust. We tell each other all the kindnesses the dead offered us while they were living. *Kindness in the mystery*. And that's it. After that, we remember them in our own ways. Privately."

Tel considered it for a moment. "You must think us superstitious."

"No." Vared turned back to face Feigh.

"I am sorry to disturb you. Sleep well."

"Goodnight, your highness."

Tel returned to his room. After two hours of twisting the covers around himself, he collapsed into a shallow sleep.

* * *

The last hours of the journey were the longest, as they always were. Caip was content to turn her face to the sun. She did not have much to say. Tel wandered the decks making petty conversation with anyone he encountered. A desire for a drink, desperate and pressing, formed in his belly. He ignored it and kept moving, after a time coming across the scribe. Without a word, the lad indicated he should follow him. Tel hesitated. The brown eyes glowed with conspiratorial hunger. The prince wanted to resist, but his body responded, and he found himself unable to pass up the chance to distract himself from his nervous, unending string of thoughts. Down to the orlop deck they skulked, the scribe snatching an oil lamp on their way.

The darkness indicated no one was on the deck. Still, Tel took the light from the boy and had a look around. Satisfied, he placed the lamp on the floor and reached for the warm hardness filling the crotch of the scribe's leggings. The young man batted the hand away and worked the prince's dripping meat free, pushing him onto a large coil of thick rope. At once, he was on his knees between Tel's legs.

The clerk groped himself through his clothes with one hand. With the other, he tugged downward on Tel's balls, sending even more blood to strain against the thin skin of his cock. The prince growled as he tongued up the fluid leaking from the slit in his knob. From the boy's throat came wordless approval.

Talented and gluttonous, he feasted. He looked up at his prince while he worked, continuing to rub himself. Tel's fingers curled around his straight black hair. Muttering filthy encouragement and praise, he took control of the rhythm. After a time, the scribe bucked and whimpered as he climaxed into his breeches. Tel answered in short order, his balls twitching in upward pulses as they emptied into the back of the young man's throat.

Tel wanted to place a simple kiss on the clerk's cheek as they put themselves back together. He moved to do so, but his companion made a fast, awkward turn to pick up the lamp.

"We should go separately. You first," said Tel.

The boy nodded. His adoring, greedy expression was gone. He headed up, leaving Tel frowning in the humid gloom.

* * *

After waiting below the waterline in the ship's gut for longer than necessary, Tel worked his unrushed way upward until he reached the open air. The deck was crowded, with the bulk of people gathered to port, near the bow. They looked across the Bay of Affas at the city itself.

Tel scanned the deck for Caip. Locating the black helmet of her hair, he moved through the people to her position on the rail. He passed the scribe, who was posted on a section of taffrail further to stern. He gave Tel a smirking glance as he spoke with another crew member, gesturing toward the capital. The singer, Vared, was standing not far from the clerk and his friend.

The crowd made a spot for their prince, next to the chief of his guard. Tel turned and leaned his back on the rail.

"Rightmajor Caip."

"Your royal highness."

"You are beaming this afternoon."

She nodded. "Home."

"I am sorry I have been so unwell."

"You can't help it."

"I cannot." Tel stared up at foresail. He felt Caip taking a close look at him.

"I see more white in your hair."

"My preference," said Tel, "is to think of it as silver."

"Silver, then."

He heard the smile in her voice. "I am getting old."

"So am I, then."

He spun his body to look at Affas. The rambling, busy port was closer. In the distance, he could see Affas Island, his home. It was connected to the rest of the city by a narrow causeway over a thousand meters in length. The broken cliffs of the isle soared up from the spray of the harbor, making it easier to defend.

Tel compared it to the royal residence he left three weeks ago. The Omelan palace had been designed and planned as an enormous monument to power. That country's rulers lived inside a singular vision. They inhabited a plan. By contrast, the Feighan palace was less a palace and more a castle made by necessity larger and larger and larger again over the centuries, until it crept over the entire surface of the island. In Omela, the seat of the monarchy was all clean, pink, marble verticality. Affas Castle was a sputter and rumble of greenish-gray battlements and crenellations. The place that had for a millennium housed the highest of Feigh's highborn was tumbling stone crookedness.

Where the causeway met the mainland sat an enormous civic plaza. Beyond the plaza, Affas fanned out. Although the populations were comparable, the city was spread over a far larger area than the Omelan capital. Affas looked to be an extension of the natural landscape with its subdued colors, lower profiles, and abundant stonework. Omela City was a bright, arrogant, human place.

His breaths were deep. He savored the aromas of home. *Here, the ocean smells more like the ocean.* His mouth flooded with saliva as he dreamed of fish prepared the Feighan way, stuffed with pearlgrowers and flash cooked right on top of hot charcoal. The respite from alcohol restored his appetite. Realizing it would have to wait until his father joined the dirt, he offered the dead king a light curse and laughed under his breath. Vith loved the dish, too.

Inhaling again to steady his emotions, he snaked his way through the crowd and sprang onto the quarterdeck, next to the captain, where he stomped the boards three times. Only the people nearest him seemed to hear, so he stomped three times again, with force. More faces turned to him. Thrice more, he banged the deck. He stood in silence for a moment

44

and had the attention of everyone.

"My father loved the goddesses and the gods, so he hated war. He did not think it was enough to talk about his devotion to the makers of the world and the plants and the animals and humankind. His faith demanded he seek peace and reject conflict. Do not allow yourselves to forget the opposition he faced in those early years, the names they called him, just for eating flesh at the same table as non-Feighans. Remember this for Vith.

"They questioned his loyalty to Feigh and the Feighan people. Worse than this, those who thrived on anger and resentment—those who profit when Feighan and Omelan dirt into red mud—undermined him at every opportunity. They tried to poison him. But my father, because he was not just a king in name but a true king from his guts to his skin, would not stop working for peace. He would not stop believing it could be grasped. He reached out, and those who opposed him saw their greatest fear become real: Cessa reached back. Remember this for Vith.

"Thank you all for helping me be my father's mouth and ears. I will not forget the sacrifices made by many people on this ship. We have peace. I thank you and I thank him. If you believe he deserves your gratitude, remember to hold the goddesses and gods in your heart. If ever again people twist our creation stories to justify the sin of violence, reject it. Remember that war made the deities leave. And remember only peace can bring them back. Remember this for my father. Remember it for my brother."

Elated approval exploded across the deck of the *Crunadam*. A chant started as he clasped hands with his people and returned to Caip's sunny face: *Remember for Vith! Remember for Lag!*

Six

Tel, Caip, and Vared sat long enough beneath the enormous stone antlers of Affas Castle's throne room that their comfortable chairs became anything but. Tel's foot tapped the plush rug, fast as a woodpecker.

"The king is anxious for your report," said Caip, managing a more than passable impersonation of Tel's uncle, Aith. He had met the *Crunadam* at the pier without any fanfare, which the protective rightmajor had griped about. "My ass."

With some difficulty, Tel stifled a laugh. "At least he sent real Feighan honey wine. I have missed it."

"As have I. The Omelans do not have a substitute," said Caip. Their goblets clacked. "I mean no insult, Vared, but your honey wine's more honey than wine." The songmaker looked at the floor in front of him. "Remember, no *your highnesses* for Aith. Even though he's a prince, he…"

"He has never been fond of the title. Not since my father became king." Tel swished the liquid in his goblet. "You are certain you will not have a taste, Vared?"

"I prefer to keep my senses within my control." He seemed to remember himself and added, "Thank you."

"A taste is all I—" Tel rolled his eyes. *Some wine would do him good. Stiff, irritating boy.* "Suit yourself, Ambassador."

Vared scoffed. "Ambassador."

Tel padded to the ornate decanter and refilled. "It is true. I will present your credentials to my brother and you will be accepted as a diplomat from Omela to Feigh." He walked to Caip to top off her goblet. "You will be properly addressed as—"

"Your excellency," said Caip.

"Yes. His Excellency Vared, Ambassador of the Queendom of Omela." Tel looked at him as he sat back down next to Caip. "Do you like the ring of that?"

"I don't know."

"Who wouldn't like a little title?" Caip asked. "Other than Aith. It's an honor."

Vared said, "I don't care about titles. I have no interest in such things." He softened before continuing. "I'm honored just to make music here."

"And make music you shall. Feigh will inspire you," said Tel. Caip looked ready to wheel on the visitor, so he steadied her with his hand. He fingered his hairline, pondering a change of subject. "It was this time of year I got this scar on my head."

"Scar?" Caip narrowed her eyes.

"You cannot see it unless you look closely. Lag and I used to race in the hallway outside this room. One time, I gave him a good head start. I was older and bigger. When I threatened to pass, he threw an elbow. Hard. I tripped, fell into the wall, and split my head open. The amount of blood was frightful, as it always is with a head wound. Still, I had to comfort him. *I could not help it, Telly.* I covered for him, admitting we raced indoors but saying I had simply tripped over my own feet. I was punished. I was always to be an example for my younger brother. I could not ride my horse for a month."

Caip's laugh was low and dry. A silent quarter of an hour passed.

"I wish we had some cards." Tel felt unable to cope with the stillness any longer.

"Cards," Caip echoed as if surfacing from a daydream.

"Yes. A game. We could play a game." Tel sat forward in his chair.

"Like what?" she asked.

"Back-to-back," they said simultaneously, enjoying the kind of laughter rooted in shared memory.

"What's back-to-back?" asked Vared.

Tel was surprised to witness the songmaker showing interest in anything. "Our...friend—" He swallowed.

"Hod," Caip said.

"Hod invented it. You sit with a partner, backs touching so you cannot see one another. Each turn, one of you asks the other anything you want. Anything. The answers must be truthful."

"And?" Vared asked.

Caip's face brightened. "And, when one of you suspects the other isn't being truthful, not really confessing, you demand to see their face. You ask them again and they must answer. And if they're lying, you get to slug them. Hard as you can."

"Nothing above the shoulders, of course," said Tel.

"It's more of a forest game than a throne room game," said Caip.

Tel nodded. "That it is. I think my arm still hurts from when I told Hod I had not kissed the cooper's son."

Caip said, "A game more for those with sixty seasons than one hundred and sixty."

"Our new ambassador is closer to sixty seasons than one hundred and sixty," Tel said. "Do you have any wisdom for the child, rightmajor?"

She made a show of thinking deeply. "Under no circumstances should you swear your life to protect a spoiled, moody prince."

Tel giggled. "I believe you are drunk."

"Hardly."

"I am getting there." Tel drained his goblet, remembering he had intended to make his report to his brother sober.

Caip finished her mead. "What's your advice for the boy?"

Before Tel could answer, Vared said, "I'm over one hundred seasons. I've not been a child for many years now."

"Don't they have teasing in Omela?" Caip asked. "Goddesses."

The air of the chamber thickened with silence again.

When Tel could stand no more of it, he sprang to his feet. "What delays him? I want to be in my own bed."

Caip sighed. "Our own beds. For the first time in *months*. Must be a pressing matter. I hope it's nothing too serious."

"He's not sent anyone, and it's been more than two hours." Vared lowered his blue globe of curls, looking at the space between his feet. "Do you not see it? He's…Your brother's making you understand he's the king."

"And I am not."

* * *

Hours later, Tel and Caip stood before King Lag. He sat on the throne, his short, pinched face below the rack crown. Usually, the crown would only be worn on the most formal of occasions. Figuring the number of times Tel had seen his father in the headdress would not use the fingers of two hands. Lag's clothing was entirely new and luxurious. Uncle Aith stood behind the throne a pace, on the king's right. Vared's credentials had been accepted. Lag had ordered an attendant to escort him to his room.

"I'm sure he didn't notice," Lag said to his brother.

"The term is unsuitable, your majesty," said Tel.

"Bluebell? Bah. I've said it my whole life. It's nothing. Besides, he's only a singer."

"It has a long, ugly history. You know this. He is a representative of our friend, Queen Cessa."

"A singer who doesn't sing." Lag picked at lint on his lush brown cape.

Aith cleared his throat. "For some of us, the memory of the Omelan brutality during the war is still fresh. It will take time for us to break the habits developed during our painful era. Besides, it's just a little barb, your highness."

"Uncle," said Tel, "your feelings about the Omelans are well-known. And understandable—"

Aith bowed his head. "Perhaps it would be best, majesty, to move onto something else." His wife and daughter, aunt and cousin to Tel and Lag, had been on a Feighan ship boarded by Omelans. Their throats were cut at sea.

"Father's memorial." Tel took a step toward the throne. "What has been decided? When will he join Mother at Foghar?"

"His ashes have been added to the dirt here. The dirt of Affas Island," said Lag.

Heat crept up Tel's neck. "His wishes were for his ashes to join the dirt w—"

"He made no such request in his will," Aith said.

"Because it was obvious. This is absurd." Tel braced against a wave of lightheadedness. "He wanted to become the dirt of his favorite place with his favorite person. And you are going to defy him and do it here, in Affas?"

Caip moved forward, so she was parallel with Tel before his brother. "No. Wait. *Have been*, he said. The ashes *have been* spread?"

"Yes," said Lag.

"You have mixed Father with the dirt already?"

Aith raised a hand. "Respectfully, your highness, you are bellowing at your king."

Tel did not lower his voice. "And who will remember Father and all those he remembered?"

"I will," said Lag, "of course."

"Of course," Tel echoed, whispering. He could not recall the last time he had witnessed his brother speak about or practice the faith. The room lurched and his head spun. He steadied himself with a few attentive breaths. "I am sorry to have shouted."

"If I may, your majesty, these discussions can continue another time." Aith turned his attention to Tel. "Nephew, you have received a lot of bad news and had a long journey. You look tired."

"Very tired," said the king.

* * *

Tel and Caip whispered a slow route through some of the least used nooks and halls of Affas Castle.

"I'm sorry. I don't know what else to say. I'm gutted. I can't conceive of what you must feel right now." Caip stopped walking and took his hands in hers. "This is…"

"Honestly, I am, more than anything, stunned. Numb," said Tel.

"It's an outrage. All of it. You were his chosen heir."

"Table declared me unfit. They have had the power to declare unsoundness for thousands of seasons."

"I'm not talking about that." Caip held her eyes shut for a time. She inhaled and exhaled before opening them again. "At least not at the moment. Your father. It's improper to not wait for your input. And here instead of…I'm sorry."

Drained, Tel sat on the floor, back against the chilly stone wall under a pair of crossed swords displayed over a forgotten queen's battle-tattered colors. Caip slid down next to him.

"Vared was right," Tel said.

"What?"

"The Omelan. The singer. He was right. All of this is about making it clear who is king."

Caip reached back and massaged her own nape. "Someone sitting atop the throne doesn't need to say much about his chair. Shouldn't."

He nodded. "It is sensible in a certain light. I would not be the first relative to challenge a monarch's claim. Not close to the first."

"You have come and shown him the top of your head."

"But he did not know I would do so."

"You're a threat," she said, still rubbing the muscles of her neck. "Not because you'd mount a rebellion, but because you're better loved than he is."

They allowed silence to join them in the hall. Guiltily, Prince Tel felt a comfortable gratitude. He was home, a monumental achievement behind him, fewer responsibilities ahead. The castle was dimmer than the Omelan palace, which was easier on his Feighan eyes. The cooler air carried old paper, buckskin, and a hundred thousand fires to his nostrils. The more he breathed it in, the more he was greedy for it.

51

Tel got to his feet and held out a hand to his friend. "Come."

"Where are we going?"

"To check on the Omelan. To apologize for Lag."

"Oh, no. Absolutely not."

"Caip."

"No. He's entirely unpleasant." Her mind was made up. She accepted his hand and stood up with his help.

"My antlered god, he is." Tel whistled.

Caip chuckled. "Entirely. And I'm tired."

"Still, I must. Lawfully, he is a member of my household. I put my signature to it." He mugged a distasteful expression.

"You may want to bring a cloak."

"Hm?"

"For the blast of cold air he brings wherever he goes."

A cackle escaped him. "That is not very nice." His second laugh was even more maniacal.

"Goodnight, Tel."

"Sleep well."

Caip walked in the direction of her apartments, not far from his own quarters. He headed the opposite way, toward Vared's accommodations. Encountering a few guards and servants along the way, he noticed they would not make even the briefest eye contact with him. His presence seemed to disconcert.

He arrived at the Omelan's room. After steeling himself for a moment, he knocked. The door opened, and warmth billowed over Tel. Vared stepped barefooted into the space between the door and the jamb. Gold light played with his features from the right. He had started a fire. Tunic shed, he stood now in black hose and an ivory shirt with the huge Omelan scoop of a collar. Tel had never seen him in anything other than all-black. He looked even thinner, his features more delicate. He was blue curls and clavicle in the firelight.

"Highness."

"I wanted to be sure you are comfortable. That you have everything you need." Tel realized this was the first time that he had seen Vared's unpainted face. It did not seem possible, but his skin was smoother without makeup than with.

"Yes. I don't need anything."

"Good."

"Thank you."

"And the room is to your satisfaction?"

"It's a nice room. Thank you."

"And Lag. My brother. The king." He lowered his voice and eased a half step closer. The singer shifted his feet. "He should not have called you by that name. He sometimes speaks as if it were the old days. He means nothing by it." Tel searched the apricot eyes and found neutrality. "He also should not have asked you to sing tonight."

"I didn't mean any disrespect. I wasn't prepared. I froze."

"Do not give it another thought. He will not. My brother finds humor in making people uncomfortable. He is harmless but enjoys embarrassing people."

"I'll forget it, as you suggest. I wish you restful sleep, your highness."

"I wish you the same, your excellency." The door had shut before Tel finished his sentence.

* * *

Vith's name had not yet been engraved into the polished slab. Tel surveyed the faces hanging above the knee-level gneiss that was Table. Its members had already demonstrated their loyalty to Lag by declaring the older brother unsound. The majority had been hand-chosen by his uncle, he now realized. Vith had left the task to his brother for the bulk of the last decade. Still, if Lag could be steered from his worst impulses, it would be with the help of these men.

All but Craid were silent. Craid was a childhood companion of Vith and had long sat Table. He had been too ill to attend when Prince Tel's unfitness was declared. Aith had his quorum and conspired to elevate Lag. It looked to Tel like his father's friend had aged twenty seasons since he sailed for Omela.

"How's Laich?" the old man asked.

"I am sure he has already completed three dramas." Tel chuckled. "He seemed pleased about his adventure. He took to Omelan food without a problem, that is certain."

"The gluttonous son of a dynast, I'm sure he did," Craid said. "Speaking of excess, I'll bet you didn't spend a single night alone."

"Nephew," Aith said, entering the chamber with King Lag.

"Brother," Lag said. Everyone stood to bow.

"My king." Tel invited a hint of extra deference into his greeting. Looking around, it hit him. He was dizzy. Only one empty chair remained. It was the largest and finest, meant for the king. There was nowhere for Aith to sit. In truth, his uncle was not the one without a seat.

Lag remained silent. He looked at Aith and raised his chin a fraction.

"Highness," said Aith, "King Lag does not require your presence at his Table. You are dismissed."

Time slowed. Needing something to focus on, his gaze rested on one of the names carved into the gneiss: *Ghail.* Her reign had been remarkable only for her corruption and laziness. Heat rose from his chest to the top of his head. He was conscious of every beat of his heart, which he felt even where his legs met his feet. His black hair grew damp and his breathing stopped. He had to remember how to begin again. Twenty and six eyes waited for him. Twenty and four of them were impatient.

He lifted his face to Lag, who looked through him. "Nearly three days, I have been home. Under the same roof as you."

"And we are pleased to have you," said Aith.

"Quiet, uncle," Tel hissed, without taking his eyes off his brother. He waited a moment. Lag dropped his gaze. "I could not have been informed of this change in that time?"

"His majesty has been—"

"I love you, uncle, but I do not speak to you. I ask my brother, the king, who knew I would attend this meeting. I have not missed one gathering of this council since our father asked me to join over two decades ago."

"Except when you've been abroad getting blind pissed and begging bluebell peasants to join you in bed," said Lag.

"I have told you," Tel barked, "not to use that word."

Lag's chair squawked across stone. Several Tablemembers flinched. The king stepped onto the enormous Table and closed half the distance to his older brother. "Who are you to tell me anything? This is why you cannot sit Table. This new reality's difficult to accept. I'm helping you accept it. I'll still need you in my government, but not here. You'll be my Minister of Arts and Culture. You've already been babysitting poets and singers, haven't you?"

Tel heard a snicker but could not identify the source.

Aith clucked. "Your father faded from us quickly. It refocused our minds and shuffled our priorities. We need…steadiness."

"Steadiness?" Tel could not believe it. "Who could my father rely on more than me to represent him? To honor *his* priorities?"

A monied merchant, a man Prince Tel did not know well, spoke up. "Enough of his priorities! Not only do you lack steadiness, but we need to be sure things do not move too far from tradition. All of us are glad for peace, but you have grown to love Cessa and her land. You have lost objectivity. With trade negotiations ahead, the kingdom needs someone who is Feighan first, before all else. Our interests must be protected."

"We do not have to fight," Aith said, "but we do have to preserve our identity."

"Our values." Lag looked down from his perch.

"Our values." Tel scanned the colossal slab of rock, long ago freed from a Feighan hillside. "Tell me, your grace, do we value women in this kingdom? Because I see no women around this Table." He turned to leave the chamber. "Do we value the people of southern Feigh? Because I see no one from south of Coltach here. The south. Where our own mother was raised."

"A coincidence," Aith called after him.

Seven

Vared's tenor, candlelight, and more than two hundred bodies warmed the cavernous banquet hall. Tel stood next to Caip, enjoying an ale.

"You're pleased you didn't cancel?" she asked him.

"You know I love a party. Especially when I am the guest of honor."

"Don't think you've ever said anything truer."

"I shall not have too much fun, and neither will anyone else," said Tel, looking over his shoulder. "Your intimidating army of sentries will make sure of that. Can they not at least stand outside the hall? We are deep in the castle, and these are my friends."

"These're not my sentries. Your brother seems to take security rather seriously."

"My brother takes keeping an eye on me rather seriously." He looked all about the room.

"You're a beast," said Caip, waving a finger. "Nothing more."

"What do you mean?"

"I see you trying to decide who to seduce."

Tel groaned. "There is no one new here."

"Nothing but an animal."

"Speaking of seduction, it seems our Omelan friend will not likely be returning to his room alone. He has the attention of quite the collection of young women and men." He swept his large mug toward Vared. At the far end of the hall, he strummed his terquin and sang a popular Feighan love song. "He must have just learned this."

Standing under a chandelier, the songmaker was a delicate stroke of black topped by a jungle of dark azure. He looked like a seedhead straining to keep from being pulled apart by the wind. The body of the terquin seemed broader than the body of the player. His voice and presence did not match the slight appearance. He always stood on the edge of things, but for when he sang. Performing, he was central, dominant. Although he was a head shorter than Tel, he was slim enough that everything about him looked long. He was overdressed for the occasion—at least by Omelan standards—in a black, formal shift that stopped midway down his thighs. The party marked both Tel's homecoming and the equinox. Vared must have mistaken one, the other, or both for more solemn events than they were. He had been amused when he learned Feighans called the equinox mid-autumn, calling the idea *absurd*. In Omela, this day was marked as the first of fall.

A small audience had dragged their chairs into a semicircle around him. More than a few mooned at him, desire unmasked in their eyes.

Caip sucked her teeth before a dry laugh. "They'll be disappointed when they realize there's no blood under that painted skin of his."

A tall man walked up to them. "Your highness." He showed the thick black hair on the top of his head. "Welcome home." He straightened and revealed a square-jawed, handsome face that had seen too much sun. "Rightmajor. Welcome home."

"Mor," said Tel, beaming, "you have come from Foghar for my party?"

Mor was a farmer and animal surgeon from the town outside Tel's country estate. He smiled at Caip. "It has been too long, your highness." After a few beats, his eyes found his prince's.

"That it has. I miss the place. Is everyone happy with the yield?"

"A good harvest, my prince," said Mor. He looked at the floor and cleared his throat. He raised his gaze. "I wanted to say that we're all very sorry for—"

A commotion rose from the other end of the hall. Vared had finished his song. He introduced a troupe of four pantos who would perform a bawdy, comedic retelling of a popular myth, the story of a catamite who stabbed his cruel warlord keeper and rose to unite the tribes of Feigh, becoming its first king.

Taking advantage of the distraction, Tel grabbed another ale and made himself small against the most shadowed section of wall available. The thought of listening to condolences this night made him sweat and itch. Caip craned her head about, trying to find the prince. She shrugged and moved to stand next to Mor in the throng. Within a few moments, their bodies were convulsing with laughter.

Tel could not miss Vared's hair among the collection of black Feighan heads. The songmaker stood at the audience's fringe, talking with one of his admirers, a young man around his age. Tel could not place the suitor. He was the son of someone with influence, no doubt. Smooth-skinned and shaggy-haired, he flashed a bright smile at Vared. The vigilant musculature of youth filled his clothes well. His finger played at a button on the front of his doublet as he talked with the Omelan.

Tel gulped half his beer while the Feighan lad reached out to lightly touch Vared behind the elbow. He moved his mouth to the singer's ear. The splendid nakedness of his countryman's desire made Tel ache. Vared straightened and shook his head, almost imperceptibly. Smiling, he said a few words before turning and heading out the nearest exit. He did not look back.

"Fool." Tel finished his ale.

He walked out of the grand banquet hall through the same archway as Vared.

* * *

Tel saw him ahead in a dim stretch of corridor. The songmaker took a quick glance over his shoulder and quickened his pace.

"Vared," Tel called. "Vared, it is only me. Prince Tel."

Vared stopped, his body rigid. After a beat, he pivoted. "Your highness. Of course." He held his terquin in front of him with two hands.

"You were wonderful. That old ballad about the sculptor and her subject? I—I have not heard it sung so well. The finest rendition."

"Thank you, your highness."

As he closed the distance between them, Tel asked, "Should you not have that in its case?"

Vared's eyes settled on the terquin in his hands. "I was playing with one of your brother's musicians in the garden and left it behind. I returned and it was gone. Someone probably disposed of it or took it for scrap." He lifted his gaze, resting it on Tel's chest. He shrugged. "It was a ratty old leather thing."

"May I see it? Do not fear. I will not play it. It would turn to dust in my unskilled hands." He took it from the singer and examined it. "Hm. Similar to a Feighan instrument."

"Yes," said Vared, suddenly animated. "The world over, it seems, people like to play strings. Every race has something quite like this. Even variations between regions of the same queendom. No one knows who built the first. There are guesses, but no certainty."

"Fascinating. Thank you." Tel handed the instrument back. "I am sorry to have frightened you. I only wanted to check on you. I did not mean to cause you alarm."

"May I speak plainly, your highness?" Vared stared at the terquin at the end of his stiff arms.

"I hope you always wi—"

"Is it customary here for a member of the royal family to personally check on a foreign guest at night?"

Tel cocked his head, his eyes also on Vared's hands. "Customary? I do not…Why?"

"Can you think of another ambassador you followed? To their room? Twice in one week, uninvited?"

"No."

"Your highness, what would a person's first thought be if they saw you coming to my room in the night, drunk?" He would not look up at Tel.

"I am not drunk."

"You smell of ale."

"I do not know what they would think," said Tel. "I do not read minds."

59

Usually.

"I want it understood that I'm here on my own merit. I can't have the court thinking anything unseemly is—"

"Unseemly."

Vared shifted his weight from one foot to the other. "I know a lot has happened to y—"

"Unseemly?"

"I think I've chosen my words poorly." Vared raised his face at last.

Tel stepped back a pace and took a vicious look at him from his feet to his eyes. "Tell me, your excellency, will the members of this court think something unseemly occurred between us merely because I am a depraved souse? Or is it because your charms are so overwhelming? Perhaps both? Perhaps I am a drunken flesh maniac and you are irresistible?"

"I know you don't remember, your highness. The night we met. After the treaty signing. You made an advance."

"I am sure you mistook an attempt at conversation as something more carnal, as you do now." Tel eyed him again, this time from top to bottom. "I am sure of it." He was hot under his beard. "How can someone able to call forth such warmth and feeling with his singing voice be so utterly wooden in his speech? Talking with you is like talking with a door."

"I'm not wooden. I...I miss home."

"I have some experience with being alone abroad," said Tel, words coming rapidly from his tight throat. "Which is why I am trying to show you some kindness. Only to be met by an emotionless door."

"How am I to let a feeling out? How am I to do it in this place? This place I don't know. This place where I'm stared at and called bluebell. To my face and behind my back. I'm to show my feelings to you, a stranger? A hypocrite? So devoted to your faith. But drunk out of your skull all the time. A monied, oversexed drunk took me off the streets ten years ago. He showed an interest in my talent. He—Who am I to show?" The boy looked around, searching for someone to answer his question, a strange, desperate terror in his eyes. "Who? I can't. I can't start giving voice to my feelings, or they'll—" He gulped for air, flinching slightly as if worried Tel would hit him. "I don't want to be here. I don't like this place, and I don't like you." His chest heaved with jagged breaths.

"You ride tomorrow to spend a few weeks at the Academy at Sonagrein, do you not?"

Touching his face, rocking from one foot to the other and back again, Vared gave a little pinched moan. He nodded.

"Then you shall have respite from my unseemliness." Tel hated himself for the bile in his voice. "I came to tell you I have arranged for you to have my best horse for the journey. They would have given you a lesser animal." In truth, he did not know why he had followed him. He did not need to inform him of a decision he had already made. "Her name is Kelseigh. She is lovely, quick, graceful, but stubborn and slow to trust." He turned and headed back the way he had come.

"Thank. You. Your. Highness."

Tel heard that the words had come at great effort, between racking sobs. Without looking back, he raised a hand as he continued across the green-gray stone. "Safe travels, excellency."

He returned to his party and drank. Two hours later, the boy who had flirted with Vared was in the prince's bed.

* * *

Tel and Caip leaned on the shady side of a squat stone building, afternoon commerce slowing into mellower evening traffic. The activity of the city's transition from day to night eddied around them.

"I will never understand how you can eat such things." Caip scrunched her nose. "Especially when you so seldom eat."

"This—" Tel was eating fast enough that he nearly choked. He swallowed what was in his mouth. "It is just a griddlecake."

"From the street." The state of her nose was unchanged. "It's incongruous, you eating street food."

"It is tasty," said Tel. "What is incongruous about it?"

61

"You realize, don't you, that you sound and move and look like a person who believes his leavings smell of gandaith petals?"

"That is only because my leavings smell of gandaith petals."

"They certainly don't," she said, widening her eyes. "I know."

"I am highborn. It is my bad luck, but am I supposed to act like someone I am not? Besides, you are the one who seems to think she is above street food. Whose leavings do not smell?" He turned a sharp look to her and continued eating. "And it is not from the street. It is from a cookshop. The woman knows her craft."

"Since you would not come out with anyone but me to protect you, it would be safer if you acted less princely. That's my point."

"We are tripping over Lag's men. His new security millenary are everywhere. Watching. And I am not eating like a prince. I am eating like a savage. I am starving. I have not eaten in a day."

"The ale leaves no room for food."

He ignored her comment. "You cannot get this in the castle." He gestured, and some crumbs fell to the ground.

"Thankfully. I'm not sure how you can eat after almost killing a man."

His mouth was full of griddlecake again. He raised his black eyebrows.

"The luthier," said Caip. "He nearly expired after realizing where he'd be delivering to and who you are."

"I admit, that is a part of princedom of which I never tire. I should wear humbler clothes more often. Their expressions are always worth the effort. Never are they pleased to see me. Only surprised. I think they would prefer it if heralds kicked their door in and sounded a fanfare and I marched in and abused them."

"You mean, they would prefer Lag's approach to his station."

He could not help his chuckle. "You are a traitor."

She watched him eat the remainder of his cake with a crooked grin. "Your errand is done, your revolting food is finished, the sun will set soon. Shall we head back?"

"Let us take a long way. I would enjoy a walk. The evening is going to be lovely. It will help my digestion."

"Your digestion may be beyond help." She raised her hood. "It's a bit chilly."

"Autumn is well underway now. The antlered goddess is smiling."

They walked without aim for an hour, enjoying the clean, salted breezes blowing off the Gray Sea as much as their usual verbal sparring. The city's outdoor spaces steadily emptied of people. Day dwellers were returning home, and night dwellers were preparing themselves to take the streets. Tel put his arm around Caip's shoulder as they turned a corner onto a tiny road paved with uneven, mismatched stones. He felt her musculature stiffen suddenly.

From behind, Tel heard quick, deliberate footfalls and understood Caip's instant lack of ease. He thought it was likely a silly overreaction, but he tightened his one-armed hug and marched them forward. Ahead of them, a dark figure appeared.

"Couldn't help notice you got your hand round a bluebell, there, sir," a man behind them said.

As soon as he heard *bluebell,* Tel remembered Caip's cloak. It was a distinctly Omelan garment, both shorter and narrower than the mantles of Feighan dress. The hood, however, was quite a bit larger. The material was not as thick. Its cheerful plum was a shade much brighter than most Feighans would consider wearing. She had admired similar pieces on Omelan women. Tel had bought it for her on their most recent trip. He had wanted to express his gratitude for her standing at his side through the negotiations. He now cursed the sentiment.

His hand was on the antler hilt of his dagger. He was certain Caip's would be on her sword.

"Only hope it's a man, not a woman. It's not safe for mongrel children to be toddlin' around Affas." A smirk colored the man's voice. "I prefer women, myself. Feighan women. But a bluebell is a bluebell is a bluebell." The figure ahead of them picked up the pace, stepping across the cobblestones, moving closer. "An' a bluebell lover, that's a special kind of Feighan. Used to be, not that long ago, such a Feighan got a special kind of treatment. Now, what was that treatment?"

Tel tried to decide what to do. He considered and dismissed options so fast, he was not even aware of all the calculations: *Run. No. We are not as fast as we used to be and do not know this neighborhood. No idea what is around the next corner. Do not move until you can make it count. Turn. Fight. Avoid violence. If it comes to a fight, let it be because they force it on us and let us know their total number. Explain who you are. No guarantee they would recognize me, and if they did, no guarantee they would care. We do not want to start talking in such a vulnerable position. Best to talk my way out of this, but best to do so behind my own weapon. If I could touch Caip's skin, I could use the stagsblood to know exactly what she is thinking...*

Prince Tel launched them to the right, into an alleyway. Piles of reeking garbage sat in small, foul ponds on both sides of the cramped passage. They spun to face the attackers from the street and draw weapons, but before they were even a quarter through their turns, a third and fourth assailant were upon them. Blades were at their backs, hands over their mouths. The two men from the street had also unsheathed their weapons.

The woman holding Tel said, "I remember. A Feighan who lay with a bluebell would be executed."

"That's right, that's right. Tortured first, if I remember my not-so-distant history."

"You do," said the woman. "Proving time and change do not guarantee progress."

The original men stomped forward while the pair behind pulled Tel and Caip backward, to the dimmer end of the alley. Rotting food and human waste seared Tel's nose. The female's moist fingers were clamped over his lips. He was already searching for the stagsblood, willing the magic of the wind to give him the criminal's thoughts. They were on the surface, waiting for him: *Make an example. There's right an' there's wrong. Purity.*

She was not here for conversation and might not take the time to realize she held weapons at the backs of not only two Feighans but of the prince and the chief of his personal guard.

Chances were good Caip and Tel would be murdered in this alley.

Antlered ones, forgive me. Let Caip act quickly. Make her know what to do.

If we die tonight, please let the dirt welcome us home. From the north, from the east, from the south, from the west, from dirt, from wind, from fire, from rain. If we live, let us welcome you home. From. The. Dirt.

A sound: *fwump.*

Orange light, bright as noon on summer solstice, filled the alley. From bottom to top, a massive pile of trash was ablaze.

Tel was a beat or two ahead of the rest of them. He stomped on the woman's foot with the full power of his right leg. With his left, he delivered a vicious backward kick, sending her to the ground. Tel unsheathed his dirk as he moved toward the man with Caip. The oaf had stumbled back a stride and a half, his forearm shielding his eyes from the firelight.

Years of dedication to the honing of her skills and reflexes meant Caip was already responding. Tel and his loyal friend formed a wordless plan of action with a half-beat of eye contact.

Caip, the better fighter of the two, launched forward to deal with the men in front of them. Tel's armed fist sailed in a wide arc toward the fiend to his right. His blade tapped the bone in the man's upper arm. Tel withdrew the edge in a blink, and his opponent crumpled. Meanwhile, the woman was stunned but moving to raise herself to her knees. Tel delivered a sickening kick to her jaw. She collapsed, flat on her belly.

Behind him, Tel heard steel kissing steel a dozen or so times before the rapid slapping of shoes on cobblestones. He turned to see both frightened men chugging as far away from Caip as they could. The rightmajor, sword aloft, continued to stomp toward the mouth of the alley, bellowing curses after them. Hand clamped over his wound, the man he had stabbed lurched into the night.

Tel closed his eyes and filled his body with a slow breath. The fire was gone as fast as it had appeared. He raised his eyelids and saw pieces of ash dancing in the air, settling on the injured woman on the ground.

She looked up at him. He hissed at the pathetic wreck. "If you knew how many Omelans have wet my cock, you would die on the spot. Such a quick death would be too good for you."

He heard Caip approach from his rear. "The fire. What in the name of the goddesses hap—"

"I do not know." Guilt bit at him for the lie. He blocked her path and guided her out of the alley. "Let us get away from here."

"But we need to take her into custody."

"Keep walking."

"She can be charged. Must be."

"Caip." His voice was full and deep with all the authority of his station. "Walk." A moment later, blocks away, he said, "I know exactly who she is and exactly how to find her."

* * *

Naked, Prince Tel performed a cleansing ritual on his balcony in scarce moonlight. He called to the four directions and the four elements. He cleaned the blood from his dirk with dirt, wind, fire, and rain. Repeating the purification on his hands, he sat cross-legged on the cold stone and prayed to his goddess and god, begging them to illuminate the path to forgiveness for his sin of violence. The thought of his dirk passing through flesh to strike bone made him heave.

He moved inside to his bed, sacramental mud under his fingernails.

Tel propped himself up on pillows and drank a spicy red wine from Andow. He had done a lot of magic in a short amount of time and was tired. As the hours ticked by, however, he realized no amount of wine would push the night to the back of his mind so he could sleep. What had occurred in the streets of Affas represented darkness, both old and new. The prejudices Tel's father and grandfather had fought against had not been defeated. They had only fled from view. The smudge of violence was, for the first time, on the pacifist prince now—it was *in* him. Frowning, he picked at the dirt under his fingernails and floated in a mist of unsatisfactory, anxious drunkenness.

Eight

Armed with dirks, Tel and Caip entered the cell holding the woman who had led the attack against them. She sat on the iron excuse for a bed. Rightmajor Caip stood straight, well outside striking distance, hands clasped behind her back. Tel assumed a more casual pose, leaning against the rough wall within an arm's length of the prisoner. Caip fired a wide-eyed expression of warning at him, which he waved off with a smirk.

He turned the wicked half-smile to the prisoner. "Lieutenant Gran. A delight to see you again. I assumed a soldier's quarters would be modest, but I had no idea. I mean no offense, of course. Still. Silver is not what draws one into service, is it? No. It is the chance glory might await. It is the unparalleled camaraderie, the siblinghood. What else? Yes. The opportunity to loyally and selflessly serve Feigh, to protect all its people." Her eyes had found a spot on the floor the instant she saw him through the barred window in the door. They had not moved. "Tell me, Lieutenant Gran, did you swear an oath to serve Feigh and protect its people? Did you give your blood to the dirt, wind, fire, and rain to consecrate your words?"

"I swore it with my blood." She kept looking at the filthy floor. Her jaw was swollen. Speaking was plainly difficult.

"I knew it, Caip. I knew it. She swore the oath to Feigh and all Feighans. I am satisfied." He made a sound of delight. A few beats passed. "Although, this would mean attacking a Feighan without cause would be contrary to your oath, would it not?"

He crouched, so his mouth was at her ear. Caip flinched but remained in her spot, hand on the haft of her dirk.

"I need your help, Lieutenant Gran," said Tel. "I do not know about such things. And Caip is so quiet. She does not teach me about the minutia of martial life. I am no soldier. I do not mean to pretend modesty. I have had some training. I can fight. I am capable of defending myself if I ever somehow stumble into a dark alley scrap. But I am ignorant of many military matters. Would attacking a Feighan not be a violation of a soldier's oath?"

Snarling, Gran said, "Yes."

Tel refused to move a muscle. "What about attacking a prince of the realm? The chief of his guard? Is that a crime?"

"Are you making an accusation?" asked Gran. "An accusation of a soldier in King Lag's security millenary?"

"You mistook Caip for an Omelan because of the cloak she wore last night. You mistook her for a—I'll not say what your friend said. But you did not know it was me. That is was us. And I do not think you figured it out, in the darkness and the commotion. But it was Caip and me. You dragged us into an alley. Whether you would have left us dead or only bleeding, I cannot be sure." He shrugged. "What I am sure about is what you were thinking. You were going to make an *example*. But there is *right* and there is *wrong*, after all. Something must be done in the name of Feighan *purity*."

Eyes wide, Gran cowered and moved across the metal bed, away from him. "How...antlered g—" She looked at Caip. "How did he?"

"I am a dynast. I read your mind." Tel's laugh was a growl.

"The fire," the prisoner said, raising her index finger to point at Prince Tel.

"Were I a dynast, Gran, do you think you would still draw breath? Strange, though, that fire. Perhaps the antlered ones just took particular interest in burning the disease you represent from their city. They created this world with the beaked ones of Omela and all the other goddesses and gods. Together they created the people of the six nations and looked over us—all of us—until violence like yours chased them away."

Gran scoffed. "You don't understand the faith."

"Oh?"

"We're special. Exceptional. Feigh is. It was the goddess and god of Feigh who led the others to create the animals and the people. And our Stag was the last god with his foot on the world. That foot was in Feighan soil until the end. The other gods, the lesser gods, abandoned their lesser people long before that. They ran off and left the Stag to grieve on his own. It is always this way. The other kingdoms can't be trusted. Untrustworthy people descended from untrustworthy goddesses and gods. They take what they want but offer nothing but disease and their backward customs. And Omelans are the basest of them all. And cowards. First sign of trouble, first time they are faced with a real fight, they fly away. They wilt. Bluebells. And half of Feigh wants friendship with them. Not just peace, but friendship. Happy to mingle and dilute what is Feighan so they can tug on some exotic blue hair when they fuck."

Furious and nauseated, Tel straightened and expelled the air from his lungs. He heard footfalls drawing closer until he saw the head fill the window. "Uncle?"

Tel felt like molten lead was filling his abdomen. At once, he realized. Lieutenant Gran would go free.

* * *

Tel ran his thumb over the embossed Stag's head adorning the leather-encased decanter from which he drank. He had snatched it on the way out of the coronation festivities, seeing no need for a glass or mug. Caip had suggested they make their exit. She wanted some fresh air, so they slinked to the extensive gardens wrapping the castle in a verdant arc from west to north. Back-to-back, they sat on the silky edge of a flower bed. The slow cooling of the year had started to dull most of the brighter colors.

"These gardens put Cessa's courtyard to shame," said Tel. He was intoxicated enough to need to concentrate to avoid slurring his words.

"The scale of them, maybe," said Caip, "but Cessa's are more elegant."

"I am amazed."

"Why?"

Tel swallowed a mouthful of wine. "I never thought I would hear you singing Omela's praises, most especially in comparison to Feigh."

She pushed out a sigh. "Doesn't feel the same."

"Home?"

"Some of that's because your father's gone. But not all of it. It's different now."

"I miss him," said Tel, his eyes on a furling, browning leaf. "If I could have one thing, it would be that he waited just a couple of months…"

"You must be angry."

"At my father?"

"Yes."

He thought about it for a time. "No. Not angry."

"At anything, then?"

"No, Caip. I am not angry."

"At your brother? Your uncle? About being attacked by that prejudiced bitch? About not being king?"

"Anger would be senseless. The state of things can only be the state of things."

"Platitude. Prince Tel offers clichés now?"

"You know, more than anyone, I did not have much fire for the idea of being king. I always dreamed of fewer responsibilities. I did not want it."

"But what about now?"

Tel thought for a pair of beats and said, "No."

"I don't believe you."

"I am not here to argue. I am here to drink, breathe the autumn air, and look at the moons."

Caip grunted. "I worry his reign will not be good for Feigh. This coronation will be the beginning of—"

"That is enough, Caip. Table will temper him. That is its purpose. We shall do the good we can. You will do more of it than me. Your heart never falters. It never desires the wrong thing. I am useless now."

She crawled around him so she could look into his eyes. He had to prevent

70

himself from tipping over when he no longer had the support of her body at his back. "Your heart is true. You're decent, Tel. You're still a prince of this realm, and you can use your power to do good things."

"I am a drunk. I am forty, and I share my bed with no one because I share my bed with everyone. I am only…I am…What am I? Minister of Arts and Culture." His laugh fell out of him, low and bitter. He took another swig from the decanter. "You see? A drunk. I was not even conscious of it. I just put it to my lips." He saw Caip look over his head. "What is it?"

"Vared." She narrowed her eyes. "Quiet as a cat."

Tel made an awkward, wobbly turn to face him. He found himself unable to look any higher than his narrow, black-clad chest. He felt Vared's eyes on him but could not give his. Heat kissed his cheekbones.

"I apologize, your highness, rightmajor. I arrived a handful of hours ago and fell into a nap. I thought I'd find you at the festivities to let you know I've returned from the Academy."

Tel swung back around, steadier this time.

"Thank you, Vared. Goodnight," said Caip.

"Goodnight," said Vared.

When he was gone, Caip said, "I don't trust him."

Tel's consciousness stood on the cliff overhanging the chasm of utter intoxication. If he did not slow down, he would lose memories of the night. Dizziness was already upon him. He stretched and set the decanter out of his reach.

He surprised himself by putting his head in Caip's lap. This affection was not the type the pair typically exhibited, at least not for the last two decades. He could feel all her muscles stiffen. After a few minutes, he felt the ice in her melt.

He was unsure how long the silence stretched. She began to play with his hair, pulling it through her fingers. He thought he might fall asleep, but a commotion tumbled into the garden.

Wanting to avoid embarrassment for Caip, he sat up. A group of about a dozen partygoers scampered into the moonlight. Their voices were colored by wine and louder than necessary. A pair of them walked off, hand in hand, deeper into the plantings and paths.

"You animals best not start a family tonight," called someone after them.

None of the revelers seemed to notice Tel and Caip sitting on the grass. Prince Tel was happy to eavesdrop while they complained about the length of Lag's coronation ceremony and as they gossiped about some of the better-known castle personalities. Tel found himself hoping they would mention his name. He thought it would be amusing to approach them as they traded secrets about him. The opportunity did not present itself, but another arose.

"What do you think they will do with the dynast?" asked one of them.

Tel and Caip looked at each other. Tel's faculties returned to him in an instant. His drunkenness evaporated.

Another said, "She surrendered quietly, thank the antlered ones. She sits near us now in the cells. Making no attempt to escape."

"Weird. Spooky," a third said.

Tel was on his feet, marching toward the group, Caip trailing.

"She will be executed. There's no choice."

"Why would the child be executed?" asked Tel as he reached them. "What has the child done?" They were all clearly surprised to see the pair. When they realized Prince Tel was among them, they became a stuttering mass. "One of you answer me. You." He lifted a finger at a young man who seemed less drunk than the others.

"Your highness." He offered the top of his head. "The dynast is no child."

"Impossible."

"Highness, she's more than eighty seasons old and used the stagsblood to murder someone."

"How does a girl of twenty years retain her powers?" Caip asked, shaking her head. "It makes no sense."

"It doesn't," another member of the group said. "But there were witnesses to the murder. Lightning from her hands."

"Stag and Doe," said Tel.

"At least she hasn't resisted," said the first man. "How would she be subdued otherwise? There's no one to fight her. Even if there was another dynast, who's to say they'd protect us?"

"Stag and Doe," Tel repeated.

* * *

Unable to sleep, Tel paced about his apartments, avoiding his giant Omelan mirror. While he once rather fancied his own reflection, he now loathed looking at himself. He knew he would see not only evidence of his exhaustion but skin not as evenly colored as it once was, a graying beard needing a trim, and deep little trenches fanning from the outer corners of his eyes.

He was haunted by the news of another living adult dynast. Whispers that some with the blood remained were ever-present and easily dismissed. Centuries ago, the dynasts began to disappear, until they were gone. Rarely, a Feighan child developed signs of mild magical skill, but their powers faded within a few years. At first, when Prince Tel's own stagsblood had begun to show itself, he had enjoyed holding an amusing little mystery to himself.

His magic had persisted and strengthened as he left childhood behind for manhood, so he had felt fearful and odd. He had not wanted to worry his parents, who were already burdened with so much responsibility. His nature had morphed from child's private joke to adolescent's closely guarded secret.

He always listened with extra care to the superstitious, hushed rumors of dynasts among Feighans. In his true heart, however, he had always thought he was alone. Agreement was nearly universal that Feigh was better off without practitioners of the dynasty, although they had once given the race an advantage over the others. Tales of their exploits were almost all aimed at spooking children. He was an oddity, an abomination. Knowing he was not alone did not make him feel any less so.

He had not seen Kelseigh since she carried Vared back to Affas, so he decided to visit the stables. The walk might tire him. He found the stable girl already dozing in the hay. Tel considered waking her but looked at her peaceful face and could not bear to disturb her. Envy of her easy snoring stung.

Moving away from her, he thought he heard a voice. Tel strained his ears but only picked up the Gray Sea roaring below. He padded toward Kelseigh's stall, at the end of a row of her own. She preferred solitude and only had company in neighboring booths when dignitaries visited with their animals. When he rounded the corner, he let out half a low gasp and covered his mouth with his hand. He stepped back into a shadow and focused attention on his breath. Lowering his mind, with considerable effort, he formed a cloak of invisibility around himself.

Vared stood on his toes in front of the stall, feeding Kelseigh an apple with his long fingers. He cocked his head. Frozen, he appeared to concentrate on listening before looking around. His eyes passed over Tel more than once. Hearing nothing more, he looked at the horse again. A lantern and fabric bag were at the songmaker's feet.

He was delicate in amber light. *Pretty as any woman could ever hope.*

"It's spooky out here. Do you think so, girl? Maybe I'll ask if you can room with me. I have missed you, my lovely." He reached down and drew a carrot from the sack. "You must not tell anyone about my smuggling. Do you understand? I think you do. Yes. Yes, I know you do," Vared spoke to the horse like a parent doting on an infant. With one hand, he fed Kelseigh the carrot. With the other, he stroked her neck. The grumpy horse adored him. His warmth and tenderness surprised Tel. He wore a relaxed smile, an expression the prince had not seen grace his face.

Tel felt like a common peeper, violating the sanctity of a private moment, but he could not bring himself to lift a foot. The intimacy of the sweet exchange held him in place like a hundred chains. Too weak to look away, his face burned.

"That's all for now," Vared told Kelseigh. "I cannot have you grow plump overnight. They'll throw me in the dungeon for sure. And I'd like you to remain sleek. If I get to ride you again, I'd like you to really give it your best gallop. Like you were running down the handsomest stallion in Feigh."

He placed a loud kiss on her muzzle. In turn, she rested her chin on his shoulder for a moment. "I must go, my girl. I'll wake up early. I do my best writing at dawn. Maybe a song about you? Yes, my sweet. Would you like that? You would? You would. Yes." He kissed her again before collecting his bag and lantern.

Turning in front of the stall, he paused to have another listen. Beads of sweat chased one another down Tel's back. Vared appeared to strain his eyes as he looked through him once more before leaving. He passed close enough for Tel to smell him for the first time.

Tel stood in silence for a long while, recovering. Unable to put a name to that from which he was recuperating, he collected his thoughts. When he felt like himself again, and when he was sure Vared would not be returning, he lowered the cloak he had cast around himself. Kelseigh reacted to his sudden appearance with a chuff and snort. She calmed when she recognized him.

Spent from the effort of holding such difficult fire magic, he shuffled to her stall. "I think I may not be your number one anymore, hm? I do not even have a treat for you, girl."

The bulk of Tel's practice with both the wind and rain dynasties had been made on animals. He had been stunned to learn the complexity of their inner lives. Cats and dogs, for instance, thought and felt in ways sophisticated enough to rival some duller humans. The minds of horses were particularly intricate.

Advanced dynasts, the practitioners of old, were able to manipulate others' thoughts and feelings in profound ways. The strongest among them—if the legends were to be believed—could control the mind and heart of another without even touching them. Tel's powers were piddling in comparison.

Stroking the beautiful beast, he pushed through his fatigue, breathed into his belly, and found her mind. She had enjoyed the journey to the Academy, taking special pleasure in Vared's affection and attention. "Not a door after all," Tel said to his favorite horse, feeling like he could sleep at last.

Nine

On a chair in his sleeping chamber, Tel squinted at a window, trying to remember. He recalled hearing the news—the female dynast had been executed—and beginning to drink. It was chilly, but he did not have the will to find last night's clothes, which were knotted somewhere in his bedding. Instead, he shouldered his nakedness into a linen shirt retrieved from a broad, solid wardrobe. It was middle thigh-length and ivory in color, with a wide opening at the chest, meant to be cinched with laces. He did not bother to close the collar. The laces trailed down his abdomen. It was cold enough to also pull on some hose, but he was unsure he could bend to do so without tipping over. Soon, he would need a fire, at least at night. He shivered. Dusted with black hairs and speckled with goosebumps, the lower two thirds of his legs peeked out from the thin, bone-colored fabric.

The first gulp of hidybrew scalded his throat in a way he found not disagreeable. Something inside his head was bashing itself over and over against the backs of his eyes. He had risen the day before determined to avoid alcohol. His intention to abstain dissolved when he learned the adult dynast woman had been executed on his brother's order.

He told himself he was making an excuse. On countless previous occasions—pleasurable times entirely free of stressors—his plan to stay sober had been swallowed by incessant thoughts of thirst and its quenching. It was easy enough to quiet his mind in those situations. Peace was as available to him as the nearest cup.

Around him, servants went about their intricate choreography, laying out linens and clothes, trolleying in a cart of food, removing evidence of the previous night's indulgences, and heaving hot water about for his bath. They had long ago learned the dance should be achieved with as little noise as possible. This quiet was nothing short of imperative when their prince sat at his window, squinting so.

He turned to look at the piles of meats, fruits, cheeses, and breads. Equal parts hungry and nauseated, he knew he needed to eat but decided he would do so after bathing. He eyed his bed, isolated from the world by its canopy of rich fabrics, wishing he could crawl back in and hide. A servant he had not yet seen this morning entered, offering a bow. Tel knew this meant she was going to speak and dreaded it.

"My prince, the Omelan is here for you."

"The Omelan?"

"Yes, highness."

"You mean Vared? The ambassador?"

"Yes."

"You may use his name," said Tel, trying a little smile. It made his temples throb. "In fact, please do."

"Yes, highness. Shall I offer him a seat?"

"Yes. Put him in the sitting room and let him know I will be right with him."

The attendant exited, and Tel waited a few moments. He finished his hidybrew and shuffled barefooted through the apartments to the parlor. Vared shifted his weight forward to rise from the couch, but Tel gestured with his left hand for him to remain seated. He glanced at the prince's bare legs.

"No need for formality. Obviously." Tel looked down at himself. "I apologize for my state. I considered dressing more fully but remembered you are Omelan. Plus, you have already seen me disrobed. In Cessa's garden." He folded his legs under himself on the sofa opposite Vared. A low, dark table sat between them.

Tel's guest looked down at his hands, which were picking at lint and smoothing the fabric over his lap. "You have a misapprehension about Omelans, I'm afraid. While we're certainly, on the whole, more relaxed about the body than the average Feighan, you're used to being among our ruling class. They're uncommonly permissive." He raised his eyes to Tel's.

It was clear to Tel that Vared could only extend his charms to horses. He bit down on the inner surface of his cheek. "I see. I have offended you. I can—"

"I didn't say I was offended."

Tel could not remember having a conversation with this boy during which he was not interrupted mid-sentence. "What brings you to my rooms? You are not worried about what people will say?"

"It's daylight, your highness. And people are everywhere about. I just...I don't want people to think I melt just because someone highborn flashes a smile at me. Or that I'm here in Feigh for the wrong reasons." He took in and pushed out a breath. He lowered his gaze. "It's I who have offended you."

Finding no sense or use in circumspection, Tel said, "Vared, look at me." It was a command, and it was obeyed. "Please accept my apology for... my advance in Omela. I am sorry. I do not remember it, but I was...not myself. I was drunk, and I had taken a dreaming bud during the ceremony. Afterward is...gone. Since then? Since that night? I am not trying to bed you."

"And I was not. I shouldn't have reacted as I did when you came to check on me. I shouldn't have yelled and said those things. To anyone, let alone you, your highness. I wasn't myself, either. I didn't lobby for this assignment, and—Sometimes, I lose control. My emotions become strong, and I have the feeling I'm struggling to breathe. Like I've been under the water too long. I...*flail*...and all of it rushes from me completely out of proportion." All the muscles of his face contracted, and he shook his head. "I'm not making sense."

"I follow."

"I didn't choose...to be here. Across a sea. Alone. I don't warm to people easily. And I haven't found a way to convince people to warm to me."

Tel snuffed a wild cackle. "Vared, I am sorry. People do not warm to us because we have convinced them. Quite the opposite."

"But I wouldn't know. May I tell you something about myself?"

"Of course."

Vared closed his eyes for a few beats. When he opened them, he said, "In Omela, there is supposed to be no shame about being an orphan, but... I don't remember where I came from." He lowered his voice as a pair of attendants passed through the room. "I don't know my parents. My whole childhood, the parts I can remember, I lived on the streets with other children. In a way, we looked after one another. But in a way, there was no trust. Knives. Thievery. Street fights. Some of us being dragged off by...for...I sang for food and silver. Did what I needed to do for food and silver or a warm night. A merchant, one of the most powerful in the capital, took me in. Heard me singing. He was drunk and foul-tempered and nasty, but he gave me an education and a bed to sleep in. That's all I had. Education, training, sleep. And staying out of his way. And now palaces and castles. Sometimes when I smell ale...or sometimes for no reason at all, I find myself feeling under the water and out of proportion. I'm not sure I've had many real friends in my life, but at least the people at home are accustomed to...the way I can be."

"Would you like one?" asked Tel. "A friend?"

"The question isn't fair."

"Why?"

"How is anyone to refuse you? You're a prince. Soldiers, singers, servants, party boys, ship's scribes? We're nothing. You think you're liked by everyone because you make conversation easily, even with the lowborn. Or because you don't abuse your servants. But you must know all the rest of us are required to make ourselves agreeable to people like you?"

"You have made yourself agreeable to me?" Tel shook his head. A low sound of amusement chuffed out of him.

"Yes."

"I do not require anything of you. I have seen your sensitivity." He pictured him in the stables, cooing at Kelseigh. An odd fear came over him. He worried he had said too much—that Vared would know about his spying. It was impossible. Still, he groped to recover. "When you sing. I have seen it. You. Show me *that*. Show me yourself. That is friendship, and it is not a requirement."

"Very well. We will be friends."

"You even make that sound like a chore. You are funny. Humor is an important quality of friendship. I need to tell you something you may not like. But my mind is made up and I ask you to trust me."

Vared tilted his head, concern creeping like dusk over his wispy features. "Continue."

"Perhaps you have heard about the incident with Caip and me? In the city? We were attacked."

"I have. This castle's much like home that way. Always whispers carrying news."

"Whenever you leave this island, you will be accompanied by two soldiers from Caip's unit. It is actually not an unusual precaution for a foreign dignitary."

"Dignitary," said Vared, around a chuckle.

"What are your thoughts about it?"

"You said, didn't you, that your mind's made up?"

"I did."

"Then I will...make myself agreeable to you."

"A joke!" Tel was stunned.

"I have something for you."

"Oh?"

"From Omela." Vared pulled two letters from between his chest and the black fabric of his blouse. "A parcel was waiting for me when I returned from Sonagrein. These were in it."

"This elaborate one would be from Cessa," said Tel. "I am not sure about this one." He placed them on the table. "Thank you for bringing them to me personally."

"You're welcome. I wanted to see you. I mean that I wanted to have the opportunity to talk."

"How did you find it? The Academy."

"Wonderful. Everything about the Feighan style—the playing, the lyrics,

80

the structures—is so direct. I mistook that directness for simplicity. I left feeling inspired." His face made it apparent his mind had drifted a long way off. He refocused. "I do not dislike Feigh, your highness. I was feeling alone here. But I feel alone at home, as well."

"I also have something for you. To say I am sorry about…the awkwardness I caused." He loved giving gifts and, in his excitement, flew to his feet. His shirt hitched upward. He scrambled to preserve his modesty—or Vared's—but was unsure he succeeded. The orange eyes were now on the floor. Tel's cheeks burned. "I will return quickly."

He strode to his cabinet and returned bearing a wooden terquin case. "You need to protect your instrument. It was only delivered yesterday. I asked that it be personalized."

Vared stared at the gift from his seat.

"Did you want it?"

"Oh, yes." Vared rose. Crossing to Tel, he said, "Of course." He accepted it and held it up to the light, regarding the flame maple's rich grain. "I haven't had a solid one before, only bags."

"It is well assembled, I believe. The luthier said the hinges and closures should hold up to travel. Perhaps not knife fights in the street." Vared laughed, stunning him. Tel noticed how his orange eyes caught the sun coming through the window as warmly as the case's wood. "We thought it was the prettiest one at the shop. Caip helped me choose it."

"She doesn't like me at all."

"Fear not. Caip likes no one. Open it."

Vared set the case on the back of the sofa on which Tel had been sitting. He unlocked and opened it, exposing the indigo velvet inside. Affixed with tiny screws, where the neck of the terquin would rest, sat an engraved copper plaque. *For His Excellency Vared, Ambassador and Songmaker of Omela. In peace and friendship.*

Another laugh escaped Vared, delighting Tel. He found it musical, which was fitting. "What is funny?"

Vared raised a cobalt brow. "I see you assumed we'd be friends."

"You said it yourself, I cannot be refused."

"I did."

They looked at one another. Tel could not believe the songmaker's grin. "How beautiful," said Vared.

Tel followed the apricot eyes to his own open collar. "Oh. This. Yes." He fingered the little Doe pendant resting against his chest. "My mother's. Rarely did she not wear it, but she left it behind the day—"

"Blue hair," cooed the young man now peeking around the doorway to the sitting room. He had emerged from the cocoon of Tel's bed. Almond-shaped brown eyes widened under shaggy black hair, consuming Vared. "You're not from here." He brought his nudity into the room. Resting his back against the wall, he jutted his hips forward. He giggled. "Hi. I'm Mil. Guess you'll be joining us?"

Vared looked at Tel's feet.

The prince emerged from his temporary paralysis and closed the distance between himself and the naked lad. Teeth gritted, he said, "No. He will not. This is *Ambassador* Vared, and he and I would very much appreciate it if you put some clothes on. Please."

Mil pouted. "You're so stern. Are we playing a game?" He let his lashes flutter. "A dirty game?" He giggled again.

"No."

"Oh."

"Get dressed now," said Tel.

"Or I can wait for you. For after Emperor Varrow leaves."

Behind him, Tel heard Vared suppress a snicker. "No. Thank you. I am quite satiated."

"*Say-she-ay-ted?*" Mil blinked with each syllable.

"Yes."

Mil scrunched his face. "Oh. You did that? Already? Right next to me in bed? Sneakier than a filthy dynast. Why didn't you wake me?"

"Please get dressed."

With a sigh, Mil said, "Fine," and left them.

Tel's hands were at his temples. "I am so sorry."

"It's understandable," said Vared. "An important man like you is bound to thirst for the company of his intellectual equals." He clamped his jaw shut over a laugh and eyed the prince.

Tel's mouth fell open. "That is not kind." He also held his amusement back, body quaking with the effort.

"Who is he? Where does he come from?"

"An apprentice to the royal tailor," said Tel. "I fear I do not even remember bringing him back here."

Vared said, "Well, you have your correspondence. And I have this beautiful case." He picked it up and patted it. "Thank you. For the gift and the comedy."

Tel did not want him to leave, at least until his latest conquest was out the door. "Thank you again for delivering the letters."

"You're welcome."

Tel followed him to the door, eyes on the sapphire mass of curls. "Vared?" He turned.

"Thank you also for telling me about you. I know it is trite to say, but I am sorry your youth was so difficult."

"It's not trite at all, your majesty. I'm sorry yours was, too." Vared offered a small, strange smile and was gone.

Tel looked at the closed door for a long time.

* * *

Prince Tel's tremulous hands poured ruby liquid from a bottle of the rotund, Andowian style into a crystal goblet. "Would you like a drink?" Craid looked at him as if confused, possibly even irritated. "I am sorry. I forgot."

"I long ago gave up sousing. Drink had his claws around my balls a long time."

"It is Caip's birthday tonight. The festivities begin soon," said Tel, gloom rather than celebration in his voice. He opened his throat and drained the glass. It was the first drink of the day, and he was surprised he had waited until evening to have it. After refilling, he took a seat on the same sofa

Vared had occupied that morning, next to the old man, who watched him closely.

"Your highness, you seem disturbed by this news. Surely it's not a surprise."

"No." Tel stared at the crystal in his hand.

"It's what is done."

"My father did not permit execution. Savagery."

"What else could be done with a mature dynast murderer? No prison could hold her."

"Lord Craid, think about what you are saying. She was in the jail, the castle jail, for days. What was to keep her from escaping? Lightning from her hands, mind control, illusion. We cannot know of what she was capable. She could have freed herself, marched to Lag's rooms, and murdered him in his sleep. No guard would stop her. But she stayed of her own will. She admitted what she did and said it was unintentional."

"She murdered that boy," said Craid, stabbing his index finger into his thigh. "Lag does not have the same view of execution as your father. She would have met the same fate if she did the deed by blade rather than by stagsblood."

"What might be done if she had set out to murder the king, or five, or five hundred more? Would we recruit an army of child dynasts to oppose her? Even if there were a thousand, would they fight her by conjuring coins or disappearing playing cards? Now we know sometimes dynasts mature, as they did long ago. They cannot all mean harm."

"She said there were more."

"What?" Wine splashed over the rim of the goblet.

"You heard correctly, highness. Before the poleaxe fell, she said she was not the only dynast in Affas."

"Goddesses and gods," said Tel, drying his wet fingers on his leggings.

"Yes, highness. Who knows whether the statement of a homicidal dynast, made in the last seconds of her foul life, can be trusted? Out of precaution, however, King and Table have a plan, suggested by Aith."

"Which is?"

84

"First sign of the dynasty, children will be sent to a new school at Fort Gontrahd. They'll be watched closely until their powers fade." Craid coughed into his fist. "Not doing so is a risk to the kingdom. When they have transitioned out of childhood, they'll graduate and begin their adult lives as they wish. Those whose powers start to strengthen will be dealt with. Hiding child dynasts will be a capital crime."

"Taking children from their families?" Tel felt overheated and dizzy. "Capital crime...For those who do not send their own children to a prison?"

"A school, highness. Where an excellent education will be provided."

Tel felt his posture deflate. "It is a fort! This will only worsen the situation. An overreaction. It will stoke paranoia."

"I see little choi—"

"Everywhere, people will see the dynasty in ordinary things, tricks of light, coincidence. Everywhere seeing dynasts where there are none. Parents *will* attempt to keep their children, to hide their powers," said Tel.

Craid watched his prince drink.

"*Think*, friend," said Tel. "*Think*." A fat tear broke from each of his eyes, gliding down his cheeks into his beard. "You have a daughter. When she was six years old, if she had levitated a bean over her plate, you would call one of the king's soldiers to take her away? What about your grandson?"

"Highness, I'm not going to engage—"

"Damn you, Lord Craid. You will not engage because you know the answer. You would do *anything* to avoid watching your confused grandson shriek as he was dragged away. I know you, and I know your decent heart, even if it has failed you long enough that you endorsed this profanity."

A heavy shadow fell upon Craid's features.

"You must be the conscience at Table. Be my father's voice. You simply must. Who else is to be the counterweight to my brother's baser instincts? Aith? My uncle only pulls him further in that direction. And the rest of Table was chosen by him. Lag has no intellectual vigor to override the first feeling that warms his gut. He needs you."

Craid looked at his lap. "Yes."

"Can you do that, Craid? Will you? At least give it some thought?"

"Yes, my prince," he answered, face open and sincere. Without another word, the late king's best friend got to his feet and saw himself out.

Tel sat motionless, staring at the table in front of him. Noticing the letters Vared had delivered, he picked them up and held them to his face, trying and failing to detect any scent of the songmaker on the paper. He had not realized what he was doing until it was done.

Quick math told him the letters could not have been sent more than three weeks after he had departed Omela. Turning the fancier of the two over, he slid a finger under the cerulean dab of wax stamped with Cessa's crowned C.

The queen was kind, thanking Tel again for his efforts over the last forty and eight seasons. She asked him to convey her best wishes to the new king. She also made an open offer to visit Feigh and meet King Lag whenever he would like. Next year, she suggested, after the negotiators hashed out the details of the trade accord. Laich, the playbard, was speaking with the keepers of Omela's history and with citizens of the capital. He had even been teaching some performers Feighan acting techniques. Cessa asked after Vared and hoped he was flourishing.

He flipped the rougher stock of the second letter over. Muddy, unstamped wax held the thin envelope together. Once he opened it, his eyes were met by untidy, labored penmanship. He could not discern whose words he was reading, so he scanned to the signature. *Turo.* He began again.

By the time he finished reading, Tel was on his feet in front of the couch, the sides of the paper curled in his clenched fists. He shook. The letter, released from his fingers, floated to the little table, which he then kicked over. Turo had been thrown from his horse on his way to the competition in Elium, his leg shattered. He was convalescing in the palace, under the care of Cessa's best surgeon, who gave him no hope of competing again. Turo would have a limp for the remainder of his days. When he was well enough, he would return to his family and work the land, as his parents did, and as their parents and their parents had.

Ten

Tel's eyes felt three times too large. He feared raising the lids, for he believed the throbbing pulse in his head was strong enough to eject the eyeballs from his skull. With his scorched throat and tongue, he swallowed and moaned. He tried to coax saliva to flow, failed, and moaned again. At first, he did not feel the nausea. It found him after a moment. Like a loyal dog, it was with him. He could not remember much of anything from the previous evening after his discussion with Craid. Replaying that conversation, he recalled Turo's letter, and something inside him split all over again. He wondered if he was in his own bed but decided not to check. Music seemed to be playing somewhere nearby. He wanted to sleep for a week. Still, it would be insufficient. He stretched his arms to determine whether he was alone or with a person or persons. Feeling no one, he was unsure whether it pleased or depressed him.

Mere flashes and smudges came to him, nothing of use in piecing together events. An abyss churned in his gut, sloshing dread in every direction. When he lost time this way, odds were he had caused himself some manner of embarrassment. In past dimness or blackness, he had started arguments, vomited in public, and attempted inelegant seduction of men whose desire for women was exclusive. After such scandal, assembling a picture of what had occurred was an anxious, dismaying search for clues. Worse, the timeline could never be made whole. The image formed through the investigation was, at best, a sketch.

Again, music.

Trepidation spread through every thought like ink added to water. He could not delay opening his eyes any longer. Finally, he looked and confirmed he was alone and in his bedroom. This information offered little comfort. His eyes, mouth, and throat screamed. The rich fabrics draped around and over his bed struck him as both prison doors and sanctuary gates. The drive to escape grappled with the desire to stay. No resolution came. It was a draw.

Making slow work of it, he moved to the edge of the bed and sat there a moment, dizzy head hanging. It was then he realized he had emptied his bladder at some point during the night. His leggings and shirts were plastered to his skin, damp and chilly. He tried to convince himself he had sweated through his clothes, that the wine and his covers had overheated him. The smell of urine made the argument impossible to accept.

I must drink less, and I must not drink at all today. A break.

The idea inspired no hope—only a bitter, silent laugh. Countless times, when he had reached some new low, when he found he had given away yet another bit of self-control, he had spurred himself toward similar goals. He had achieved several weeks-long periods of dryness but had hated himself during each of those. Foul-tempered and quick to lash out, it was unbearable to be himself. Worse, the people around him had suffered. He would begin drinking again, in a controlled fashion. Before long, it would accelerate into another humiliation.

He willed himself to his feet and came near to vomiting. With concentration and care, he shed his clothes and tossed them on the bed. Throwing his body across the mattress, he wrenched the bedding from it, including the pad meant to keep his skin from being poked with quills.

He ended up on his backside when he yanked the covers to the floor, almost losing the contents of his stomach again. When his head stopped spinning, he got to his feet, found a pitcher with some red wine in it, and dumped the contents all over the pile of bedding and clothes. He could not bear the thought of someone knowing he had lost control of his bladder and hoped the scent and color of wine would mask any evidence. The sting of tears visited his eyes. He offered himself vicious curses until he regained composure. Using a cloth and basin, he cleaned himself. Still, he detected the stink of ammonia.

Again, music.

Unsure if either—odor or sound—was real, he wondered if he was going mad. Rather than reaching a conclusion, he put a few drops of spicy Andowian perfume on his skin and wrapped a hooded cloak around himself, raising the cowl over his head. The song faded.

Tel knew of one unfailing method for making himself feel well. A drink would quiet his mind and steady his pulse. Those effects would be nearly instantaneous. Not long after that, his concern over last night would float away, at least for a time. His mood would lift. Saliva flooded his mouth at last.

He clenched his jaw. "You must not."

Deciding distraction might be his best tactic, he thought of a volume he had been reading. It was a dry but fascinating history of the reign of his great-great-great-grandmother. A quick search of his chamber did not reveal the book. He concentrated, which caused his head to bark. After a moment, an image of it—sitting on the carpet next to his favorite sofa—entered his mind.

Once he was through the door to the rest of his rooms, he realized he had not been hallucinating. He froze and strained his ears. Music—singing—from the sitting parlor. He crept on the balls of his feet toward the sound. With care, he peered around the jamb into the room, hiding most of himself behind the wall.

Vared was on his couch again, terquin across his body, lounging more than sitting. He cleared his throat. "Two-and-three-and…

Between the nations
Mm-mm-mm-mm
Stood the wives of the gods
Stag and bird, snake and worm, fish and frog
In their wrath and mm-mm-mm-mm
They were deaf mm-mm-mm
Hear our words, mm-mm-mm, mm-mm-mm."

It was clear he was writing as he sang. Even with his lyrical fumbling and casual posture, his voice rang true and clear. Tel stepped into the room. "That was pretty."

Vared sat up and gave a weak smile without looking at him. Instead, his eyes found and clung to the rug.

"Good morning," Tel offered.

"You're alive."

"Barely."

Eyes still on the floor, Vared said, "We weren't sure you'd be up so soon. If ever."

"We?"

"Caip and I."

"I feel like I had quite the evening," said Tel. "I hope her birthday was as much fun."

Now Vared lifted his gaze. "It was not."

"Oh?" Tel wanted to cry, knowing the blame was on him somehow. "If I—I am sorry."

"She said you'd say that. That you were sorry. Again." He shifted his weight forward to stand. "If you will excuse—"

"No, Vared. Take your seat. Stay."

"I'm here to make sure you're not dead. You're not. She didn't want you to be alone. But she couldn't stay."

"Sit. Caip could have asked one of her people to watch me. But she asked you. And now you know who I am. What I am like. What my problems are. And now you can tell me. As if I do not already know. As if the entire kingdom does not. Your queendom, too."

A dense kind of silence settled about them.

After a time, the rapid drumming of Tel's fingers against his thigh broke the quiet. "Speak, Vared. Speak."

"Your highness, you embarrassed her, and you embarrassed yourself. Not for the first time, apparently. You warm your belly and can't help but make yourself the center of attention. A spectacle. She's tired of forgiving you. She might. But she's *concerned.* Feels she's allowed this…behavior. And I don't blame her. Since we've gotten here, you've done nothing but prove that Table right. Carrying on like a madman. But you're the prince, who can't be refused. So, she has to watch you drink yourself stupid or dead. Send me home for speaking my mind. But I will speak it. Caip can't." He swallowed. "You're not my prince. I'm Omelan."

Tel was surprised by the heat and familiarity with which Vared had addressed him. It occurred to him that he should be outraged. Instead, he felt penitent. "I want to explain…" He squeezed his eyes closed, trying to think. He could not, so he opened his mouth and spoke. "I want to explain to you how it feels. How I feel. All the time. It leaves me only when—No. It does not even leave when I drink. Not anymore. It never leaves. Not for even a short time. It used to. Now it is always with me." Making a paddle of his hand, he struck his ribcage with his fingertips. "In here. For one hundred seasons." It was both truth and excuse. He allowed himself to fall onto the couch opposite the songmaker. "I am so…" He pulled the cowl from his head but could not meet the orange eyes.

"If you want me to stay," said Vared, "I'll stay. If you want me to leave, I'll leave."

"There is no fault to be found in anything you said. Or in what Caip thinks or might have said. The truth is so much worse. And I am ashamed that once again you are witness to an embarrassing situation."

"What happened to them?"

"To?" Still, he would not look up.

"Tell me about your mother and your first man."

"Var—"

"Tell me."

He finally looked at Vared's face, so youthful and well-balanced. It made him conscious of how last night—and thousands of nights before—must be written in harsh penmanship across his own features. "Do you always make a habit of ordering royalty around?"

"Only you."

"Ah." He lowered his head again.

"Tell me."

"There is, a week's ride from here, a castle at Foghar. It served as a retreat of sorts for my family for gods know how long. The favorite place of my father. My favorite place. And probably the favorite of many queens and princes and kings and princesses before us. A few generations ago, a new retreat was built. A bit closer and a lot grander. My father made the old estate mine because I love it so. My true home. Where I feel most comfortable. The castle. The land. Bigger than the city of Affas and your capital and ten more capitals. Endless fertile dirt tucked in a great valley, rocky forested hills on either side. Falls and brooks and streams, all flowing to the river.

"The beginning of autumn—what you would call mid-summer—was endless rain. Father was here in Affas, unable to escape. My brother was never fond of Foghar and remained with Father. My mother, Hod, Caip, and I rode out for the season. We were trapped inside for weeks. We read, played games, bickered. Hod and I—we did what two boys of that age who loved one another would do. Over and over and over again." A wistful suggestion of a laugh escaped him. "The rain stopped. We had indoor madness, all but Caip. She was not feeling well, so she stayed in bed.

"Mother and Hod and I prepared a picnic and rode out to the river. Her favorite spot. A perfect day. Shaded and with a small, sandy beachfront. Of course, the river was fat and angry, so the beach was covered over. We ate and enjoyed the sun, which hadn't really dried the ground yet. Hod and I talked on the blanket about the future with the arrogance and confidence of adolescents. Mother said something about our eyes being tangled again and stood up. She walked to the riverbank, singing.

The lovers met in the light of the moons
 Oh, their tangled eyes
 Kissed and promised until noon
 Oh, their tangled eyes
 And those around them called them fools
 Oh, their jealous eyes."

"Lovely," said Vared.

"It is. But Mother did not finish her song. She…I want to say screamed, but she did not. She made a sound—I still hear it perfectly—a sound like

92

she had dropped something. Anything. An apple. Like an apple had fallen from her hand. *Ooh.* And she was in the water. Slipped on the soft dirt.

"I am not sure Hod's feet touched the ground once he stood. By the time I looked up, he had already launched himself off the bank. His beautiful body was arcing toward the water. Hung there long enough for me to realize they were both gone before he was in the river. And I walked to the edge of the fast water and did nothing. I stood there. I decided I did not want to live without them, but I lacked the fortitude even to fling myself after them. Not to rescue, but to die. Stood there for ages, begging the mud to collapse, so the river could pull me to where they...I could not do it myself, but I would not have fought it. I waited so long. Do you believe me? That at least I wanted that?"

"Why wouldn't I believe you?"

Tel considered the question, an urge forming in his solar plexus. It was, at first, the barest fleck of an instinct warming his abdomen. Then, it swirled into a storm of desire inside his chest and gut. He wanted to touch Vared, to read his thoughts with the stagsblood dynasty. If he could invent a pretext for grabbing his hand, he reasoned, he would know his mind—even his feelings. In a beat, the contact would reveal whether Vared was revolted or concerned or bored. He struggled against the notion until able to release it, thinking it further evidence of insanity. "Because you do not know me well."

"But I know myself." Vared pulled himself forward on his cushion. "And what's different? You lost the queen and Hod. I lost my parents. You witnessed your loss. I have no memory of mine. I know none of the reasons or circumstances. That's a difference. But they're both huge... *events* looming over our every moment, every thought. Every emotion. You had the pressures and expectations that come with being you. But you had the privileges that come with being you. I had the pressures and expectations of the street, and then of my patron. But I had the privileges of spending some years in a household of means. Not the same, but similar. You choose one route of escape, of forgetting. I choose another. It's the only other real difference."

"The whole kingdom knows how I escape. How do you?"

Vared laughed. "By hiding behind my terquin. And by being the way I am."

"What way?"

"Unwarm. Aloof. Not social. I don't have anyone."

"You are part of my household. You are of my blood now, for what it is worth. And after last night, you have Caip, apparently. Strangely."

"I didn't find her as intimidating once we were commiserating about dragging you half-conscious back here," said Vared, chucking. He shielded his face with his hand. "I'm sorry."

"I am the one who owes an apol—" Tel shook his head.

"What?"

"I have apologized a thousand times before. I have just realized how *worthlessly*. Scarcity makes worth—and there is, if anything, a surplus of my apologies. A glut. I would only be saying sorry to soothe myself. Like I soothe myself with drink."

"I see."

"What happened last night?" asked Tel. "What was I like?"

Vared tucked some of his curls behind an ear. "You..."

Even his ear is small and fine and pleasing. "I what?"

Getting to his feet, Vared smoothed the black fabric over his narrow frame. Tel thought he looked almost too fragile to remain upright. "Your highness, it occurs to me that telling you about last night would offer you some of the soothing you've just mentioned. And I'm overdue for sleep. Enjoy your day."

Prince Tel was alone in his sitting room. He still smelled piss.

Eleven

Tel did nothing but not drink. He ordered his rooms emptied of all alcohol, which apparently mystified his servants. Under sweating skin, his bones chattered. On the second day, he saw unknown things moving in the far corners of his vision. He heard distant whispers. The sights and sounds were illusions, he knew. Nonetheless, they distracted and distressed. With effort, he ignored them. He twitched and muttered his way in and out of sleep so light it only hinted at proper rest.

The first half of the third day, his tremors were extreme enough to render him unable to stand. When out of his bed, he moved about by crawling. His limbs could not be trusted to observe his wishes. It was difficult even to speak, but he thought for a moment about calling for an attendant to bring him a small cup of ale. *Just a few sips for steadiness.* He groaned at his foolishness. *That is always how it starts.*

That evening, the shadow of the Stag's rack glided across his bed.

"I have given you much," said Tel's god.

"And taken much." Clutching his damp pillow, Tel rolled onto his back. "I hate you."

"Yes."

Tel squinted but could not see his face. "You have come to…"

"I have come, fruit of my Doe, because you need giving and taking."

"Will you? Please?"

"I have."

The antlered one was gone. A haze of scent—the musk and umbra of forest—lingered.

* * *

Tel and Craid walked the interior perimeter of the castle wall, hoods raised against a sharpened breeze. "My brother must see—must be made to see—his reactions are out of proportion. He cannot send three dozen men stomping into a small, isolated town because of a *rumor* of a child dynast. This is precisely what I worried about. A matter of days."

"Yes." Lord Craid trailed the prince by several paces.

"He is a new king with no experience in government. No interest. He is trying to establish his authority. Sending a message. But he makes a bad policy worse with these tactics. Like a fire spreads through the woods, this will spread across the countryside. It will only make the whole issue more fraught. I must get through to him."

"Highness?"

Tel spun on his feet to face him. Craid was even farther behind him now. "I am sorry. I have an unpleasant excess of energy."

"So it seems."

"Frankly, I worry I am losing my mind. It is difficult to focus. I have not had a drink in four days. Should I not feel better? Because I feel worse. Like I will step out of my skin. This, not politics, is the reason I wanted to walk with you this evening."

"I see."

Tel kicked a fist-sized stone from his path. "I thought, as you have been dry so long, you might be able to help me."

"You've turned to the wrong person for advice, y—"

"Craid. Please."

"The nervousness will pass. Give your thanks that the quaking did not kill you. It has killed more than a few souses."

"I am determined to drink less," said Tel. "I will have a dry month to defog my head if it *does* kill me. Then, only occasionally. Perhaps you have a suggestion?"

"I do."

"Share it. Please."

"If you try to drink less, highness, you'll fail."

"This is your advice? Do not try?"

"Let us sit, Prince Tel." He indicated a cobbled path leading to the edge of the royal gardens. They found a bench. "Have you tried to drink less before? Have you taken a break from the drink and then set your mind to enjoying your wines and ales more reasonably?"

"Yes. But I—"

"How many times? Once? More than once? More than twice? More than five times? Ten?" Craid shook his head, chuckling.

"Several times."

"My prince, you and I aren't of the type that can slow their drinking. The thirst we have for the stuff asks more of us. Some people are like this. Born, perhaps, with some sort of…misalignment of the mind. A tendency. I tried your approach. The number of times, I don't care to consider. My breaks were weeks, months, even a full four seasons. I followed that with another four seasons of drinking a glass here, two cups there. A miserable lunatic at every stage. After a time, I could not resist the third cup. Then the fourth. Before long, I was starting fights and pissing the bed again."

"You pissed the bed?"

"Yes. Many times. The woman eventually made me sleep on a pallet."

Tel bent and rested his face in his hands. "But what of the misalignment? The tendency?" He straightened his posture and fidgeted on the bench. Seeing his knee bouncing involuntarily, he groaned. "You still thirst?"

"For fresh milk," Craid said, heat in his voice. More softly, he added, "Nothing more."

"In that case, surely you could have a real drink."

"A real drink just brings the thirst once more."

"Never drink again," said Tel.

"Perhaps worthy of an experiment, highness. Unless you like pissing the bed." He winked.

Tel drummed his fingers on his thighs. "How do I get through this…this *way* I feel? How do I stop thinking about the thirst?"

"Stay busy. Think about something or someone else. I drove my children to the brink of madness, I doted so. But now, nearing the end of my life, I don't regret it. If anything, I wish I could've started doting sooner. And I think they'd agree."

"Caip." Tel's voice was a rough whisper. His face was in his hands again.

"We've not really spoken of your father."

"No."

"He wasted away so quickly."

"He suffered." Tel lifted his head and faced Craid directly.

"I won't lie to you, my prince."

"Thank you for that."

"I must have your forgiveness that I was too unwell to be at T—"

Tel raised his palm to stop him. "There is no need for forgiveness, my friend."

"We were outmaneuvered long ago. You've been gone so often. These last years, especially. And your father, feeling the pride of his many accomplishments, left so much of Table's business to your uncle, even its very composition. I see now—"

"I see, too, Craid."

"It was underhanded. Something must be done about it. About it and this business with soldiers kicking in doors, raving about security."

"Something," Tel scoffed.

"You have friends in the capital. *Many* friends in the south, your highness."

Tel's eyes widened. "Do not say it."

"Lag will work to erase what your father's done. What his father did. I'll be the only one at Table to object. My term is up soon. I may be dead sooner."

"Stop."

"Highness—"

Tel looked about. "Are you deaf, old man?"

Craid gave his eyes to the turf. "He was glad to have gotten to visit Foghar one last time. I know he wished you were with him."

"He went to Foghar?"

"He rode out and spent a few days. He knew it was...He was gone the same day he returned to Affas. I think my grief contributed to my sickness."

Eyes burning, Tel knew he should have been comforted by knowing Vith saw the valley at the end. Instead, he fantasized about punching Craid in the mouth.

* * *

King Lag stood on the dais before the formal hall, having just concluded over an hour of remarks. The speech had served to draw a contrast between the new leader and his father. From internal security to a fishing rights agreement with Kamber in the northern Gray Sea to the fresh trade negotiations with Omela, Lag had announced a new, sterner approach. Feigh and Feighans, he had argued, were exceptional and must act as such.

Behind him was his banner, the new colors of the kingdom, a dull brown field surrounding a white disk. Lag was perfectly placed during the address, directly in the center of the flag, the rack crown on his head. It made for a striking tableau. The impeccably outfitted king was framed by blazing white. When he finished, the hall, crammed full of courtiers and hangers-on, thundered with a chant echoing the closing lines of the speech: *Whole Feigh! United Feigh! Pure Feigh!* Aith drifted from a shadow near the platform, striking the gloved palms of his hands together with each word. King Lag clapped along and strutted the stage, encouraging the people before him.

When the chanting quieted, the crowd began to mill around. A dazed Tel darted through the attendees until he reached Caip, who was speaking with Mor. "That was dark," he said, hoping only his friends would hear. "This is supposed to be a celebration."

"Your royal highness," said Caip, "warmest winter."

"Warmest winter, rightmajor." Although he had spied her when the festivities had begun, he got his first good look at her. "You are stunning tonight." Her hair was wilder than usual and threaded through with dainty crystals. The tiny jewels winked in the light. Her brocade gown was a soft yellow with a raised silver-white pattern. It was cut close, highlighting her sturdy femininity.

"Was there anything else, your highness?" Caip showed him a smile, but the rest of her face remained rigid.

"No," said Tel. "Anything else? Why?"

"Goodnight to you, then." She stepped away and returned her attention to Mor. Over her shoulder, Mor gave his prince an empathetic—or pitying—look.

"Caip," Tel complained. She faced him. "Caip, I am trying. I have given it up. I know I have been a—"

"I want you to picture two piles of stones, each stone representing a day. One pile is three days. One pile is one hundred *seasons* of days."

"It has been four d—"

Her glare had teeth. "Fine. Add your fourth stone. Goodnight, your highness." She put a hand on Mor's back and guided him a few meters away.

Tel spent the better part of an hour chatting with various attendees, dodging more than a few direct offers of ales and implicit offers of sex. He knew he must not drink and could not imagine bedding someone without drinking. Even conversation was a challenge. Anxious and foggy, he was incapable of his usual repartee. He felt like only the smallest essence of himself—a kind of bare awareness of his own identity—had been placed into the body and mind of a different person. Worse, this person was lousy at parties. Hoping to avoid any further socialization while he gathered the energy to escape to his rooms, he cast his eyes downward.

"Your highness."

Tel's features clenched themselves into a pained expression. With effort, he relaxed it to something more neutral and turned to face the speaker.

"Vared." The songmaker stood before him, relaxed and smiling. His feet were covered below the ankles in clean fabric shoes. A long way above them was the hem of a formal Omelan shift. The black fabric of the garment shimmered. His lips and eyes were painted more vividly than usual. The torchlight made his apricot irises seem to dance. In his cobalt curls, he wore three leaves which had turned in the cooler weather—one red, one orange, one yellow. "You look...well."

"So do you," Vared said.

Tel fumbled around his head for something to say. "Warmest winter?" It came out of him a question because he had been asking himself if it was the right remark.

"Nonsense. This isn't the first day of winter. This is mid-autumn. Worthy of a party but nothing so ostentatious. In the civilized world, we celebrate winter in many weeks."

Tel giggled. He asked himself if his laugh always sounded so, hoping not. "You are performing tonight?"

"No," Vared said. "The protocol minister declined my offer. Feighan performers only."

"Oh. I am sorry."

Vared's eyes had a slight, playful roll in their sockets. "I get to absorb Feighan culture as an observer tonight," he said, sweeping his hand toward the partygoers. "You are not drinking."

"No." Tel realized he was standing on the balls of his feet. Embarrassed, he let his heels touch the floor again.

"And you feel..."

"Good. I feel good. Nervous. Generally nervous. Also, I do not know how to be at a party."

Vared said, "Then we'll leave. You've done admirably."

"Before midnight? That is the biggest moment."

"It's only mid-autumn."

To his horror, Tel's little giggle was identical to his last. "Where would you like to go?"

"I'll walk you to your rooms. There are so many parties in this castle. And it seems to be my duty to get you home from them safely."

This time, he refused to laugh. "You are a wicked Omelan."

"Do you mind taking a longer route? I have something I've wanted to ask you for a while."

Tel's throat was dry in an instant. "I do not mind."

They wound through the crooked corridors used for the most part by servants. The celebration meant the halls were more active than normal for this time of night. They greeted cheerful, often intoxicated, celebrants on their stroll. Other than this, they did not speak for a while. Prince Tel was anxious to know Vared's question but chose not to talk first.

When they had not encountered anyone for a few moments, Vared said, "I was hoping you could tell the rest of your story."

"Story?"

"The creation story. From your religion. You told it the night of the signing of the treaty. The other morning you heard part of one of the songs I'm working on about the goddesses and gods as Feigh's people see them. I'd like to know the rest."

"Did I not tell the complete story?"

"I don't believe so. The Stag made the young one a dynast and left the world to find his brothers."

"We do not know if he found them," said Tel. "He may still be looking."

"But what of the child dynast? And the other dynasts?"

"I believe your history has it much the same as ours. Like all history, it is muddy and nonsensical. We do not understand how the dynasty is passed. Sometimes, it appears to be familial. Sometimes, it seems random. Each person with the blood can work four different magics. Northern dirt, eastern wind, southern fire, western rain. The four dynasties. Usually, the dynasts are better with some, weaker with others. Were. Some say the dynasts were utterly pure in the beginning, living to serve their non-dynast sisters and brothers. To keep them safe. We are told they were corrupted, somehow. They helped Feigh remain the most powerful kingdom by far, but some of them turned against their non-dynast Feighan kin.

"Like the rest of humanity, some were creative, some destructive. I would guess most were both, in one proportion or another. As we all are. Over the centuries, dynasts became fewer and fewer. Those rare people now born with the blood see their powers naturally slough away. At least, that is what we thought." A twinge of regret—guilt—pulsed under Tel's sternum. If anyone knew the dynasty could still last into adulthood, it was he. "And now, it is a crime to fail to surrender a child showing magical ability. A *capital* crime. The children are to be sent to Gontrahd and..."

Vared knew enough to lower his voice. "You're not in agreement."

"Saying so is criminal itself. What happens if a child's powers do not disappear? Would we execute them before they became strong? It would be like executing all people at sixteen because a few grow up to have twisted desires. There would be none of—I am sorry. And I should not."

"You needn't worry about me, your highness."

"I sense that. I know." Tel nodded.

From ahead came the sounds of a commotion—footfalls, laughter, and playful shrieks drawing closer. A pair of adolescents blasted around a corner into the hallway. The female chased the male, his doublet in her fist. They seemed to hardly notice Vared and their prince.

Vared's arm flew out. He grabbed Tel by the fabric at his lower back and pulled him out of the way of the wild, charging duo. They ended up pressed together in the wind created by the young pair sprinting past.

"Sorry," said Vared.

Tel felt the heat from Vared's mouth on his neck. Some spirals from the dark cloud of blue tickled his nose. The hair smelled faintly like spiced oil and the first muggy day of the year. Vared's balled hand released his jacket and flattened against his back.

"Thank you. Do not apologize," said Tel. He both wanted to open the distance between them and detested the idea. Decorum demanded he step back, but the agreeable fragrance begged him to stay put. Time crept, and he floated in this middle space for a long time. It was not long enough.

They each moved backward a pace, their first physical contact ended.

"I thought they were going to knock you over," said Vared. Biting his plump, painted lower lip, he looked up at the prince.

Tel felt dizzy. He had to break eye contact, which caused a burning ache to flash in his gut. "They were, but you rescued me."

"Do you think they're in love?"

"Mm?" Tel struggled to clear his head.

"The girl and boy who just now almost killed a prince."

"Of course," said Tel, wistful amusement in his voice. "They are, at the very least, well on their way."

"Good for them."

"It is," said Tel, nodding.

"So, you have had it? Love. Like that."

"Yes. Once."

"Who?" Vared clenched his eyes shut, raised his chin, and forced a sigh from himself. "Of course. I'm foolish. Your Hod. I apologize. I had a love of a kind once. Didn't have our preference, but let me believe it was a possibility with just enough peculiar sweetness. Why do they do this to us sometimes? It was a painful thing. And that was before he took everything from me at the point of a knife."

The thought made Tel angry. "That is terrible."

"It was…how it was, in the capital."

"We have street children in Feigh, as well. And adults. And people who are not on the streets but have very little. Hod's family had nothing. Caip's father, before he was old, was my father's chief groundskeeper. He met Hod's father over an ale in a tavern and hired him. It made him able to take care of Hod and his mother. And it brought Hod to me. One's lot in life is so much down to chance. Whether they have a drink in a tavern on a certain evening. I do not think about it enough."

Vared's irises found the prince's and held them steadily. "You do not."

"Maybe it could be my focus," said Tel. He felt warmth spread over his cheekbones. "Our family has always given silver to the poor, but… Perhaps I could convince Lag to take an interest in the roots of the problem. Problems."

Vared made a strange sound in response.

"He scared you tonight."

"No."

"My brother went too far. He is too invested in appearing formidable. My brother does not understand the maxim that the only message conveyed by a man carrying on about having a big cock is he has a wee one." He watched Vared stifle a laugh and drop his gaze to the stones of the floor. "I am sorry.

That was vulgar."

Vared stopped walking and offered Tel a devilish smile. "I have heard the word before."

"I know. But you are so—"

"How am I? Tell me, your highness. I am so..." His grin grew even more wicked.

The dizziness returned to Tel's head. "You are so courtly, refined, graciou—"

Defying possibility, Vared's smile widened.

"I am going to stop talking now."

Vared tittered and began walking again. "Not yet. Have you ever heard of a non-Feighan dynast?"

"Nothing more than rumors. No one has accounted for this. Since it seems not only to run in families but to appear at random, I would expect to hear of stagsblood the world over. As for hereditary passing, my people have not cross-mated much with people from the other queendoms and kingdoms. Other than Sheruck, we have been the most isolated of all the nations."

"Purity," said Vared.

"Purity." He realized with disappointment they had reached the door to his apartments. For a few moments, they made hushed small talk in the hallway. They wished each other a good rest.

In his quiet rooms, Tel sat wondering if Vared would play the terquin before bed, if he would be too tired to scrub the paint from his face, if he slept on his belly or his back or his side.

He meditated, lowering his mind—both to find relaxation and to play with the dynasty. The magic seemed to come easier now. It was within reach with less fuss and a smaller expenditure of his energy. Perhaps drying up had increased his strength. He pondered how frightened Vared might be if he came to know his secret nature.

Later, in bed, the stagsblood began to thrum inside him in a way he did not recognize. He was consumed with thoughts of western Feigh, the region of the kingdom he least knew. When he finally found rest, he dreamed of the dark forest that crawled up the Chreok Mountains.

Twelve

For the next ten days, Tel continued to struggle with sleep. Despite this, the stagsblood strengthened further, and he began to take more pleasure in his spiritual and magical practices. Thoughts about wine or ale continued to hover like summer flies around a horse. He was pleased they remained only thoughts. They failed to grow into any real thirst. Throwing himself into the minutia of official business, he established a demanding routine and, in this way, prevented notions of drinking from gaining enough momentum to become desire. He spoke with Craid almost every day. His old friend suggested he develop an answer for these thoughts. He took the advice to heart, and when confronted with his own mind attempting to sabotage his abstinence, he responded by asking himself, *What else can I do?*

Tel invited the heads of charities to the castle and asked them about the people they aided. He took a special interest in his talk with the woman who administered an orphanage important to his late mother, Queen Fyor. Over Caip's objections, he followed up by donning ordinary clothes and walking into the heart of the city to observe good works in person. No one seemed to recognize him, which was a relief to both Tel and the watchful rightmajor.

He managed to avoid complaining—other than inside his own mind—when he sat and listened to a pair of counters review his finances. Unsure of why he needed to be reminded he had more silver and land than anyone could use in ten lifetimes, he bore it with a neutral expression tacked to his face. He made some plans for his money, including backing three new ships to ferry goods to and from Omela.

With much greater attentiveness, he took an early morning update on the status of the people and land of Foghar Valley. This year's harvest had been excellent. He received a list of all the babies who had been born since his last visit. It had been an incredibly productive year in that respect. The antlered ones had shown mercy to families, and no mothers had been lost to childbirth.

After the meeting, he stood at a window with his steaming cup, letting the nippy air and weak sunlight cross his face, considering how he might begin a letter to Cessa. Just as he decided on the shape of an opening passage, he heard Craid's voice behind him.

"Your highness."

Tel watched a gull riding the breeze over the northern edge of the island. "Lord Craid."

"My prince, Ambassador Vared has been arrested."

Tel spun around, burning his hand with hidybrew. "What?"

"I rushed here," said Craid. He was bent at the waist, hands bracing his thighs. "He is in a cell. Orders of the king."

"What for?"

"I'm unsure. All foreigners on the island have been jailed."

* * *

Tel and Caip stood just inside the entrance to the old building that housed all the royal cells, glaring at Gran. Caip asked, "Lieutenant, on what charge is the ambassador being held?"

"I won't say."

"Not only do I outrank you by a long height, Gran, but a prince of this realm stands before you," barked Caip. "Answer my question, or you will most definitely find your career is over in very short order."

Gran chuffed and inched her head closer to Caip's. The rightmajor did not budge. "On orders of the *king* of this realm, I'll not say. And your bluebell's not going anywhere."

"We will see him," said Tel, waving a hand. Gran did not give way. Moving as near to her as possible without touching her. He titled his head, somehow imbuing this small gesture with tremendous menace. His stagsblood crackled. A realization bloomed. His powers had advanced enough that he could conjure a fire inside her chest hot enough to vaporize her. He would deal with the horror of that knowledge later. For now, he used the fact to his advantage. She could not cow him. "Knowing exactly who and what I am, Gran, I expect you will answer this question with extreme care. Did the king say I could not see Vared?"

Her boldness managed to hide only most of her fear. "No."

"Ah. Find yourself out of my path."

Gran could give him her eyes no more. A swift sidestep removed her from his way.

"And," Tel said over his shoulder as he and Caip strode away, "if a single blue curl…Well, I do not expect I have to finish the sentence."

When they were out of earshot, Caip regarded him with large eyes. "That was impressive."

Sickness at his own hypocrisy churned his stomach and sat dully in his chest. So readily had the pacifist become willing to threaten. Tel cursed himself silently until they reached the round anteroom. He looked at the disinterested soldier serving as guard and said, "I will need to be let into each prisoner's cell for a few moments."

"Ain't no one Isn't anyone here but the one from Omela, highness." The guard showed him the top of her head.

"Where are the rest?" asked Caip.

"Other blocks," said the guard. "This one's to be kept by himself."

"Bastard," said Tel, to no one. "Let me in to see him."

The guard looked at Caip and said, "I would need to search your person, highness." She cleared her throat and returned her eyes to her prince.

Tel's response was a simple look, which caused the young woman to droop.

"Fine."

"You'll not find any trouble for this, soldier," said Caip. "I'll keep you company while Prince Tel has his visit." It was soft friendliness wrapped around a more baleful core. "Take him to the cell, come back here, and you and I can chat about military life."

The young guard nodded at Caip and, without a word, escorted Tel down the catwalk.

He first saw Vared through the little window in the heavy door, standing in the middle of the miserable chamber. Apparently unharmed, the songmaker drew his fingers in quick, rake-like motions through the halo of blue.

Unlocking the door, the guard swung it open. She nodded at Tel and returned to Caip.

"Your highness. I heard your voice," said Vared.

"Before anything else, I cannot take you out of here right now," said Tel, stepping into the cell. "But I will speak with my brother as soon as I can and sort this. I am sorry. And if I cannot sort it, I will break you out."

Vared chuckled.

Tel moved a pace closer. "I am serious."

"I asked for you the instant they took me, but they didn't seem inclined to deliver the message."

"What have they said their reasoning is?"

Vared shrugged. "Nothing. Only that they've rounded up all of the foreigners at Affas Castle."

"That is all I know, too. I hope you do not hate me."

"I don't, but I confess to not finding your country all that lovable at present." Vared's grin brightened the dim cell.

Tel sputtered and shook with laughter. "That is fair." He sat on the floor and hugged his knees.

"Your highness, sit on the bed. Your clothes."

"This is fine. You have a seat."

Instead, Vared sat near him, on the floor, mirroring the pose. "I'm filthy already." He looked around the cell. "I suppose this is justice, of a kind."

"How so?" asked Tel.

"Well, I never really wanted to talk with people much. Or to be around them, unless I was singing. So, in a way, I've gotten what I asked for."

Tel tilted his head. "You talk to Caip and me."

"This is the farthest I've ever been and will ever be from home. It's shifted something in me. Besides, we've established that you, Caip, and I all escape. We hide."

"We talked about you and me, not Caip." Tel lowered his voice a fraction. "How does Caip hide?"

"She hides behind her duties to you."

"Oh?"

"And it makes it hard for her. She has two relationships with one person. It's why she is angry with you. A friend might slap the mead from your hand and tell you to stop the foolishness. But, would the person sworn to put her body between yours and a blade? We hide, the three of us, but it doesn't make us happy."

"Ah. You have spoken to her about this."

"No. Of course not. I don't want her to hit me," said Vared. "Only a guess." Tel chuckled, which caused a smile to open across Vared's face. "You have still not drunk."

"How do you know? Another guess?"

"I can see it."

Feeling for a flash like a child caught doing something he should not, Tel looked away.

"Your eyes are clearer than when…than before. Greener. I can't see the color in this dark, of course. But I can see you haven't drunk. I can tell."

"Everyone says I have brown eyes. I did not see the green in my eyes until I purchased an Omelan mirror and looked at myself in the sunlight. I was well older than you."

"I've noticed that mirrors are very rare here," said Vared. "As I've noticed that you'll always be well older than me."

On the revolting floor, they giggled until they had no breath. Vared clutched his stomach. Tel rocked back and kicked his feet.

* * *

111

The rings around Tel's eyes were dark as his beard. His mood was darker. He slumped in a chair in the hallway just outside the Table chamber. After seeing Vared, he spent the better part of the previous afternoon and evening visiting each jailed foreigner. He tried to uncover the reasoning for Lag's maneuver but could find nothing. Even Craid professed to be ignorant of the logic for imprisoning so many people. The old man said he suspected the king would reveal his motives at Table. Frustration—and the lack of drink to blunt it—caused a sweaty, fitful, shallow sleep.

Soldiers blocked him from entering the chamber. His would be the last business of the council. Knowing this was meant to further humiliate him, he sat and waited as he was asked, muttering curses under his breath. When the door finally opened, he wobbled past the guards.

"Brother," said Lag. A woman knelt at his feet, buffing the nails of his right hand.

"Nephew," purred Aith. "Again, you look positively exhausted. Unfortunately, there's no seat for you."

"How can we help you?" asked Lag, eyeing his attendant as she worked.

"You know very—" Tel took a breath. His voice sounded shredded. "My king, I came to ask on what charge the foreign visitors are held. Why have you jailed them?"

"Uncle." Lag gestured with his left hand to indicate Aith should explain.

"Trouble in Hebe. Terrible trouble, I'm afraid," Aith said. He clucked his tongue.

Tel found Craid's burdened face over the gneiss slab and asked, "What sort of trouble?"

Aith shook his head. "Most unfortunate. A group of Omelans entered the Hebite palace in the darkness. They cut the throats of the entire royal family. Then, the cowards drank poison."

Tel moved two steps closer to his uncle and brother. "Who sits on the throne of Hebe?"

"There was a dispute over succession," Aith said. "No clarity on the matter. The relatives and their women and men began to clash in the streets and in the countryside. Lord Gawash—I believe you know him—raised a force and put down all the squabbling parties. He consolidated power and wears the crown."

"Uncle thinks he'll be a good friend to me," said Lag.

Tel saw a child playacting as monarch. This, along with the thought of Gawash leading an entire nation, nauseated him. "I see."

"I wouldn't be so certain of that," said Craid. "I've had dealings with him, myself. I'm not convinced he's trustworthy." He drew distasteful looks from around Table.

"You've already made your distrust known. Thank you," Aith said, with the side of his mouth. He returned his attention to Tel. "Naturally, we had no choice but to remain as cautious as possible with foreigners. Particularly *Omelans.*"

"What evidence do you have that any of them intend harm?" Tel asked.

"None," Craid said. "They were released."

"On my orders." Lag wore a stupid grin.

Exhausted, Tel turned to leave with a dismissive grunt.

"Except," said Lag.

He wheeled around to face them again.

"Except for the songmaker," Aith said.

Craid leaned forward. "What?" A few other Tablemembers murmured. This had not yet been disclosed to the council.

"Without evidence. Without reason," said Tel.

"We have evidence. A letter to Cessa was intercepted." From his clothes, Aith produced it. His smirk was small and tight.

"It's now the practice of this kingdom to intercept personal missives?" asked Craid.

"We do," growled Lag, "whatever we must to keep me and this kingdom safe." His fist landed on the ancient stone with a smart bang.

"And there is evidence in this letter that Vared was plotting to slit throats? Impossible." It pained Tel to raise his voice.

Aith opened the letter. "No plot to slit throats, but very unflattering toward our king." He began scanning Vared's words, reading fragments aloud. *"My impressions of King Lag are not yet certain...our first meeting was tense...a suspicion of foreigners...extra guards and soldiers in the city...seems to take his cues from his uncle..."*

"No word of this is a lie," said Tel.

"He's spying." Lag glared at his brother.

"He's much kinder about you, of course," Aith said, sneering. *"As you said, Prince Tel is keen and charming...beneath his vices, one can see he brims with decency...well-liked by his people."* He made a show of pocketing the pages. "How sweet, nephew."

"Your little songbird's a spy, Tel." Lag smirked.

He wanted to scream but paused. "Your majesty, *Ambassador* Vared is simply reporting some basic observations to our friend, Queen Cessa. If you wish he was more flattering to you, perhaps you should have avoided harassing and addressing him with a slur when you first met. Perhaps you should not have celebrated the arrival of winter with such a dark speech. And perhaps you should have not made Queen Cessa's personal emissary a prisoner."

"You are not king, *brother*." Lag hissed at the woman attending him, making her flinch and scurry away. He sprang to his feet. "And you're not the only one with a keen mind. Everyone has always fallen all over you, but I'm the one with the mind to keep Feigh safe. You have a mind to give it all away. To water Feigh down. You say yes to everything. It's why so many people love you. But that love comes cheap and easy."

Tel looked at the floor, shaking his head. "I only hope we can prevent this, which Cessa will consider an outrage, from undoing years of work."

Aith raised his hand in a blade. "Your majesty, if I may? Obviously, Prince Tel's upset to hear someone of his household is under suspicion. Tel, the singer will be released, but he will not be permitted in the castle or in the city after sundown. When he's here—for formal functions, performing, so-called diplomatic duties, and the rest—it will be during daylight, and he will be under close guard. This will be the same for all off-Feighans. It is not merely because of his letter or because you have made him *of your blood*. He was only held longer so we could explain it to you. King and kingdom will be kept safe. Foreigners engaged in espionage, disloyal Feighans, dynasts, blood diluters—they'll all be sent to Gontrahd from this day forward. Your Omelan boy should feel lucky he won't be among them."

Craid stood. "I don't understand. This is madness, your grace. Gontrahd was to be a school for the dynast children. Now we are—"

"My kingdom," said Lag, "will have secur—"

"Is it madness to keep your king and capital safe?" asked Aith. "Of course not. To that end, no foreigners will be permitted to rest their heads within the limits of Affas."

Thirteen

Letting his legs fold, Tel ducked Caip's swinging waster. He did not expect to sink so far into the mud under his feet. The deep, carob mire kept hold of his boots. Unable to spring backward quickly, he could not dodge the next strike. It landed with too much force for practice.

"*Ow*. Antlered goddess, Caip. I know you are angry, b—"

"I'm not angry."

"Cow leavings," said Tel, massaging his shoulder.

"I'm here to spar. To do my duty. Not to discuss personal matters." She landed another blow.

"*Ow*. Caip, stop. Stop. I am an ass. I have been an ass. Self-involved and unappreciative and embarrassing, and there is nothing I can do to erase it. Absolutely nothing. I cannot alter what is behind us. I would if I could. I would for you. But it is impossible. No matter how hard I wish for it. I can only try to be less self-involved and unappreciative and embarrassing. Caip, I need you to be *both*."

"Both? Both what?"

"I need you to choose to be both my friend and the prince's most loyal advisor. There are so few left to trust. And I trust you. With my life. I am asking for both, not because I deserve it. You and I know I do not. I am asking because I hope I have not burnt through all the friendship and loyalty."

Rightmajor Caip spat in the muck to her left before brandishing her waster. "Let's spar." She lowered her center of gravity.

"You must choose," said Tel. "You can say yes to one or to the other or to

116

neither, but I need to know."

She threw the practice sword to the ground. "For a long while, it hardly ever occurred to me that my friendship and loyalty to you have cost me so much. A life of my own, really. A family, maybe. But how could I have a man or a family to watch over when I have to watch over you? For a long time, I forgot this. Because I had accepted it. Because to be your friend and to serve my kingdom is a privilege. An honor. And then, more and more and more, over these last years, I watch you drown yourself. And that's what I gave up a life for? So you'll be dead in five or ten years, and I'll be alone?"

"I understand."

"Tel, *shut up.* You couldn't possibly."

He stepped toward her. "I am trying every day to do better."

"I lied. I'm *so* angry. And *that* makes me angrier. It's meaningless. Stop talking. Start doing."

"Too angry to be my friend? My right hand?"

She looked at the low, slate sky and screamed, jumping up and down on the balls of her feet. Tel thought she looked like the little girl he played with so long ago. "I'll be your friend. And I'll be your chief. With two conditions. First, if you start getting drunk again, understand that I will not stay to watch you do it. Second, you must allow me to be neither for a moment more. Neither friend nor chief, for three beats. Right now. And you must not be a prince. For three beats."

"I do not underst—"

She screamed again. "Just two people, Tel. No prince. No rightmajor. No friendship. Three beats. Yes or no?"

"Yes."

Tel did not realize her right fist had struck the left side of his face until he was in the mud. He pressed the heel of his hand into his eye.

"Caip, I am a pacifist."

She was already striding away from him. "And I'm a soldier."

* * *

Tel and a party of more than fifty women and men scrambled through their final preparations for the weeklong journey to Foghar. The cheerful, lemony sun was not yet high enough to melt away the light frost of an early winter morning, but it promised a comfortable day's ride.

A groom approached Tel and Caip, leading Kelseigh. "Your royal highness."

"The best girl in all of Feigh. All the world." Tel stroked and nuzzled the horse's neck. "The fussiest but the best. But you are Vared's girl, now." He eyed the songmaker, who was out of earshot, busy securing some of his belongings on a cart. By touching Kelseigh, Tel could feel her inner life with the wind and rain magic. She had recognized Vared's name and thrilled at hearing it. "Take Kelseigh to Ambassador Vared. I will have Pony." He referred to a smallish horse, sweet but unremarkable.

"Pony?" asked the groom.

"Yes. Pony, please. Quickly."

"I am stunned," Caip said.

"They are a match. Trust me."

As the groom led Kelseigh away, Tel and Caip watched a hooded figure approach Vared. They exchanged some words. Vared tittered. When the cloaked person lowered his cowl, Tel recognized him as the young man whose flirtatious attention Vared had deflected weeks before in the banquet hall—the same young man Tel had taken to bed at the end of the festivities.

Vared had a furtive look all around, causing Caip and the prince to pretend to be occupied with one another. They looked back in time to see Vared and the lad share a quick kiss and exchange a few words. As the handsome Feighan sauntered away, a smile beamed from beneath Vared's blue curls. When the groom handed Kelseigh's lead to him, the grin only widened.

Caip giggled. "If I didn't see it with my own eyes…"

"Good for him," said Tel, watching the toe of his boot dig at the frosted turf.

"How does he feel about leaving?"

"Unbothered," said Tel. "Or so he says. Looks forward to seeing a less settled area of the country. It will give him a chance to talk to Feigh's real people, away from the commerce and politics of Affas. How do *you* feel about it?"

"About going to Foghar? You know it's my favorite place just as much as yours. She gestured to the score of King Lag's soldiers whose watchfulness was upon them. "Besides, we're clearly not wanted here."

Aith stood among the military women and men. He caught the eyes of the prince and the rightmajor and gave a compact nod.

"No," said Tel. "We are not."

* * *

Fingers of golden firelight stroked Vared's high, delicate cheekbones. He stepped to a surprised Tel and said, "I am hungry," as two dozen members of the traveling party had before him.

"You do not have to follow our way to eat of the hunt," Tel whispered.

The huge amber eyes did not blink. A few azure spirals near his temples twitched in the wind. "I am hungry."

Tel's stomach fluttered. He gave a slight nod. "All right. What have I to feed you?"

"Northern fruitfulness, eastern clarity, southern passion, and western joy."

Four times, Tel dipped his middle finger into the chalice of blood and said, "Dirt, wind, fire, and rain." His dripping finger trembled in front of Vared's face. Although he had shared the ceremony with off-Feighans before, this felt transgressive. "You are nourished," he said, painting a red streak across Vared's waiting lips.

"Nourished by the antlered ones," Vared said, eyes still unblinking. He stepped past Tel to receive his small share of the flesh of the buck felled by the arrow of one of Caip's women.

When all completed the ritual, the heart was put on the fire. Once done, it was offered to Prince Tel by the man who cooked it.

"I am hungry," said Tel.

"You are nourished," said the smiling man.

"Nourished by the antlered ones." Tel had his first bite of the heart.

After a rowdy dinner, the crowd around the fire thinned, many choosing to find their tents early. They had paused two days to camp and hunt but would set out near first light. About a dozen of them remained, chatting and digesting.

"Don't stay up too late," said Caip, rising from her place at Tel's side. "You'll be in a foul mood and impossible to be around."

"It makes little difference. I do not sleep anymore."

"But rest your eyes and your bones." She walked to her tent, which was closest to his.

After a time, Tel sensed someone next to him but could not take his eyes from the fire.

"May I sit with you?" It was Vared.

"Of course."

"Thank you."

"I could," said Tel without looking at him, "watch the fire for the rest of my life."

"It's seductive, isn't it?" asked Vared. "Hypnotic."

"It is," said Tel. Finally, he turned to the man at his side. "It demands attention."

"You've been avoiding me."

"Nonsense."

"Four days," said Vared. "Hardly a word."

Tel faced the fire again. "I am feeling guilty."

"Why?"

"Your arrest. I should have seen it coming. And having to take you away from Affas."

"I can say I have been locked in a cell now. In a foreign land. And I'm enjoying the journey. The countryside is beautiful. I'm certain Foghar will be likewise."

"We can send for him," said Tel. "He could visit. He may stay with us for as long as you want."

"Who?"

"Vared. You know who."

"It's not necessary."

"I do not want you to feel any lonelier here than you already must."

"I haven't had the kind of attention he gave me in a long while," said Vared. "It was nice. He was nice. But there's no future in it. He's a friend. It was a diversion. Physical. And I needed that. I'm sure you've noticed how much more relaxed I am." He enjoyed a quiet chuff of a laugh. "A good lover. As you know."

"He told you."

"Frequently. He's...proud to have been with you. A prince."

"I was drunk."

"He was quite satisfied."

Tel opened his mouth to respond. Unable to think of anything to say, he closed it. His cheeks grew hot.

"Your eye," said Vared, "looks even worse today than yesterday."

"It *feels* a bit better. It is still tender, mainly when I touch it."

"Stay here." Vared stood and padded away from the firelight, returning a moment later with a leather pouch. Sitting again, he said, "Come."

"What is this?" asked Tel.

Vared rifled through his little pouch. "Just scoot closer. And turn your head this way so I can see." He adjusted Tel's face by grabbing his chin. "I'm unable to grow a beard. Yours makes me envious. You'll be warmer this winter." He released Tel's chin and held an index finger in front of his face. "Do not move."

Tel could not see what he was doing with his hands. "Will this hurt?"

"No. You've painted me tonight. Now, I can return the favor. I think this shade will match your skin. With a little care, we can hide the bruising." He got the angle just right by taking the chin in hand again. With a finger of the other hand, he applied something cool and slippery to the area all around the eye. "Why always younger men?"

"Hm?"

The Omelan rolled his eyes. "Why always younger men?"

"Not always."

Vared squeezed Tel's chin and rolled his eyes again.

"I…I like prettiness. I like…teaching." He could feel his own embarrassment in the pulse of his wrists.

"You like telling young men what to do."

"No—"

For the second time, Vared squeezed. For the third, he rolled his eyes.

"Yes," said Tel. "A bit."

"A bit."

"I thought you said this would not hurt."

"It wouldn't if you knew how to duck a punch, your royal highness. I'm barely touching you."

Tel felt self-conscious. He tried to see the people on the other side of the fire. They were at least pretending to not watch them.

"One day, maybe you'll let me properly paint you like an Omelan gentleman. Why you Feighan men walk around so plain—even on special occasions—I'll never understand."

"You look just as nice without make-up as you do with."

Vared stopped working. "You think I look nice," he said, like he had caught a child sneaking an extra treat.

"I—"

Vared narrowed his gaze. "You look nice, too, in the rough, Feighan way."

From scalp to heel, Tel's skin prickled and heated. He wished Vared would hold onto his face forever, but no more than he hoped to run all the way to Sheruck and never see him again. For a moment, he thought his stomach might empty itself.

"There." Vared handed Prince Tel a small, framed piece of glass.

"Like I was never hurt at all."

* * *

Over the second half of the journey to Foghar, Vared gained the respect and affection of even the party's most skeptical members. He pulled his weight around camp and remained cheerful company even when hard at work. Those who knew Kelseigh's personality were impressed with how he rode and built a rapport with her. After sundown, he kept the women and men entertained with Omelan stories and songs. One night, around the fire, he inspired most of the party to goad Tel into singing with him, saying he had heard their prince's voice and had found it a pleasant surprise.

Vared even started drilling with Caip during their stops. Everyone else would eat or rest while the pair practiced grappling or swinging wasters. Each session, they attracted a small audience. The onlookers always shouted encouragement at Vared—and taunts at Caip. He lacked the rightmajor's strength, but Vared was agile and a quick student.

The three friends rode parallel for the trip's last leg, leading the long line of travelers. Conversation grew sparser. As the final day cooled, the rough road brought them to a crest overlooking the valley surrounding Foghar Castle.

Vared, Caip, and Tel stopped their mounts. The sun was still just high enough to illuminate a measure of the land's beauty. Rugged hills and dense forest lined either side of the fields and houses. Some of the trees still held onto a few leaves. The surviving foliage was painted with the muted shades of late turning season. A river sliced the whole region in two, winking grays and sunset pinks back at them, reflecting the colors of the sparse, fat clouds hanging over the whole of the basin.

"Lovely," said Vared.

"There," Caip said, pointing. "Mor's land. The best of the valley." She sighed. "I can smell the cooking fires."

"I am starving." Tel laid his hand over his stomach.

Caip looked around him and addressed Vared. "I enjoy seeing him eat more often than once every three days."

"I hadn't seen him eat at all until this trek," said Vared.

"*He* is right next to you both. Unless he has died of hunger and is now a shadow on the way to the black. Come on, Pony." He touched the horse's ribs with his heels. "You never talk about me like I am not here."

"Now he's talking to Pony," Caip said.

Vared whistled. "Should we tell him horses can't speak?"

"That is what you think," said Tel, giggling.

Fourteen

Between their arrival at Foghar and solstice, proper cold skirled from north to south between the hills, bringing cleaner, thinner air to the valley. Tel made efficient use of the shortening days, continuing to ask himself how he could be useful. He rose early from improving sleep to make or receive visits to or from the locals. Frustration had mounted among residents because King Lag demanded increased tribute in silver or the fruits of their toil. Tel decided to cover the additional banalities with his own coin. The area needed a new mill to keep up with extra yield resulting from the introduction of Omelan planting and harvesting techniques. Finding his terror of babies had lessened, he made sure to meet each of the newest inhabitants of Foghar Valley. He even cooed at them in the manner he had always found ridiculous.

It was Feighan custom to observe solstice in a simple, private manner. Omelans marked the shortest day of the year more festively. On the other side of the Gray Sea, it was the most important event of the calendar, set aside for parties, gift-giving, and looking forward to the return of longer, warmer days. Even in the Omelan capital, where one might not see one's breath at all during the entire year, the parties were raucous. Tel had experienced more than one.

He arranged for Caip to take Vared on a trek to explore the wilderness for the day. When the sun set, she would perform a solemn solstice ritual for the songmaker, in the Feighan style. She would return him to the castle after the ceremony. With luck, he would be surprised with a celebration reminding him of home.

Prince Tel fussed and fretted over every detail. He scrambled to gather enough candles for the festivities. With his bow, he personally brought down two of the game birds they would serve. They were the Feighan species closest to the fowl Omelans enjoyed in their traditional feasts. Tel recruited every musician in the valley and arranged for them to rehearse a few Omelan songs.

As the first party guests arrived, Tel paced the great hall, checking this and rearranging that. He lingered over his mother's diadem, which sat in a glass case on a shelf at the far end of the chamber. The half-crown was a simple band of twelve overlapping silver leaves—one for each of the gods. The two largest leaves—one for the Doe and one for the Stag—formed a peak at its center. Like the woman, it was humbly, elegantly beautiful. Telling himself Queen Fyor would have enjoyed a party like tonight's, Tel shook off the melancholic moment to continue his preparations.

As would be done all over Omela at similar gatherings, each new arrival took a candle at the entryway. Once lighted, they placed the candles on the floor in concentric rings, creating a nucleus of warmth and illumination around which the partygoers would make merry.

A soldier charged with lookout stuck his head into the great hall. "They're coming!"

The guests quieted as Tel dashed to the entry, an unlighted candle in his hand. He stood in the archway, feeling sweat surface on his skin. When the songmaker was in front of him, Tel passed the candle. "Light returning, Vared.".

"Light returning, Te—your highness."

Tel swung his body out of the way, allowing the dome of candlelight to reach the smoothness of Vared's lips, cheeks, and forehead. The deep blue of his wild hair came to life. His eyes were two small flames.

Tel swallowed.

Vared lighted his candle and began to move toward the collection of tiny fires in the middle of the chamber. As he took his first step, the musicians started an Omelan tune of the season. An untrained but strong alto sang a somber, gorgeous melody. Vared stopped.

Tel swallowed again.

Vared turned back and mouthed, "Thank you."

After the extravagant meal, Prince Tel rose in front of his chair and asked for the partygoers' attention. "I am gratified to have all of you in my home tonight. I am, of course, less gratified to see our guest of honor is much more popular than I." Chuckles filled the hall as he turned to address Vared. "It is custom to mark the lengthening of the days with the giving of gifts, is it not?"

"Yes, your highness."

"Good," said Tel. "We have a couple for you." Caip nodded at him, stood, and strode out of the great hall. A tall man approached the prince's table carrying a large package of rough paper tied up with string. He set it in front of Vared. "This is Dun, the best trapper in the valley. We noticed you are woefully unprepared for the coldest Feighan days, still ahead of us."

Vared opened the bundle with care, revealing a blazing winter ermine cloak. Dun beamed.

"Thank you," Vared said, showing the trapper a shy smile. He turned his face to Tel. "Thank you."

"Show us," cried someone in the hall.

His embarrassment was evident, but he played along, standing and donning the white, calf-length garment. His hair never looked bluer. The hall filled with clapping. When it concluded, he said, "Phew. I will never be cold again." Dun pulled the cloak from Vared's shoulders and hung it over his arms.

Caip crossed back into the room and called, "We have more." She walked to Vared's place and presented a sheathed smallsword. "Because you have the natural feel for the sword, Prince Tel thought you should have this."

Vared unsheathed and inspected the blade.

Tel said, "It was my great-grandmother's. A fine swordsperson. I think it is about the perfect size for you. Unfancy, but a well-made weapon. May you never need to use it."

"This is your great-grandmother's?" Vared asked, placing his palm over his solar plexus. "You honor me, your highness. You all honor me."

"Light returning," said Tel.

"Light returning," the crowd bellowed.

Tel beamed. "Now, for dancing."

"Wait." Vared put a hand up. "Although I didn't know we were exchanging gifts, I have one for the prince." He turned to one of the local musicians. "I can fetch my terquin, unless I can borrow your instrument for a moment?"

"Of course," the player said.

Although Feighan lutes were not identical to Omelan terquins, Vared showed no hesitation with the instrument. He readied himself as everyone gathered around him. "This is a ballad based on a story I heard Prince Tel recite the night our war was finally ended." He began strumming. "I wrote it with him in mind. I know the story's important to all of you, especially his highness.

Between the nations
Between the armies
Stood the wives of the gods
Stag and bird, snake and worm, fish and frog
In their wrath and in their raging
They were deaf to their pleas
Hear our words, drop your swords, show us peace
Forward they still marched
Showed mercy to no one
So I ask you now why you ignore
The grief of the antlered one
Still the nations
Still the armies
Spill blood under their feet
Form their lines, draw their swords, murder and siege
To their greed and to their hatred
Humankind closes their eyes
The glories of victory are not worth their price
Forward they still march
Show mercy to no one

So I ask you now will you ignore
The grief of the antlered one
Will the nations
Will the armies
Heed their own history
Hear our words, drop your swords, show us peace."

When he played the last note, Vared showed the hall a slight smile. Many of the eyes watching him glistened in the candlelight, Tel's included. Vared's tenor would cause skin and spine to tingle if he sang the contents of a counter's books. The sentiment of the ballad and the Omelan's masterful delivery edged Prince Tel close to shaking apart. Like the rest of the crowd, he brought his hands together like rapid thunder.

When the applause died, Vared shouted, "Now, we dance!"

* * *

They danced in Feighan and Omelan fashion both, the music growing faster and the people growing drunker over the next pair of hours. The event was a success, pleasing Prince Tel. His faith was a bit restored. Everything that had occurred since their departure from Affas proved that many Feighans had within them the capacity to offer a warm embrace to foreigners, even Omelans. In fact, they seemed to do so easily.

Just as he decided the drunkenness and din were too much, Vared appeared alongside him.

"Your high—"

"I want you to call me Tel in private, as you almost did earlier. There is no need for the formality if it is just you and me. Or you and Caip and me."

"Would you accompany me while I step outside and test my cloak?" asked Vared. "I'm afraid the party's too rowdy for me, even if it is solstice."

"I would enjoy that. I could use some air. I was just now plotting my escape."

"I know. Your face is easier to read since you stopped taking your comfort."

Tel resisted the temptation to explore the statement. Vared jogged back to fetch his new cloak and threw it over his thin frame. Crossing back to Tel, he looked like a fair-weather cloud crowned with sapphire. They stepped outdoors into bracing relief, crunching past shrubs, sculptures, and benches, to a large field where Tel sometimes liked to read and bask in the sun during warmer weather. They took their time, creeping across the breadth of the empty space without aim.

Vared said, "I enjoyed marking the solstice in the forest with Caip. The Feighan way. It was wonderful. But to return and have a reminder…Thank you."

"You are welcome."

"I'm not sure I'm worthy of anything as fine as this cloak," said Vared.

Tel shook his head. "Worthy? I will not hear it."

"Or your family's sword."

"You are, quite legally speaking, a member of my household," said Tel. "Of my blood. You cannot play with wasters forever. And it is impolite here to question a gift."

"I'll mind my manners, then."

Tel cleared his throat. "The song…"

"Did you find it satisfactory?"

"Satisfactory? It was beautiful. Like…like the story itself. The best gift I have ever received."

"I'm sure y—"

"I will not hear it, Vared."

They looked up at the stars in silence until Tel sensed Vared looking at him. Tel gave him his eyes and asked, "Is it warm enough?"

"The fur? Yes. I'm perfectly warm. But you have no cloak."

"It is inside somewhere."

Vared opened the ermine, extending his right arm. "Share mine."

"Share?"

"Join me in here." He titled his head to his right. "There's plenty of fur. Just to warm your back and shoulders."

"I am not that cold. My Feighan blood is thicker."

"Tel."

How is anyone to refuse you, Vared of Omela? For a beat, Tel thought he had said it aloud. He was grateful he had not.

"Come here," said Vared.

Without another word of protest, Tel moved to him. Once he had the fur draped over himself, Vared's arm slid across his broad upper back. Tel was overwhelmed by two drives, equal in strength. He wanted to run. He wanted to not move for the rest of his days. This duality reminded him of when Vared had pulled him from the charging young lovers' path in the corridor in Affas. Pushing all the mental noise aside, he mirrored Vared, draping his arm across the Omelan's back.

"Better, yes?"

"Yes," said Tel. "It is."

"Sometimes, it's good to lower the shield of pride."

"I—"

A hooting tumble of revelers pierced the quiet, running at them from the direction of the castle.

"That's him," cried one.

"You can't hide that blue mess anywhere, Vared," said another, through playful laughter.

A half-dozen young women and men barreled across the crunchy grass. Tel lowered his arm and maneuvered out of the fur cloak in a smooth step. Pivoting to face the approaching group, he shared a quick look with Vared. The meeting of their eyes communicated much in an instant. Unfortunately, it was as if it had been in a language Tel did not understand, even the half he had spoken.

He heaved his finest royal smile onto his face and showed it to his people. "I hope you are all enjoying the solstice party." Vared turned but remained close enough for Tel to feel the ghost of his warmth. "Have you come to stargaze? That is what Ambassador Vared and I were doing."

"I think," shouted a tall girl, "I'm drunk enough I'd see two of every star. Like the moons."

"The moons are small tonight, and it makes the stars easier to see," said the boy next to her, as if announcing a profound discovery.

"Come back inside, Vared. I told everyone about the funny song. The one with the one-handed Omelan flesh-peddler. You have to sing it. You must." She clasped her hands together in front of her chin, begging.

"I'm not sure," said Vared, "it's appropriate for the solstice. Or any other day of the year, frankly."

"The party's now far past appropriate," said the moons expert.

From the back of the cluster of the prince's guests, a shivering man said, "Come on, Vared. It's cold out here. Don't be such a no-fun son of a dynast."

Tel felt the orange eyes on him as he took a half-step towards the drunk young people. "I am sure the ambassador would love to sing the song for you."

"You should come and hear it," the tall woman said. "Your majesty," she added.

"Highness," hissed someone behind her.

"I do like a raunchy tune, but I will enjoy the stars and the clean winter air a while longer."

Two women took Vared's hands in theirs and started dragging him toward the castle. "Come on," one of them slurred.

"Perhaps the ambassador would consider playing it for me another time," said Prince Tel.

Vared turned to look at him over a shoulder. "Of course."

Cold and jumpy, Tel stayed in the field regarding the silver-flecked dome overhead until his neck ached. He considered how to best spend his time and energy over the many cold weeks ahead. *What else can I do?* Fyor and Hod entered his mind—a mundane conversation they had shared in this field while he read a short distance away. They had loved each other with fierceness due to their kindred worldview. The queen and her son's lover both saw only the best in people. *It is how they were able to love someone as stormy as I.*

As he shuffled back to the castle, the stagsblood vibrated, begging him to go west, urging him toward the Chreoks. He thought he might glean the reason for this new drive to move, but it remained a frustrating distance beyond his grasp.

* * *

The next morning, Caip strode into the library, hair damp from drilling in the field. Her eyes widened. "Des, old friend. What are you doing all the way up north? Such a wonderful surprise."

The former Tablemember and close friend of Tel's parents rose to greet the rightmajor. "Caip." They shared an embrace.

"When I heard you wanted to see me in here, I expected to see you and Vared," Caip said to Tel.

"He is still sleeping," said Tel, "so I borrowed his rehearsal space when Des arrived to tell me he had something important to discuss."

"Oh?"

"Have a seat, Rightmajor Caip," Des said, neatening his remaining wisps of gray hair with his fingers. He was stronger of body than he should be at his age. His kohl eyes sparked but carried woe. When Caip was settled in her chair, he began. "An ugly series of incidents in Athair. Tensions have been high. King Lag has no one from the south sitting Table. Things worsened with news of the increase in taxes. The number of the king's armed women and men patrolling the streets has nearly tripled. They're aggressive and disrespectful. The southeast of Feigh is seen as less Feighan because we supported Vith's peace efforts early and in strong voice.

"They've already taken a cross-corded couple—a Feighan and a Sheruck-ian—to Gontrahd. Disloyal people, they say. Spies. Someone reported a child dynast to the king's troops. They came to collect the boy, and the neighbors swore to protect him and the family. A standoff. A siege, really. Ended with more than a dozen dead. Eleven citizens, including the child and his sister, and a few of the king's soldiers."

"Terrible." Caip turned a grave expression to Tel.

Des leaned forward. "It only gets worse. People have begun ambushing the king's forces. Now more arrive. And they vex Athairians at every turn. I fear extensive bloodshed, rightmajor. Feighan against Feighan in one of the kingdom's oldest cities."

"Already bloodshed enough," she said.

"Agreed. There is…"

"A complication," Tel said, looking at the floor.

"The pace of these occurrences," continued Des, "seems to be increasing. The most recent event—the thing that inspired me to make this trip—was particularly…" The old man cleared his throat. "Someone painted the side of a building near where the king's soldiers are garrisoned."

"Painted a building?"

"Yes, Caip," said Des.

Tel lifted his face and leaned toward his friend. "Orange, green, the cross, the ring."

A little gasp scurried past Caip's lips. "Your colors."

Des leveled his black eyes at Caip. "And the words, *Health and wisdom to King Tel,* tall as a man."

Fifteen

Tel decided he must go to his brother at once.

He and Caip raced, hunted, reminisced, and argued their way across the countryside. She had insisted on taking at least a detachment of the guard, but he had not wanted their approach to convey even a hint of threat. At night, they shared a tent, which made the strengthening winter cold more bearable. He found himself forgetting the excursion's aim and enjoyed his old friend's company in a way he had not in twenty seasons. The night before they would arrive at Affas, they stoked their well-banked fire deep into the dark hours.

Side by side, they stared at the waving and jumping of the flames. The crisp breeze turned into a more forceful, stuttering wind. Snow began to fall—the first of the season. Tel and Caip noted this with some excitement and watched the whorls of compact flakes twist around them in silence for a long while. They moved closer against the chill.

"I am miserable sometimes," Tel confessed, "over and over reliving the mistakes I can remember, trying to figure a way to go back and unmake them. And the ones I cannot remember—how would I unmake those? I convinced myself if I meditated on my regret long and hard enough, I would be able to alter it all. Undo it."

"That would be magic, Tel."

"Yes."

Caip rubbed her hands together. She pushed them into the dome of heat made by the fire, opening her palms. "Impossible."

"But you know I am sorry?" Tel shifted forward so he could see her face.

"For the humiliations and the worrying. For forgetting you. Even when you have been next to me the whole time."

"I know."

"And I know it means nothing. That the being sorry is...mine. Mine to feel. But I need you to know how deeply—" Tears skated down his face, some clinging to his beard, some landing in the white dusting of snow. "How deeply I feel it."

She gave him her eyes. "I know it, Tel. I do."

"Thank you," he whispered, because he could not find his throat. He convulsed, overcome, and wiped mucus from his nose with the back of his hand, not caring if she saw. "You are the best fr—I love you."

"And I love you." She lowered her hands, resting them on her knees. "And, yes, I can find only so much meaning in your *sorry*. I'm much more moved by you sharing your thoughts, like this, and by you staying dry. Don't punish yourself too much. It's another form of selfishness, just as much as forgetting everyone and everything except the drink." She turned her face to the sky, letting the cartwheeling snowflakes land on her cheeks. "And it's dangerous. Make yourself miserable too long, and you'll find a mug in your hand, promising it'll help you feel better."

"Yes. Of course. May I rest my head on your shoulder?"

"Yes, Tel."

He could hear the rolling eyes in her voice but took advantage of her permission. "Thank you." He stayed still, leaning against her, for a few moments. "I wonder if Foghar is seeing this weather. I will miss Vared's first snow."

"You're sweet on him."

"I am sure I do not know what you mean."

She nudged his head off her shoulder. "Well, *I* know what I mean. Because I know you as you don't even know yourself. And I know you're sweet on Ambassador Vared of Omela because my eyes work. Not since..."

"Do not say it." He found he did not have the energy to dissemble. "But he is..."

"He is," said Caip. She made a little sound of amusement in her throat. "I

136

know."

"I cannot. I do not. I do not do *that*. Something inside me broke when they went into the water. I know I am not the first to have that kind of break. Craid says the pain of the breaking may be why I took solace in ale in the first place. There is...*appeal* in the thought of..." Without closing his eyes, Tel saw Hod's body curling through space toward the swollen, murky river. "And I know. I know people put their insides back together. But I have not found the way."

"Maybe the way found you."

He wanted to show her a wilting look for her mawkishness but could not sculpt his face that way. Instead, he almost cried again. "I cannot find the courage. I have no reason to think he—Of course he does not. He is so young. And I am not. Even if he does, if he later changed his mind, or if something happened to him...Please do not push me about it. I am the way that I am. Such a thing is not for me."

"Very well, my friend. Very well. He may never forgive you. For leaving him in charge of Foghar. *Lord* Vared." She scoffed and enjoyed a long chuckle.

"He is a member of my household. I left him Kelseigh."

She pulled his head back to her shoulder. "I'm sweet on Mor."

"What?"

"I care for him. A good deal."

Tel snickered. "He has been trying to woo you without appearing like he is trying to woo you for sixty seasons."

"I know," she said, chuckling again. "And you'd know it's been working for the last dozen or so seasons if you ever paid any attention to anyone but yourself."

Knowing he deserved it, Tel decided not to protest. "I did notice how close the pair of you seemed at the solstice celebration."

"There was something about that night," she said with an easy sigh.

"Yes."

"He's a good man."

"And," said Tel, "he has the best wool in Feigh. And the best apples. As he will be more than pleased to tell you."

Caip gave an amused shrug. "And *after* the party…"

Tel sat up straight and turned to her. He grabbed her by the shoulders, shaking her body. "And after the party?"

"Yes."

"Antlered ones, Caip. How long were you going to wait to share this?"

"I've been angry. So, I was going to wait until exactly now."

"Fair."

Her expression became impish. "But if it comes down to your brother taking one of our heads, it's yours. Mor's a very good lover."

"Also fair," said Tel, pulling Caip's head to his shoulder. He extended his free arm and opened his hand to the cold air. They rested their eyes on his palm, where snowflakes became water.

* * *

Tel sat in the overheated, cramped den in his uncle's rooms. Aith had offered him a low chair near the screaming fireplace. Between them stood a table with a marred, dusty surface. The uncle did not meet the nephew's eyes when he said, "Curious how you and Lord Craid always find yourselves arguing in opposition to King Lag and his ideas. In opposition to Feigh. You spent years selling your father the Omelan view of things. Now, you're troubled when a soldier wants to ask a foreigner some simple questions on the streets of our own capital. You fret when we decide to keep the whole kingdom safe by watching the children with the blood. You gripe when the king moves to put down an uprising."

"To give anything but my best counsel would be disloyal," said Tel. "I offer it in good faith."

Aith grunted and got to his feet again. "How's your pretty songbird?" He walked to a cart sitting against a dull brown tapestry.

Tel shifted his weight on the chair. He watched Aith closely. "Vared is enjoying Foghar. He says he will have dozens of new tunes about Feigh to leave with us and take home to Feigh."

"How wonderful." With three thuds, Aith placed a crystal decanter and two metal mugs on the table at Tel's side. "It is so early in the day, but sometimes I get a devilish thirst in the mornings. As long as it doesn't become a habit, I see no harm in allowing myself to quench it."

Lips pursed, Tel continued to eye his uncle.

Aith poured two tall cups. When he put the top back in the decanter, he slid one of them toward his nephew. He drank his entire mug in slow, deliberate gulps. "I feel so wicked." He looked at the second mug and then at Tel. "Will you not join me?"

"No. Thank you."

"Of course. How clumsy of me. You're trying the dry life. I should eliminate the temptation." He gave Tel his unblinking eyes, took the second mug in his gloved hands, and drained it. "So satisfying."

Tel felt no enticement, only nausea and unease about being alone with his uncle. Beneath that, the stagsblood wailed. The urge to mount Pony and ride west took hold again. He thought it a mad idea but had the sense that relief—safety—was to be found at the feet of the Chreok Mountains. "I came here to speak with Lag. Why am I being barred from seeing him?"

"You are not being barred, Tel. He simply can't find the time. Entirely too busy with government."

"I am *here* to discuss *government*. A prince of this realm seeks audience with his king about matters of..." Tel looked at his lap. After a handful of beats, he raised his head and allowed himself a full breath. He showed Aith a crooked smile. "If my brother is entirely too busy with anything, it is with visiting with tailors and sleeping in and having his feet rubbed." He shook his head and rocked forward. "If there is not anything else, Uncle Aith, I think—"

"There is something." Aith pulled folded paper from inside his doublet. "Obviously, the king needs you to renounce any claim to or desire for the throne. Formally. Publicly." He stood and searched the surfaces in the parlor. "There must be a quill and ink somewhere. *Ah. Yes.* You'll sign this letter, so he, Table, and all the good people of Feigh know you're not a traitor. And so the insurgents in Athair know they rally to no one. A ghost." Aith placed parchment, inkpot, and quill on the scratched table next to his nephew. He stabbed his index finger on the spot for Tel's signature.

"I will read it, if you remove your finger."

"Of course."

"Why always the gloves, uncle?"

Clasping his hands in front of his belly, he said, "A skin ailment, your highness. More unsightly than anything."

"Your hands seemed fine before my last trip to Omela," said Tel, without looking at Aith. He continued to scan the document.

"Yes. Yes." Aith brought his palms together in a half-dozen rapid, soft claps, leather on leather. "If you sign, I can bring it with me to Table. It will please them."

"It would please most of you. Not all. Not Lord Craid." Finally, he lifted his gaze. "I will not sign this. I will reject any claim to the throne but will not put the name my mother gave me to all the rest of these leavings."

"Excuse me? Leavings?"

"Uncle, your ears work fine, old as you are." He picked up the letter and began reading. *"I offer my loyalty and service to my brother, King Lag, and to a New Risen Feigh...freely devote myself to the return of the Feighan Race to their rightful station on the world...my life to my king and kingdom if its sacrifice is required to defend the superiority of the Feighan faith."* He let the letter fall to the table. "Leavings. My fath—*your brother*—would wipe his ass with this. And it would not be up to the task."

Aith's laugh managed to sound both dark and giddy. "My brother—*your father*—is the one who allowed the rack crown to be snatched from your head, fool. Surely you can't think he didn't know this was coming. Do you long to know why? Do you? Because you're a drunk embarrassment. He clung to the notion you'd one day right your ship. But you've done so too late. And everyone around you knows this change is just temporary. That you'll one day—one day soon—crawl back into a barrel and drink yourself to death. It's your destiny. You were always self-important. The peacemaker prince! Bah. Those last three years of diplomacy didn't require the crown prince's personal attention. The work was done. To your credit, it was largely done by you. But again, long ago. These last years, however, have seen a man who indulged his baser appetites become ruled by them. Following his thirst and the whims of his balls to humiliation. And your father watched it happen. Watched a prince full of potential, brimming with intelligence, become what you are today. King Vith kept you on the Omelan task because even you could not cock that up. Even blind drunk and sniffing after any man who crossed your path. Thank the antlered goddess your poor mother was not here to witness your long, sad slide into disgrace."

Tel rose, oddly placid. "Uncle. Despite all you have said, I still love you." He moved to the old man and pulled him into an awkward embrace. Aith did not have the strength to break the hug. His nephew's arms were too powerful. Tel's face met Aith's sagging neck. There, he placed a kiss and read the man's mind and heart with the stagsblood. He did not permit himself to show any reaction to what the wind and rain magics told him. After three beats, he let go of his uncle and moved to the door. When he reached it, he spun around.

"And if I am to be denounced as a traitor, please execute me while I am here in Affas. Another day or two. Three at most. I should hate to have to make this trip again just to have my head separated from my body. Especially in winter. But make sure you are ready for what will come after. Lag is weak. Strong leaders do not triple the number of eyes watching their citizenry. He is weak because many of his people are unhappy. He does not need a martyr for the Athairians to look to." Tel narrowed his eyes and took a single step back into the room. "It could be a disaster for him. I do not want that crown. I accept that Lag sits on that throne. But once I am dead, there will be nothing to do or say about what happens in my name. Drunk and useless as I have been and may be, I still know my history. Unhappy subjects with a dead figure to carry all their hope and a tyrannical ruler to receive all their rage…Well, that kind of situation does not make for security and stability."

* * *

Halfway to the window, Tel prayed, telling the antlered god he should have let him be born a peasant. Had he been reared by a poor family, it would be unlikely he would find himself clinging to an outside wall of the castle in the freezing night air while maintaining a cloak of invisibility. He did not know how high he was off the hard ground and did not like thinking about it.

"This is absurd," Tel said aloud. He panicked for a flash, then realized he could not be heard at this height. *Nor in this godsforsaken wind.* He was uncertain he would make it the rest of the way. While he was strong enough, his hands were becoming more unreliable the colder they got. He was losing sensation past his wrists.

Pain is only information. Caip's frequent training reminder came to him and spurred him to keep climbing. *"Prince Tel is dead* is also only information," he muttered.

He could not be sure how long it took, but eventually, the window was within reach. It was a gamble, but one that logic told him had the best odds. He had tried to see his brother since he arrived but was turned away by surly guards each time. On the other side of the shutters was the outermost section of the king's apartments, what was little more than a vestibule. It was most likely empty. *It had better be.* Tel's raw fingers demanded he place his bet as soon as possible.

His precarious position made easing the shutters open much harder than he had imagined. He almost lost his grip on the stones three times before he could lift his stomach onto the sill.

He caught his breath before allowing himself to fall into the vestibule. The blood returned to his hands. He closed the shutters and listened. Nothing reached his ears but the wind behind him. In the quiet, he realized how fatigued he was. It would not have been possible to maintain the cloak for too much longer. He had not considered the extra expenditure of energy. Although the use of magic had come to him at a smaller cost in recent months, there were limits. He allowed the cloak to fall away and stood straight, trying to look like he had not sneaked in.

Stepping into a narrow hallway, he saw the closed library door and felt his chest burn. He had spent countless hours in that room, absorbing his father's wisdom. A careful reading of history, King Vith had taught him among the books and scrolls, showed that all the world's queendoms and kingdoms had both committed and been victims of atrocities throughout the centuries. Humankind had long teetered on the fulcrum between creation and destruction. It was a monarch's responsibility to place the weights she or he had been given by the gods—their natural talents—on the correct side.

He walked to the left, to the formal parlor, where he found Lag and a female servant sitting on their legs on a broad sofa. The servant had a bowl of fruit between her knees. His brother was wearing the rack crown, even at night in his private rooms. Seeing Tel, the woman squeaked.

"Brother," said King Lag, his voice uneven. He straightened his back. "How?"

"I needed to speak with you. Without Uncle. So I found a way," said Tel. He looked at the servant. "You may go."

Lag nodded, and the woman got to her feet.

"I won't be long," said Lag. He resumed popping fat red grapes into his mouth. He tilted the crystal bowl toward his older brother, who grabbed a small bunch and lowered himself onto the couch. The fruit was the most colorful thing in the room. Lag's changes to the décor had been radical. Browns predominated. The fabrics were luxurious, but the effect was grim. A long, quiet moment passed.

"Haven't seen you eating like this since we were boys," said Lag.

"I stopped drinking and my appetite came back."

"You'll end up with father's paunch if you're not careful."

"With Caip forcing me to drill constantly? A paunch is a long way off for me," said Tel.

Lag chuckled. "I'm getting big as a horse. I'm not allowed to lift a finger for myself."

"You are king. Make them allow it."

"Bah."

Tel scooted closer to his younger brother on the cushion of the sofa. "You *are* the king. You understand I know this, do you not?"

"Uncle isn't sure."

"Brother, you are my king." Tel took Lag's hand in his. The stagsblood should have instantly conveyed his thoughts and emotions. Instead, Tel found only neutrality. All within Lag was noise—a rush of sound like the white water of a river. No meaning was in it. He silently cursed the antlered ones. "I have no designs on your crown. My life is lived in service to this realm—your realm. You must not take too seriously the incidents in Athair." Still, contact with his brother's skin yielded nothing useful. He squeezed Lag's hand and let it go. "To overreact now would only serve to exacerbate the situation. Their rallying to my name is just a sign of frustration. You must not make it worse. Ease off and give them a voice at Ta—"

"And reward rebellion?"

"No. Just hear them," said Tel.

"I hear whining."

"Brother. My grace. I am trying to help you."

Lag scoffed. "I don't need your help. Or anyone's. I'm king. Under this crown because it's the will of the Stag, I know what's best for Feigh."

"Father alw—"

"I need to rest," said Lag. "When I don't get enough sleep, my face gets puffy."

"Your face."

Lag rose from the couch and put the bowl of fruit on his brother's lap. "I don't know how you talked your way in here. Don't do it again without an appointment. I'm busy. I ought to have my entire guard hanged on the other end of the causeway."

Exhausted, Tel sat in the parlor for a while, his mind racing. When he had touched his uncle's damp skin, he had seen in him the skewed deviousness and hatred he had feared but expected. Much worse, he was a mature dynast, and a powerful one. Aith knew his nephew had the blood, too. Tel believed this was why he had taken to wearing gloves—to avoid Tel's touch, or the touch of another with the blood. Contact would tell anyone with even minor powers the true nature of the old man in an instant. Recent months had shown Tel he was anything but the only person in whom the stagsblood powers had outlasted adolescence.

His uncle's magic eclipsed his own. Tel had felt an echo of raw power. Dynasts with gifts of such extraordinary magnitude might be able to control the minds and hearts of others without even touching them.

The longer he sat on his Lag's couch, the more convinced Tel became. Aith was strong enough for such use of the wind and rain dynasties. Tel believed this strength allowed his uncle to dictate every move his brother made, to shape each decision. Lag had always seemed susceptible to Aith's worldview. In Vith's absence—and because of Tel's laziness, naivete, and self-absorption—they were emboldened to reveal the dark depth of that worldview.

For gods knew how long, the uncle had held the younger nephew on a psychic tether. With this magical leash, Aith was reshaping Feigh. It explained the blankness Tel had found when trying to read his brother. Aith had made of dull Lag a vessel to carry his wrath and prejudice.

Sixteen

When they reached the valley after a brutal journey eastward through the ceaseless, icy gale, Caip asked if she might take a night or two to spend with Mor. Major Dar could remain in charge of the guard. Thrilled, Tel granted the request and urged her to take longer than that. He would see her in a week.

Vared must have had warning about his approach—a good sign his soldiers had remained alert under Dar's command—because he met him outside the castle. Tel was delighted to find Vared standing in the yard, wearing the white cloak. Even in the dark of evening, Tel saw he looked tired. Impossibly, it only made him lovelier. His beauty shone because of—not despite—his vulnerability.

"Your highness."

"Lord Vared." Tel smirked and knew at once he had miscalculated.

"How was your journey?"

"Productive. I learned some things I needed to know. I missed home, though. I—"

"You'll also want to know about some events," said Vared. "I thought it important to prepare you before you entered the castle."

Prince Tel felt chilled, and not only because of the winter air. Vared was different. His detachment had returned. It reminded him of their first few conversations. He thought of their talk on the deck of the *Crunadam*. "Continue." He ignored the sensations—sharp and dull both—in his chest and gut.

Vared said, "The home of Gunda, her man, and their children burned."

"Goddesses and—"

"A total loss. Several offers from the people of the valley, but I felt they were most easily accommodated here. Probably only until mid-spring, but I moved them into one of the cottages. Six of Caip's women and men are now in the great hall. We already have the material and labor promised to rebuild the home come warmer weather."

"You did well." Tel could not help his smile. He stepped closer to Vared. "This is precisely why I left you in charge."

"Thank you, your highness."

The songmaker appeared to try to remain neutral, but Tel read some relief in his eyes.

"Vared, is everythi—"

"There have also been six cases of the winter sweat. We've limited contact between the sick and the healthy. Mor has been helpful. He has a preparation with the yellow spice to purify the blood. Still, we may lose three."

"May the antlered ones look over them."

"Yes."

Tel leaned in. "Speaking of Mor, Caip has gone to see him. They are in love, it seems."

"Interesting."

"Yes." Tel felt a small frown appear, against his will. "You are upset with me."

"No."

"I see now that I should have prepared you for taking responsibility."

Vared looked at his feet. "You always do what you want. The rest of us..."

"I am sorry." Tel lowered his head, trying to take his orange eyes.

Breaths coming faster, Vared would not give them.

"I am sorry," said Tel.

"You disappeared."

"Yes. And I—" Tel stopped speaking.

Vared trembled. It looked like he was trying to hold something powerful at bay. He seemed unable to get enough air. He croaked, "I was alone."

Tel wanted to hold him, but his face was alive with panic. "Vared. When I am feeling overwhelmed, when my mind is very high, I focus on my breathing. If you can breathe in a way that fills your belly, it will bring your mind low."

"I don't want your help."

Tel swallowed. "I am here, that is all…"

With what looked to be a great effort, Vared spoke again, flatly. "I'd like to retire if you'll permit it, your highness."

"Of course. Sleep well." Tel swallowed again, loud enough that he heard it.

Vared vibrated under the ermine as he walked away, leaving Tel standing in the snow.

* * *

Behind the castle, Tel and Caip packed snow into compact balls. They tried to hit the trunk of a tall, straight, white-barked tree with their missiles. This was one of the few physical activities at which he had always bested her.

She missed by the width of a fat man. "Goddess damn it."

"You are even worse than usual," said Tel, shaking his head.

"I know."

"You are in love."

"Quiet. I'm concentrating." She was closer this time but still wide. Tel's next shot hit home with a *thuck*. She reacted with a growl.

"Tell me about it. Please, Caip. Distract me."

"You've seen Mor. He's handsome. You know him. He's big-hearted and intelligent. He cares for other people. He cares for me, proving that nothing's impossible."

"But how do you feel?"

She tossed a fresh snowball between one hand and the other. "Lucky. *Yes*. Lucky. He could have his pick. But he's pined after me for so long.

148

And something in me is different, and I allowed myself to pay him some attention. I asked myself what I was *doing*, ignoring him. He hasn't asked anything of me other than to be myself and to give him some of my time. He doesn't want me to change or to take a post where I won't have to trail you all over the world. I'm fine for him just as I am. And that's a rare thing. Especially for me. I'm not easy, and I know that."

He beamed at her. "You are happy," Taking her into a hug, he felt his eyes grow wet in the cold. He released her. They looked at one another.

Caip tilted her head and narrowed her eyes. "You're a good deal softer since you gave up the drink. I think I like it, but I also think you should start again immediately."

"I feel exactly the same."

Laughter folded both their bodies. Through her hoots, Caip said, "You're sincere and sensitive, and I'm in love. What's become of us?"

Tel howled. "I do not know."

"You two are having fun," Mor said, approaching from behind.

"Yes," they said in breathless unison.

Remembering the purpose of Mor's visit, Tel's face tightened. "How…"

"You were right, highness. He's improving. The fever's broken. He'll be tired for some time. But he's on his feet and has returned to his room."

Vared, sick with the winter sweat, had not been able to walk under his own power for days. Feeling responsible, Tel had doted on him, rarely leaving his side. The boy had been too weak to protest. Tel had moved the Omelan to his own bed, so he could be on the most comfortable mattress in the valley. There, Vared had muttered and rambled and perspired on the prince's sheets. Tel had taken shallow sleep in a chair.

"Thank you, Mor," said Tel. "I think the spice made a difference. You will stay for supper?"

"It would be my pleasure, highness."

Tel, Caip, Mor, and Dar enjoyed a meal of stewed game bird over root vegetables. Vared declined, telling Caip he might have a bit of stew later. He remained in his room.

Conversation among the four diners was easy. The guests enjoyed some wine with their supper. Tel was surprised he found no interest when he looked at the pitcher being passed among them. Feeling the opposite of thirst for the stuff, his gut churned at the thought. Watching Caip with her new lover fascinated and delighted him. They obviously tried to avoid paying one another too much attention, but their success was limited. An hour after the meal, the pair rode off to Mor's house, leaving Tel and Dar to play cards.

The major continued to drink and before long had the glow of intoxication about him. Tel had never seen him drunk and found it amusing. His play became slower. His decisions were more reckless. Tel wondered how many times people had witnessed him in this state—or a state far worse. He felt the sting of shame.

After a couple of hours, Tel grew bored with cards his company. Asking himself if drunk people always repeated themselves like this, the little twinge of chagrin returned.

"Dar, I am afraid I am tired," said Tel. "I have not been sleeping well. I need to crawl into bed."

The major's glassy eyes met Tel's clear ones. "What if I joined you?"

Tel froze and made a dumb sound.

"We could…" Dar's smile was dumber.

"I did not know you enjoyed men." Prince Tel looked at his companion. His rugged maleness was attractive. That much, he could not deny, but the appraisal conjured in him only the notion of lust, rather than lust itself.

"Not my favorite, but my woman's far away. We could…relieve each other. There're things I know about two men being together. I'm feeling good. Could feel better."

It was less appealing than the wine. "Major Dar, you are the second in command of the personal guard of a prince of this realm. A prince you just propositioned."

This seemed to get through to Dar a bit. He sat up straighter and said, "I'm sorry. You aren't known for…discretion. I'm sorry."

"Please go to your bed and sleep this off."

Dar stood. "I'm sorry."

Tel rose and indicated the direction of the great hall, where the major's bed was located. "I know. Go to bed. We shall forget about this. It did not happen."

"I'm sorry," said Dar, stepping toward his prince.

Placing the flat of his hand on Dar's muscled chest, Tel stopped him. "Go. To. Bed."

Dar hung his head. "Night."

"Yes. Goodnight."

Dar wobbled away to the hall. Craving some cold on his skin, Tel shook his head and puttered into the winter night. After a few moments surveying the sky and breathing deeply, he ambled toward the dormant garden, where he found Vared sitting on a bench.

Tel took a seat next to him. "I hope you have not been out here too long. It is cold."

Vared was bundled against the weather, wrapped not in the ermine but a large blanket. He drew a long, slow breath. "No, highness. And you don't need to hover. To watch over me constantly."

"I see. I apologize." Tel snapped to his feet and stomped a few paces away before turning back to him. "Goodnight."

"You stay." Vared stood. "This is your home."

Prince Tel strode toward him, jaw clenched. "It is yours, too. Sit down and enjoy it."

Wide-eyed, Vared complied.

Tel wheeled, marching back in the direction of the castle. "Glad you are feeling better."

* * *

During the next few snowy weeks, routine returned to Foghar. Caip, Tel, and the soldiers drilled outside when they could and in the great hall when the weather was unfriendly. Vared isolated himself in Tel's library, writing and playing songs. He took some afternoon walks with Caip, avoiding all

151

but necessary, polite exchanges with his host. Devouring Feighan histories, he constructed a catalogue of songs appropriate for his diplomatic mission.

Queen Cessa wrote that Lag had recalled the Feighan trade negotiators for the winter. She was unsure any summit would mark the first anniversary of the treaty, as had been planned. That formal conference was also meant to be an opportunity for Vared and the Feighan playbard, Laich, to present some of the work they completed during the exchange. She included a note from Turo, who was recovering faster than anticipated. He had soaked up the attention the Omelan nobles had lavished on him for the past months but would return to the farm soon.

With gusto, Tel threw himself into his physical training. Soon, he was as fit as he had been in fifty or sixty seasons. He read in the evenings and played cards with Dar, whose behavior remained appropriate. At night, he made a habit of finding an hour or two for mind-lowering. He practiced the magical skills he could. He visited the horses to work with the wind and rain dynasties, beginning to see inside the animals' minds without touching them, even bringing them instantly to sleep by planting a suggestion with the psychic tether. His grasp of fire magic increased, allowing him to more easily maintain invisibility. He was surprised to find he could now also conceal objects, making them wink out of view. Disguise was harder, although he could alter his appearance for short periods. His ability to create flame and lightning with the dirt dynasty increased. He could now direct them in plumes and bolts, which was quite exhausting. Conjuring small objects—coins, strange white crystals, even a feather—was a new skill of the dirt dynasty. Making them disappear, rather than simply hiding them, was much more challenging.

One cold night, tired but exhilarated by his progress after a stagsblood session, Tel decided he would sit up for a bit and read in bed. He picked a volume he was about halfway through, an unchallenging but pleasant romance, the perfect reading for right before sleep. The backdrop was a war between Sheruck and Kamber. The lovers were soldiers—one from each side—who ended up at the bottom of a ravine during a battle as the first winter storm of the year approached. The armies collected their dead and moved away. Both were injured and forced to rely on one another to survive and escape. The tone of the story gave Tel no doubt the brave women would wind up together in the end, somehow. Finding the *somehow* was the fun of the book.

He was only a few sentences into the chapter when three knocks landed on his door. "Your highness, are you awake?"

"Yes," said Tel. "Come in." It was Caip.

She opened the door.

"Is something wrong?"

"Yes."

She seemed in a daze. "Sit." He patted the mattress next to him. "What is it?"

"News from the south. Someone sent a rider through all this cold and snow. The unrest in Athair has continued. It's...worsened. Apparently, it's spread through the whole city. They're refusing to pay tribute to the king. Lag sends more and more troops, and they bother the people. Riots. Mysterious fires at the shops and homes of people perceived to be disloyal to the crown. Mass hangings and decapitations in the streets. They hanged old Des and let the loyalists defile the body, Tel. Your mother's friend is dead, and her home is a a battlefield."

Prince Tel had closed his eyes, wanting to disappear. The Chreok Mountains tugged at him. Hot in his veins, the stagsblood buzzed.

Caip cleared her throat. "They call for you. They display your colors."

After a long silence, Tel asked, "How do I tamp this down?"

"Tamp it down?"

Tel lowered his eyelids. "Reason needs to be restored."

"Reason."

"Yes," said Tel.

"They have no one in Affas to protect their interests. Or even to say a word about them. Your brother demands they pay more than anyone else. Not only this, but troops—strangers from all over the kingdom—descend on them and kick them around. Drag their children to Fort Gontrahd the first time a loyalist whispers *dynast*. Burn their neighborhoods. They're terrorized and responding as any people would. They're *being* reasonable. And they're asking for their king."

"I am no king." Tel let his weight fall back into his pillows. He grunted. "Goddesses and gods damn it!"

"Your brother's no king."

Tel snapped back up to a seated position. "No. No. He *is* the king. That is fact!" He lowered his voice after a mindful breath. "I will not tell you he is a great king. Or a good king. He is, so far, a very bad king, in my estimation. But king he is. It is the way of things. The people do not choose their queens and kings. I do not choose. You do not choose."

"But your people have chosen you."

"A few people. A few, Caip. And what is the result of their choice? Death. Death in the streets."

"Would you not be a better king?"

"Rightmajor, lower your voice. The servants. The soldiers under you, they may be part of my guard, but they answer to Lag. You speak your treason under my roof."

She did as she had been commanded and spoke softly. "All of them would fight for you without hesitation. They'd risk the axe or the rope for you tomorrow. I know them."

"If that is the case, I am surrounded by fools."

"Answer my question," said Caip. "Would you be a better king than Lag?"

Tel leapt from the bed, almost knocking her over. He shouted, "Yes! Yes! Does that help you? Yes, I would be a better godsdamned king than him or Aith. Aith, real king of Feigh." Chest heaving, his fists were clenched at his sides. He turned to the fireplace and began poking at the blazing logs with an iron tool. "He is evil, and my brother is dull. And I am a lot of things, but I am not deliberately cruel or stupid. So, yes, damn you. Yes!"

"And you're angry about it."

"What? I am angry? I am angry? I am not angry. I accepted it faster than anyone else. It is you. It is all of you." In a quick motion, he swept all the objects off a nearby table with the poker. Everything crashed to the stone floor. "You are angry. I am not angry."

Dar burst into the room, half asleep. "Your highness, is—" Tel turned away from him.

Caip stood and walked to him. "Everything's fine, Major Dar. Go back to bed." Dar looked at her, stammering. "Go to sleep."

"Goodnight, your highness, rightmajor."

"Goodnight, Dar. And thank you," Caip said. The major left. She returned to her place on the bed. "Come sit, Tel."

Tel said, "I am sorry."

"Don't think of it again. Come sit."

Just as the prince settled next to her, Vared stepped in through the open door. He surveyed the mess on the stones. "I heard the noise. I was worried. I wanted to check—"

"Nothing to worry about, Vared," said Caip.

"The prince…"

Tel hung his head. "I am fine. Go away."

"Goodn—"

"Now," said Tel. "Close the door." He heard the door latch. Without moving, without looking up, he spoke to his oldest friend. "Nothing would improve if I tried to take the throne from my brother. Things would markedly worsen from one end of Feigh to the other because it would mean war from one end to the other. Which would bring death and a thousand other miseries. And on top of that, a thousand more. I know this reign will be ugly. But do I add to the ugliness by asking young people to splash their blood all over the kingdom? Would it be just to meet their violence and hatred with my own? Which side of the scale would that weight land on? Creation or destruction? We will survive this king and hope the next monarch is better.

"You all think I am spoiled. A dilettante. That I simply playacted diplomacy to travel the world and bed boys and drink wine. But it is not the case, even though I mindlessly did those things. I swear it. War is waste—of life, of treasure, of time—and waste is the only true sin. I feel this in my chest and my belly because my mother and father put it there. And they were right.

"Even in peace, people starve. Children go parentless. Disease is everywhere. Caip, you are a soldier. There is honor in it. But imagine if your honor was put to a different purpose. Think of it. Call it naïve. You have before. But the goddesses and gods would disagree. They saw our foolishness. The goddesses were crushed for their seeing. And the gods left us here to use our gifts to end it, not continue it. I will not add to what drove them away. I will not help my brother or my uncle. I will oppose them in any way I can. If they decide I die for speaking my mind, I will die without regret. I will continue to raise my voice. But I will not raise my sword. And I certainly will not press you or some innocent girls and boys to do it for me. Do not ask me to."

"I won't," said Caip. "I won't ask again."

When she left, Tel's doubts did not allow him to sleep.

Seventeen

Prince Tel continued his daily practice with the stagsblood and took to fighting through the spring mud into the forest. There, he was free to work with flames and energy. He did not permit any guard to follow him, saying he would be meditating in nature and must not be disturbed. It was not a total falsehood. He had scorched a tapestry in his bedchamber with a bolt of lightning, requiring him to make a stuttering, inexplicable excuse to an attendant about tripping on the rug with a candle. His proficiency with the dirt dynasty had grown too much to safely test the limits indoors.

One afternoon, a new level of clarity and relaxation—of mind-lowering—came to him all at once, and he threw a dozen bolts from his hands, twenty and five or thirty meters in length. The pure energy crackled from his palms, frightening him. His final argent streak of lightning felled the tree it struck, vaporizing part of the trunk. That section of the tree simply did not exist anymore. He watched the bulk of the tall sycamore tip and crash through the branches of its neighbors, landing on the wet forest floor with a *thud* softer than he expected. Debris knocked loose from its fall whispered down for what felt like an hour. Once his breath returned, he hooted and pounded his chest. Exhilarated, he darted from the forest and loped down the slope toward the castle.

He wanted to tell someone, to demonstrate. As he rushed homeward, he remembered he could share it with no one. Fatigued and starving but euphoric, he rounded the back of the castle to discover Vared's blue head in front of about a dozen mounted horses. The songmaker was talking with the rider of a strong sorrel at the lead. Vared looked tiny before the beast.

A few more strides revealed the identity of the person in the sorrel's saddle. It was Lieutenant Gran. Tel barreled toward them.

"Vared," said Tel when he reached them, huffing. "Are you all right?"

"Yes, highness. The lieutenant and I were catching up."

"I haven't seen this Omelan since he was…under my care in the cells at Affas," said Gran. "Charged with spying, if I remember."

Pleasing Tel, Vared did not take the bait. "She was just asking where you were, Prince Tel. I was explaining that I didn't know, but she seemed to suggest I was lying."

"Well," said Tel, spreading his arms, "here I am, Gran."

"Your royal highness." She peered down at him, scrunching her nose like she had smelled something noxious.

"Foghar is so far from home," said Tel. "How can we help you?"

"Foghar *is* home now." She dismounted. "Not the castle, of course, but the valley. No. We aren't permitted to sleep under the same roof as an off-Feighan." She jerked her chin toward Vared.

"Ambassador Vared is a member of my household—the household of Foghar," said Tel. "He is of my blood."

She spat on the ground to her right. "I'm sorry. Bad taste on my tongue."

Tel felt himself sneering and forced his features into a more neutral expression. "Besides, I have not invited you. Neither to my castle nor my land."

"Table Head Aith asked me to take some of the best from the millenary," said Gran. "He and your brother are concerned about you. There's been some unrest in the kingdom. We want to make certain it's safe here. I rounded up my ten best and rushed to you."

Prince Tel lost control of his face and smirked at her. "How kind. Of you, of Aith, and of my brother. As you can see, we are all safe."

Gran returned the crooked smile. "We'll be sure you remain that way. There is, I believe, a field beyond your gardens. A splendid place for a permanent camp. And close by, so we can keep careful watch, your highness."

"Please make yourselves comfortable." Tel gestured in the direction of the field. He put an arm around Vared's shoulders, turned, and walked him toward the castle. When they were inside, he let Vared go under the chandelier in the foyer. "I know you are…displeased with me, but do not, under any circumstances, leave these walls without one of Caip's soldiers with you."

"Very well."

"I mean it," said Tel. "Do not so much as walk to the stables to brush Kelseigh or go piss on a tree without someone at your side. Gran is not to be trusted. She is a bad person."

"I know exactly who she is."

"Good. The trade summit is now in question, but Cessa and Lag have not recalled you or Laich. Whatever happens, your time here is half done. Before you realize it, you will be sailing for home."

"Yes," said Vared.

The amber irises looked up at Tel. It struck him how long it had been since they were alone, at least while Vared was not feverish and had his whole mind. This knowledge—the amount of time—had mass. It hooked itself onto the heart in his chest, pulling it down to his gut. The orange eyes seemed to search his. Tel sensed Vared was on the edge of speech. They stood on that border together for what felt like an impossibly long moment. Tel both willed him to speak and dreaded what he might say.

Vared broke the anticipation. "Thank you."

* * *

Craid and his grandson, Nik, arrived at Foghar one early evening during the height of the spring rains. Gran's watchful soldiers were first to greet them, but Caip chased them off.

When they started the journey from Affas, Nik told the prince, the old man had been well enough to ride his own horse. At about the midpoint, he had purchased a rickety wagon from a greedy townsperson, using most of their silver. He had fashioned the best cover he could, hoping to keep his feverish grandfather dry during the second half of the muddy slog.

Tel and Nik lifted Craid onto a sofa in the front sitting room. Along with Caip, they hovered around him, drinking hidybrew, expressions carved by worry. The elder's babblings were constant and incomprehensible.

"He seemed to age another forty seasons in three days." Nik fingered his black beard and hair. A tear clung to one of his proud cheekbones.

Looking at the old, thin wreck on his couch, Tel shook his head. "Why did he insist on coming all this way? You said something was troubling him before you left?"

Nik opened his lips as if to answer but froze. He pressed a balled hand against his mouth for a moment, squeezing his eyes shut, before inhaling a jagged breath and beginning again. "He didn't think he had long, even before we left. He'd resigned from Table. A protest. A fishing vessel from Kamber collided with a Feighan ship where the Sleeping Sea meets the Gray. Both sank. Even though the Kambs apologized and offered reparations, Lag declared war. He's seized merchant ships to supplement his fleet and ordered conscription, beginning in the Athair region. Grandfather was the only one at Table to raise an objection. It seemed to crush him. He said he needed to speak with you, your highness. That he had more than this to tell you. A message he refused to send with someone else."

"We are at war?" asked Caip.

"And drafting southerners," said Tel, just louder than a whisper. "My antle—"

"There's more," Nik said, Craid sputtering and moaning behind him. "Your brother has named himself Emperor."

Tel laughed before clamping his palm over his mouth. He looked at Caip. "Excuse me? Of what empire?"

"Kamber isn't simply to be defeated, your highness. They're to be made part of the empire. Part of Feigh. As far as your brother is concerned, Kamber's already Feighan territory. If his invasion is successful, the Kambs will observe our faith or..."

"This is monstrous," Caip said.

"And now there is no voice of reason at Table. Not even one." Tel stared into the cup of hidybrew encircled by his fingers.

Vared stepped into the room, a bit out of breath, his skin dewy. "I've removed my things from the library. We can move Lord Craid whenever you're ready. There's enough space to fit this sofa easily. And another sofa in there for you, Nik. You'll find two bedrolls."

"Are you sure I'm not inconveniencing you, Ambassador Vared?"

"The library's warmer than here. And I can play in my room. It's plenty spacious," said Vared. He looked at Tel with an unreadable expression. "The prince was too generous in offering me a separate room for music in the first place."

Craid's grandson reached out and took the singer's hands in his. "Thank you."

Vared's eyes fell to their clasped hands. "My pleasure."

"We should move him now." Tel set his mug down. "Caip and I can carry the couch. Nik, stay here and rest. Ambassador Vared, will you walk ahead of us and make sure we have a clear path?"

With each careful step, Craid shivered and rocked on the cushions of the sofa.

Soon after, Mor arrived. He prescribed the yellow spice. Voice low and grave, he offered little hope. Tel, Caip, Mor, and Nik visited quietly in the sitting room. Every few moments, one of them checked on Craid.

When it was Tel's turn, he looked at his sick friend and asked, "What did you want to say to me?" Realizing he might never have his answer if he did not act, he moved to Craid and placed curled fingers against his sopped forehead.

Prince Tel's mind came low. The old man's confession was right near the surface, bobbing on a lightless sea of regret and confusion. Tel was almost knocked to his knees by the tide of grief and shame. Haunted by months of foul nightmares, Craid had begun sneaking the drink and had continued on and off for more than four seasons. He had been badly hungover the morning Table declared Tel unsound. Craid's presence at that meeting would have kept him on the throne.

Tel did not allow himself an emotional reaction. He sensed rage and despair were luxuries he could not afford, for they threatened to shove him toward madness. Dully, he floated back to the sitting room.

Caip and Mor were readying to leave for the farm. Nik thanked them all and retired to the library. Dazed, Tel padded up the broad stone staircase. Halfway to the second floor, he saw Vared sitting in shadow on the top step. The sight of him pulled Tel from his haze.

"That's what I was like when I was sick?"

Tel sat next to him. "Intermittently. Yes."

"You stayed with me most of that time."

"Yes," said Tel.

"I remember more than you think. I remember I was so cold."

It felt to Tel like his stomach flipped beneath his skin.

"I asked you to warm me," said Vared. "You refused."

"You did not have your mind."

"But you stayed."

"Yes."

"Why?"

"You are part of my household. Of my blood," said Tel.

"Not really."

"That offends me. These things mean something to a Feighan."

"I meant no offense. Thank you."

"You are welcome, Lord Vared," said Tel, smirking.

Vared stabbed him in the ribs with his elbow and said, "I'm sorry...about the way I've been."

"Since I returned from Affas."

Vared looked at his long fingers. "Yes. I didn't think about it. I didn't mean to be that way. I was furious when you first left, but after a while, I counted the time to your return. And Caip's. But I saw you when you came back and I went cold. I have wanted to...not treat you that way. But I was stuck in the cold place, like there was a chain and weight around my ankle and I could not move it no matter how hard I stretched." He turned and took Tel's eyes. "Caip helped me find those words. She helped me understand."

"You talked with Caip about this?"

Vared nodded.

Tel saw himself cradling the blue head against his chest, but the vivid image frightened him, and he chased the thought away. He realized he wanted Vared to have comfort and ease more than he wanted anything else. "I should have asked. But to me, it seemed like the most natural thing in the world, choosing you to watch over Foghar. There is no one else of my blood who cares anything for it. Caip. Caip is family. But I needed her to be with me. And I needed you to be safe."

"I'm worried for you, Tel."

"I will be fine."

Vared swallowed. "Everything feels like it's getting more dangerous."

"War again," said Tel. "I thought for a time we could really have a world without it."

"Many more people want to avoid fighting. To live in quiet. But other people stand between us and quiet. Those who value peace must be the *right* people. People born with power. Like you. Like my queen."

"I miss that warm old cow," said Tel. "Oh, my goddess. I am so sorry. That was inappropriate. I am tired."

Vared's laugh rattled his whole body, rocking him on the step. He covered his mouth. "I hope I didn't wake Nik. Poor Nik."

"You find him handsome."

"No. He's not unpleasing. But no."

"The way you looked at his hands when he touched you. I thought…"

"No." Vared closed his eyes and gave a little sigh. "I find touching strange. The way people do it when they only know you casually." He raised his eyelids and looked directly at Tel. "Almost as much here as in Omela."

"You touched me," said Tel. "Put your arm around me. In the field."

"I remember. And I asked you to warm me. Do we know each other only casually?"

Tel shook his head and looked between his boots. The silence hanging over the flight of stairs took on the quality of a summer afternoon before a violent thunderstorm. He raised his head, meeting Vared's gaze.

Holding his eyes was excruciating, but letting go felt impossible until the sound of a soldier's barking laugh bounced up the staircase from the great hall.

Tel said, "I had better...I am tired."

"Of course."

After a few slow steps toward his room, Tel turned back. Vared had not moved. "I counted the time, too." He went to bed and dreamed he started drinking again.

Eighteen

From the corner of his eye, Tel saw Caip fill the archway between the sitting room and the corridor. He closed his book and faced her, knowing what was coming. Rainwater from her black cloak and black hair pooled on the stone hallway floor, forming small puddles around her black boots.

"You've sent Dar away with Nik."

Tel set the book next to him. "Yes."

"He's my best." She did not move from the entrance to the room.

"Precisely why he accompanies Nik south."

"South?"

"To Athair," said Tel.

"Why?"

"Why?" Tel drummed his fingers on the leather-bound volume at his side. "And you are always calling me naïve. Would Nik be safe in Affas right now? With his father gone? He thinks his best chances are in the south. Dar will make sure he gets there in one piece. The rest is up to Nik."

"It's not safe in the south. The best, most seasoned among Lag's ranks flow down to crush the insurgents and round up young people to fight Kamber in the north."

Tel snarled, "It is not safe anywhere, Rightmajor Caip." Before continuing, he collected himself. "I have given them plenty of silver. They will keep a low profile. Would you please come into the room and talk with me? You are hovering. Looming."

Every movement crisp, Caip strode into the sitting room and placed herself on a chair against the far wall.

"Thank you. He wanted to go south, so he will go south. He will take his chances."

"Could you not have discussed this with me?" Caip asked, lowering her hood. "Warned me, at least? Dar is—It's important that I know if I'm going to be losing my right hand like this."

"You are right, of course. I should have spoken with you," said Tel. "I apologize."

"Thank you." She relaxed her posture, allowing the back of the chair to support her. "He took Craid's ashes?"

"They will add him to the dirt on the way. The place Craid met Nik's mother."

Something caught Caip's eye. "Vared, what's wrong?"

Tel turned to see him standing in the archway, wet and agitated. "Vared?" Tel flew across the room to him.

"I'm sorry." Vared's whole body vibrated until he shattered, moaning. Tears mixed with rain on his skin. He hung his head. "I'm sorry."

Tel pressed Vared's wet face into his doublet. He did not decide to embrace him. Instead, it merely happened. "Tell me. You can. Anything." Vared cried against his chest, breathless and trembling. The soaked blue curls wetted his black beard. He worried for a few beats that Vared's frazzled state might be worsened by the hug. He was relieved to feel him relax against his chest. Vared wrapped an arm around him.

A moment passed before he could find the air to speak. "I like to walk in the rain. I thought they'd be in their tents. I didn't think they saw me. I walked into the forest—just a bit—to see how many buds were coming in. I'm writing a song about the Feighan spring."

Tel backed up a half-step and took Vared's face in his hands. Some of the kohl around his eyes ran down toward his cheeks in thin, black threads. "And you took no one with y—"

"I'm sorry, Tel." Vared hid his face.

"No. No." Tel's chest felt raw and hollow. "This is not your fault."

"What happened?" Caip asked. Tel had not noticed she was behind him, within arm's length.

"They were suddenly *there*," said Vared. "Walked right up. A woman and a man. Gran's people." He appeared to try to stave off more tears by clamping his eyes shut. "They asked what I was doing in the woods. Said that it's suspicious to be out there in the rain. That I was already accused of spying. I told them I'd return to the castle, then, and started to walk back. They followed me. Closely. And…"

"And what?" Tel's entire frame tensed. "Go on."

"I walked faster and faster. They walked faster and faster. She said…all sorts of nasty things. That I must be good. In bed. Because…"

"Because?" Tel growled, settling into a slight crouch.

Vared cast his eyes to the worn rug. "Because you'd do anything for a good lay. Even let a spy share your bed. Even treason. And…maybe I'd show them how good I was."

Tel's vision narrowed. A flash of heat enveloped his body. When it dissipated, he was left cold to the bone. "Excuse me." Vared moved from his path. "Caip, stay here with him."

"Tel!" she cried.

He could hear her moving toward him. Without turning, he barked, "Rightmajor Caip, stay with the ambassador."

His movements felt both outside his control and of his own mind. He considered and dismissed using the stagsblood. *I cannot be found out.* Instead, he walked to the great hall, still serving as quarters for some of his guard. He saw what he needed leaning against the far corner, behind a pallet bed.

Within three beats, he was marching through light rain, across the garden, into the muddy field on which the sad tents squatted. No one was about in the wet. He found the biggest tent, moved the flap, and stepped inside. Gran sat against the central timber support. She stopped shoveling food into her mouth from a wooden plate and froze.

Tel raised the bow and loosed the arrow. *Ffffft.* The iron tip found the wooden column. It bored into the post just a thumb's width above the crown of the lieutenant's head. She appeared to want to shout for her soldiers but choked on her mouthful of food.

He stepped close, bent his knees, and hovered in front of her. She continued to work bits of her meal out of her windpipe. "I am a godsdamned prince of Feigh. Vared is an emissary of the government of Omela. And he is of my blood. If I hear of one of your people harassing him again, I will come back." The quality of his own voice surprised him. "I think a second visit will see my aim much improved. You and your women and men are not to even speak to him."

Tel stomped out of her tent and back across the mud, cursing himself for failing to keep Vared safe. *Must I send him home?* The thought of the singer crossing the Gray Sea made him want to wail.

* * *

He spent the remainder of the day trying to balance his need to check on Vared with the Omelan's distaste for his doting. Caip, smirking, took pity on him and did some of the peeking in on the boy. She insisted on spending the night, fearing retaliation from Gran. They ate and played cards into the evening. Tel retired early.

Although he longed for his bed, he decided to honor his commitment to himself by meditating and practicing with the dynasty. He thought he might be at the limits of his capabilities but believed he would be well-served to continue to work to keep his skills sharpened.

He shed his clothes, throwing them over a chair. Legs crossed, he sat on the floor in front of the fire. The stones were warm on his skin. He noted his mind was busy and knew the best way to quiet it was to attach his focus to an anchor. The sounds of the fire were suitable targets for his attention. Within seconds, his mind began drifting downward. Soon, the popping and hissing of log and flame detached from anything material—it was just *noise*. The stagsblood roared to life. He felt the call of the western forests and mountains again.

After a while, other sounds found his ears, stirring him at depth. Soft and distant but unmistakable, tenor and terquin drifted into his bedchamber.

The music did not originate in the library. It came from Vared's room. He was playing the song he had given Tel—the song about the antlered god's grief.

Dynasty thrumming, Tel's mood darkened. He had delighted and gloried in the dark threat he had brought to Gran's tent. Not only had he sinned against the Stag, but he had been prideful in his sin. He had not honored the anguish of his deity. With dread, he contemplated how many more such transgressions were ahead of him.

* * *

Not long after it started, Tel knew it was a dream. Still, he could not bring himself back up and into the waking world.

He, his mother, and Hod sat on a blanket at the bank of a muddy river. It did not look the same as the river that took them but *was* the river that took them. Hod cut bloody pieces from a dead buck. When he plated the portions, they became sections of cake. He handed a slice to Fyor, who ate it with a few efficient stabs of a fork. Tel refused his plate. Hod ate with his fingers.

Across the river, two armies clashed—one clad in brown, the other wearing orange. Countless swords glinted in the daylight. Before long, they were dulled with blood. The brown held their orange enemies' heads under the rushing water until their struggling ceased. The victors simply let the dead be taken by the raging current. Arrows, many of them flaming, sailed over the river, landing all around the three picnickers.

"Move," urged Tel. "We have to leave." His mother sang while Hod watched her, dumbly clapping along. A lighted arrow landed in Tel's navel. He could smell his cooking flesh. "Do you not see?"

"Quiet," said Hod. "The queen's singing."

The arrowhead was buried so deep, Tel could not remove it no matter how hard he yanked. "It hurts. Please h—" He noticed Aith on the other bank, walking down into the water. The river raged around the old man.

Cadavers floated by him. Still, Aith retained his poise, drawing closer, crossing the river.

Soon, his uncle was under the water, in the middle of the flow. Tel kept watching. He knew Aith would not stop crossing. Before long, the top of his head reemerged, and he continued his trudge toward them.

"Please," said Tel. "I would like to leave now." He was still trying to pull the iron tip of the arrow from his stomach.

Hod turned fierce eyes to him. "Quiet. I'm young and handsome."

"I cannot leave without you. He is coming." Tel raised his arm and pointed his index finger at Aith, who was stepping onto land. "Mother!"

Fyor stopped singing and turned toward Aith. "Telly, that is just your uncle. Say hello." Facing Hod again, she resumed her song. Aith stood behind her, dripping. He bent over and unclasped her necklace.

"I think you want this, nephew." Aith smirked. The chain and Doe pendant dangled from his gloved hand.

Finally, Tel freed the arrow from his flesh. He stood, raised the bloody thing, and charged. His mother and lover paid him no mind as he leapt over them to get to Aith. As he reached him, the old man dodged, somehow hooking Fyor's necklace around the shaft of the arrow.

Tel's momentum carried him into the foul, rushing water. All around him were corpses and pieces of corpses.

"We'll do this again," Aith called.

Tel fought to keep his head above the water. Some of the bodies traveling with him downstream had faces he recognized—his father's, Craid's, Nik's, Cessa's. He decided to try to let the river pull him down. It obliged but threw him onto a narrow beach in short order.

He recovered and stood, walking for a time through tall grasses, which eventually gave way to shorter tufts and mud. Far ahead of him, he saw Fyor and Hod on the blanket at the riverbank, same as before.

Relief soon gave way to horror. The pair were undressing. His mother spread her legs. Hod mounted, sticking himself inside her.

"No. No. No. No. No. What are you doing?" He ran to them, his shouts becoming incomprehensible. Aith walked through the river toward them again, the brown and orange still warring on the other bank. Tel tried to turn his head, to close his eyes, but an unseen force made him watch.

Arrows landed around their rutting. Hod said a name of one of Tel's string of conquests with each ugly thrust. "Lod. Tar. Mat. Fel. Caip. Pod. Het. Can't remember. Marvo. Fon. Dek. Lart. Pened. No name. Who knows? Vidur. Can't remember. Turo..." Uncle Aith stood above them, watching, a grin slashed across the putty of his face.

The sounds of his mother's building climax broke the spell. "Stop it!" cried Tel. "Stop it. Why do you do this?" He stepped nearer, determined to rip them apart with his bare hands.

His mother began to moan, "Vared, Vared, Vared, Vared..."

Tel charged. He tripped and stumbled right by them all, into the river. Now it was not water, but ale.

"We'll do this again," Aith said.

He hacked ale from his lungs. The current carried him for a short distance before once more depositing him on land. This time, it was night. Dread sickening him, he walked, knowing he would find himself at the bank again.

He was surprised to see Vared standing where his mother and Hod had been. The blanket was gone. Vared wore fabric shoes and his shimmering black shift. He noticed Tel approaching and beamed, loosing all his beauty into the darkened world.

Prince Tel's heart skittered.

As he closed the distance, he saw the violence on the other shore below the dull, ruddy moons. The river churned under a carpet of orange and brown dead. Once again, his uncle began to cross.

"I'm happy you're here," said Vared.

Tel said, "It is not safe."

"I feel safe with you." Arrows from the other side landed in the soft earth around him.

"But that does not mean it *is* safe." Alarmed, Tel eyed Aith as he drew closer. He was nearing the middle of the river. Soon, like twice before, he would be under the water for a time, only to break the surface and bring new horrors to the more peaceful bank.

"Will you swim with me?" asked Vared.

"No, Vared. I—"

Vared tilted his beautiful head. "Please?"

"I cannot."

"But *I* must," Vared turned and walked toward the water, the crazed thicket of sapphire bouncing with every footfall.

"Why?"

Vared looked back over his shoulder at him. "You just said. It's not safe here. You've convinced me. I'll trust you until the end of my days." He waded into the river and walked toward Aith, who beckoned him with a curled finger. They met in the middle and were gone, under the water.

The dream spat Tel out, cold and sweating. For the first time in months, he ached for a drink to settle his nerves. He knew his uncle had used the wind and rain dynasties to create the nightmare.

* * *

Praying in the quiet of the morning, Tel asked the Stag and Doe for steadiness and wisdom. He sat in meditation. Once he found calm, he cleaned his teeth and face, dressed, and broke his fast. Stepping outside to survey the day's weather, he was happy to feel real spring warmth in the morning air. It would be an excellent day for a ride.

When he heard Vared talking with an attendant, he waited a few moments before heading toward the songmaker's room. He paused in the hallway in front of the door and almost walked away. It took him some time to muster the courage to knock. He felt foolish standing there, waiting, nervous in his own home.

"Good morning." Vared had not yet painted his face.

"Good morning. I am sorry to bother you."

"You're not a bother." Vared dismissed the idea with a slight roll of his eyes.

"Do you have plans for the day?"

"No. Are you going to change that?" He smiled at Tel from under a cobalt eyebrow he had pulled into a peak.

"I…" Tel returned the smile but could not maintain eye contact. A slight, nauseated embarrassment forced him to order himself to pull his mind together. "It is beautiful outside. Would you like to take a ride? On horses?"

"On horses?" Vared raised his brow again. "Not on sea monsters?"

"I…"

"You're odd today."

"I had…not very much sleep. I apologize," said Tel.

"Stop apologizing. I'd love to take a ride with you. On horses. May I have an hour?"

"Of course."

"Excellent. I'll see you in an hour." He began to shut the door.

"Vared. It will be only us. Wear your sword."

"Very well." Vared closed the door.

Tel shut his eyes and shook his head, chastising himself for his strangeness. Electing to prepare and saddle the animals himself, he drifted to the stable and fussed over Kelseigh and Pony. The stagsblood told him both were pleased to have the exercise and company, although Kelseigh tempered her enthusiasm. He let her know that she would be with Vared, which perked her up.

When Vared arrived, the mare danced a bit. He went to her and gave her some scratches and baby talk. "I may ride her?"

"I told you before, she is your horse."

"I wish I could take her home with me."

Tel frowned for a moment before brightening his expression. "Horses can be sent over the sea. Or you can come see her whenever you wish." He swung himself into Pony's saddle.

Vared mounted Kelseigh. "This is the only time I'm tall as you."

"That is because Kelseigh is our pretty giant."

"Yes, she is." Vared leaned toward the horse's ears for more baby talk.

Tel had to stop himself from staring. "Shall we?" he asked, looking anywhere but at Vared.

"Yes. Where are we going?"

"Somewhere I have not been in a long, long time."

Unhurried, they rode through town, needing to stop as much for the people to say hello to Vared as for them to greet their prince. The songmaker was gracious and charming, eliciting smiles from the women, men, and children.

Beyond the houses and farms, they veered off the road, onto a narrow trail that cut downhill through the edge of forest. The warmer air and brighter sun had begun waking the world after months of slumber. Vared marveled at the gandaith shrubs bounding the dirt path on both sides. He fingered the tiny lavender petals of the blooms. "These are wonderful. The fragrance! We don't have these in Omela. Intoxicating."

"Take some. People all over Feigh celebrate the arrival of gandaiths. Pick them and keep them in their homes. Twenty months in the year, and they are with us for less than one. They will be gone in a week. Two at most."

"Such a short life. But this is good. Too much beauty for too long would spoil us to everything else in nature." He removed a panicle and tucked the stem through his hair and behind an ear. He faced Tel. "Does this look ridiculous?"

The sight—the prettiness—almost knocked Tel off Pony. "No." He struggled to recover his wits. "Of course not."

They rode in quiet until the path veered to the left and out of the wooded area. The land sloped gently down to the river. Vared raised himself on the saddle. "See that rock and the little copse of trees?"

"Yes."

"Race you there."

"A race?" asked Tel.

"Yes."

"Very well."

"But before," Vared said, turning to him, "I should mention that you cut quite an attractive figure on horseback."

"What?"

"Go," said Vared, nudging Kelseigh through a canter and into a full gallop, giggles trailing behind him like a banner in the wind.

Tel urged Pony to give chase. "This is not fair," he called. "Kelseigh has such long legs."

Nineteen

Tel and Vared sat cross-legged on the dirt, watching the river a few meters in front of them. It was swollen with spring rains and melt. Still, compared to the day it had taken Hod and Fyor, it was docile.

"You've not been here since?"

"No," said Tel.

"Why today?"

Squinting against the sun, Tel looked at him and then at the river again. "It was time. I have never put this behind me. Not really. And…"

"And?"

"And I thought…" It seemed to Tel like his organs were flitting about his torso. "I knew it would be easier with you here."

"Not Caip?"

"No."

"How is it?" asked Vared. "How are you?"

"I think I was right. I think it is easier. But not easy."

"Good." Vared's hand glided over the damp, chestnut dirt until it rested on top of the prince's.

Tel wanted to take that hand and pull Vared to him, to pull all the prettiness into his lap. He considered doing so but thought of Hod. "Something came to me just now. Something I have never considered. I told you this was the first time I have been back here, but that is not truthful. It is more correct to say I have never left."

"What about trying the Omelan way?"

"The Omelan way?"

"Of saying goodbye. Are you willing?"

"Yes." Tel realized if Vared had told him he must build a dam with his hands and the Feighan dirt, if Vared asked him to divert the river through forest and hills and mountains to empty into the Sea of Queens, he would be willing.

Vared lifted his hand. "You simply tell the kindnesses they did you."

All thought fled Tel's head. He wanted Vared to return his hand to his. Suddenly nervous, he reminded himself to breathe. "It has been so long. I am afraid I will forget some."

"Do your best."

"My mother. My mother. She gave me life. Fed me. Taught me how to talk. Encouraged me—Is this what you meant?"

"Exactly what I meant," said Vared. "Go on."

"Encouraged me to disagree. Taught me manners, which I sometimes observe. Held me when I cried. She looked upon Caip and Hod as her own. She took care of my father and helped him be a great king. Protected him and Lag and me. Taught me about the faith. Helped me understand what we lose through violence. Met my bratty behavior with love. Did not judge me or fear me when I told her I...when I shared my deepest secrets. Gave me appreciation for art. Music. She helped me to not fear the unknown, to welcome strangers." He closed his eyes and shook his head. "I cannot remember everything. Not right now. Ask me tomorrow. I will only have more. There was so much." He swallowed with his scalding throat. Tears threw themselves down his face. Opening his eyes, he noticed a wet streak on Vared's cheek, too.

"The goal—" Vared cleared his throat. "—isn't to remember everything. The goal is to realize you can't. Her kindness was without end, just as she is. As her love was infinite, she *is* infinite. We can't fathom it. We only have kindness in the mystery."

"It is so inadequate."

"Yes. Now Hod."

"He...goddesses and gods, he was so beautiful. And I do not mean his appearance, though his smile and his eyes were kindnesses themselves."

He hesitated. Praising Hod in Vared's presence caused inside him a guilty tugging.

Vared pivoted to face him more directly and scooted nearer. "Go on."

Tel looked at Vared's knee, unsure whether it touched his own or was only extremely close. "Hod taught me people without guile exist. He taught me how to relax. He found the unserious parts of me and coaxed them out. No one makes me laugh like he did. I was so self-important. Am. But he still let me be myself. Always stood up for what was right. Gave me love, physically. And often." He chuckled. "Met my bratty behavior with love, just as much as Mother." He lost himself to a fuller laugh. "Gave me perspective. Helped me see the privilege of my station. He thought I was pompous. Ridiculous. But if you could have seen the way he looked at me." He wiped his face and thought for a minute, Vared watching closely. "That is not all. But it is a lot. More important than anything, though, was his time. He gave me so many days, so many hours of his short life. As did Mother. Hod's final kindness was giving away his life for her. For me. He tried to save her. While I did nothing."

Vared closed his eyes. "Maybe watching him trying to save her made you see it was hopeless. So, in trying to save her, he saved you. And think how many lives you have saved through your work for peace." He looked at Tel. "And the lives they will save."

Tel brushed drying mud from his boot with a hand. "There is just a different war now."

"Not your fault," Vared said, giving his head a little shake. "Neither is the loss of your mother and your lover. Maybe soon we can talk about the kindnesses you did them."

They sat without speaking for a long time. Vared got to his feet and walked to where water met dirt. Tel's heart thundered under his ribs. For a beat, he was certain he would watch Vared be carried away by the river. He opened his mouth to ask him to step away but did not want to seem hysterical.

Vared cast a noble silhouette. It was strange to see him with a sword at his hip, but it fit. He held his tiny, elegant frame erect. He should be too delicate for such an upright pose, yet there he was. Even standing casually, he looked like a plant stretching to find the sun. Never did his movements seem anything but effortless. When he turned back to face Tel, his hand was over his heart. "You've honored me by sharing these things."

"No." His eyes fell, unable to bear holding him for too long. The sight made him ache. Day by day, it grew harder to deny.

"Yes. I treasure our friendship."

Friendship. The word was a serrated blade plunged into Tel's chest. The knife dragged itself downward, opening the rest of his torso. "Me, too."

Vared floated back and placed his willowy body on the dirt next to Tel. "It's difficult to match."

"What?"

"Hod," said Vared. "What he represents to you. How could any suitor match that? One hundred seasons, and you have found no one to live up to him." He shook his head. "This is inappropriate. I'm sorry. I was thinking aloud."

"No. It is not inappropriate. We are friends," said Tel. He wanted to scream. "And it *has* been one hundred seasons. But I also have not searched. For that. And I have never had suitors."

"Have not had or did not entertain?" asked Vared. With that, he rested his hand on top of Tel's again.

Prince Tel regarded the long fingers covering his. A bewildered intoxication swirled from stomach to head. Even at his drunkest, he did not feel this out of control. He and Vared watched the river as the sun eased itself toward the horizon, filling the Feighan spring sky with dusty grays and pinks.

* * *

Foghar's miller, Daina, crossed into the sitting room, Caip trailing, and showed Prince Tel the top of her head. Under severe black brows, her lively hazel eyes danced in the sunlight falling from the window near Tel's chair.

"It is good to see you, highness. My trip was fruitful. We'll soon have a pair of new quern stones. The search took me halfway to Affas, close enough to learn a bit of news. It's credible. If you've heard it, forgive me."

Tel eyed Caip. "Go ahead, Daina," he said.

"The emperor's women and men have been pushed out of Athair. The whole city's held by rebels who name you their king. The loyalists have surrounded the city. A siege, but it's useless. The rebels have access to the sea."

"What of Lag's ships?" asked Tel.

"Occupied up north with all the isles of Kamber," said Caip.

"Of course," said Tel.

Daina continued, her tone conspiratorial. "There are a couple of his ships out there, but they're easily evaded. Rumors say Lag and Table are worried you'll take your place in front of the rebels and lead them to the capital."

"No. They are *trying* to draw me in. This is what they want. I will always be dangerous if I am alive. If they murder me in cold blood, I am martyred and even more dangerous. But if they defeat me on the battlefield, that would be that. The best way to neutralize my threat is to see I fight them and lose."

Caip nodded. "Their position is superior—by far. It's a good gamble on their part."

"Pardon." The miller swept long raven strands from her face, tucking them behind her ear. "But you're both wrong. They may have a military advantage, but that's only down to numbers. But you have numbers, too. You need only ask the people to join you, and many will. Every woman and man has a sword. From courtiers in Affas to farmers in the east and west to fishers in Athair—all of them."

"Thank you, Daina, for visiting." Tel offered her a compact smile.

She stepped a bit closer to him. "No one loves Lag."

"*I* do, damn you. He is of my blood." The blast of words was involuntary. "He is my brother."

"Of course, my prince," said Daina. "Sorry."

"Thank you for bringing us this news. It's appreciated." Caip put a hand on the woman's shoulder and steered her out of the room.

Daina continued as she was led out. "This whole valley would stand between Gran and you if they had the chance. It's the same elsewhere across Feigh. Not just in Foghar or Athair."

"Thank you, Daina," said Tel, teeth gritted. "Keep me apprised regarding the progress with the mill."

Caip returned after a few moments to find Tel staring, grim-faced, through the window.

"There's more," she said. "Gran's asking for you."

"What could she want?"

"She's in the garden. Neutral territory, she says."

"This is my land. None of it is neutral," he snapped. "I *allow* her to—" He closed his eyes for a pair of beats. "I am sorry. That was not for you."

"I know. I'll come with you."

"Thank you. That will not be necessary."

Caip opened her mouth, closed it, and nodded after several beats. "All right. But be cautious. She's a snake."

"You insult snakes," said Tel.

Among the brightening greens of his garden, Gran sat on a bench. The sight of her struck him like an ink spot on a crisp, white shirt. He leaned against a young tree. "What is it you want?"

"If I had everything I wanted," Gran said, "you'd very much rue it."

"Even your threats are lies. If you had everything you wanted, I would rue nothing. I would be ash in the dirt."

She enjoyed a laugh. "You'd not be honored with a burning."

A chill slashed down his back, but he hid it with a relaxed smile. "Please tell me why I am here, then."

"One of my soldiers just returned from Affas. She wanted to deliver the information herself, but I decided I'd enjoy seeing your face. One of the perks of command."

"My brother has proclaimed the moons Feighan territory."

"You're clever. I do enjoy your quickness," she admitted. "We might be friends if you weren't a bluebell lover."

Tel refused the bait. His face was still.

"Not the moons," Gran said, "but the empire does expand."

"Oh? Success in Kamber?" He knew it was impossible this soon. *Maybe ever.*

"Hebe." She searched his face, only to find his stoic mask intact. "King Gawash has agreed to take Craid's seat at Table. He'll serve as Emperor Lag's viceroy in Hebe."

"In the name of your fight for purity, a foreigner will sit Table? Dissonant, to say the least."

Lieutenant Gran gave a little grunt. "He'll accept the faith. As will his people, one way or another. Tempting as it sounds to eliminate off-Feighans from the world, it's simply not practical. They'll be given a choice. If they accept, they'll be given a useful status."

"Useful? An underclass, you mean. Non-citizens."

"A prince bellyaching about an underclass. Hypocritical, to say the least." Gran chuckled. "Gawash will be in Affas soon. Your uncle said he mentioned in a letter he's anxious to see you. Perhaps you can visit while he's there."

"I will pass," said Tel.

Smirking, Gran said, "There's still time to reconsider, of course. You may decide you want to attend the cementing of this arrangement. A chance to witness history."

"I will keep that in mind." He took his weight off the tree and stroked an unfurling bud with a finger. "Enjoy the rest of the afternoon."

"There's more."

"Oh?"

"Our unit has been recalled." Gran shrugged, smirking again. "We ride to Affas midday tomorrow. It was decided there's no threat here."

"Safe travels, then, Lieutenant Gran. Mind yourself when you arrive on the shores of Kamber to fight for my brother. And *Viceroy Gawash.*"

"What do you mean by that?" Childishness colored her question.

He did not answer. "Thank you for offering me the opportunity to witness history. Do you know what has always fascinated me about it?

History, I mean. It is littered with important moments—*planned* moments. Prearranged events. Occurrences everyone sees coming. Like Gawash traveling here to ceremoniously pimp his people to my brother. But the most important parts of history? The thunder that shakes the world and shifts fate? Those are the events no one sees coming." He leveled a violent smile at her and left her on the bench.

He was confident the lieutenant was being withdrawn to give him space to move toward their trap. That night, he penned a letter to Cessa.

Twenty

"Will you fight, or will you not?" Vared huffed.

"Will I fight? You are completely subdued. You are at my mercy." Tel had Vared's pretty, painted face in the dirt of the field, not far from the spot he had loosed his arrow in Gran's tent. His knees ground into the turf on either side of Vared's body. His right hand held tight to his own left wrist in the blue curls behind the songmaker's neck. Vared's entire right arm was useless, as it was caught in the ring formed by Tel's upper limbs.

"You're bigger than me," Vared griped. "And I'm much better with a sword."

"When you asked me to train with you, I thought you meant with wasters. It was *you* who wanted to grapple." Tel applied a bit of extra pressure to the neck to punctuate.

"I hoped to make you argue for it. Stag knows you'd enjoy watching me play with my sword."

Warmth trailed from Tel's ears to his cheeks. His head swam. The surprise and embarrassment threw him, and his muscles softened. Vared took advantage of the subtle shift. At once, their fortunes were reversed.

Tel was on his back, between Vared's knees. The Omelan applied no force at all. His knuckles were in the dirt on either side of Tel's head. Breathing hard and wearing a wicked smirk, he gazed down at him.

Tel was as frozen in place as if five champions were holding him down. *The goddesses and gods can take me to the black now. There could not be a prettier sight at the end of a life than what I see. Not on all the world and in all time. Not on all the world and in all time.*

184

"What are you thinking?" Vared pushed off from his knuckles and sat across Tel's hips. He flattened his hands on Tel's chest.

For a flash, he believed Vared was reading his thoughts. Dismissing the idea, he recovered. "I am thinking you said *Stag knows* a moment ago."

"You must be having an effect on me," said Vared, beaming.

Tel swallowed.

"Will you fight, or will you not?" This time, Vared asked with softness and gravity. Tel began to grumble beneath him, adjusting his weight to scramble away, but Vared cut him off. "No. Tel. No. Don't be upset with me. But I see you constantly thinking. I see you go inside yourself. I'm not asking so I can give my opinion or urge you to one course or the other. This isn't my matter, except that I care for you."

Tel allowed his eyelids to fall. He filled his lungs all the way. Releasing the air, he looked up at Vared. "I do not see how I fight. I do not see how I do not. Both are traps. My brother and uncle want me to oppose them violently so they can put me down. And chances are they would. If I do not try to stop them, my passivity is endorsement. And they are doing dangerous things. Destructive things. Needlessly terrorizing the families of child dynasts. Forcing the faith on good people. Banning foreigners from this place and that. Declaring Feighans disloyal. Sending people in their prime to Kamb shores to die for…power? Purity? I do not even know. They are on their way to swallowing up half the world. I want to run, and I hate that in myself. I want to fight, and I hate that in myself even more. I make leavings of the principle around which my whole life has been arranged. Peace is an absolute good." He realized how comfortable it was to have Vared's weight on him this way, as natural as a jay on a branch.

"I'm not certain there are absolutes."

"I am not certain of anything," said Tel.

"I know you're in an impossible position. And whatever you choose, whatever you do, whatever you don't, I'll think highly of you still. I don't care a whiff what the prince of Feigh does. Only Tel. Because he's a good man. So, if he runs, I'll be happy he's safe. If he fights, I'll pray he stays so. The prince of Feigh is not my prince."

"You dare show royalty disrespect?" Tel raised his finger at him in mock outrage.

"Only Feighan royalty. I'm Omelan from the soles of my feet to my blue hair."

"Peasant!" Tel rolled, throwing him off his hips. Vared eluded Tel's attempt to get a handle on him, using his wiry strength to wriggle free.

They wrestled for a few moments, observing none of the rules of grappling bouts—neither Omelan nor Feighan. Struggling against one another fiercely but with good humor, they grunted and giggled in equal measure. Vared's body froze when a pair of boots appeared a few inches in front of his face.

Caip cleared her throat. "You know, not too terribly long ago, grappling—if that's what you're doing—was done by naked combatants."

Vared said, "Now *that* sounds interesting. I'd like to hear more ab—"

Tel cupped his hand over the songmaker's mouth. "How are you, Rightmajor Caip?" he asked as Vared squirmed.

She said, "I have something to tell you."

* * *

Tel stood under the feathery green of a tree in the muggy but not unbearable breeze typical of days near the heart of summer in the valley. In front of him were the couple and a happy throng of witnesses. Behind him, a neat orchard and handsome stone walls stretched across verdant flatness. He had offered the castle for a venue but now thought Mor was correct that his own land made the perfect setting.

Having the highest station, Tel served as the officiant. The bulk of the Feighan handcording rite was focused on preparing the person who performed the ceremony—a spiritual cleansing. As Tel worked himself through a slow circle to call on the directions, he accepted four offerings, each symbolizing an elemental power.

Vared had suggested the offerings should be made by Gunda's clan—the family of four he had moved to the estate after the house fire. Caip and Mor had adored the idea. Gunda brought Tel a stone ring for the north, which he fit over his thumb. Her husband, Tak, gave him a passerine feather for the east. He tucked it into his black hair. Their adolescent daughter drew a streak of ash across his forehead for the south. The little boy brought a pitcher of water for the west, emptying it over his hands.

Prince Tel had corded a couple once before at a much grander affair in Affas Castle. One of the women had sat King Vith's Table for a decade. Tel had been close to drunk and had not given the duty a second thought. Now, he faced the solemn responsibility with great nervousness. This was his best friend. It did not help that he felt awkwardly underdressed. Tradition demanded he approach the ritual with humility. Shoeless, he wore a simple, cream chemise with chestnut leggings. The only embellishment was the ceremonial fabric cord, which he had tied around his waist. Although he always dressed more casually in the valley, he felt naked without at least a proper tunic. Stealing a glance at Vared, he wondered what he thought of all this.

Tel swallowed, looking first at Mor—dashing in his finest formal outfit—then at Caip. Vared had offered to paint her face for the occasion. She accepted but demanded a subtle hand. His work highlighted the warm brown of her eyes, the pretty swoop of her brows, and the friendly roundness at her cheekbones. Her dress was the blue-green of the Sea of Flowers on a cloudless summer day, decorated with dainty embroidery work in silver. His friend's sturdy beauty hit Tel like a rock to the face, but his failure to notice for so long struck him harder. Close to falling apart, he wanted to embrace her and confess—to tell her again how sorry he was about so much.

When he could speak, he said, "Caip. Mor. My friends. I am Tel of Affas, prince of—No. My friends. I am Tel of Foghar."

All the people of the valley hooted and clapped, including Caip and Mor. Tel felt overheated when he caught Vared's eyes and saw him grinning widely while shaking his fist in the air.

"I hope you will do me the honor of allowing me to cord the hands of

Mor of Foghar and Caip of..."

"Foghar!" Caip said, like anything else would have been ridiculous.

"Caip of Foghar," repeated Tel, a ripple in his voice. The guests roared their appreciation again.

"We will," said Mor.

"We will," said Caip.

"We will," echoed the crowd.

"Thank you." He untied the cord from his waist and held it up for the celebrants to see. All were silent. Caip put her left hand in Mor's right. Tel wound the entire length of the cord around until it obscured their hands, securing the fabric with a knot at the top.

"The six pair of deities who made the world showed us the sanctity of love and the sacred potential of the number two. Each of the proud races could not have been made without that love and potential. We would not *be* without that number. By agreeing to bring their lives together for the next sixteen seasons, Caip and Mor honor our divine origin. By agreeing to soberly decide in sixteen seasons if they wish to be corded again for sixteen more, they honor themselves. For only by freely and fully and individually choosing to join their lives can they continue to honor the power of the number two. Mor and Caip, will you, for sixteen seasons, give one another the best of the north?"

"We will give the fruit of the dirt," they answered in unison.

"Caip and Mor, will you give one another the best of the east?"

"We will give the clarity of the wind."

"Mor and Caip, will you give one another the best of the south?"

"We will give the passion of the fire."

"Caip and Mor, will you give one another the best of the west?"

"We will give the joy of the rain."

"And will you, good people of Feigh and of Omela, give them your best?"

The crowd chanted, "Of the north, of the east, of the south, of the west. Of the dirt, of the wind, of the fire, of the rain. Yes!"

"Mor of Foghar and Caip of Foghar now stand before you freely handcorded."

The crowd broke into ecstatic yelps and surrounded the couple. The struggle for the prized positions—along the inner ring around the pair—resulted in the expected, good-humored, mock violence. In their stoutest voices, they demanded the newlycordeds kiss. Of course, custom dictated they make the wait as agonizing as possible. When their lips finally met, the people of Foghar exploded with joy.

Once the couple parted, those in the crowd with partners found them and shared the traditional kiss-after-the-kiss. Prince Tel looked at his feet until it was over and the party could begin.

* * *

Like before, Tel could not escape the dream, despite knowing he was asleep. He sat at a long, narrow table in a dim stone chamber. A candle flame danced over the scarred brown surface in front of him, giving the only light. The darkness kept him from seeing the other end of the table. To his right stood the first boy he had been with after Hod.

The boy was the son of one of his father's lesser ministers. Tel could not remember which. The family had arrived at Affas several weeks after the accident, and the eldest son, about his age, took to following him around day and night. Near the bleary end of the third season after the drownings, they had gotten drunk together in a dusty, disused part of the castle. *I know you want my cock,* Tel had told him. The boy had said, *Yes.* Tel had smirked and told him, *Take off your clothes and show me your hole.* He had used him without so much as a kind word.

"I know you are not real," said Tel. "I know this is not real."

"It doesn't matter," said the boy.

"I know Aith is giving me this dream with his magic. Forcing it on me with the wind and rain dynasties." Tel worried his uncle might soon be able to control him with the magical tethers. *What if he has already begun?*

"It doesn't matter," repeated the boy. "Hear that rain? Falling all day in sheets." He put a crystal goblet on the table and into it poured wine the color of a garnet. "Drink."

Tel lifted the glass to his face and inhaled. Saliva flooded his mouth. He had a sip. The familiar heat coursed from his tongue to his gut. "I should not. But I have—"

"You've missed it."

"Yes." Tel thought of Craid, loving and detesting him both.

"Faster."

Tel finished the glass, and the boy refilled. "I cannot remember your name."

"You haven't missed me."

"That is not tr—"

"Drink," said the boy, glaring at the goblet.

Prince Tel did as he was told, the sound of falling water in his ears. A lighted candelabrum appeared across the murky chamber and floated until it came to rest on what must have been the other end of the table. Tel's eyes focused, revealing Aith. The stone antlers stretched up behind the old man. His uncle lowered himself onto the throne of Feigh. He seemed too far away to be so crisply visible. This room was much larger than the real throne room. Most of the table was still shrouded in the blackness.

"This one loved you," Aith said.

"I know."

"Drink," the boy and Aith commanded.

Tel drank. He looked at the politician's son and saw for the first time the mischievous Feighan handsomeness. "Why did he stay young? Why did you stay young?"

"You got old." The boy refilled the goblet.

Tel stammered, "Am I supposed to say sorry? I do not understand why I am here."

"Are you, nephew?" asked Aith. "Are you sorry?"

"Yes."

"I agree. You're sorry," said Aith.

Tel pleaded with the young man. "You understand I cannot change any of it? I know I should not have been careless with you. You were so kind. And

I did not deserve such kindness. I was grieving and lonely. Even Caip was away, starting her training. I had no one. These are excuses, I know. What I do not know is how to make it right. What else can I do? That I can see the ways and *feel* the ways I was unfair to…to everyone…is my punishment. I swear I can feel all of it. Anytime I stop."

"Drink," the boy said.

"Punishment? Splendid notion," Aith said, clapping his gloved hands together several times. "Can you see, nephew? That you've been kind only to outsiders for the bulk of your sad life? Omelans? They get respect. Affection. The rest of us? Feighans? We get carelessness. Used." He gestured again to the boy. "A beautiful Feighan man stood in front of you, begging you to let him make you happy. You could've corded ninety and five seasons ago. Had a life, here, at home. Focused on your family and your people. But you chose to get pissed and suck bluebell cock and make peace with the queendom that has muddied the dirt of this world with Feighan blood forever. Then, you got dry. A new Prince Tel. Tel the Sober. Tel the Good. But behold the wine-stained lips. Pathetic. Pitiable."

"This is not fair. You are conflating—You are confusing me."

"Punishment!" Aith swept the candelabrum into his palm, and a harsh scraping sound filled the chamber. He was dragging something behind him.

Tel could not see what was happening. The candles moved closer, lighting the planes of his uncle's face in spasmodic flickers. Aith stopped and rested his candelabrum on the table. The glow revealed a mass of blue curls. Tel's eyes adjusted and left him no doubt. Vared was face up, atop the table, his head nearer the prince's end.

"Can't you see, nephew?"

In a blinding instant, the room was illuminated. Tel's vision again sorted itself. From the ceiling, between the stone antlers, water began to fall in a narrow but steady ribbon, landing on Vared's face. Vared sputtered for a beat before falling silent.

"This endless wet." Aith clucked. "I'll save him." He raised the source of the scraping sound, a large poleaxe, from behind his body. Moving the weapon over Vared's head, he held the broad blade horizontally, so it diverted the flow away from his nose and mouth.

The songmaker coughed the water from his windpipe but did not otherwise move.

"Vared," Tel said, "you can get up. We are dreaming. I am. But get up now."

Over Vared's head, the blade wavered in the air, allowing more of the stream to fall on his face. Aith clucked again. "My strength isn't what it used to be, I'm afraid."

Tel tried to stand, but his legs would not work. He looked at the boy. "Why can I not move?"

"You're drunk. Drink."

"No!" Tel swept the goblet onto the floor. "Let me move."

"I simply cannot hold this anymore," said Aith. He lurched toward Tel and the boy, burdened by the poleaxe in his hands.

The stream of water widened, crashing down onto Vared's face.

"Would you hold it for me?" Aith asked the boy.

"Yes."

"Good." Aith sprang forward and buried the blade in the boy's chest.

"Why would you do that?" screamed Tel. "He is innocent."

"Was, until you put your seed in him."

"Vared," said Tel. "*Get up.* You will drown. Please."

His uncle was walking away. Without turning, he waved a hand and said, "Save your bluebell, traitor."

At once, Tel was free. He sprang into a run toward the center of the table. He swung his legs onto the surface and stood. Taking hold of Vared's feet, he dragged him from the thickening column of rainwater.

Vared did not stir. Tel squatted over him, panicked. The paint on his sweet face was streaked into thin, colorful mud. "You have to breathe. You have to breathe. You have to breathe." *Goddess please goddess please goddess please.* Tel's trembling hands hovered over Vared's belly. "Goddess, please." He pushed his palms downward.

He awoke in his sweat-dampened bed.

Twenty and One

Tel and Vared took advantage of a warm morning and mounted Pony and Kelseigh while the sun still sat low and bashful behind a thin veil of haze. They made a long, unrushed walk-and-trot from the castle. Tel wanted Vared to see his favorite place on the world. For most of the route, the prince listened while the songmaker recounted his harrowing youth, his eventual adoption by a nasty and influential merchant, and his days in Queen Cessa's service. Tel found himself several times on the edge of tears, both because Vared was granting access to his unvarnished story and because he had suffered so.

"We tie them here," Tel said when they had gone as far into the forest as the horses could manage. "We will travel the rest of the way on foot."

"It will be steamy today," said Vared, petting Kelseigh's neck after securing her.

"The forest will shield us from the worst of it. And the water will be cold."

They slipped deeper into the woods. A comfortable stroll soon became a challenging hike, each step upward. The floor of the wilderness was littered with stones and boulders of pale feldspar and glassy quartz.

"We are climbing the mountain." Exertion dampened Vared's hair.

"Only a hill, young one." Tel's laugh was gently taunting. "And do not worry, we will not be climbing to the top."

"I've been tricked. You invited me for a ride and a *little* walk."

"We Feighans are so big and powerful, all things seem little to us."

Vared scoffed.

"You may kill me, but there is a much easier, gradual path. The horses can travel almost the whole way. It is the route my father took in recent years. But that is no fun."

Vared narrowed his eyes and emitted a low growl. He turned his head. "That's—I hear water."

"Just wait."

They walked in silence for a while. Tel's spirits were buoyed by the physical effort. The feeling was something akin to drunkenness but without the dull murk. Each of his senses sang. The pleasure of exertion even masked the now constant buzzing of the stagsblood and its strange pull westward. He led the way through the growth, which was thick despite not yet reaching the density of late summer and early autumn.

"The trees are different here," said Vared. "So large. Like Feigh is older than Omela, somehow. And all these wildflowers."

"I am told you have similar forest in the north of your queendom. Perhaps one day we can see it."

"Together?"

A tingling dizziness slowed Tel for a few beats. "If you would like."

"I would."

They soon reached a rocky downward slope. At the bottom was a stream. "This empties into the river. Everything empties into the river here. Be careful. I have slipped on these rocks more times than I can count. I have the scar to prove the worst of them."

"On your shin and calf," said Vared.

"Yes."

Discovering the loose rocks along the way, they eased down the slope. Vared was surefooted and relaxed. When they reached the stream, Tel held his waterskin in the flow. He passed it to the younger man.

"Thank you. I'm thirsty." Vared drank, water spilling down his chin. He laughed at himself. "I'm a greedy savage." He dragged the back of his hand across his mouth.

Tel appreciated the gesture, surprised at the rough boyishness. He took the skin and drank. "So cold."

"Wonderfully so."

Prince Tel backed himself against a crooked tree and looked up at the jeweled viridescence of the canopy. He felt the weight of Vared's orange eyes on his face. The pressure stayed until Tel returned the gaze and asked, "Why are you looking at me that way?"

"I swear you have two expressions," said Vared. "You either scowl, or you smirk."

"And which am I doing now?" asked Tel.

"You're smirking."

"Should I scowl?"

Vared laughed from his belly.

Tel's crooked smile etched itself deeper into his skin. They each had a second swig from the waterskin. Pushing himself off the tree, Tel said, "The tough part is ahead of us, but it is not that long and worth the trek. I promise."

They trudged ever upwards through the rocky woods, parallel to the stream. Before long, they were drenched with sweat. Vared stayed close enough for Tel to smell something essential of him. It aroused a strange, wobbly hunger. When he thought he might have to scream to break the trance, they reached a broad flat of thinner growth. Tel pointed ahead.

"Beautiful," said Vared.

Before them was a cliff, the height of more than a dozen tall men. From it, a waterfall plummeted into a broad, shallow pool. This pond drained into the brook along which they had been hiking. "The first part of my favorite place. My father's favorite, too. Are you brave enough to get in? Even deep in the summer, it is colder than you can imagine. Now, it will be even harsher. Especially for a soft boy from the south of Omela."

Vared was already stripping. He disrobed entirely and, without a word, bounded to the pool, tossing his clothes onto the dirt. He waded in without hesitation. "Won't you join me?" He did not turn back.

"How does it feel?"

Vared called, "It's...*bracing*. It's horrible. Horrible. But I think I'm getting used to it."

Tel shed his clothes, trying not to look too long at the unexpectedly sturdy globes atop the back of Vared's legs. Even at its deepest, the water came up only as far as the middle of his thighs. Tel stepped to the pool and hissed his way in.

Vared walked around the sheet of falling water. Tel saw through the cascade blurred shapes and colors that were both a vague impression of a man and the unmistakable figure of Vared. Something pulled Tel through his nervousness. He joined him behind the fall.

Tel urged himself to remain respectful but could not resist a reflexive glance at the area under Vared's navel. He thought he saw him do the same. They exchanged strange smiles. Tel looked downward at the water, which seemed to allow him to breathe. When he lifted his eyes, he saw wet, blue-headed Vared crossing the distance between them. Vared reached up and grabbed the back of the prince's head, pulling it downward. Bounding percussion filled Tel's chest.

"Thank you," Vared shouted alongside Tel's ear, over the roar of water. "It's wonderful here."

"You are welcome. I am too cold."

"Who's soft now?"

They shared a laugh, the songmaker's hand still in Tel's hair. Vared seemed to remember himself and withdrew his touch. Tel felt a protest forming in his mouth. Instead, he looked down at the water between them again.

Together, they plodded through the pool, back to the dry edge. In silence, they allowed some of the water to drip from their bodies. Tel kept himself from looking below Vared's shoulders. They pulled on their breeches and boots.

"You were especially beautiful at the cording," Vared said.

"You are terrible." Tel gave a breathy chuckle, shaking his head. "Always teasing me."

"I'm not teasing." He squeezed some of the wet from his long curls onto the forest floor. "Which you know."

"I do not."

"The night you told the story of creation at the treaty signing, you were impressive. From head to heel, skin to guts, royal. They were shields. Your garments and bearing. Here, in the country, you dress more simply. Fewer layers and billows. And at the cording, you had no shields. Maybe that or maybe I know you now. But on both occasions, you were who you are. Wise and sad and smirking."

Tel could not look at him but was listening with care. "Sad."

"Like your head and heart carry the burdens of two lifetimes. More."

"Oh."

"You already know I didn't want to come here. To do this exchange. Then, when I saw you, knowing I'd have to spend time with you, I was instantly nervous. Scared. A different kind of—"

"Why?" Tel raised his eyes. "Because I am highborn? I do not want anyone to be frightened."

Vared chuffed. "Because your face is the softest *and* the hardest thing I've ever seen. How is that possible?"

"Why are you saying this?" Tel wanted to scramble away but needed every word.

"Because you have a reputation. Had. Not of a bad man, but of... a troubled man. The idea that I would even catch your attention was ridiculous, but...I think I did. Right away. The night of the signing. And you were pissed drunk but still charming. And, then, Caip needed you, and you asked me to wait. And you never came back. I waited for hours."

"Vared, I—"

"I know, Tel. I know. You were drunker than I thought. I'm not saying this to make you feel guilt."

"Then..."

Vared took a step closer. "Because I want you to understand I wasn't being cruel those first weeks. It took me time to forgive you. And after... I wasn't trying to hurt you. I was trying to keep hold of myself. To keep *being* myself. Not someone who'd be impressed because...you're a prince. Or because you gave me gifts. And you *are* beautiful. And wise and sad and smirking." He took another step.

The shame of not remembering his first conversation with Vared goaded

Tel to run, to leave him in the forest. He fought this drive, forcing himself to keep his feet planted. "I do not know what to say."

"You must."

"I only know—" Tel felt the tension in his jaw. He pushed the words out. "The people who have hurt you. On the streets. And your…patron—this old fiend who took you in…I would—" He realized he had balled his hands at his sides. His chest heaved. *You would do what, Tel?* He knew if he were to punish the ones who had harmed Vared, he would owe himself the same treatment. Never had he felt so inadequate. He draped his blouse over a dripping shoulder. "Come," he said. "I will take you to my tree."

Vared tied the sleeves of his shirt around the perfect skin at his slender waist, watching Tel, painted lips slightly parted. He nodded.

Tel began walking, instantly loathing himself even more for the change of subject, which may have only hurt Vared again. "There is no real path from this approach. Be careful of prickers." They fought through close growth. Tel tried to find the easiest way, his stomach fluttering, his chest aching. After a quarter of an hour, the ground cover thinned. "Almost."

Vared's yelp was like the songmaker himself, slight but impossible to miss.

Tel's organs dropped in his abdomen. "What is it? Thorn?"

"No. My neck. Like a hot knife." He explored his nape with his right hand and brought his hand in front of his face. "No blood."

"Let me see," said Tel. He moved toward him.

Vared recoiled. "It's on the back of my neck."

"I think you have been stung, probably by a yellow needle. If I take the stinger out, you will feel better."

"It's…intimate for us," said Vared. "For Omelans. Me."

"You are of my blood." He moved closer.

"But—"

Tel took the final steps, destroying the emptiness between them. He looked down to see Vared staring at his chest. "Give me your eyes, Vared." The songmaker raised his chin. The twin amber flames shone at the prince. Their gazes were bound now, the connection singing with meaning. Tel finally saw in that link the welcome, the permission for which he had been waiting, underneath his awareness. He realized it had likely been there for weeks. Vared knew him drunk and sober. Vared had been hurt by him. Still, Vared offered himself with his eyes.

Swallowing, Tel felt all his anxiety shrink away. Once he began moving his head through space, there was no way to stop what he had started. It would have been as impossible as stopping the falling of tossed stones back toward the world under their feet.

Their first kiss was both a placid thing and a collision. Tel paused for further blessing—a deeper invitation. Vared provided it, separating his lips and skimming the prince's tongue with his own. Still, Tel hesitated, wanting to stand in mindful appreciation of the moment. The shorter man rested a forearm on either side of the taller man's neck, encouraging. Tel's tongue crossed the threshold, and Vared softly moaned. It was a tiny sound of relief, of an impatient wait concluded. Bringing his hands to either side of Vared's face, Tel took another taste. It only made him hungrier, but he moved away, looking down at the beauty he now held between his palms.

"Now may I see your neck?"

"Yes." He looked as drugged as Tel felt. Turning his body, he raised the curls from the delicate column of his nape. Tel was nearly taken by the compulsion to devour the smoothness there. Vared's taste sat on his palate, the smell of him hung in his nostrils, and the sight of him was long ago branded into his eyes. He wanted to have him here. He wanted to ease him onto the carpet made of autumn after autumn of shed leaves and mount him. More, however, he wanted another simple kiss. The forest floor was not good enough for him. He wanted to make him a bed of the finest pillows—soft enough for the slumber of the antlered ones—and upon it, map his mouth with his own. Such a bed and his tenderest, most skilled kiss would be unworthy of Vared of Omela.

Shaking off his intoxication, Tel located the welt and the tiny brown barb at its center. "Ah. I will remove the stinger with the side of my fingernail. It should not hurt."

"Yes."

"There. Easy." He rolled the stinger onto the pad of his index finger and brought it around Vared's head so he could see it.

"Such a small thing should not cause so sharp a pain."

"Less the stinger than the poison, I think. You have never been stung before?"

"Never."

"I will make a paste. It will pull the poison from the welt." He squatted. Raking the rotting leaves aside with his fingers, he gathered some dirt in his palm and added two drops of water from the waterskin to make a thick mud. With the umber paste, he covered the site of the sting. "I have no idea if this is a legitimate treatment, but it is what my mother did, so it is what I do."

"It feels better." Vared turned around. "Thank you." He grinned and looked away. "Yours drives me crazy."

"Hm?"

"Your neck." Vared covered his face with a hand, plainly embarrassed.

Tel's whole body caught fire. "I am glad. Thank you." When he had some of his wits back, he asked, "Shall we? The tree?"

"Yes."

They hiked in silence for a few moments. Tel stole glances at Vared, wondering how long he would have to wait for a second kiss. They came alongside and eventually walked upon a proper path.

Vared said, "We could've just taken the horses all this way?"

"Yes," said Tel, "but we would not have seen the waterfall." *And you would not have been stung. And I might not have kissed you.*

"I suppose it was worth it, then," said Vared.

When they arrived, Tel said, "Here. Off to the left."

"Your tree's a fallen tree?"

If each of them had a twin, they still would not come close to encircling it with their eight arms. The giant's death had taken several lesser trees down with it. "Fell the year after they drowned. Spontaneously. There was no gale. No storm. It decided it had had enough and wanted to rest. But it gave me my cave."

"Cave?"

Tel led him around to the base of the tree. "You see how the earth has clung to the roots? It forms a disk of dirt. In all the rains and snows over the seasons, it has solidified. I have sat out an afternoon thunderstorm under here and stayed dry as an Andowian desert. I come here to pray and meditate. As does my father. Did." He walked under the ceiling of sod and roots, barely needing to stoop. Vared followed. Tucked into the roots and mud all over the dome's inner surface were curled, yellowed notes and keepsakes.

"These papers would tell me a lot about you, I bet." Vared dragged the backs of his fingers over some of the mementos above his head. "A star." He indicated the center of the back wall of the cave. The largest gnarled roots radiated from a central point, forming a five-armed shape.

"Beautiful, is it not?" Tel sat. "Would you like to play a game?"

"A game?"

"Sit. We call it back-to-back."

Vared lowered himself to the dirt. "I remember."

"I have told you about it?"

"When we first arrived at Affas."

"That is right. In the throne room," said Tel, noting how different and distant life in Affas seemed. "Very well, then. Back-to-back."

They oriented themselves and scooted until skin met warm skin. Tel was surprised by the power of the relief brought by being in contact with him again. Nearly as strong was the drive to use the stagsblood to probe his thoughts and feelings. He was desperate to know his interior, to confirm or dash his own hopes and be done with the matter. It would be a violation with which he could not live, so he ignored the urge.

"Who has the first question?" asked Vared.

"You have never played before. The honor goes to you."

"All right." Vared took in and set free a long breath. "Do you miss the drink?"

Tel closed his eyes. "No. Surprisingly." He opened them. "I have had only one or two real bouts of thirst. Sometimes I reach for a glass with my hand.

At a meal or a party or when I am nervous. I think only because it was so long my custom. The drink was at my side as much as Caip was—more—for decades. I still think about it often, but I do not fret about it. Craid said… he said he still had periods when he would have thoughts. *Most thoughts are rubbish,* he told me. So, I dispose of them. He told me to only worry about a thirst that will not leave."

After a few beats, Vared said, "You were truthful."

"Yes. My turn."

"This is terrifying."

Tel's wicked laugh rang into the woods. "It can be." He decided to simply ask what he wanted to know. "After the exchange is concluded, when the year has elapsed, will you see me? Somehow. Here or in Omela?"

"You're thick."

"Thick?"

"Dense as a milk cake," answered Vared. He chuckled. "If you paid any attention at all, you'd know the answer. Stars in the sky, how is one so intelligent so slow?"

"You are being truthful?"

"Why wouldn't I? My turn." He took a quiet moment.

Tel spent the pause inhaling the equilibrium of scent offered by the forest—half brown death, half green life. It was old and new in divine balance. A bit of the tang of Vared's body found his nose, too. His cock stirred.

"I have it." A smile was evident in his voice. "Do you hold a secret from all people? I'm not asking for the secret. But do you have something inside of you—trivial or grave—no person knows?"

The dynasty danced strangely in Tel's veins, dissimilar to any magical sensation he could remember. "No," he said, in an off-handed manner. After a few beats passed, he convinced himself the casual answer sounded suspicious. "Being a member of the royal family and a diplomat has provided my mind with more than enough secrets to hold. None of them were only mine. And I do not like to clutter my head with extra information."

202

"I believe you."

Those four syllables struck Tel in the abdomen like the arrow from his dream.

"I like this game, but could we play another time? I miss seeing you," Vared said.

The arrow drove itself further into Tel's guts, tunneling through flesh. "Of course."

They spun on their buttocks to face one another. "That's better," said Vared, showing Tel the sweetest expression he had ever seen. Vared regarded him through his blue lashes. In and around the apricot eyes was a whiff of mischief. "I like it here. The water. The woods. This tree, especially. I hope you'll take me again."

The arrowhead twisted, boring inward until he was run through. "Vared. Vared, I lied to you. Just now."

"Oh."

"And I am sorry for it. I have a secret. Only one living person knows it and came to know it recently."

"Caip."

"No. Not Caip. Other than him, only two have known, and they are gone."

"Your mother and Hod."

"My secret...I thought I might die with it. But circumstances have changed. And it wounded me to be false with you. I may need to soon share this with...Circumstances have changed. But I want you to know. Before anyone else."

"You don't need to tell me. I only asked if you had—"

Tel blurted, "Do you know I mean you no harm?" He ground his palms into his closed eyes and combed a hand through his raven hair. "That I would never injure you and that I would stand between you and anyone who intended to hurt you?"

"Yes. I know that."

"Promise me, even if you are frightened, you will remember this. That I would not hurt you. That I would stand between you and pain. You must promise me."

"Tel, wh—I promise."

"This secret is best told without words."

Twenty and Two

Tel allowed his eyelids to fall closed. *What if knowing curses him, like Hod?* He pushed this aside, labeling it rubbish, and looked inward. After a beat, his mind was well-lowered, so he held his palms in the air between his ribs and Vared's. He opened his eyes. Vared was frozen, holding his breath.

Above each of the lined flats of his hands, a loose ball of white light appeared. Vared shrank backward but kept his seat, legs crossed. Tel made the fist-sized globes of energy change colors. One shifted through the rainbow until it was the blue of Vared's hair. The second stopped when it reached the warm orange of his irises. Tel shrunk the blooms and made them brighter. Vared squinted. Placing his hands in his lap, Tel made the blue sphere chase the orange in wild arcs and loops under the dome of dirt, roots, and disintegrating papers. They paused a moment, hanging, until one pursued the other into the woods.

He returned his right hand to the space between them and conjured a sour apple in his palm. After taking a large bite from the fruit, he held it out before the boy again as he chewed. When he swallowed, the apple faded in his hand until it disappeared. He looked at Vared, trying to assess what he was thinking and feeling. His expression was opaque. He did not raise his eyes to regard Tel. Instead, he continued looking where the apple had been.

Tel passed his left hand over his right arm from fingertips to elbow, cloaking it, bit by bit, with invisibility. He reversed the motion, making the forearm visible again. At this, Vared gasped, covering his mouth.

"It is painless. I am only hiding it."

"Is—Could you hurt someone?"

"I would not hurt anyone. Least of all, you."

"That's not what I asked. How powerful are you?"

Tel answered, firing a bolt of energy from the cave, making the air scream and hiss. The lightning struck the side of a cow-sized boulder, blasting away a third of its mass. It fell to the forest floor in smaller rocks, pebbles, and dust. Above them, birds fled the trees.

"What else can you do?" Vared asked, too much white in his eyes.

"I can read the thoughts and feelings of those I touch. Plant a suggestion in their minds or hearts. Sometimes, I think I receive thoughts and feelings without touching people, but I cannot make any sense of those."

Vared scooted away from him a bit, without seeming aware of it. "Have you…"

"Never. No. Never. I have wanted for so long to be able to see inside of you, so I might know…but I could never. I would find no peace after such an invasion. Never, I swear it."

"I believe you." Vared's body remained tense.

"You are Kelseigh's favorite person. She looks forward to being with you."

"You can—Horses, too?"

"I am a dynast. I have so seldom been tempted to share it with anyone other than Caip, but I cannot help but let you see me entire." He had a closer look at Vared's face. "Are you frightened of me?" He leaned forward and took his hand.

Vared's eyes filled with tears. He pulled his hand from Tel's and rocked up into an awkward squat. "I need to go." His attention darted about the space. His breaths were rapid and shallow.

Tel knew Vared was approaching the brink of panic. He had seen him like this before. To give him some room, Tel eased his body backward on the dirt.

"No!" came Vared's sharpened scream. "I cannot find my way back. I need you to take me."

"I was not going to leave—" Tel rose slowly and brushed debris from his clothes. "I would not leave you."

Vared trailed him rather than walking at his side. Tel's throat and chest burned with every step.

* * *

The next afternoon, Tel and Caip returned from a clearing in the forest, where they had taken a couple of unusually quiet hours for archery and sword work. They found Mor walking circles in the yard, clearly watching for them. Vared hugged his knees on the grass.

Caip knitted her face. "What is it, love?"

Mor looked at his prince. "A young woman and her daughter, coming from southwest of here. Walked into town, dirty and starving. Says they escaped your brother's forces two weeks ago."

"How old is the child?" asked Tel.

"Eight seasons or so." Vared stood. "I rearranged things. They're in the littlest cottage."

"Good." Tel tried and failed to hold Vared's eyes.

"Does she know she's safe now?" asked Caip.

Mor said, "She's scared. Beyond scared. But I think she's more scared of what's behind her than she is of us."

"I will speak with her," said Tel.

"No," said Vared. His hand flicked out, and a few of his fingers curled around a few of Tel's. He looked at their hands and withdrew his more quickly than he had sent it out. "Let me watch after her. They don't need to see you. They don't need to be overwhelmed by seeing a prince for the first time right at their lowest moment. Let them rest. Get their bearings."

Caip nodded.

"Thank you, Vared. Whatever you need to make them as comfortable as possible. I will speak to her tomor—whenever. When and if she wants to. I leave it to you."

* * *

The young woman was ready to see the prince by early the next evening. Vared insisted Tel and Caip go to her. *Foghar Castle might be humble in your estimation, but it's a castle still.*

The prince, the rightmajor, and the woman sat on overturned crates in front of the cottage. The little girl stayed with Vared a handful of meters away, bouncing and babbling on the lawn.

"I am glad you are here, Ruitha," said Tel.

She twisted strands of her black hair with her fingers. Her left leg vibrated in front of her. "Me, too. Your highness. Thank you. We came so far. A few days in, I realized I didn't know where we were going. People said to go to Prince Tel."

"You should not be thanking me. I should be apologizing to you. For my brother's people."

Caip gave Ruitha an empathetic but direct look. "We'll need you to tell us what happened. We know it's a fresh, uncomfortable memory, but it will help us understand."

Ruitha's eyes appeared to defocus. "They came to conscript those of the right age. Just swooped in on the town. Not even a town. It's hardly a village. Less than a hundred. Just a bunch of houses with farmers and craftspeople inside. And several of our young adults already marched for the emperor. Probably put on ships to Kamber, so there are even fewer of us."

"How many of them? The emperor's women and men?" asked Caip.

"Let us break," said Tel, tight-jawed, "the habit of calling my brother that."

"Twenty, twenty and five. Maybe more," answered Ruitha. "Not everyone can join the service. Not all of us. I'm not eligible. I have Ofya. She needs me. My brother—" Her throat caught. The speed of her fidgeting increased.

"Ruitha, perhaps we could talk another time," said Caip. "If you would r—"

"No, rightmajor. Allow me a minute." She appeared to subdue the emotions threatening to overwhelm her. "My brother and my man. They... told the soldiers. Enough of us have gone. The soldiers said if we weren't willing to help, we must not be real Feighans. We must all have Kamb or Omelan lovers. Maybe we were even hiding some. My brother got upset. Just as he would when my father would talk in the old way about off-Feighans. The soldiers called him names. Threatened him. My man tried to reason. To explain that we couldn't give more women and men. Respectfully. The harvest really *is* just months off. We need some strong backs..." She cleared her throat.

"One of them said—I'll remember it always for the way he said it. It was so...dark. One of them said my man was making sense. They couldn't take all of us. Then, he told me to choose. Since I couldn't spare both of them, I should pick. He expected me to choose my brother or my man to go with them." She absorbed her tears with the loose, ratty cuffs of her sleeves. "He said I was taking too long. I needed to decide. Then—" She croaked, overcome. A frustrated grunt came from her chest, like she was willing herself forward. "Just as I was about to answer. He was screaming in my face, and I was about to tell him, and...*one, two.* He stabbed them. I didn't even know he had his blade out. But he stabbed them. Just like that. *One, two.*"

"Sacred Doe, I am sorry." Tel rode a swell of rage. He wanted to smash something—to destroy anything.

"Even after this, they wouldn't leave. I had to beg them to let me burn Fas and Sol. They ate our food and drank our ale and slept in our homes. And watched us. Bothered us. One of the women, she was especially nasty, slept in our house. Mocked my crying. But she had too much ale one night. They all did. And I didn't know when they would leave or what else they would do before they did. I took Ofya and ran."

"We'll do our best to keep you safe," said Caip. Tel heard the disguised anger in her voice.

"I had to get her out of there." Ruitha gave a start, her head whipping around until she found her daughter with her gaze.

The girl sat on the ground, watching Vared. He threw a large stone into

209

a lazy upward arc. When it landed, he imitated the sound of the impact. *"Plonk!"* It sent Ofya into hysterics, which Vared seemed to find contagious. Side-by-side, they shared a belly laugh.

"You are tired, Ruitha," said Caip. "If you would like to sleep. We will mind Ofya and bring her to you when she is sleepy."

"How does she have so much energy still?" Ruitha asked. "After all this? I'm so tired."

"Sleep, Ruitha. So you can keep up with her tomorrow." Caip placed her hand over the young mother's.

Ruitha nodded and stood. "But don't you want to know…"

"Know what?" asked Caip.

"What choice she had made." Tel frowned. "Her brother or her man."

Ruitha nodded. "Yes."

"It's not important," said Caip.

"It is. It is." Tel stood and moved to Ruitha. "Not because one choice was good and the other bad. It was ugly. Impossible. But because you need to speak your reasoning out loud."

"Yes. Thank you. Yes."

"I would hear it if you would let me." Tel reached for her, placing a hand on each of her upper arms. "I would hear it."

She gave him eyes like bruises. "Fas. My brother. I would've sent him to war. Only because he was childless. And Ofya needs Sol. But now…If I'd found the courage to say my brother's name…"

"No, no, no, Ruitha. There is no sense in that." Tel took her in an embrace. "Never forget, the ones who did this—my brother's people—are responsible. They will be held to account. On this, you have my word. And your reason makes sense to me. For Ofya." He let her go and showed her a gentle nod. Calling some authority into his voice, he said, "Now sleep. She is in good hands."

"Thank you, your highness."

Caip rose and walked with her toward the cottage. When they reached the little stone step, Caip turned back and looked at Tel, a question on her face.

* * *

A handful of evenings later, Tel sat fidgeting in the garden. Caip approached at the appointed time and joined him on the bench. The sun had set hours before, but the night's air carried true summer warmth. The Stag's eyes cast their moody light across the valley, making it feel like dawn or dusk.

"It's lovely out," she said.

"It is."

"What's happened between you and Vared?"

"I did not ask you here to talk about that."

"I don't care. You've been avoiding one another for over a week, both of you trying to act carefree, which only exaggerates the fact that you aren't. When you do cross paths, it's impossible to be in your presence. The atmosphere thickens. Like foul pudding."

"I kissed him." The memory caused an awful pang—behind his eyes, in his throat, and through his guts.

"You must be a terrible kisser."

He whacked her thigh with the back of his hand.

"He didn't react well? Surprising."

"What would be surprising about it?"

"You two have been aching for one another for months. And months. Both thinking you're so subtle about it. But all you did was miss months of…one another. The pair of you are dense."

Dense as a milk cake. Tel's laugh was short, quiet, and bitter.

"But the kiss wasn't good?"

"Of course it was good," said Tel. "I have not had one like it."

"So, what happened?"

He closed his eyes and fiddled with his hairline. "I turned out to be not what he was expecting. A different man."

"What did you say? I'm sure it can be fixed. Decide what you feel and go to him and tell him. You're forty and one. You shouldn't be wasting time."

"Listen to you," said Tel, stopping himself from rolling his eyes. "The

211

romantic."

"Mor's done this to me. But I mean it. What is it you feel for him?"

It took him a while to find his throat. His eyes stung, and nausea came over him. He waited until the sensations abated. "Respect. I respect him. I want for him the best dreams in his head. He deserves more than any man could ever give him in a hundred romances. Me, especially. Behind his... shields...he is so tender, even after the world has hurt him so much. His gifts are—they put me in awe. In worship. I worship him. And my respect and worship do not permit me to press or try to woo him. I cannot do that. I cannot be the entitled royal, expecting to be given what he wants. Not with him. I would only ever ask him to be alive and to pursue his pleasure. If he wants me, I shall give myself to him. If he wants the world to be rid of me, I will put my own neck under the axe's edge. If he asks for this castle, it will be his. If he asks for nothing, it will be his."

She moved her head in a series of slow nods and pulled him into an embrace.

"Why are you hugging me?"

"Because I don't want you to hurt, Tel. Because I adore you."

"Please remember this feeling." He squeezed her upper body into his. "Please remember."

She pushed herself out of the hug and searched his eyes, which caught someone approaching.

"Ah, Dar," said Tel.

The major showed the top of his head. "Your highness. Rightmajor."

"It's good to have you back, Dar," said Caip.

"Good to be back."

Tel straightened his posture. "We have two subjects to discuss tonight. Major Dar, please tell Caip what you shared with me yesterday."

"First, Nik's safe in Athair. He'll continue to do the contingency planning Prince Tel asked him—"

"Planning?" Caip narrowed her eyes.

Tel raised his hand in a blade. "Let him finish."

"The fighters who hold Athair number somewhere above two thousand.

Their leaders are convinced they can have another thousand or more."

"Nothing compulsory," said Tel.

"As you instructed, highness. No one will be pressed into service."

Caip's fingers came to her lips. "Goddesses and gods."

Dar continued, "Rightcolonel Sitha's four hundred soldiers will march for you if you send word, along with the two hundred or so already stationed in and around Coltach."

"And you have asked a sample of these soldiers if they will fight...next to someone *different* from them?"

"Yes, highness." Major Dar answered. "And to a woman and man, they will. Others will hesitate, maybe even refuse, but the ones I polled aren't troubled by it. They're troubled by your brother much more."

"Different from them?" Confusion pulled at Caip's features.

Tel rose from the bench. "My friend. I ask you again to remember our hug a few moments ago." He raised his arms to shoulder height. "I have the blood." From his hands burst two great plumes of fire, more than two meters in length. "The blood of the antlered god." Orange light and heat streaked over the planes of the faces of the rightmajor and major. Three beats later, they were again solely lighted by the moons.

"I—Of course," said Caip. "*Of course.*" Her face collapsed into her hands. "The fire in the alley with Gran. So many other—"

"Remember our hug, Caip," said Tel. "We will talk of this after you have slept on it. If you want to leave, I will let you go. I have kept things from you, my friend. But I *respect* you. I would happily give you the castle. I would happily give you nothing. But I would prefer it if you accept more than nothing. Lead my army. It sounds like you would start with thirty and six hundred behind you. And a dynast prince next to you. We can grow the army with a bit of cunning and luck. We will need more than a bit, for the other side has some sixty thousand here and twenty thousand in Kamber.

"I can no longer cling to my love of peace while so many Feighans have none. They are terrorized. When I set this plan, I knew it could be abandoned. I assumed I *would* abandon it. But I needed to explore options. And I needed to think. Just when I thought I might go through with it, I began to waver. Because of the evil of violence and the whiff of self-interest. But Ruitha and her little one arrived just in time to show me what to do. I will knock my brother from the throne and knock my uncle into a pit. That, or I will lose my head. If you join me, you may, too. But I will not hide that head while thousands of people call on me to raise it high and end this wickedness.

"Dar, now you know it was no stranger I had in mind when I asked you to test the sentiment about fighting alongside a dynast. I do not understand why I matured with my powers intact, but I know I did not ask for it. It makes me no better or worse than if I could not make the fire or disappear myself. Pick a few people and ride out tomorrow to see how many from the area you can recruit to march under the cross and ring.

"Caip, decide if you can forgive me. And if you can, we will begin planning, and I will share what I have already arranged. I leave for Athair in twenty and five days with all who will follow."

Tel walked toward the castle. When he was far enough away that it could not be seen, he allowed himself to tremble. He was frightened and tired, and he had not even begun.

Twenty and Three

As the hot afternoon considered surrender to evening, Prince Tel changed into a festive but simple outfit to ride into town. While colorful, his attire was free of billows and puffs and embellishments. More and more, he eschewed layers of princely garments in favor of plainer ensembles. Cheerful, grass green leggings disappeared into knee-high boots of creamy, brown leather. A quilted doublet in a mellow, rusted amber closed around a thin tunic of a brighter orange.

He would join the people of the valley to mark the anniversary of the end of the Kamb occupation of northern Feigh with dancing, drinking, and four spit-roasted forest hogs. Although the fighting ceased centuries ago, the Feighan victory was still observed as a significant holiday across the kingdom, particularly in and around Foghar. A unit from the region had been crucial in dislodging Kamber's hold on the capital.

At the stables, he found Kelseigh still missing. He had not seen Vared all day and had paced about, trying to not fret about it or ask if anyone knew where he had gone. Because he could not manage to smooth the worried etchings on his face, a handful of attendants and soldiers had asked him if he was well. Vared had left the estate without escort. Tel was, by turns, furious and sick with fear.

What else can I do? Castle or nothing. It is not my choice. He would try his best to enjoy the celebration. His people were excited to have him here for the holiday for the first time in sixteen seasons, and he would play his role. After fussing over Pony for half an hour, he saddled him and took the road through the heart of the valley until he reached the open meadow used for the festivities. At the paddock's center, a giant pyramid of wood of all kinds stood ready to be ignited. It would be Tel's honor to bring the bonfire to life.

The smell of roasting meat greeted him before any villager. His stomach rumbled, and his mouth flooded. Increased appreciation for food was one of his favorite aspects of avoiding the drink, and he looked forward to the rustic feast. After tying Pony, he spent a full ninety minutes being welcomed by his people. He sat in time to hear a smith tell the story of his daughter's recent birth. The child arrived a bit earlier than he and his woman had anticipated, and he relayed the story with humor and pride.

Tel giggled through the smith's tale and enjoyed other folks' updates, struck by the possibility this might be the last time he would see many of them. *This could even be my last summer on the world.* He was not too seduced by the darkness of this notion. Instead, he chose to savor this time with good Feighans.

Someone called Vared's name, and Prince Tel leapt to his feet. The response was involuntary. He could see the unmistakable, slight, cobalt-topped figure in his periphery, securing Kelseigh before ambling, terquin case in hand, toward the revelers. Tel pretended not to notice and made a ruse of having stood only to start a friendly competition. "Did someone bring a rope for a tug of war?"

Someone had, and Tel organized the game. Determined to not lift his head to seek out Vared's, he joined in round after round until he felt he might collapse. A pair of young men rescued him, telling him it was time to light the bonfire. Soon after that, they would feast. Most of those in attendance gathered near. Despite his best effort to avoid notice or care, he saw Vared had taken a seat on the grass twenty meters away. He played a quiet song to a small audience, who sat entranced.

Telling himself everyone would know soon enough, he considered using the stagsblood to ignite the towering pyramid. He chose instead to observe tradition and tossed an oil lantern onto the base. When it smashed, the gathered townspeople hooted their delight. He watched the flames spread up and around the structure. It was as difficult as ever to pull his gaze from a fire. He was surprised when Mor sidled up to him.

"Your highness." His tone was warm. He showed his prince the top of his head.

"Hello, Mor. I was worried I would not see you tonight. Is Caip here?"

"Of course."

"Is she—"

"You have a long, complicated friendship. She loves you like a brother. She always will. But leave her be tonight, your highness."

Tel heard the certainty in Mor's voice. Although he felt none of that sureness, Tel understood in an instant there existed territory of Caip's interior he would never know. This territory was for Mor and Mor alone. The realization made him burn with an odd, resigned envy. He felt no hostility toward the man, just the sensation of melancholy chewing at the soft tissues of his chest. "I will not bother her."

"And if I may ask of you one more thing, my prince?"

"Ask it, friend."

"Do not stop until your rear end is on top of that throne and your head's under the rack crown," Mor whispered. "And please keep her alive."

Tel's eyes widened. Mor gave him a small, tight nod. "The more likely scenario is she keeps me alive."

Mor chuckled as he walked off, no doubt to find his partner. "Happy night to you, your highness."

Finally, it was time to eat. Tel and most of the attendees did so with gusto, enjoying an unrushed and casual feast. The mood was joyful. Caip offered Tel a brief smile from a distance. Seeing that it changed her eyes as much as her mouth, his throat stung with gratitude.

Once the children had taken their fill and retreated to the outskirts of the celebration to play, the adults laughed over jokes and friendly taunts, which became more vulgar with each mug. Tel was happy to be so relaxed when surrounded by overindulgence. He was, however, preoccupied with thoughts of Vared—and with chiding himself for those thoughts. Even over the raucous sounds of the feast, he caught fragments of distant tenor, terquin, and silvery laughter.

* * *

Many of the townspeople had left the paddock for home, especially older residents and those with children. Both the flames and conversation had mellowed. It became much trickier for Tel to pretend to ignore Vared when people called him closer to the fire to share some music.

Vared complied. Tel tried to balance the amount of attention he paid him as he approached, wanting to avoid the appearance of tension or awkwardness. He knew it was irrational, but he felt as if all of them—the arresting songmaker included—could read his thoughts as easily as if he screamed them at the limits of his voice. He tried to look at him, but not too much, all while maintaining a neutral but not unfriendly expression. *This is absurd. I am absurd.*

When he stepped into the dome of gold light, Tel noticed the difference. He had shortened his curls a great deal. His dainty cheekbones were entirely visible, now that the hair had retreated from his features. What was a massive, feral tangle was now a pleasing, balanced, blue vessel for his face. When the Omelan turned to show a smile to a young woman, Tel's breath hitched. A peek—a tantalizing sliver—of the nape of his neck was exposed to the night air. Warm light and gray shadow from dancing flames tickled the perfect skin.

Something in his movements and posture was changed, as well. After puzzling over it for a few beats, Tel knew he was observing the telltale signs of drunkenness. Just as it came to him, he saw Vared gesturing for a drink. A mug was placed in his hands. He made a show of taking a large swig, to the applause of the crowd.

"What'll you play?" asked the woman at whom he had grinned.

"Hm." He readied his terquin. "Prince Tel was kind enough to send me to the Academy at Sonagrein not long after I arrived in Feigh. I'll sing a little song the students taught me. They said almost everyone in the kingdom knows it. If you do, sing with me."

His strumming was jaunty as he tore into the introduction, to which he could not help adding his charming, nimble-fingered trickery. He struck the strings with atypical force but maintained graceful dexterity as he locked eyes with Tel until the prince could look no longer. It took a bit, but nearly everyone indicated they recognized the tune with hoots and cheers before he began singing.

You better mark my warning
I give it to you freely
Take care you don't lose your head
'Cause you'll lose your head
Fooling with th' stagsblood
I'll tell you of my best friend
With a dynast he was smitten
So he gave her his dong
It rotted off before long
From dippin' it in stagsblood

Tel's experienced a gauzy sort of deafness and did not hear the chorus. He carved a cheerful expression onto his face and even managed to bob his head in rhythm as he withdrew a good distance inside himself. He set to calculating how long he would have to stay at the affair to avoid the appearance of tension or offense.

Surfacing from his own depths after what he guessed was another two or three tunes, he got to his feet to begin the tedious process of giving his goodbyes. As he clasped hands and wished folk well, he refused to look in Vared's direction. He made his way through the townspeople, his brief visits bringing him in wider and wider orbits around the fire. Behind him, he heard the singing and playing stop before a round of applause.

Daina, the miller, walked alongside him as he shuffled across the grass toward Pony. "Won't you stay? We'll celebrate until dawn, I think."

Tel said, "I think people will enjoy themselves more without a prince of the realm lurking."

"But we'd love to have you stay."

"I am tir—"

"She's right. You should stay." Vared emerged from the gloom and caught

219

up to them. "Aren't you having fun, your majesty? Highness."

Tel saw Daina take note of the shadow that slid across his features and excused herself. "I'm terribly thirsty. Sleep well, your highness."

"Thank you, Daina."

"Why are you leaving?" Vared asked, insufficient space between the words.

"I would like to sleep."

"What about fun?"

"I have enjoyed myself," said Tel. He moved around Pony and fiddled with leather. "Thank you," he added, feeling the muscles under his ears tightening.

"Don't you like my hair?" He let his mouth hang open while he played with his curls. It was theatrical flirtation.

The question and Vared's manner infuriated Tel. He swung himself into the saddle.

"I think," slurred Vared, "you don't want me to have fun. Because you don't get to have any fun anymore. You don't even like a fun little song. Maybe you should have some mead and relax. Like me. I like to have fun. To drink sometimes. To go to bed with someone. Get my cock wet. Where are you going?"

Tel fantasized about dismounting and punching him into the dirt but instead said, with forced casualness, "Home. I am going home."

"You don't think we should talk?"

"Goodnight, Vared." As he rode Pony away, he turned to see the songmaker weaving back to the revelers, muttering. "Have fun," he called back, venom on his tongue.

He rode up to one of Caip's soldiers. "Make sure Ambassador Vared stays safe. Keep your distance. Do not bother him. Let him do whatever he likes. But do not let anything happen to him."

"Understood, highness."

* * *

The sun screamed down on Caip and her drilling troops. Their ranks had increased. Over a dozen young women and men from the valley had joined them.

She cupped her hands around her mouth and bellowed, "You are—to a person—soft and slow. Too much mead last night. You think a larger, better-equipped force will show you sympathy because you're hungover? Move!"

Fully outfitted and armed, she paraded them back and forth over the field, pausing at the end of each pass to execute a tight choreography of movements and postures. A drum pulsed.

"Goddesses and gods, hold the damned formation. You look like leavings out here." She jogged alongside a raggedy line. "You're not even awake."

Tel watched them from underneath the visor he made of his hand. Despite the untidy work of the soldiers, his chest was full. He enjoyed seeing his friend doing what she loved so. In her, he had every confidence. If he were to take Affas, it would be because of Caip.

Caip trotted over to Prince Tel. "I'll have them in better shape than this."

"I know," Tel said. "And there will only be more to make ready as we go south."

"We'll need to be twice as clever as we are strong," she said.

"That we will. Our ranks will expand. We are on the side of peace." He shook his head. "Listen to me. The doublespeak of warmongers. I will stand in front of the Stag for this after my life here."

"Stand in front of him now," said Caip. "Go to the forest and ask for him. You can't lead this endeavor with your heart in two. Get it whole. We *are* on the right side. No one thinks you're a warmonger. Your whole life's work shows the opposite."

"There will be war in my name. I am not sure it is forgivable."

"You speak like you live outside reality. What are we supposed to do if attacked? Stand peacefully? You don't believe so. I saw you in that alleyway in Affas. You sensed danger and fought to survive, as you'll do when we march. Peace is an ideal. It's perfection. Or…it can only sustain itself in perfection. We're women and men. We weren't made perfect. If the Stag

221

and the rest of them wanted peace, they should've made us better. All of us."

"They made me particularly flawed, I fear." Tel cast his gaze at his feet and took a pair of slow, full breaths. He raised his face. "Caip, I am sorry I kept it from you. For a long time, I resented the prejudices and superstitions about dynasts. I told myself they kept me from being myself. I was superstitious, too. Because I shared it with Mother and Hod, and they were taken from me. From us. And then I found the longer I held such a secret, the more impossible it became to release my grip. I—"

Caip appeared to absorb what Tel had said for a moment. She gave a slight shrug. "I didn't even know you showed the blood when we were young."

"It started with the rain and wind. Sensing the thoughts and feelings of others through touch. Nothing spectacular. Do not worry. They are more trouble than they are worth. And I never read you. When the other magics began to develop, the dirt and fire, I was old enough to need to hide it. Or to feel I needed to hide it."

She crumpled her features, thinking again. "Stagsblood or not, makes no difference to me. At least, it won't over time. The shock of it will fade. I've thought of a thousand reasons you would've hidden it. It stings you didn't tell me. And it stings I didn't see it. Because, truly, I should've. That's not the real belly punch, though. You kept that you were considering a challenge to Lag from me. You sent Dar to do what I should've been sent to do. And you kept that from me, too. I've earned your trust. Your confidence."

"And you have it." Tel regarded her heart-shaped face, pausing until he had her eyes again. "You have it. Dar is capable of what I asked of him. More than capable. I knew you would have argued that it should be you to explore raising an army. But I needed you here, with me. To be my constant. My steadiness. Remember, when he rode out with Nik, Gran and her goons were here, watching us and harassing Vared. I needed my best with me. Here. Keeping us safe. Especially him." He lowered his eyes, feeling his skin warm and prickle. "Rumors in the capital say Lag's troops are making no progress in Kamber since the first wave of the invasion. A standstill. Between five and ten thousand more will be sent north in ships."

"Excellent news, if true."

"It is a tragedy, Caip. A waste. More death on both sides," Tel said, voice wavering. He took a few beats and found steadiness. "But, yes. For our purposes, it presents an opportunity. It takes soldiers off the table for them and betters the odds for us. Anything keeping those ships off the southern Gray Sea is good for us. We can only hope they continue to underestimate us. Our threat to them increases as their respect for us decreases."

"Have you thought about…about what happens if you take the throne? About what happens to your brother?"

"When Aith is eliminated, Lag will be rudderless and will sue for peace. Trust me. He is an ignorant, bigoted fool, but he is not in control of this kingdom. I will figure out how to deal with Aith first."

"How can you be sure?"

Tel turned his attention to the drilling soldiers. "Aith is a dynast. A powerful one. Twice as powerful as me. More. He invades my mind with the wind and rain dynasties while I sleep. He gives me nightmares. He does not seem able to influence my waking thoughts. That may be because such magic is outside his ability or because I am also a dynast. It may be that he will find a way. I am uncertain. But I am certain he is using the tethers to control Lag. Our focus must be ridding the world of him. Somehow."

He faced Caip again and found her only response was a slackening of her jaw.

Twenty and Four

The morning blazed hotter than any had for eight seasons. Tel arrived before even the rightmajor, armored in leather and anxious to burn some energy. The rest of the soldiers trickled in while the day's steam thickened over the valley. As they reached the green silk of the field, Caip paired them off. Tel had not practiced a single maneuver, and his black hair was damp already.

Vared was last to arrive. At first, Tel assumed he intended to spectate, but then he saw Caip match him with a partner—and a formidable one. This was not to be some easy session like the singer had been taking now and then with Caip. Tel had asked for training to be intensified. They would be knocking each other around all day.

He set his mind again to ignoring the Omelan as best he could. "You are to forget I am your prince and try to knock my cock into the dirt," he told his partner, a taller, muscled corporal with a nose that had clearly been shattered more than once. Tel figured the enormous soldier lacked his speed, even if he had a significant advantage in brute strength.

The corporal grinned, and a sound—half chuckle, half growl—crossed his lips. "For Feigh, then."

Tel's eyes found the glossy network of scars stretched across the giant's fingers and knuckles. "For Feigh." He swallowed.

"Begin," cried Caip.

Tel winced and braced himself, lowering his center of gravity in preparation for an onslaught.

The corporal held his position. "Heh."

"What is your name?"

"I'm Bin. Of Athair. Like your mother."

"Athair? Soon you will be home." Tel began a careful arc to his left. Bin's response was not immediate. His movements to keep Tel in front of his body—at a safe angle and distance—lagged. Corporal Bin showed no concern, no vigilance. He did not see his prince as a threat. "Tell me, what do you think about being a traitor for me?"

"A traitor to your brother?" Bin wiped beads of sweat from his brow with the back of his mighty hand. "I don't give a horse's set o' balls about your brother. He's dumber than me. And you'll let me cord my woman."

"Your woman?" Tel picked up the pace of his dance, watching for an opportunity, waiting to spring. "Why would you not be allow—He has forbidden cross-cording again."

"Yes."

"Tell me about her."

"A sailor." Bin smiled. "On an Andowian merchant ship. Came into port back home a few seasons ago. Small but strong as a bear. Doesn't take any leavings from me. Or anyone else. A blessing to a pair of eyes, too. You'll let her live here with me, yellow hair and all."

Tel swept his eyes sideways to locate Vared before turning his attention back to his sparring foe. "Yes." He saw something cross Bin's eyes. Tel lunged forward, attempting a thrust with the waster. Bin dodged, and Tel found himself within the taller man's reach. Bin brought his elbow down, striking the place his neck met his shoulder. He crashed to the grass at Bin's monstrous feet.

"There. Your cock's in the dirt, highness. You're welcome."

"Thank you." Tel rocked in pain while he massaged the impact point. "So much." Sure he now had an opening, he rolled and tried to take Bin down by the legs. The beast did not budge.

"Get up, highness. You need to focus." He offered his hand and pulled Tel to his feet. "I know you can fight better than this."

"Right." Tel slapped dust out of his clothes. "Let us—" A cry of pain slashed through the sounds of friendly taunts and wasters meeting in the air. He saw the blue head on the ground beneath his hulking opponent, in much the same position he had been a few beats before.

Tel marched across the field. "Ambassador Vared, a moment of your time?"

The songmaker moaned and spun onto his back. He rubbed his lip, streaking scarlet across his face. "I'm occupied at the moment, Prince Tel."

"Get up. Now. Please." He moved to give him his hand but decided against it.

"Very well."

"The garden." Tel strode in that direction.

* * *

Under the hanging foliage of an ancient sulking tree, filtered speckles of sunlight landed on Vared. The breeze shifted the leaves and branches, making the bright dapples dance over his skin and hair. Tel looked up at him from a bench.

"You're the one who suggested I learn how to fight."

"I meant—" Tel heard the heat in his voice and paused to begin again. "I meant for you to take some exercise. Perhaps learn some skills in case you found yourself in trouble. So you could escape. Not so you could stand and fight soldiers."

"You think I'm too weak for it. Too dainty. I'm n—"

"Would you please sit with me?"

"I'll stand."

"Stand, then." Tightness returned to Tel's throat. He waited for it to dissipate. "It is not that I think you are weak. Or that you are incapable. But these women and men, myself included, have trained to fight for years. Decades. We are going to war. And you are going home."

"I'm not going anywhere."

"We are here for a few more weeks. Then we will head south. At Coltach, you will board a ship for Omela. Your departure will more or less be timed for the end of the exchange. You will have completed your full four seasons of service to your queendom."

"I will stay. With you."

"No. You cannot."

Vared rolled his eyes and took a seat next to Tel. "I don't have anyone in Omela. I have you and I have Caip here. I know you're angry with me. The bonfire. I can't remember, but I can imagine. I remember my mood. Sometimes, I don't like how I feel for you. It's so...predictable. You're powerful, and the stagsblood dynasty only makes you more powerful. While I'm just—I was disgusted with myself for so easily...And now you want to be rid of me."

"Look at me." Tel swung a leg over the bench, so he was straddling it. Vared mirrored him. "I have no power with you. If you knew what I saw looking at you, what I hear listening to you. What it is like to smell you. Months ago, you asked me a question. *How is anyone to refuse you?* But the question is for *you*. How? I am sending you home to keep you safe. Against everything I feel. Selfishness would have you stay. To have you in my sights. To have you in my tent at night."

"Let me stay. Keep me safe."

"I cannot. The odds...are not good for our side."

The orange eyes found the stone of the bench between them.

"You know it is true," said Tel. "So. I will do the unselfish thing and send you home. We will say goodbye at Coltach. As if—"

Vared lifted his gaze and took Tel's eyes. "And if you win?"

"I will send for you. Or choose an heir, abdicate, and come to you, if that is what you prefer. I do not care for power. I give it to you. I only want justice in my kingdom and less fighting on this world. And you."

"I still choose to stay." Vared hung his head. "If I lose you when we're apart, I won't be able t—"

"You *will be* able. You *must be* able," Tel spat. He waited until his flash of anger dimmed. "If something happens to me, you will *survive*. You will. No one knows this better than me. No one. Grief makes time a strange and vicious thing. Each beat will feel like a year, yet seasons will pass unnoticed.

And you will have somehow breathed through the whole nasty stretch, even when you had no will to do so. Then, you will sometimes notice your breathing. A long while after that, you will appreciate the breaths now and then. And you will write a ballad so, in a century, at least Omelans will know that many people in Feigh, most of us, did not want trouble with the rest of the world's people." He searched Vared's expression for understanding. The songmaker nodded. "I am sorry I scared you with…I should have been more thoughtful about the way I told you I am a dynast. It seemed so wrong to keep it from you another moment. But that was only more selfishness. I wanted you to see and accept m—" He was paralyzed by the sight of Vared gliding across the stone. Their knees met.

"I am of your blood. If it is stagsblood, then I am of stagsblood." Vared tilted his head and brought it through the air to Tel, who accepted his kiss.

Their mouths joined with more urgency this time. Copper from the fresh cut on Vared's lower lip greeted Tel's tongue. All apprehension and hesitation fell away. They devoured one another, which only resulted in further, deepening hunger. Pretense evaporated. Vared's fingers wound themselves into the back of Tel's hair. Their bodies pressed together—mouth to mouth, chest to chest, cock to cock—over the polished stone of the bench. They melded, hot.

For Tel, the union straddled the border between satisfaction and disappointment. He experienced contentment because the tension of anticipation—only worsened by their first, tenderer kiss—was broken. A knotted muscle gave way. The sudden relaxation gifted so much relief. He gloried in the crashing of their wet mouths. A dim regret shaded the ecstasy because he knew even the deepest, most fully appreciated kiss can only demonstrate its limitations. It cannot last forever. The lovers cannot be closer than this. One cannot crawl inside the other's skin and live and die there, though both may desire it. He knew there would be future kisses, though. They would have some weeks, at the least, and he would happily try, as many times as Vared would allow, to find a kiss closer than this one.

Tel had lost any concept of time before Vared said, "I have to stop. My lip." He gave a little laugh and touched the swelling with a finger as he pushed himself backward. He stood, catching his breath.

His own lips were warm and raw, so Tel understood. "And I have to stop before I mount you under this tree like an animal."

Vared's laugh was sturdier this time. "You mean, before *I* mount *you*." He heaved a direct look at Tel. The Omelan's whole face shone with truth and mischief.

Tel had never been the passive sexual partner, even with his decades of debauchery. He had made a couple of clumsy, unpleasant attempts. Still, it was headily arousing and right. "Yes, Vared."

The songmaker walked back to the bench, eyes still on Tel. Vared bent to kiss him again. Tel eased onto his back as Vared's mouth took possession of his. Vared ground the swollen hardness in his leggings against him. He nipped Tel's lower lip between his teeth, and every muscle of the larger, older man melted under him. "Yes, Tel," he said, mouth still on his. "I see the part of you that wants to practice yielding to someone else." Vared mashed his bulge against Tel's once more, wicked satisfaction crooking his whole face. "The part that pretends to be a wise teacher, but really is an eager student. The part that wants to know just how dainty I am *not*. So, it is not you who will mount. Not for a long time."

"Yes." Reality wavered before Tel's eyes. He pinched them closed, feeling Vared move away. Tel remained on his back, breathing to quiet his twitching stomach and skittering heart. He was filled with internal chatter. He worried about his sexual prowess as he had not since his first few encounters. Because he had not been with anyone since he had gotten dry, he had no idea what his performance would be like. He opened his eyes to see Vared playing with a broken section of sulking branch, looking down on him with what seemed to be warmth. "What?" He sat up.

Vared grinned. "You're going to win. It just came to me. It'll be hard and you'll sacrifice. A lot. But I know it as I know this stick will fall to the ground if I let go."

"I wish I had your confidence." Tel wanted to weep.

"You may borrow some of it, if you wish," said Vared. "I have more than enough in you."

"I have to leave tomorrow. Caip made me realize I need to…do something. I could be gone a week or two. Do not torture me about it. Shortly after I return, we will leave for Coltach. From there, you will sail for home. But we will have a few weeks on the way. Would you share my tent? If you do not mind that it will not go unnoticed."

Vared snorted, sputtered, and placed a hand over his flat stomach. "Dense as a milk cake." He shook his head.

"What?" Tel asked, giggling, still lightheaded and aroused.

"Don't you know everyone sees us? They *see* us, Tel. Before *we* see us."

Prince Tel's answer was half croak, half groan.

* * *

Tel walked into the woods for two days. Even the shade boiled. Like the constant pull toward the drink he once felt, the blood urged him to the wilderness of the far western reaches of Feigh, but he did not have the time for that. He wanted to go to the little cave made by his tree but knew he must go deeper, into strange forest. When the sun made its second trip over the edge of the world, darkness settling, the prince of Feigh settled, too. Water was near. He would do only the work of the faith until he had what he needed from the woods—no stagsblood magic.

The first morning at his little camp, he took some water, shed his clothes, and prayed for his antlered master to come to him, forgive him, and guide him. To wait, he lowered his mind and let it empty. His whole being listened. The forest dimmed. He did not eat.

The second day, he prayed for the Stag to come and feed him. He meditated again until the pain of stillness was terrific from his black hair to his filthy toes. The forest dimmed.

The third day, he asked again in prayer and waited again in meditation. Still, he drank water and ate nothing. He was glad the rain hid his tears, even though no one was watching. The forest dimmed.

The fourth day, he swore and demanded. He would not eat. He would not move. He would stay right here. The physical pain was the strongest his life had known. As night arrived, he abandoned his search for the Stag's will and used the stagsblood to try to form a tether. With the dynasties of the east and the west, he reached out, searching for Vared, not knowing if his gift had strengthened enough to make contact. He knew in his bones that his uncle had some mastery over this form of magic. The scoundrel had sculpted his dreams with it. Finding how to use it himself might prove invaluable in neutralizing him.

Knowing Vared was in the world by *feeling* he was in the world would also lighten his heart, which was burdened by the songmaker's absence and his own failure to hear the antlered god.

Hours passed. Repeatedly, his mind sank low and burst high in frustration. He could not see past the chatter—the grasping, the *wanting* to find him—to the opening, the allowing. In need of an anchor, he could find nothing suitable, neither sight nor sound.

Realization plowed into his mind. *He is the anchor. If I hold him and him only in my head, letting all else fall away, even the wanting, I may find him.*

It became so easy. Vared. And only Vared.

There. There he is. He was obsessing over a fragment of a new song and fretting over Tel's mysterious trip.

Tel withdrew. He had already transgressed enough. Vared would rightly be horrified if he knew of the intrusion.

Later, he would only remember of the fifth day that he thought he might die in meditation.

The sixth day was senseless. Weak, he asked forgiveness for his demands of the Stag, for using the blood when he had promised he would not, for reaching into Vared's mind, for the drinking, for the selfishness, for the waste, and most of all, for what he was about to unleash on the dirt of Feigh. The sounds of the forest ridiculed him. With dusk a short way off, he needed to interrupt his meditation to empty his bowels. He cackled, as he had not eaten in days and could not see how he had anything to empty. Dizziness took him as he stumbled away from the camp.

He woke, his throbbing head resting on a bloody rock at the bottom of a small trench. Somehow, he had stumbled into it. He could barely move. A sharp, dead branch, thick as a baby's wrist, was lodged deep in his right shoulder. With great effort, he extracted the wooden dagger. He moaned against the scarlet rock.

The stink of sweat and seed hung in his nostrils.

"I have given you much," said the prince's god, looking into the trench.

"And—Yes."

"You get angry, but you never doubt," said the Stag.

"I do. But no. There is Hod. But there is Vared."

"Yes."

"Will you forgive me?" asked Tel. "For the war?"

"I do not know. You have not yet done it."

"How can we stand in peace if who and what we love dearest is threatened?"

The antlered one was silent for a moment. "I do not know. We have given you a mystery. You do many things in it. Kindnesses. Hatreds. I am in a mystery. How to love all of you when you are so—"

"So like you made us," said Tel.

"Yes, fruit of my Doe. You must get up now. Use my dynasty to seal your wound. Eat in the morning."

Two hours later, Tel sat, legs dangling into the trench. Covering his left palm with scorching white energy, he brought it to his shoulder and cauterized the gash.

Twenty and Five

Starving, bruised, and marrow sore, Tel arrived at his castle a couple of hours before sundown to find a half-dozen Hebite men in his yard, playing a card game. They paid him little attention, which irritated him. He walked into his home, stomach lurching.

He wanted to call out when he stepped inside but could not seem to make his voice work. The sounds of conversation met his ears. He followed them to the dining room, where he found Vared, Caip, and Gawash. The rightmajor was seated at one end of the table, her face showing an expression designed to convey impassivity. Because he knew her so well, Tel saw the anger, visible as the fur on a dog. Vared sat on the other end. Gawash sat perched on the table near the Omelan, legs hanging in the air. His upper body was cheated forward. He hovered over the blue head, close enough to enrage Tel.

"Respect to Hebite culture, Lord Gawash, but we do not sit on tables in Feigh. It is rude. Sit in a chair or stand, please."

"It's Viceroy Gawash." He oozed off the table.

Vared stood. "Tel." His eyes flicked to the Hebite. "Your highness, what happened?"

"Goddesses and gods." Caip's back stiffened.

He had forgotten his filthy, injured state. "A long story I will tell you another time when we do not have *such an honored guest*." He poisoned the phrase with treacle. Vared stepped to him. "For now," he said, stroking the Omelan's jawline briefly with the backs of his fingers, "suffice it to say, I am grateful to see you." Tel was unprepared for the tears that clung to his

233

eyes, through which he viewed the prettiness he found so overwhelming. A small streak of greasy dirt from his fingers remained on Vared's skin, making his beauty all the more undeniable.

He laid his shimmering eyes on Caip. "And you, my friend." He was likewise almost crushed by the gravity of her loyalty. "I missed you more than you can know."

"I'm surprised by this emotional display, Prince Tel. I've come so far to your...*lovely little house* to see you. I'm glad you're back from your mysterious errand. In time for dinner, which I was told some time ago would be ready soon. You look...I want to say *terrible,* but that's unkind. I suppose I only mean you look like you could use a bath and a drink. This evening's a reunion of sorts. It calls for a celebration. Surely, some wine."

"I do not believe we have any." Tel shrugged. He winced, his shoulder barking to be heard above his general achiness.

Gawash scoffed.

"I have given up drinking."

"What?"

"Fogs the mind. Slows the body. But I am sure one member of my guard or another has something that will get you pissed. Caip?"

"Absolutely." She moved to rise.

Gawash waved a hand. "Thank you. I'm fine."

Tel let his sore muscles rest in a chair. Both Vared and Caip eyed him as he lowered his body too slowly. "What brings you here?"

"Antlered goddess and god, Tel," said Gawash. "Do friends need a purpose for a visit in Feigh? I had a break in the business of Table and wanted to check on you. I know the last year has been—"

"A relief." Tel smiled but wanted to slap the words of the faith out of the pretender's mouth.

"A relief?" Gawash's mouth hung open.

"You observed once what a *reluctant* king-in-waiting I was. I no longer have the awesome responsibilities of being sovereign. In fact, my brother does not even seek my counsel. My way of looking at the world has...fallen out of favor."

Gawash chuckled. "That it has."

"I appreciate you checking on us. As you can see, we are all well. Will you be heading back to Affas after dinner, or somewhere else?"

"I thought my men and I would stay here for a few days."

"Unfortunately, that is impossible," said Tel. "My little house does not have the room."

"The singer has already told me you accommodated soldiers in the great hall for the winter. That would do nicely for my guard. I thought I'd simply share a bed with you again, but it seems that won't happen." He looked down the length of his nose at Vared, lips pulled into a sneer. "Unless?" The hairless head swiveled to Tel. He winked.

Tel wanted to look at Vared's expression but could not manage to face him. His cheeks felt like rocks in the sun. "The great hall or a tent outside are your only choices. And we have guests coming. They should arrive by nightfall tomorrow. I am afraid we must say our goodbyes in the morning, Viceroy Gawash. I hope you will remember to give my brother my best and tell him I look forward to seeing him soon."

Gawash stammered. "I had hoped to speak with you privately about some matters of state. I also wanted to talk with you about the faith. I know you're particularly devoted and thought after din—"

"I have had a trying journey. We will have to save our discussion of politics and religion for our next visit," said Tel. "Where is that food? I am famished."

* * *

After the hushed meal, Vared went straight upstairs. Gawash invited Tel on an after-dinner walk, which he refused. Smirking, the Hebite insulted Feighan food and said he would not be able to digest or sleep without some exercise.

The moment he was out of sight, Caip said, "It's difficult to be in the same room as him."

"He is—"

"You slept with him? Even for you, that's—"

"I know."

"You are in a *lot* of trouble. A heap." She looked at the ceiling under Vared's room.

Tel made a sound of dread. "At least Gawash does not seem suspicious."

"He's impossible to read. You'll be pleased to know Dar was able to muster one hundred more from the area. I had only counted on another few dozen. We now number more than one hundred and fifty here. Dar has them camped in the town paddock. He's training them. Or attempting to. It's our good fortune they're out of sight. Gawash has only seen the number we left the capital with. He has no evidence you're raising an army."

Tel nodded. "Good. The goddesses and gods have protected us."

"What happened to you?"

"That's three thousand and seven hundred and fifty if we can get to Athair," Tel said, eyes defocused.

"You asked for the Stag?"

"Still difficult odds."

"Tel, talk to me."

"Tomorrow, Caip." He eyed the ceiling. "I have even more difficult odds to face tonight."

"But—"

Tel labored to get out of his chair, then stopped, half-risen. "Wait. Wait. Would it be possible for you to organize taking Gawash and his guard into custody overnight?"

"I don't see why not."

He straightened. "And chances are, it can be done cleanly? No loss of life."

"Most likely. But why?"

"Information. Leverage. We need to take every advantage we can *when* we can."

Caip said, "If you order it, I'll make sure it's done."

"Take them."

* * *

Dejected, Tel began to pivot away from the door to Vared's chamber when it finally opened.

Vared looked at the floor. "Hello."

The neutrality of the greeting was violence. Tel asked, "Would you like to talk?"

"What's to talk about?"

Greater violence. "Please." He took a step toward him.

Vared held his hand between the two of them. "I am tired. You are tired. Very tired."

"I had a difficult experience in the forest."

"See? Not tonight."

"Vared."

"If you're feeling lonely, perhaps you could find someone to share your bed. *Again.*"

"That was not—We never shared a bed. Not for a night. Not like—"

Vared looked about the hallway. "Come in here. No one needs to hear this." He stepped aside, and Tel crossed into the room. Even though he had closed the door, Vared lowered his voice to a whisper. "Did you fuck him, or did you not?"

Tel's eyes widened at Vared's use of the word. "I did. But it was in the past. I did not know you. There is no need for this je—"

"Oh, no. No. You're not going to do that. This isn't about jealousy. You'll not make me into that person. This is about *judgment*, Tel. He's disgusting. Everything he says drips with bad faith."

"I was drinking. And he had given me an herb. It was also not an easy night for me. You saw me in Queen Cessa's garden. The death rite for my mother and Hod. And more death. My father."

"You were drinking? You lost your people? That's what you say? You have a convenient pardon for decades of your life on both accounts, then."

Tel said, "You are right. Of course." He felt the sick pressure of shame

237

and regret from his throat to his groin. "Very well. Goodnight."

"I have something you'll want to see. It's important."

"Important?"

"I found it. At your tree. The cave. Tucked into the sod and roots. It looked so much newer than the rest. I didn't see it when you brought me there." Vared went to a table piled with books and scrolls. From one volume, he removed a folded piece of paper. "Forgive me for reading it."

Tel took it in his hand and forgot about it at once. "You went to the tree?"

"I was missing you. For some reason." He gave a little shake of his head and walked to the door. He held it open. "Sleep well."

"Sleep well." Every muscle crying out, Tel shuffled to his chambers. He placed the paper on his bed and disrobed. Lowering his body into the warm, perfumed bath he had requested, he wondered if he had ever felt so tired.

After cleaning himself, he dozed for a time in the tub. When he woke, he dreaded even the short walk to his bed. When he reached it, the paper was waiting for him. He crawled into the covers and read. Wide awake at once, he sat up straight against his pillows.

> *My brightest boy,*
>
> *I hope you find this. I know you still sometimes come to the tree. I see now so clearly what my own brother has done. I have given him much responsibility over the composition of my Table. Blindness. All at once, it came to me. They are all now in the middle of their terms. I am dying and have no hope of replacing them. I have been lazy, wanting to enjoy my accomplishment, our accomplishment, peace. I missed what he was arranging.*
>
> *If I go to the black and you have not returned from Omela, Craid will be the only one to stand between Lag and the throne. He is old, sickly, and in recent months, often absent from Table.*
>
> *I am trying to live. I am not certain I will even make it back to Affas. If I am wrong and outlast your trip, I know you will be a good king, but I worry the drink will rob you of greatness. I fret it will snatch*

from you some of the mass you could add to the right side of the scale. I love you, so I must tell you directly. You take too much comfort in your mugs and goblets.

It will seem like madness, but Aith hovers, even in my dreams. He is a danger. He has never freed himself from the bitterness of losing his family to Omelan hands. He does not understand that his kind of loss, our loss, is why we must avoid war. His ideas are relics, and your brother is susceptible.

I have only not been stalked here because this final trip to Foghar removes me from the capital. You are rightfully the next sovereign of this land and its people, and I have failed you with my bumbling. Even though you are lost in the drink, this is your responsibility. This is my will. It may not matter, but this is me.

Vith

Tel refolded the note and stowed it in a drawer. He wondered if Aith might have not only invaded his father's mind but also made him sick of body—if he had killed him.

He asked himself why he was not more upset. Should he not be shaking with rage and grief? Instead, his blood was cool. He would follow his plan and devote his life to destroying his uncle and ridding Feigh of his beliefs. His mind quieted without trouble. He let his exhaustion and pained body take him down to sleep.

* * *

He woke. The bed was moving. Only the softest moonslight shone in the windows.

"I couldn't sleep." Vared slid across the mattress until they were touching.

"I am quite hurt and tired," said Tel. "I would prefer to be feeling better our first time."

"You are presumptuous. I didn't come here for that. You're still being

239

punished for your bad taste. I came because I couldn't stop worrying about you. That note."

"It helps me know I am doing the right thing. Because it does not feel like it always."

"Your poor father."

"Yes."

"I would've liked to know him."

"He would have loved the song. The one you sang at solstice."

"Your song. I hope so."

A moment of silence passed. Tel felt the tempo of their breathing synchronize. "Vared?"

"Mm."

Aware of every cut and bruise, Tel rolled to face him. "Did you also come because you missed me?"

"No. I'm furious with you," said Vared. He placed a kiss on Tel's forehead. "You're on punishment. I just told you."

"I deserve it. You know...with Gawash...I was different then. And it was just..."

"Yes. I don't want to talk about it."

"All right."

"I thought you were hurt," said Vared, snickering.

"I am. You have seen me."

"Not *all* of you is hurt."

"So? Yours has been poking me since you crawled into my bed." Tel turned over and faced the other way because that was how he had slept since he could remember. "Do you think you will be able to sleep now?"

"Yes. This is better."

"It is."

* * *

Tel sent the two guards away and walked into the great hall carrying a neatly bundled linen napkin. Gawash sat on a pallet in the far corner, arms bound behind his back.

"Such a big room for such a small man." Tel clucked.

"Where are my soldiers?"

"Town. I have some of my best figuring out how we will *accommodate* them. And you, of course. You will be reunited with them soon. You can all keep each other amused. You will be released once I am well south of here."

"South."

"An indirect route, but we are off to Affas to remove my brother from the throne. Which, as you know, means to remove my uncle from the throne."

Gawash let out a reedy, staccato laugh. "Liar."

"Lying is too much trouble."

The viceroy repeated his laugh. "How? Who with? A few dozen men?"

"And women. We value women in this kingdom."

"Foolish. You're not this stupid." He laughed yet again.

"Are you hungry?" Tel held out the little linen package. "I know mirth can be exhausting. You must need to replenish your energy. It's spicy bread. One of my favorites."

"Funny." Gawash shrugged his shoulders to the extent he could.

"Of course. Sorry. Come off the pallet. On your knees. Face that way."

"A man on his knees facing *away* from you. First time for everything for Prince Tel of Feigh."

"Are you hungry or not? Do you want to move your arms a bit or not?" Gawash swung around to kneel as instructed. "Do not fuss. My dirk is quite sharp, and I would not want to accidentally stab you ten or eleven times."

Gawash turned and showed his profile, speaking over his shoulder. "Hilarious. A waste you're a prince. Should've been a panto."

Tel pulled out his antler-handled blade and made quick work of sawing through the cord binding his prisoner.

Gawash rubbed his wrists and rolled his joints. Tel handed him the bread. "Aren't you concerned I'll try to escape? To attack you?" He asked his questions around a mouthful of bread.

"Hm." Tel bent down, placing his dirk on the floor within reach of Gawash. "Escape. Attack me."

"You have armed people in and around this castle. I wouldn't make it far. I get it."

"Perhaps this would help. Make things a little fairer." Tel held out a flattened palm. A sound, akin to the noise of paper slowly ripping, accompanied the sight of an identical dirk shimmering into existence in his hand. He bent and put it on the floor. With his boot, he gave it a gentle nudge. It slid across the stone to join the first weapon. "There."

Gawash laughed for a third time. Now, it was wilder. "Very well. You're… *one of those*. You've intimidated me. I'm legitimately frightened. I mean it. So, ask me what you want to know."

"I do not need to ask." When he bent down to pick up the original dirk, the other dimmed until it was gone. "I swore I would never touch you again." He placed his hand on the smooth brow and felt Gawash's entire body stiffen.

"What're you doing?"

"It is done." Tel removed his hand and wiped it with vigor on the outer thigh of his leggings. "And just as I suspected, you are mostly useless. They do not trust you. Consequently, they tell you very little. Still, I had to see what you might know. Even you intuit that you are just a pawn. You are full to the brim of little anxieties and panics. Terrible. But you do offer one piece of information. One fact that will get me through the day smiling. They have totally underestimated me. Believed I would have made my play before now. They think I will stay isolated here or cross the sea in exile, despite their goading. They have no idea of my plan. No concern about me at all, really." Now, it was Tel who laughed as he walked away.

"Because it's insane," Gawash called after him. "It's no plan, Tel. It's suicide. Even with your magic tricks. You can't win. They have the largest, best-trained army on the world. You'll lose. And even if you escape with your life, you'll lose that pretty Omelan, too."

Tel froze.

Gawash continued, "You know it. You excite him now. You're a prince, and he's nothing. You're still handsome, but how long do you expect that to last? Sixty seasons older. A joke. And a sad one. How long before you go ugly and your cock goes soft? Think he'll stay for that? And waste more of his youth watching you slide into a cremation fire? Even if he stays, he'll resent each of his lengthening days and each of your deepening wrinkles."

Tel walked the rest of the way out of the hall. When he got to the other side of the door, he turned to one of the guards. "Take him to the others. Tie him up again. Tightly."

Twenty and Six

The dynast prince of Feigh tried and failed to clear his head after a long day of planning with Caip. He could find no real quiet. Now that he had set so much in motion, Foghar felt too still and stifling. This valley and this castle had been, his whole life, a place of air, space, and comfort. Now, the verdant hills and gray walls closed in, choking. He knew he would be able to breathe once they set out for Coltach in the morning, at least for a time.

The feeling of tightness could not muffle the beauty of the place, however. Through his window, he let his eyes record every rock and leaf within reach of his sight. The wounded, pink-orange sun bled as it eased itself beyond the horizon.

Two quiet knocks on his door were echoed by a pair of spasms in his chest. He had no doubt Vared would be on the other side. Still, he prayed for it to be so. "Come in." He heard in his own voice a mote of dread.

The door swept open, unhurried. "If you're busy…" He was a wispy blue flower in the archway.

"No."

"Or want to be alone."

He knew it would be easier to send him away, just as it would be easier if he could have a drink. Some part of him denied himself the softer way, like a parent providing firm instruction. "No."

Vared stepped into the room and pushed the door closed with his back. He stayed there, leaning. Like the prince, he wore leggings and a linen shirt, though Vared's featured a wider neck, in the style of his queendom. His clavicle was exposed. "You have been in here most of the day."

Tel looked at the floor near the Vared's feet, feeling the orange eyes upon him. He was unable to lift his gaze, though he wanted to do so. "Caip and I have been working. It is quieter up here."

"It's been busy downstairs."

"You will be ready to ride come morning?"

"I will."

"We will have you sailing home in a few weeks."

"I don't want to go home."

Tel pulled his eyes from the stones and looked at him. "So you have said." Feeling the rigidity in his throat, he paused to find evenness. "So you have said. Many times. But go home you must."

"Because you say. Because you're a royal and I make songs." His face was as sour as the words.

"Will you say that in twenty years if I am of one mind and you are of another? Will you always rely on that little jab? Every disagreement, I should yield to you? So it does not appear I am lording my station over you?"

"You're older than me. The highest of the highborn. *And* you're a warlock. Tell me what that would feel like. Put yourself in my place."

Tel scoffed. "I hate that word."

"Tell me. Imagine."

Tel scoffed again, this time rolling his eyes.

"Do it."

"I do not know what you are asking me." In the elegant creature leaning against his door, he saw firm earnestness. "Very well." He closed his eyes, withdrawing, trying to understand. "I would feel at a disadvantage. Scared, I suppose. I would feel subject to the whims of...the, uh—"

"Older, highborn warlock."

Tel opened his eyes and admonished him with a look.

"You're doing the imperious eyebrows. Only a royal could have such eyebrows."

"Fine. Yes. I would feel powerless," said Tel.

"And? What would you want?"

"I do not know. I do not know. Must we play this game? Why do you not simply tell me what you want?" Vared looked at him with a tilted head, expectation naked in his expression. All at once, Tel understood. "Vared, would you please sail for home? So you will be safe? Would you do it because I ask?"

"Yes. I'll hate it, but I will. Because you ask."

"Thank you."

"I *will* hate it."

"I know," said Tel. "I feel cheated." He realized the gravity of that truth. A part of him had been buried by his own hand—the part of himself only wanting to flee with Vared. He longed to shed the responsibility to right his land. He could happily spend his days listening to him sing. They could disappear. They could cross the Gray Sea. He ached to put something in the Omelan dirt.

"I understand."

Tel felt the weight of the loss of him, and it had not yet happened. He hung his head a bit, certain the premature grief was making his face look old. "But you need to do it, too."

"Do what?"

"Be in my place. Tell me what it would feel like."

"I'm rich. I have a castle. Servants. It feels wonderful."

"Funny."

"Tell me what you mean."

"Try, Vared. Be me. I will be you. I am young. Much younger than the prince. Much. I have nothing material. But I am beautiful. Talented."

His pretty face screwed in thought. He did not rush his pondering. "I would worry whenever someone got close. About what they really wanted. About if it was me."

"Yes."

Vared's features were swallowed by gloom. "That's not me. I don't want anything, Tel."

"I know. And I do not think of you like that. When I am alone with you, all that falls away. Even when I see you across the room. But our worries, our darkest wonderings—they do not feast on truth. They sustain themselves on...something else."

"We should starve them, then."

"We should."

"Good."

"Vared?"

"Mm?"

"Would you step away from the door and actually come in?"

Like him, his laugh was small and pleasing. He took a few steps toward Tel. "There. Better?"

"Much." His chest and stomach twitched. Thoughts formed slowly. He tried to know what to say. It felt like an hour passed.

"I feel nervous," said Vared.

"Why? I do, too. But why you?"

"*Telllllll.*" He colored it with both sweetness and exasperation.

"I am not certain your hair will grow long enough by the time you get home to restore you to Omelan decency."

Vared's hand stroked the curls at the back of his head. "I'll wear scarves or high collars, like when people lose their hair." He looked down. "I only cut it to...have an effect on you."

"I had guessed. For what effect were you aiming?"

"Well, I couldn't expect an Omelan reaction. Anything. As long as it was intense."

"It was. Both intense and Omelan." Tel tried to hold his features steady, but a crooked smile burst through the mask. Fire rushed up his neck from his abdomen. He looked away.

Vared asked, "Could we sit?"

"Yes." He gestured to the little couch against the wall. "I never sit here. I use a chair or sit up in bed." Again, he had to avert his eyes, feeling the heat of embarrassment. Mentioning his bed might have been a misstep.

"And who's this?" Vared searched the painting hanging above the sofa. He sat.

Tel delighted in the way Vared had taken his seat. He had almost stepped onto the cushion before dropping onto his folded legs. It was a boyish maneuver which again brought to his mind his age. "Some relative or another. I have never been able to discover exactly who. I like it because he looks like he has a secret."

"Like you."

"Hm?" Tel lowered himself onto the couch.

"You always look like you have a secret."

"I suppose I always have, for the most part."

"Pure mischief."

"You have thought a lot about my face."

Vared shrugged. "I confess."

He had to look away from him again, overcome by bashfulness. "I have, as well. Thought about yours. Your face." He was not sure if it was Vared, the lack of drink, or a combination, but he had never felt this kind of awkward fear. Desperate, he leapt at honesty. "Why is this so difficult?"

Vared turned his body and scooted closer, near enough for Tel to smell him. "I don't know, exactly. But I'm glad it is. What do you do at night?"

"How do you mean?"

"Your routine. What would you be doing before bed if you were alone?"

"Ah. Well, I would read a bit. I would pray. I would lower my mind for meditation. I would practice with the stagsblood. Then, I would sleep."

"What would you pray?"

"For steadiness. Right thinking. A sense of peace for myself and peace on the world. To be free of the thirst. For my mother and Hod and my father. Lag. At least, I would pray for all of that if I was not feeling selfish and sorry for myself. And you? What do you do before bed?"

"I play sometimes. Often, something I know well. It relaxes me. I might get in bed and write some words I could turn into a song. Not to actually *assemble* a song. I do that in the morning, usually. But I like the way my thinking gets at night. When I'm most tired. Freer. And right before sleeping, I take stock of my day. *Kindness in the mystery.* What kindnesses did I do? What kindnesses were offered me? When and how and why was I unkind? Can I do anything about it tomorrow to repair it?"

"Lovely."

"I didn't do you kindnesses, at first."

"I do not blame you," said Tel. "I did not even remember…"

"Still, partly, I don't want to do you kindnesses. I didn't want to end up here. I don't only mean Feigh. I mean *here*. With you. I resisted. I *know* you have to worry. When someone smiles your way. Why are they smiling? You or your station? And I had to worry the same. Him or his station? But the minute I saw you speak in Omela, I saw the troubles on your face. Even later, when you were sloppy and drunk and embarrassing. Even now, dry, I see the troubles on your face. And I want to take them. From you. Not your station."

Tel shook his head. "You should have no troubles."

"Let me decide what I should have." He moved closer. "What else do you do? At night."

"That is it. I have told you," said Tel.

"That's not it."

Tel felt warmth bloom over his cheekbones. "No?"

"Well…That's not it for me. At night."

"No?"

"No, Tel." He swung a leg around the prince, so he was in his lap, knees on the cushion on either side of him.

"What else?"

"I touch myself."

"You do?" He wanted to look away. The strange Omelan eyes burned but held him.

"Every night. You?"

"Sometimes." Tel felt himself harden.

"Sometimes?"

"Often. Not every night. I am older. I do not…require…as much relief as I used to."

"I require a lot."

"I know." Tel's cock pulsed.

"Every night. I think about you."

249

"No."

"Yes. You? Do you think about me?"

"No," said Tel. "I would never allow myself."

"I want you to." He took Tel's face in his hands.

"Think about you?"

"Touch me."

He let his trembling hand explore the front of Vared's tights. When he gave the fattest part of the hardness a little squeeze, Vared put his mouth on his, in his. One tongue battled for the greater taste of the other. After a time, Vared's right hand moved around to the back of Tel's head. He grabbed the hair there and pulled.

Tel looked up at him and found something animal in the prettiness. Vared pulled harder.

"Yes," Tel mouthed, without sound. He was unable to find his voice—and unsure of the question he had answered.

The prince's chin was tilted up, exposing his neck. Vared lowered his mouth to the bare skin, just shy of contact. He let the heat of his breath tease for a long time. Finally, lips met throat and slowly traced a route up to ear. He whispered, "I know you're hurt still. Tell me to stop now. Once I start—"

"No."

"I won't be able…"

Tel could not discern whether Vared's lips were touching his ear as he whispered. His mouth may have just hovered achingly near. It made him feral. In normal circumstances, he would now take control and find his way on top of his lover. This partner was smaller and weaker, but Tel's paralysis was utter. All his willfulness evaporated under Vared, leaving him free of burden but frightened. It was thrilling, like sitting saddleless upon a robust horse and allowing the beast to go at the strongest gallop.

Vared sat back a bit and pulled his bone-colored shirt off, dropping it behind him. From above the lean tower of his torso, he beamed a wicked grin down at Tel. "We're not the brightest, the pair of us. You too," he said, indicating with a finger that the prince should remove his shirt.

"Not the brightest?"

"We've waited too long for this."

Tel struggled and grimaced as he worked the shirt off himself.

Seeing his wrecked body, Vared gasped. "Tel!" He climbed off him. "Stand up."

He did as he was told. The boy assessed him, eyes lingering over the raw, glossy shoulder.

"Is it—Do you find it unattractive?"

"No. Of course not. I just worry…"

Tel could not stomach being even a few feet from him any longer. It appeared Vared felt the same. They moved to one another simultaneously, colliding in a kiss that was cousin to violence. Tel's hands felt enormous on Vared's slight waist. They bumped into a table, causing the younger man to lose himself to giggles.

Tel froze, mouth open, looking at him. "You are so godsdamned beautiful."

"Prove it." Vared's eyes shone with impish twinkles. He walked backward toward a wall, wriggling his leggings off. Leaning against the stones, his long cock swayed before him.

Praying he was as skilled as he had always believed, Tel stepped to him. He dropped to his knees, unrushed, never breaking eye contact, until he had the smell of him in his nostrils—clean but ancient, wild, and male. That virility was secreted deep, under Vared's delicate appearance and demeanor, and being invited to reach it felt like a privilege. A kind of headiness, a drunkenness, overtook him. He inhaled and closed his eyes. Needing to taste that scent, he wet Vared's balls. His essence spread over his tongue. Tel did not hear himself growl.

He surrounded the base of Vared's twitching cock with his fingers. Tongue lapping at the tip, he coaxed the last rush of blood into the thing. He tortured, doing soft, wet work at the head and the head alone until the Omelan begged wordlessly. Tel removed his lips and tongue, squeezing the hilt as he looked up. Vared returned the look and begged again, louder.

He took all of him in his mouth, opening his throat, holding his nose in the blue hair. Yet again, Vared nudged him with a whimper. Tel was a beast now, frenzied by the smell and taste and sound of him, overwhelmed by the elation of a long wait ended. Gone was everything other than his devotion to this man, to his body, to the meat in his mouth. His drive to please was as pure as it was intense. In this way, it was immaculate, already unlike any coupling he had experienced.

"Tel. I can't. I'll—Not yet."

It felt unnatural to stop, to shatter the singlemindedness, but he would give him anything for which he asked.

"Come up here. I miss you."

The prince stood and looked at him, feeling a slight embarrassment that his hunger had been so exposed.

"Give me your mouth." Tel obeyed, and they kissed again for a while, Vared flicking at his nipples until it was the prince who moaned. The singer purred a laugh. "I've found your weakness."

"I am only weakness right now."

Vared fingered the little Doe pendant around Tel's neck, smiling at it. He formed a fist around the charm. With his knuckles, he pushed against Tel's chest, moving him across the rug until the back of his knees met the bed. He offered no resistance. Before the Omelan, he stood defenseless. Tel's submission was total, baffling, and numinous.

Vared narrowed his eyes. "Naked."

He removed his leggings.

"Bed."

Tel eased himself onto the mattress. Vared stood at the side of the bed, staring. After too long, he said, "Look at you."

"What?"

Vared put one knee, then the other, onto the bed, and crawled unhurriedly toward him. "Mm."

When the younger man reached him, his legs fell open. It had happened without thought. Vared knelt between his black-haired thighs.

The songmaker leapt on him, and they kissed again. Each moved to get as much of his skin in contact with the other's as possible while their mouths merged. Tel threw his legs around Vared's waist. They were cock to cock, grinding and bucking and mashing. The prince leaked, the constant trickle making the friction all the more pleasurable. He came near to climax, but Vared seemed to sense it and eased the pressure.

"What is this?" Vared's fingers ran over a small, raised bump on Tel's right thigh. "It's hard as stone."

"I forget it is there. Lag and I had a fight in the garden at Affas. That is, Lag had a fight. I was a pacifist by then. I simply defended myself. We were adolescents. I was scraped up badly. The grit worked its way into my skin and...stayed."

"The Feighan dirt is a part of you."

"No one has ever noticed."

"I'll soon know everything about your body." Vared reached down between them and squeezed Tel's cock, coaxing from him a little whispered moan and more sticky fluid. Features set by wickedness, he brought two fingers up to the prince's lips. "Taste." Tel welcomed the slick digits into his mouth, savoring arousal and sweat. "Share." Vared replaced his fingers with his tongue. It was their most rapacious kiss yet.

Tel's body rocked with a spasm when Vared's wet fingers landed in the valley between his buttocks. He withdrew the touch, causing the prince to reach for the singer's hand. Tel guided it back to where it had been and encouraged him with a greedy kiss. The teasing was gentle at first, fingertips tracing little orbits around his hole. Vared ended the kiss, moving down Tel's body to take his leaking meat into his mouth. With each stroke of his lips and tongue from tip to base and base to tip, he applied a bit of further pressure to Tel's opening.

Mouth agape, dumb with excitement, he looked down at Vared sucking and teasing, wanting what was coming but unable to see how it could happen. As if in answer, the Omelan flattened himself on his belly and began to open him with his tongue. Tel had never received this type of attention before and lost himself in it. He stopped just short of stroking himself to climax. Not until his arousal came near to cresting did he realize his cock was in his hand at all.

Vared moved away and off the bed. Tel began to form the question, but he realized what he was doing. He could not see him but heard him rummaging through the collection of potions and powders he seldom used. Returning with a pretty little jar of emollient meant for the face, he crawled back over the prince and kissed him. It was deep but sweet. "No one has ever...*taken* you?"

"Never successfully."

Vared kept his face near Tel's. They regarded one another, the prince still unsure of the reality of the moment. The Omelan seemed to be trying to communicate something with his eyes. Tel smiled up at him, trust entire. Smiling back, Vared used some of the cream to stroke him with slow skill.

"Vared?"

"Yes?"

"I would like to stay facing you."

"And I would like to stay facing you." Vared slickened his own cock with the emollient.

The prince saw him touching himself and responded with a sound of need and wonder. Vared pressed his now slippery finger into him with a sting. The unpleasant sensation subsided as he stroked and teased the little spot just inside and upward. He began to draw the finger in and out.

"Good, Tel."

Hearing Vared say his name made him senseless with longing. "More."

He obliged and added a finger. Tel whimpered, moving his head side to side on the mattress. When he stopped his flailing, Vared quickened the pace and increased the force.

Prince Tel was crazed by the invasion. He was crazed *for* it. From his solar plexus, he groaned.

"More?"

He could only manage a nod and accepted a third digit. Vared stroked his hole with growing vigor, but his face conveyed only a determined tenderness.

Soon, Tel worried he might lose consciousness if he did not speak. "More." His own demand surprised him. Vared withdrew the fingers, which both relieved him and left him feeling an odd sadness. The songmaker swept a pillow under him, lifting him a bit off the bed. Tel gripped the sides of Vared's torso.

He aligned himself, cock huge and wet and poised. "Tell me you're mine."

Tel's hands slid down until they held the muscled teardrops of his buttocks. "*Have* been."

Vared began to work his way inside. He pushed the head past the first point of resistance, causing Tel to cry out and unconsciously back away. "Are you…should I stop?"

"It burns."

"I w—"

Tel gritted his teeth. "*No.* If you stop, I'll die. Please. I can do it." His chest heaved. He knew Vared would not hurt him. The only true injury was not having this.

In a slow, single stroke, he buried his cock inside him.

Tel heard himself emit a little extended yowl, a whine from his throat unlike any sound he had ever made. Vared remained still. Tel felt his hole yielding around the monstrous thing. He caught his breath. "More."

As Vared began to fuck, he kissed Tel. The kiss dissolved away in the quickening rhythm, and their faces simply rested together, touching, as they grunted their exertion. By the time Vared was at full speed, Tel had shot his semen between their torsos. He had not even been stroking himself. He had simply clamped his hand around his cock without realizing it.

His climax did not dampen his desire. Vared crashed into and retreated from him over and over again. The pleasure of receiving him—of bucking himself up to match and accept—was beyond orgasm, and he felt his ego shatter and fall away like glass. He was not himself anymore. Thoughts and wants dissolved but for a singular need. Under Vared's sweat and strength, he was pure appetite. That hunger was for this man and his seed.

It was not long before he planted it deep and laid his soaked head on Tel's chest.

"Your hair is my favorite thing on the world," said Tel when his breathing slowed.

"Your ass is my favorite thing." They both snickered. He tasted Tel's tongue again and propped his head on his hand, elbow on the mattress. He eased his cock out of him.

The prince gasped at the sudden emptiness. "I am relieved you enjoyed it."

"You used a contraction."

"Contraction?"

"When I was trying to pry you open."

"Did I?"

"Yes."

"I'm sure I didn't." He stuck his tongue out. "But if I did, it is because that long, fat thing turned me into an animal with no respect for language."

"The first to take a king. Even if I don't care about your station, perhaps that's how I'll be remembered."

"A prince," Tel corrected.

"You're leading an army tomorrow to take the throne, aren't you? Because you and many others believe you're the rightful king of this place?"

"I am." He hoped to conceal the terror this realization elicited. "I do."

"Then I've just been inside a king."

Tel rolled up onto his side and elbow, mirroring Vared. "And I hope you will be again, soon."

"Maybe sooner than you think, your majesty."

"Yet another burden of the crown."

"Good." Vared looked at him directly. "It's really when you sing."

"What is?"

"My favorite thing on the world."

"Please. I am terrible, I am sure."

"No. Your voice is lovely. Especially when you think no one's listening. To hear you being musical…it makes my chest nervous."

Tel leapt on top of Vared and kissed him on the mouth. He tasted the sweat on his collarbone and licking his way up his neck to an ear. He nibbled the lobe, the younger man wriggling beneath him, before sitting up and looking down at him. The Stag had blessed him beyond comprehension. He felt like his ribcage was expanding against the inside of his skin, threatening to break him open.

"You would stay with me, knowing the risk?'

"Yes, Tel."

"I do not want to be apart from you."

"Then don't send me home," said Vared, shrugging.

"I will not allow you to fight. Do not bother to try."

"Very well, your grace."

"Very well."

"You've made me happy."

They kissed again for a long while.

Vared's cock returned to life, so Tel took it in his hand and began to sing. By the end of the first line, the Omelan vibrated beneath him with laughter so loud, Tel thought it might wake the entire valley.

You better mark my warning
I give it to you freely
Take care you don't lose your head
'Cause you'll lose your head
Fooling with th' stagsblood
I'll tell you of my best friend
With a dynast he was smitten
So he gave her his dong
It rotted off before long
From dippin' it in stagsblood

Twenty and Seven

Before opening his eyes, he felt Vared against him, warm. Still, the sight—the reality—of him there, peaceful, was a giddy blessing. Watching him inflate and empty with the comfortable rhythm of sleep, Tel quietly reveled in early light filtered through cobalt twists.

His face was lengthened by the relaxation of rest. Slender but well-defined blue brows sat untroubled above placid, smooth eyelids. His jawline was strong but fleshy. It ran to the little cup of his chin. If he did not know him—and had he not had the entirety of him inside himself just a few hours previous—he might think he was looking at a woman of uncommon allure. That the prettiness concealed such raw, wild power thrilled. The space in Tel's body that Vared had twice filled the night before ached in a way that was strictly pleasant but for the sense of absence.

Bit by careful bit, he eased himself away from him. When he got one leg over the side of the bed, Vared croaked. "No."

Tel rolled back to him, grinning, and kissed him. "But I must arrange things for our little plan."

"You're...not regretful?"

"Who is dense now?" asked Tel.

"And we'll share a tent tonight? And I'll remain with you?"

"Yes, my veery."

"What's that?"

"A bird with a beautiful song." He saw his expression. "If you do not like it, it will only encourage me to call you it more." He kissed him again, this time with wet depth. Pulling away, he carefully regarded his face once

258

more. The ludicrous beauty caused a grin to streak across Tel's face. He launched himself off the bed.

Downstairs, he found the castle and its grounds were kinetic in the mugginess that had not, even in darkness, blown away. Caip barked at some of the greener arrivals, who, seeing Tel approach, showed the tops of their heads.

"General, a moment. please."

"General?" she said once they were out of earshot.

"I have promoted you. Just then. When I said it. Congratulations."

"Quite a promotion."

"Quite a woman. If we have any chance, it will be because of you."

"Some of them are not ready for a march, let alone a fight." Her face was bunched with concern.

"You will guide and shape them on the way. I have no doubt. And soon, if we survive long enough, you will have more. Many of them will be seasoned."

She strode toward a cluster of troops who had been with Tel's personal guard a long time and promoted one of them to chief in much the same way her best friend had just done, leaving the freshly elevated man slack-jawed. "We take this one stage at a time," she said, turning away from them to assess another group. She formed a visor with her hand and shook her head. "First, we need to get to Coltach to join Sitha."

Vared crossed from a stone path to their location, dressed in the short style of shift reserved for special Omelan occasions. When he reached Tel, he kissed him. It had been no mere peck. Seeing this, the women and men of Tel's guard clapped and whistled. Vared buried his face in the prince's chest.

"This is," beamed Caip, "the least surprising surprise in history."

"How soon can we set out?" asked Tel.

"Two hours."

"Good. We are taking a minor detour." He looked into the lively apricot disks of Vared's eyes. "In the meantime, make sure they all know about this." He pulled his father's note from his doublet and handed it to her.

* * *

At the riverbank, dressed in a soldier's leather armor and garb, Tel stood on the spot where his mother and first lover had gone into the water. To one side of him stood Caip, rod straight. To the other, Vared's curls danced on the eddies of a slow, intermittent, thick breeze. Before the triad were about one hundred and fifty soldiers and a small group of camp followers—Ruitha and little Ofya included—fanned over untidy grasses. Some in the ranks muttered and whispered.

Tel walked forward to be among them. "No more of you are leaving?" He weaved through the women and men. "Give me your eyes as I pass you," he said, now beginning to clasp hands and pat backs. "Not one of you is afraid of my blood? I repeat, no reprisal. I have kept a secret from you all for too long. From my people. There is wickedness in secrets. But I am not wicked. Give me your eyes, I said." Having reached the end of a line of troops, he spun on a heel and walked in the opposite direction, cutting this way and that, assessing their sweaty faces. "Leave now if you do not believe a dynast can lead Feigh to peace and justice. Leave now if you believe the old superstitions. I will not blame you, my Feighan sisters and brothers. I think the usefulness of those ideas long ago expired, but I will not blame you. And if you stay, you stay. I will expect your loyalty until the end. You will be loyal to a dynast. You pledge this by keeping your boots on this Feighan dirt, and you pledge it now." He continued to plod through the group, looking into their eyes. The brash squawks of birds in a nearby tree cut through the rush and splutter of the river. "Very well."

He took his place between Vared and Caip, where he slowly removed his boots and clothes. Once nude, he unclasped his mother's chain and secured it around Vared's elegant neck. Tel saw comprehension of the gesture register on Vared's face. A tear streaked over his cheekbone and down his chin.

"No, Tel, I—"

"Of my blood. Of your blood."

The blue head nodded.

Caip blessed Tel with the symbols of the elements—dirt, wind, fire, and rain. Next, she asked the Stag and Doe to witness the coronation and to consecrate it by sending the powers of each of the directions—north, east, south, and west. Tel knew everyone present would think she sounded strong and sure, but he detected the subtle tremulousness in her speech.

She took a few paces forward and looked at the women and men she would command in war. "Who is to love and protect Feigh, the land of the precious Stag and Doe?" Caip asked them.

"Tel of Foghar!" they cried with force. Every hair on Tel's body tingled as he lowered himself to his knees in the dirt that was the last solid bit of the world under the feet of Fyor and Hod.

"Tel of Foghar is to be your king?" she asked.

"Yes!"

"And who, Tel of Foghar, surrenders you to the house of Feigh and places the crown on your head?"

It stung him to remember Lag had chosen his uncle for the honor, but he looked up at the young man next to him, unable to help the thin crack of a smile that broke his solemnity. "Vared of Omela."

"Tel of Foghar is of your blood, of your house, Vared of Omela?"

"He is."

"And you release him from your house to the house of Feigh?"

"Freely, I do."

"And you accept responsibility for the house of Feigh, so long as you are of sound mind, Tel of Foghar?"

"Freely, I do."

From a humble sack, Vared pulled Fyor's diadem of silver leaves. Tel eyed his lover's quaking hand. Vared slipped behind his back, to the north. Walking in a slow circle, north to east to south to west, the Omelan called, "A fruitful reign. A clear reign. A passionate reign. A joyous reign." He completed the circle.

Tel felt him place the little crown on his head.

"Feigh, you have a new king," Vared said.

"Stand, King Tel of Feigh," Caip said.

Knees dirty, Tel rose. The crowd chanted in loudening repetition, "Health and wisdom to King Tel!"

He watched Mor embrace Caip. Seeing them together brought more joy than it ever had. It cut, as well. His closest companion had found someone who thrilled her, at long last, and this day represented a parting for them. *Stag and Doe, keep their separation temporary.*

In the excitement, Vared rushed to grab Tel's clothes. He shoved them into the king's arms. "That's enough. Cover up. You'll drive me crazy. Not to mention these animals." He winked at him.

* * *

Tel asked Caip to march their diminutive army as hard as possible for the rest of the day. They moved southward along a country route chosen for the low risk of encountering any of Lag's troops. Once they made their temporary village and everyone ate, Vared took out his terquin and entertained a good many women and men by singing Omelan children's songs to Ofya. A couple of musicians joined him. Tel stood a few meters away, hypnotized by Vared's talent and charm.

Caip ended his reverie, appearing alongside him, her voice taut and strained. "Walk with me, your majesty?"

They strolled the length of the camp together. About fifty meters beyond the tents stood a copse of trees. They leaned against rough bark, watching the army prepare for sleep. "It is quieter than I would have guessed," said the king.

"Most of them are exhausted because most of them are new."

"Mm," said Tel. "The weeks of marching will have everyone in better condition."

"I have two concerns—"

"Concern is your role, after all," he said, chuckling. He had misjudged her mood.

262

"First, there are rumblings. Rumblings *you* wouldn't hear but that I hear, and my trusted people hear."

"Oh?"

"A very small minority are uneasy about you...and the stagsblood."

"I will not blame them for their uneasiness."

"I'm saying we might lose some. A few. Not many."

He rubbed his face with both hands. "What? A dozen already left. Did I n—I walked among the rest. Goddess curse it! I told them to make their choice at the river."

"You did. And for that reason...Because you were so clear..." She closed her mouth and her eyes.

"What, Caip?"

"You know the punishment for desertion."

He nodded.

"And you have the stomach for this?"

"My brother and my uncle. Gran and Gawash. They all think I have the stomach for nothing. I have made my decision with care. I have weighed these values against those. This virtue against that. Temporary violence for lasting justice. My soul is already marked before the eyes of the Stag. I have decided. I will answer to him one day, in the black. Meanwhile, people would be wise to avoid testing my stomach."

Caip absorbed what he had said for a few beats. "Good."

"If they see me working as hard as them, marching with them, they will trust me. I must believe that."

"Perhaps. But be ready."

"I am," he said, perturbed. "You have another *concern*?"

"Yes. Our goal's to get to Athair by way of Coltach without a fight."

"You are worried we will be intercepted. Or that we will happen upon—"

"You haven't let me finish," said Caip. "We can't control who we happen upon, or if we're ambushed. But is there something we *can* control?"

"What do you mean?"

"Originally, I thought we should just get everyone to the larger force in Athair. The march to Coltach should improve their bodies. And it should improve cohesion. Avoid a fight and focus on the fundamentals until our odds are better. *Slightly* better."

Tel crossed his arms in front of his armored torso. "However?"

"What if we can give them a test? Get them in a fight? Something we can control. I'm not talking about storming Affas by autumn. But something to give a sense of accomplishment. Pride. Faith. It would do a lot of good."

He leaned his head back on the tree. "Then we will get them in a fight."

"How? Where?"

"I know just the opportunity." He pushed himself off the tree. "We can discuss it tomorrow. I am tired."

"Goodnight."

"Thank you." He started walking toward the camp. "And General?"

"Yes?"

"Make sure the banner guard can manage to keep my colors out of the dirt tomorrow. Or assign some others to that duty."

"Yes, your majesty."

He heard the smile in her voice. Returning to the fire, he hoped for a song or two, but the musicians were nowhere to be found. He walked to his tent and noticed his guards bowed more slowly and deeply than before.

He slipped into the flap and smiled. "You are here."

Seated on a chair he had pulled to the center of the tent, Vared said, "Waiting."

The sight of him, hair disheveled, brought a woozy flutter to Tel's skull. His skin heated. He looked down.

"Give me your eyes, Tel."

He obeyed.

"Show me the top of your head."

Tel felt an excited confusion flash across his own face.

Vared's expression was still. "Show me the top of your head."

Tel bowed. His cock was already fat with blood, making the maneuver uncomfortable.

"Good."

Tel knew to keep his eyes on the floor. He was dizzy enough to worry he might tip over.

"Kneel."

Again, Tel obeyed.

"Come to my feet."

Hot and painfully hard, on his knees, he shuffled to Vared's boots.

"Give me your eyes now, Tel. Good. You can't be king always. It isn't good for you. So. I've decided for you. Because you cannot decide. Tell me *thank you*."

"Thank you, Vared." He did not understand why, but the sentiment was genuine.

"Now tell me you're beautiful."

"You are *so* beau—"

"No, Tel. That *you* are beautiful."

"Vared—"

He put a hand under Tel's bearded chin. "You're not king here."

Feeling an alien, embarrassed thrill, he got the words out. "I am beautiful."

"Good. Stay on your knees. Spin around and show me the back of your neck." Tel did as he was told. From his seat, Vared leaned over and kissed, licked, and nibbled his nape. Tel lost track of time and puzzled at how powerfully exciting he found this new attention. He felt drugged and thought he might climax in his breeches. Then, Vared pulled away. "Now, I'm hungry. When I turn around, very soon, I'd better see that hole—*my hole*—on the bed. Understand?"

"Yes." Silently, Tel stripped and mounted the bed, raising Vared's meal in the air.

It was different from the previous night. Vared teased mercilessly with his tongue until Tel was nearly mad with desire. The prince whimpered and groaned and begged senselessly into the pillows and blankets. Vared flipped him over. When he began to push his way in, he demanded Tel's kiss. The taste of his own hole aroused Tel even more, and he opened around the warm hardness of Vared's cock. He pulled him in.

They did not fuck in the usual way. The songmaker did not thrust. Instead, their bodies wrestled, pressing not for leverage or escape but for contact. They were like grappling combatants, except that the object of the match was to get as close as possible to one another. Moaning into one another's wet mouths, they tried to grind themselves into one flexing, sweating physicality. Vared only broke the kiss when he neared climax, saying he wanted to see Tel's face as he emptied into him. Still inside, he coaxed the Tel's seed out with a few determined pumps of his hand.

Several quiet moments passed, their breathing finding evenness in the warmth of the tent. Tel shifted his weight to get out of the bed. "No," Vared said, grabbing his wrist.

"I am just going to get something to clean us—"

"No. I want to...Let's stay like this tonight." He was himself again, asking rather than demanding.

"Whatever you like, veery."

Vared winced. "There it is again."

Tel planted a quick kiss on his lips.

"Don't make me call you *warlock*. Of course, you're king now, outside this tent. You could have me executed."

"I am a king today because you told me I was a king last night. And I could have had you executed when I was just a prince."

"True, warlock."

"I hate it so much." Tel snickered. Then, with mock gravity, he said, "Execution it is."

The singer rolled the little Doe pendant between two fingers. "Thank you. For this. And for letting me stay. You'll keep me safe, and I'll keep the royal hole happy."

"A perfect arrangement." Vared could not have seen him chewing on his bottom lip.

* * *

For the next ten days, Tel and Caip were merciless. When not marching, the army drilled alongside the camps they made. Sleep was minimal. The king and his general allowed for enough to hold insanity and dangerous discontent at bay. Tel did not exempt himself from the grueling routine, pushing himself harder physically than he ever had. He was older than most of them by a stretch but avoided complaint and showed as much vigor as nearly any of them.

Even Vared trained. Like Tel and Caip, he marched alongside his mount all day, then practiced smallsword and grappling as the light leaked out of the evening. After a few nights, the king stopped hounding him about overexertion, finding him immovable. Tel was staggered by his lover's marked improvement.

One dusk, Corporal Bin caught the dynast king staring dumbly at a fierce demonstration of the Omelan's new prowess and said, "Your little flower has feathery petals, but the stem is iron, eh?"

The first moonless night, Tel, Major Dar, Bin, ten seasoned troops, and forty green but promising soldiers departed camp. Caip had expected to be at the head of the operation, but Tel insisted it was important she remain behind to watch over the other hundred or so women and men, including Vared. She put up a milder protest than usual. Whether that had been because she was less willing to argue with a king or because she agreed, Tel did not know.

In the paltry starlight, they staged themselves out of sight but within striking distance of their target. The king made himself invisible. Dar needed to clamp his hand over the mouth of a young man who had, until recent days, tended a bit of dirt in Foghar Valley with his parents. He was so disturbed, he let out a sound that was a hybrid of a gasp and a scream.

Tel shed the magical cloak. "It is still me," he whispered. "Still Tel. I am son of Vith and Fyor. Same man I always have been. The same person who went to Omela to make peace. With your help, I will stop my brother. I will end the warmongering and the rounding up of children and good foreign people and farmers like you who cannot afford his taxes. *We* will stop them from sending your sister and brother north to kill folk because they have red hair and we have black. The same Tel who took his comfort neck-deep in barrels of ale and balls deep in any ass that moved." Several of them stifled laughter. "I would like to sleep in Affas Castle one day soon, so I can look after the land the antlered ones looked after long ago. And I will look after it just the same if I can make lightning with my hands or if I cannot. But I can only sleep in Affas—and I can only look after Feigh—if you all stay with me. And convince others to stay with me. Stagsblood or not, I believe I will add more to the good side of the scale than the bad. Just as my father did. Will you stay with me?"

Mouth still covered by Dar's meaty hand, the man nodded. The king raised the magical cloak again and faded from their sight. "Thank you." He enjoyed a silent chuckle about how unnerving his disembodied voice must be.

His long strides covered the distance in a short time. A careful approach was unnecessary. Even if he disturbed the ground as he moved, the gloom would hide it. The breeze served to disguise any noise of his footfalls. When he arrived at the foot of the timber edifice, the light wind also hampered his ability to listen, which he strained to do.

Hearing and seeing nothing of consequence, he began to circumambulate Fort Gontrahd, where Lag had ordered the dynast children and other undesirables taken. He saw no one staffing defensive positions—the situation the rumor mill had told him to expect and the one for which he had been hoping.

Twenty and Eight

Nearing camp, King Tel grew uneasy. The sun had begun its lazy descent toward the horizon, but the heat of the day had not flagged. While the women and men around him talked of longing for food, the king's stomach felt full of sand.

Soon after they crested a little rise which served to hide the camp from the west, the tents came into view. He realized something was amiss but failed to understand at first precisely what was wrong. To get a better view, he jogged to the front of the group. Dar must have recognized something in his face or body language because he joined him at the tip of the unit. It looked as if a few of the tents had been taken down. Moving a bit closer, Tel saw. They were knocked over.

"Goddess, have they been attacked?" Dar asked.

"Go have Bin hold the prisoners with a few people. If they make a sound, he is to put a blade through their throats." Tel was surprised at the ease with which the violent words had flown from his mouth but ignored it. He continued to try to discern what was happening at the edge of the woods below.

Before he knew it, the major was alongside him again. They led the soldiers unoccupied with prisoners down the slope. Cutting toward the western edge of the encampment, they kept their profiles as low as possible. Their movements were quick but near silent. Sand now filled the king from his bowels to the back of his mouth.

A small, protruding rock ripped free from the soil under Tel's foot, nearly sending him to the ground. As he righted himself, he saw the unmistakable

269

figure of Caip standing among a cluster of soldiers. He surmised from her posture that, while tense, she did not feel any imminent danger. He accelerated down the hill toward her.

When he was close enough to see her face, her troubled expression was plain. Feet peeked out from under two makeshift shrouds near her. He saw nothing because he could not see any blue curls among the tents. The feeling of being packed with sand made it impossible for him to speak as he barreled toward Caip.

She looked down between her feet for a few beats. The panic it caused dislodged something, and Tel heard himself scream, "Where is he?" He was moving too fast to see if she answered, and he heard nothing but his own repeated question. "Where is he?"

Tel ripped one shroud away, then the other. Vared was under neither. He spun in place, trying to find him. Caip was speaking, but he could not understand her. Something in him wanted her to be quiet. Seeing his own tent, he stomped to it and lifted the flap.

Vared was there, sitting at the foot of their pallet, legs crossed at the ankles. His orange eyes were fixed on the floor. Their ascent to meet Tel's was slow.

King Tel cleared his throat. "I thought…"

"I killed one of them." His speech was flat and breathy.

"Are you hurt?"

"No."

Tel had his first deep breath since he and the soldiers had reached the ridge. "What ha—Do you want to talk about it?"

"Not now."

"That is fine."

"I think I'd like to go to sleep. Now that I know you're here."

He had said it like a child. It nearly ripped Tel open. He clamped down on himself and said, "That is fine, too."

"I know you need to…to talk with Caip. But stay with me a while."

"Of course."

"Until I fall asleep." Without undressing, he crawled toward the head of the bed. He curled on his side on top of the blankets.

Tel moved his body against him. After a long, silent vigil, Vared's breaths slowed and evened.

* * *

Standing over a fire near the center of the encampment, not far from Tel's tent, Caip turned a log over with her sword. It popped and hissed. "We lost five. They lost three times as many."

"They had someone stalking us?" asked Tel.

"That's my guess."

"They were so outnumbered," said Tel. "And in the middle of the afternoon? Foolish."

"Who doesn't expect a surprise attack in the night?" She had a brittle laugh. "They followed the stream and came up through the woods. Probably knew you took a third of our force with you."

"Still." He shook his head, lost in the flames.

"It speaks to their lack of respect for us. We were fortunate. Very fortunate. A few of our people were walking down to the water to bathe. They saw them and were able to alert us. Still, they penetrated the camp and killed some good people."

"This is already so awful," said Tel, throat burning.

Her hand came up to shush him. "Don't do that." She gritted her teeth, looked around them, and lowered her volume. "Absolutely not. Tel, this is nothing compared to what's coming. Steady yourself. We did well. We need to move faster, though. We have a handful of prisoners, but a few others ran. I don't think there's a larger force nearby, based on what one of the prisoners told me. They were to join the ones at Fort Gontrahd. You could verify the truth of the prisoner's statement? By touching her and using the stagsblood?"

"Yes. And you are right. About steadying myself. About what is to come. But thinking I had lost Vared. Seeing him that way."

271

"He was remarkable, Tel. The one he got was bigger than him by a lot, too. But he came out of that tent and engaged him without hesitation. Stepped between the oaf and one of our inexperienced boys. Saved his life."

"Of course he did." His mouth was dry.

"He's like you," said Caip. "Has the advantage of speed and agility. I was trying to get to him, but I had to fight my way there. I saw the whole thing. He let the big man overcommit with too much of his weight. Once he was off-balance, Vared danced around him and got him in the side."

Hearing it made him proud. Feeling the pride nauseated him after a moment. *Hypocrite.*

Tel asked, "Did Ofya see any of this?"

"No. Ruitha had her down for a nap."

"Thank the Doe."

"Tell me about Gontrahd."

"It is so foul, Caip. And I had to...experience it, in a way, reading their soldiers with the stagsblood."

"The children?"

He looked at his friend, feeling the rush of tears, tasting salt. "No children. Burned. In the courtyard. One by one, as they arrived. A danger to the kingdom." He laughed humorlessly. "The *empire*..."

"Precious antler—" She swallowed, blinking away her own tears.

The king struggled to find his throat. "They burned adults, too, but not before they *amused themselves* with—"

"Torture?"

He nodded. "We lost no one. I blasted through the postern door with the lightning. Our people tumbled in. It was over before it started. We freed nine people they had locked up. They returned to camp with us. An Andowian, two Omelans, one Kamb, three Hebites. And a pair of *disloyal* Feighans."

"I met them. When you were with Vared," said Caip.

"If you have not already, do not bother," Tel said, "to meet the soldiers we took prisoner. Nasty lot. I read them with the stagsblood. They relished their roles. True believers in this Feighan purity nonsense. Child murderers."

She looked as far away as the moons. "You have your first victory. Victories."

Tel felt as distant. "I burned it to the ground. With the blood. Pure rage."

"They will know."

"An empty fort would have told them as much. And they have already attacked us. They know we are on the move. You need to sleep. Extra watch on tonight?"

"Yes."

He stepped forward and embraced his friend, seeing how it surprised her. "Thank you."

* * *

In an endless sea of grass taller than him, Tel walked under a ceiling of clouds, each stride raising a *shh* to his ears. Otherwise, silence. After a long while, he sensed someone at his side. He stopped and turned to his left. His uncle stood there.

"I know this is a dream. And I know you have sent it to me along a tether with the wind and rain magics. Where are we going?" Tel resumed his walk.

Aith was sweet. "We're going to see your aunt and cousin."

"But—" He decided against reminding him they were gone. *Maybe here, they are not.*

"I've missed them. It's been a long journey back to them, but it's almost over now."

"How much farther?" Tel asked, but Aith was gone.

The sward moved around the king as if stirred by wind, but the air was still as a boulder. The whole enormous stretch of green waved and undulated, tickling Tel through his clothes. Disconcerted by the sensations, he walked faster. Some blades of grass were glossy and sharp, nicking his face and hands as he struggled forward. He could not see Aith. Denser and denser was the growth. He felt like he was swimming through it. All around him, it moved, more animal than plant. His boots no longer touched soil. "Uncle? Uncle? Can you hear me? Where are you?"

All at once, the resistance disappeared, and he tumbled out of the grasses, landing on flat, brown dirt.

"Nephew!"

Tel shook his head, stood, and brushed the debris from his clothes.

"Nephew!"

One hundred or so meters before him was a platform in the middle of the field of chestnut dirt. What looked like a dusting of snow surrounded the feet of the structure. Feeling cold, he looked down. A black Omelan shift had replaced his clothes. His feet were bare, sinewy legs exposed to his upper thighs. He trotted toward the platform.

As he grew closer, he saw that neat, careful stacks of timber formed the platform, which was a bit more than half a man's height. Despite its broader than usual footprint, it was unmistakably a Feighan funereal pile. It sat upon an enormous circle of odd, iridescent chips of white stone.

"Nephew, at last." Aith now wore the rack crown.

"How did you make it here before me?"

Uncle Aith gave a little shrug. "I let myself be pulled down to the Feighan dirt, which brought me."

Tel formed a visor with a hand and spun around, searching. "Where is here, though? Where are we?" Beyond the brown dirt, on all sides, were walls of giant, sage blades under a slate sky.

Aith tilted his head a fraction and offered an empathetic, closed-mouth smile. The expression did not look at home on his face. "I just told you, Tel. Where Feigh brought us."

"I do not understand."

"Would you like to see your aunt and cousin?" asked Aith.

Tel tried to crane his neck to see around him. "Are they here?"

"Yes. This way."

Knowing what he would see, anxiety rippled through Tel.

He was right. Aith's woman and child were there, dead, on the platform.

"Come closer, nephew."

"I do not want to."

"But you will."

They crunched their way across the little pearl chips. The flakes of stone dug into the flesh of Tel's feet. His aunt and cousin were unshrouded. Tel saw the wide crimson yawns where the Omelan sailor's knife had opened their throats. He squeezed his eyes shut, revulsed and angry. "I know this is a dream, Aith. I know you are tethered to me and putting this in my head. What is the point of this? Let me wake up. I will see you very, very soon."

"The point is the funeral, nephew." His tone was saccharine patience.

"Let me wake up."

"Not before we've burned them."

"Then burn them."

"But you will burn them. With the dynasty. Not before our last guest arrives, though." He surveyed the sky. "Ah, here he is." He pointed to a tiny black smudge against the clouds.

The dark spot shot across the ashen heavens, moving closer. The suggestion was of flapping wings followed by easy skates along the current, like a bird in flight.

It *was* a bird.

No. He knew it was much too large to be a bird—a racing blur of blue and green, at least the size of a man. It did not slow as it neared the field of brown. He thought it might crash into him, his uncle, or the platform. Reflex made a shield of his arm. After a beat, he heard the little stones disturbed by an impact much less intense than he anticipated.

"Welcome," Aith said.

Tel lowered his arm to see Vared standing there, folding massive green wings at his sides. "Hello, warlock," he said, affection plain. He smiled. "You look so handsome in Omelan clothes."

"Veery."

"Why am I here?" asked Vared.

"For the funeral." Aith had spoken as if referring to a holiday party. He rubbed his gloved hands together.

"Why isn't he sad, Tel? Whose funeral?"

"Turn, come, Vared. This way." Aith stepped closer to the pile.

Tel scurried to put his body between them. "Say his name again, Uncle, and I will kill you where you stand." He turned to Vared, who was moving closer to the timber. "Fly away, Vared. I will stay for the funeral. You do not know them."

"He knows them." All Aith's sweetness was gone. "He killed them."

"I've never killed anyone," said Vared. "Except that one man. For Tel."

For me.

"Look, songmaker," said Aith. "You killed my family, too. Look!"

"Oh, no. No. I killed them? Tel, did I kill them? Even a child?" Vared began to sob.

"No, veery. Of course not." Tel moved to comfort him.

"Why would I do that, Tel?" Blubbering, Vared pushed his lover away. "Why?"

King Tel moved back in front of him. "You did no such thing. Vared! You do not have to look. Look away."

"I cannot. I cannot look away." He was hysterical. "Why would I do this?"

"Why, indeed?" asked Aith, disgust on his tongue.

Vared's whole body seized with sorrow. Impossibly red eyes threw sheets of tears down his beautiful face. He choked, beating his enormous wings on the dirt. Green feathers danced in the air about him.

"He can't breathe, Tel," his uncle said, like he was stupid.

Tel tried to spin Vared around, but he would not budge. He kept himself between the boy's eyes and the bodies on the wood. Vared knocked him to the ground with a great wing. The tears flowed pink now, tinged with blood.

"He can't breathe, and he can't look away, nephew."

Tel scrambled to his feet, nearly blind with frustration, muttering. "I must stop him from seeing. He cannot breathe. I must stop him from seeing. I must stop h—" He lowered his mind, and the platform caught fire. Still, Vared quaked, skin turning color from the lack of air. The blaze was not fast enough. Tel doubled the flames. He tripled them.

"He cannot breathe. He killed for you," taunted Aith, before turning to dive onto the blazing pyre.

When Aith's body hit the flames, they burned a searing white for a beat and disappeared. Nothing of the lumber or dead remained.

"Vared. It is over. They are gone. You did nothing wrong." The Omelan's condition was unchanged. "Vared, just fly away. Look at me. Just fly away, Vared. You must. Please! Vared!"

"I'm here. I'm here. I'm here, Tel. Don't worry."

It was real now. Tel was awake. Vared's delicate face, molded by concern, hung in the air near his. They were in their tent.

"You've had a dream," said Vared.

"Yes." Tel was breathless.

Vared kissed him. He kissed back, gratefully, mouth lost and desperate and searching—until his thankfulness was swallowed by passion. He pulled him closer. Vared answered by swinging a leg around him, so he was on top. Tel's hands knitted into his soft, blue curls.

Twenty and Nine

King Tel tugged a strap, making sure the pannier was secure on Pony. The stagsblood touch told him the little horse wanted him to be in the saddle for the day.

"Oh, Pony," he said, scratching the animal's neck. "I would like nothing more. I am tired, but I cannot be the spoiled king. I will walk near you again."

"Your majesty?" Tel turned to see a large-eyed boy standing there, a bit too far away for conversation. Seeing the king's face, he stepped forward a couple paces. "Idiot," he spat, after a few beats, clamping his eyes closed. "Not you, your majesty. Me. I forgot." He offered the top of his head.

"You can breathe, soldier. I dropped and buried my leavings behind a tree this morning, same as everyone else in camp. My tent is just bigger and nicer."

"Yes, your majesty." He bowed again.

Tel laughed. "Just one bow and one *your majesty* is enough. What can I do for you?"

The boy shifted his weight, foot to foot. "I wanted to thank you."

"What for?"

"Vared saved my life. I...froze. That big one would've taken my head off."

"Ah. You should be thanking Vared, not me."

"I will," said the boy, "But he's your man, isn't he?"

The heat of embarrassment and the dizziness of desire visited Tel's head. He chuckled. "Again, you would have to ask him. Fortune should smile on me so brightly. I am certainly *his* man."

"They are just like us," said the boy.

"Who?"

"Blue—Sorry. Omelans."

"Yes. Of course."

"My family's for you. Always have been, from what I remember. They loved your father. They were sad when Lag became king. My mother and father wanted the warring to stop. But I think I had some of the old ideas about Omelans. Everyone likes Vared, though. Reminds me of my sister. The way he walks, like he's not touching the ground. The way he pays attention to everything. How he's quiet at first, then very friendly. She sings, too. My sister."

Tel absorbed what he had said with a smile. "Do you think you will have children one day?"

"I would like to convince my girl to cord with me. And start a family."

"When you have that family, remember your king asked you to teach them about how Omelans are. And Hebites and Andowians and the rest. Tell them about Vared."

"I'll do that, majesty. And I promise I won't freeze again."

"I believe that. A man willing to change his mind—to let it grow—is a courageous man."

"Thank you." He offered a little bow again and turned to leave.

"Soldier?" The young man turned. Tel rocked onto the balls of his feet and continued, "If you speak to Vared, you can leave the part out about fortune's smile. I do not wa—"

The boy sputtered before enjoying a loud and hearty laugh. "I think you two are past the need for games like that, don't you?"

When all was ready, at least an hour later than the king had hoped, Caip bellowed the order. The little army moved with crisp neatness, forming up in front of Tel with an efficiency he found heartening.

The breeze was a mercy, making it feel cooler than it had in weeks. Tel's flag opened on that gentle wind. He eyed the pumpkin-colored cross and ring on the green field. Next, he found Vared, looking as straight and serious as any of the rest. He was among the others, with no place of honor, although he would undoubtedly march alongside the king most of the day.

"A little more than a day ago, many of you were completely untested." Vared's expression remained stone. "Now, I stand before women and men who have had their first two tastes of victory. Let that sweet flavor sit on your tongues. Do you taste it?" As one, they shouted in the affirmative. "Good. Now swallow. There are also five of us—good people—now in the black. And children. Many. The children of Gontrahd. Children with the stagsblood. Children like me, your king. They are in the black. Let the bitter flavor of that flood your mouth. Do you taste it?" Again, they answered in unison. "Now swallow. Remember this flavor, so the next time someone to your east or west is in danger, you will do anything to avoid it again. Do not look for the bitterness. We have tasted it together, and that is enough. We will taste it together again. That is enough. Do not seek it out. Do not hold it on your tongue."

He walked among them now, talking directly to them, seeking eye contact, like he had at his riverside coronation. "There are those on the other side with the bitterness of four hundred, eight hundred seasons ago still in their mouths. Those we rescued from the dungeon of Gontrahd can attest to that. Anyone among you who loves bitterness that way may leave now. You are not welcome in the new army of Feigh. Treat our prisoners well—all of you—no matter how foul they have been. If you fail at this, you will answer to me.

"Keep your eyes open and your posture tall, siblings. They know we are on the move. We may not make it to Coltach before we are engaged again. If we remain ready, if we protect the person to our east and the person to our west, if we do not hold the bitterness on our tongues, we have a chance. We will still surprise, even if they know we are coming. Will you do these things for Feigh?" For a third time, they boomed their agreement. "General!"

Caip joined the king and led her army forward.

* * *

Even though Tel and Caip pressed to get to Coltach as soon as possible, the going was slow. They cut through wilderness and unpopulated countryside wherever they could. They did not want to risk conflict along the roads, so they avoided them when able, no matter how difficult.

In the middle of one afternoon, they skirted the grassy boundary of marshland. Maps of the area were useless in their vagueness, and the king and general hoped the wetter ground indicated a lake or pond nearby. They aimed to pitch camp near a good source of fresh water, although the muck seemed to stretch on without end. The heat was nearly unbearable. With pride and appreciation, he noted the only complaining he heard about it was the griping in his own mind.

When they at last found themselves looking at a small body of water, Vared wordlessly knitted his slight form to the front of the sweat-sopped women and men. He removed his boots and rushed toward relief, shedding clothes along the way, hooting all the while. After dunking himself, he called encouragement to the three dozen or so following suit. The pure, playful joy of the moment—conveyed by Vared's mad smile—almost stopped Tel's heart.

With that sweet, dull ache in his chest, he turned to the work of setting up camp. Compared to evenings only a short time ago, the speed and ease of the operation stunned him. Rather than bellowing orders, Caip was free to lower her head and quietly tend to her own tasks.

Later, in the middle of all the tents, Tel stood, twenty and five soldiers sitting in an arc around him, relaying the tale of his first, tense meeting with Prince Belo of Omela. He saw the smudge of wild blue enter his periphery. When he paused for some laughter, the smudge moved closer.

"Your majesty," Vared said. "I'm sorry to interrupt, but I need you for a moment."

The soldiers nudged one another and raised eyebrows, mumbling suggestively.

"No," Vared said, "General Caip and I."

Their puckish mutterings only grew lewder.

Giggling, Tel turned to Vared and said, "I will finish telling them about your prince some other time, then."

Vared led him to the little lake. "They love you already, you know."

"I hope—What is it?"

"Leave them be, sometimes. You're forever trying to be at the center. Either that or hovering. Evaluating. You mustn't hang and flutter about them constantly. You're working them hard. You're working yourself hard. And you're working even harder to be ordinary. To be among them. They'd die for you. You have nothing to prove. Let them relax." He placed a little kiss on Tel's cheekbone. "Be ordinary with me."

Tel nodded, and they walked in silence for a few moments until they reached Caip, who stood watching Ofya. The little one seemed happy to look at her feet while she twisted at the waist, swinging her arms and babbling. Tel came alongside Caip. Vared walked to Ofya.

"Where is Ruitha?" asked the king.

"Sleeping early. We offered to give her a break and wear the child out."

Tel sat and hugged his knees. Caip mirrored him. Together, they watched Vared and the child by the water. Before long, Tel's body was rocking with laughter. The Omelan crawled around the dirt, pretending to be a cat. He rubbed against Ofya's leg, groomed himself, and slinked to and fro in an elegant, feline manner. The pantomime was excellent.

"Kitty, kitty, kitty," Ofya said, Vared meowing and purring at her feet.

"He's good with her," Caip said.

"He is."

"Hm."

"Hm, *what?*" asked Tel.

"Have you ever thought…"

"Listen to you. So domestic, suddenly. Just because you began a great romance behind my back while I was occupied with my drunkenness—"

"Have you?"

"Not really. Again, I was a little busy getting pissed to make much of a father. Not to mention the added complication of finding a willing mother. I am sure if I were going to bring a little one into the world, I would have done so already. You?"

"There's no way to know how much longer I'll remain fertile." Caip pursed her lips for a few beats before shrugging. But, if we get to the other side of this war, I'd happily make a baby with Mor."

"What you do is a form of mothering, is it not? Leading women and men. Inspiring them. Disciplining them."

"I suppose."

"I am sorry," Tel said, "I am just now getting to know you. I was—"

"Busy getting pissed. I know. And I always thought you would get around to it. You're a good man at your core. Even when you were drunk. At your core. And you'd be a good father."

Tel pointed to Vared and Ofya, chuckling. They had reversed roles. While the little girl hissed and stretched and preened, the curly-haired adult scratched her head, saying, "Kitty, kitty, kitty."

* * *

Somehow, Ofya's vigor did not wane for a few hours. When her energy finally gave out, it faded all at once. Her cheek, still fat from babyhood, rested against Vared's chest. He had taken the girl from Caip's arms when the general retired. Singing her a sweet Omelan lullaby, he had walked back and forth over the little beach until she was deeply asleep.

He returned to where Tel sat in thought and whispered over her raven hair, "Take her, warlock. My arms are tired."

Tel's answer was to freeze and widen his hazel eyes.

"Just to walk her back to the tent. Don't tell me you dislike children."

"Of course—" He remembered to whisper. "Of course, I like children. I just do not know how to hold them. I have spent much of my life in debauchery."

Vared rolled his eyes. He did so with such aggression, Tel thought it looked painful. "Take her." He was insistent.

Tel rose and returned an eye roll meant to outdo Vared's, confirming it was a bit painful. "I do not want to hurt her. How do I do it?"

"As soon as she is in your arms, you'll know how to hold her safely. Unless you're a monster." The Omelan songmaker stuck his tongue out at the king of Feigh. Tel felt himself relent. Gingerly, Vared moved the child from his chest and placed her in his lover's stiff arms.

Vared had been right. After a few beats, instinct took over. Tel relaxed, cuddling Ofya to his body. She stirred and leaned away enough to get a good look at his face. He met her appraisal with a smile and said, "It is just me, King Tel."

She looked at him as if she did not care if he was a bear or the antlered god himself. It both humbled and delighted him. "Nn," she said, nuzzling back to his tunic.

"Not so difficult, is it?" Vared whispered.

"No. It is quite nice," Tel whispered back, managing to make it sound grudging and exasperated. With one of his long, delicate hands, the singer stifled a laugh. The lively glimmer in his orange eyes made Tel dizzy.

"You're beautiful right now," Vared said.

Tel began to form a protest but instead said, "Thank you. And thank you for this." He cuddled Ofya and kissed her head.

"Let's get her to her tent and get us to ours."

"Yes," Tel agreed.

When the short walk was over, he did not want to wake the child. He enjoyed holding her and felt terrible about rousing her. "Ofya. Ofya. Your mother misses you." She looked at him. Even in her half-dreaming, half-awake state, her eyes were enormous. They were the darkest brown, but the irises still brimmed with warmth.

"Ruitha," Vared gently called, holding the flap of the tent open.

King Tel lowered the girl to the ground. She rubbed an eye with a plump fist. Looking at her brought upon him a terrible feeling of responsibility. Within a few moments, she had helped him forget all his burdens and made his awareness of them vivid and entire. He looked at Vared and wanted to cry.

"My love, come here with me," the mother said. It was a hoarse song.

Ofya tramped into the tent, like an oddly proportioned, drunk adult.

"Thank you," Ruitha called.

"Sleep well, you two," said Tel.

"Goodnight." Vared allowed the flap to close. When they were a few paces away, he said, "I was so frightened she'd ask about her father. Or uncle. What a thing to grow up with that kind of loss."

"Veery, you grew up with that kind of loss. Two times over. No father and no mother."

"I suppose."

"Are you so unselfish it did not even occur to you?" They had reached their tent, and they both gave the guards standing outside it a quick smile. Tel gestured for Vared to go ahead of him

"I'm not unselfish," the songmaker said, stepping inside. "I just don't think of it a lot. And you lost your mother, too. Did you forget that?"

"I suppose I did. But I was also more or less a man. And I think of it frequently."

"Mm. I know you do." Vared looked up at him and encircled his torso with his ropey arms.

"You are so strong for such a little thing," Tel said, burying his face in the hair on top of Vared's head.

"And you're so sweet for such an oaf." He squeezed Tel. "Did I overstep earlier?"

"When?"

"When I told you to give the soldiers space."

"No, Vared. No. Of course not." He pried the younger man off himself so he could look at him. "On the contrary. You help me remember...I have a different experience of the world than other people. I need that. I need you." He paused, feeling his own features fall.

"What is it?"

"I have made a decision." Vared made a little sound and turned away from him. He felt the air inside the tent change. "Is something wrong? What is wrong? I have not even said—"

"Nothing's wrong. I'm not sure why you're asking." He still did not look at Tel. "You have made a decision. That's what kings do." It was like they had returned to the first weeks they knew one another. Every syllable was jacketed with ice.

"Vared." He could read in the small movements of his lover's shoulders and head an internal struggle.

Vared spun on him. *"I need that. I need you,"* he said, mocking Tel's highborn timbre. "You need me, but you're about to push me onto a ship and send me across an ocean. You need me? But you send me to another continent while you face your biggest test?"

Tel began the slightest move toward him but rethought it. "I would only keep you here out of selfishness. I need you to be safe. I almost lost you, vee—"

"Veery. How many pet names have you given? How many on your long list? How many before me?"

"That is not f—"

"Not fair? You'll be rid of me just like them."

Tel felt slapped.

"Nothing to say?"

"Will you let me sp—"

"You need me." Vared scoffed. "On a different continent."

"Vared, are you trying to make strife between us, so the parting is easier?"

"Don't do that. If you want to read my motives, just touch my skin, *dynast.*"

Tel wanted to scream, but his blood went cool. "Well, *I* do not want strife. I will have a walk and hope you are calmer when I return." He moved toward the flap of the tent.

"You're leaving? Won't I be gone soon enough for you?"

The words froze Tel at the opening of the tent.

Vared continued. "Too many hours to bear between here and the sea?"

Tightness in his chest, hands balled into fists, Tel turned and took a step toward him. "You. Are. Hurting. Me."

"You're hurting *me.* Why must I leave?"

"To keep you safe. We are at war."

"I'm a grown man. I fought and killed a grown man. I saved a life. I can keep myself safe."

"It will not be like that," said Tel. "They will target you. They can get to me by getting to you. You are my weakness."

"Let them try. I'll kill them, too."

Tel moved another step closer. His chest heaved. "Vared. I will be *dead* in two seasons."

Vared's mouth fell opened as he searched the king's face. Closing his eyes tight, he groaned in apparent frustration and rage. It was the lowest tone Tel had ever heard from him. Vared's hand flew to his own neck, where he clawed the skin enough to split it. He stumbled backward. He stumbled again. Trying to ease himself to the floor, he fell half the distance, landing on his backside. "Stop saying. Stop saying. Stop saying that. Stop leaving." With each syllable, he had less breath. "Shut up, Tel. Stop saying that." He looked about himself, searching. "I ca—breathe. Breathe." He stuttered little gasps and gulps. "Tel. Tel. H...Tel, help." He looked around again, still fighting for air, still drowning. His hands fumbled on the floor beside his legs as if trying to find something he could not see.

Tel's alarmed trance shattered. He moved to sit behind Vared on the floor. The boy was between his legs. "I am here. I am here. Do you feel me?"

Vared's nod was desperate.

"You trust me?"

"Yhh—" It was a horrible, strained sound.

"You are breathing here." Tel placed a palm flat against the very top of Vared's chest, near his throat. He patted the bones there. "Here," he repeated, applying a little pressure. In front of him, Vared still sputtered and rocked. "I need you to breathe here, veery." He slid the palm down, so it rested on his belly. "Here. Just breathe here. Not up there. Down here. I will sing to you, and you try to move my hand. Just listen to my voice and breathe. Listen and move my hand."

The only song he could think of was the one his mother loved so—the one she sang right before she slipped into the river. He sang it to Vared—barely louder than a whisper—and sang it a second and a third and a fourth time. Between lines, he stroked his lover's stomach and encouraged him to breathe.

Midway through the fifth rendition, Tel realized the Omelan's respiration was slow, deep, and even. When he finished, Vared said, "Once more." After the sixth time through, he said, "I wish you sang more."

Tel said, "I am embarrassed, singing to you."

"I know. But you sing well."

"Thank you."

"Come with me to Omela. Run."

"You know I cannot. Ofya is just one of many."

"Yes," said Vared. "Yes. I know you can't."

"There is nothing I want more than to be near you, Vared. Not a castle. Not a throne. Nothing."

"I know that, too." He turned his damp face to Tel. "You don't really think it's hopeless?"

"No. Not hopeless. There is magic in the world. I do not mean the things I can do with the blood. True magic. Deeper magic. Ofya's innocence. Me not wanting to drink anymore. Meeting you."

They sat in silence for a long while, holding one another, before they moved to the bed to sleep.

Thirty

Sitha's delicate appearance surprised King Tel. Long and bony, it looked like a moderate gale could carry her away to Andow. Even as she strode to him, waves of black remained obediently tucked behind her ears, revealing the angular strokes of her face.

She offered the top of her head. "Your royal majesty, I am Rightcolonel Sitha. I offer my loyalty and the loyalty of seven hundred and forty and one Feighans, if you will accept."

Tel fought off an impulse to hug her, an urge he would not have felt four seasons prior. He allowed himself to smile at her. "I will, Sitha. You have, in less than a minute, quadrupled the size of my army."

"You will want to see the ships, I imagine. The *Crunadam* and a dozen from Omela."

"A dozen? She has come through. More than I had hoped." Tel turned to Vared. "Have I told you before how much I adore that queen of yours?"

"You have mentioned it, yes." Vared smirked.

"The songmaker," said Sitha, smiling as she assessed him.

Tel nodded. "This is Ambassador Vared of Omela, songmaker and—"

"I'm the king's man."

Tel felt a burst of pride he would have found embarrassing to admit.

"The rumors are true, then." Sitha narrowed her eyes for a few beats. "Yes. You're good together. Big and small. Blue and black. Young and—"

"Thank you, Sitha. It's a pleasure to meet you," Vared interjected, stepping forward to take her hand in his and lead her a few paces away. "You're from this area? Lovely." He turned back to Tel and winked.

With her usual crisp professionalism, Caip merged the two forces, then marched them through the town on the main thoroughfare. The everyday activity of the citizenry ground to a halt. People stepped into the afternoon heat, lining the road to greet the king. Tel's elbow grew sore from all the waving, but his spirits were high. He knew some people loyal to Lag must live in Coltach, but the enthusiasm of the reception felt genuine. Most of these Feighans—no doubt because of their affection for Vith—placed their hopes in Tel. He prayed to the Stag and Doe they did not have to pay a price for their faith.

"What's that?" Caip strained her eyes to see ahead of them. "Who are they?"

Tel could make out nothing but smudges in front of them on the broad public square.

"Goddesses and gods," she said, awe in her voice. "Tel," she whispered.

Step by step, the picture sharpened. He could not believe it, even when it was clear to his eyes. Hundreds of people stood on the square, dressed in black. A blue head crowned each.

"You Feighan bastard!" a familiar voice barked.

"You Omelan prick!" he yelled back.

"I have brought one thousand friends."

Tel jogged toward the square as one of the Omelans broke from the group and moved toward him. They met in the middle. "Belo," Tel said, embracing him.

Clearly surprised by the hug, Prince Belo of Omela said, "Good to see you, my friend."

"Not nearly as good as it is for me to see you."

* * *

At a cockeyed table in a dim corner of Coltach's finest inn, Prince Belo and King Tel enjoyed a private afternoon meal of fishes, pearlgrowers, sea plants, and starchroot. The Omelan ate like he was famished but retained his manners.

"My mother regrets she was not able to send more. We cannot risk it with Gawash to our north. He has moved many thousands to near the border. As have we."

"A thousand good people is more than I asked for," said Tel. "We will be more Omelan than Feighan until we reach Athair." It amused him. "I wrote to ask to borrow the ships and buy the equipment. I did not ask for people."

"Equipment. We have more than swords and armor. Wait until you see." Belo raised a blue eyebrow.

"And I certainly did not guess she would send you to deliver them personally."

The prince washed some food down with a gulp of ale. "This is not a delivery, your majesty."

Now Tel raised a brow. "What do you mean?"

"I will be staying. If you will have me. You are a friend to Omela. The queendom is a friend to you and to Feigh. The Feigh of King Vith and of King Tel. I will fight for you. Please do not talk to me about it being an uphill struggle. Or of it being a risk to the queendom. We know the situation and have decided. If your brother is not stopped, he and Gawash will be making war with us sooner or later. Either have me or do not."

Tel sat back in his chair and swallowed hard with his burning throat. "Of course, Belo. Of course."

"Good. You look well. Not drinking agrees with you." He pushed his plate forward and relaxed into his seat, mirroring Tel.

"Thank you. You are sickening in your handsomeness, as ever." He chuckled. "It is shocking how much better I feel without it."

"It shows," said Belo, grinning. "And you eat now. Extraordinary. But there is something else, no?"

"Something else?"

Belo nodded and appraised his friend through narrowed eyes. "Our songmaker."

Tel attempted to maintain a neutral facial expression, but it cracked and fell away, revealing an embarrassed smile. "I…It is that obvious?"

"To see the two of you. It is clear."

"Yet another kindness your mother has done me. He is…" Tel found it difficult to qualify what he thought and felt. He shrugged, feeling foolish but not uncomfortable.

Belo's face exploded into an expression of delight and, he pounded the table. "Nothing is impossible. Tel of Feigh dry and holding a man for longer than a night. Truly I can say I have seen everything on the world."

"And how is Doma? The children?"

"Well and healthy. And more than I deserve, as always. I see them too little. After this campaign, it will be time to domesticate myself. To be a father and husband and to prepare to be king."

"Preparation is impossible," Tel said. He explained how he believed Aith had manipulated his dreams—and his brother—with the stagsblood. When he disclosed he, too, was a dynast, he did not even check for onlookers or eavesdroppers. His lifelong secret dwelled in the light now. He made a little fire with one hand, a bit of lightning with the other.

The Omelan prince's reaction appeared to straddle fright and wonder, as Tel had expected. After a few moments, Belo said, "A weapon on your own."

"But we must not forget, they have at least one dynast, too."

"Come with me. To the shore outside the city." Belo chuckled. "I will show you something they do not have."

They rode out of town until they encountered a small detachment of Belo's people. Beyond the soldiers, in the road, a dozen curious objects were arrayed. Little two-wheeled carts sat in a line. On each cart was a metal tube. Belo followed Tel as he walked to the alien things. The tubes were broader on one end than the other. Slots were cut into the top of the wider halves, which terminated in a closed bulb shape. The skinnier side of each tube was open at the end.

"We call them *findos*."

"Hm." Tel could make nothing of them.

"You have seen our skycolors. They led to the findos. These do not loose decoration, though. Would you like to see?" Tel nodded, uncertain. "We shall want to back up a good deal. Everyone, his majesty is ready."

The two royals strode to the border of the road opposite the dunes, stepping through unfriendly shrubs and grasses. All the soldiers but one put distance between themselves and the findos, bending their knees and squatting low to the ground. The one still in the road carried a slender pole about the length of Tel's arm. At its end was a lighted slowmatch.

"Watch the piles there." Belo pointed to collections of wooden items stacked crudely into tall mounds beyond the grasses. The refuse was nearly one hundred meters away, Tel guessed.

"Now," ordered Belo.

The soldier touched the slowmatch to each of the twelve little vents before scurrying away. She squatted into a crouch near some of her comrades.

"Your ears." Belo shielded his with his hands.

Tel did the same. Still, he heard the world itself crack apart a dozen times, like thunder had clapped inside his own head. He felt the blasts in the depths of his chest just as much as he heard them. The piles down near the waves shattered. Wooden shards launched high into the air. He looked at the Omelan prince, who smirked. "I might have pissed myself."

Belo chortled. "Now you know the value of the findos," he said. "We are making them fast as we can. We thought you might find these useful."

Possibilities raced through Tel's mind. "What happens if someone is…"

"It's hard to imagine they would feel any pain. I will show you how they work. It is like magic."

* * *

Tel and Vared faced one another in the pallet bed. The sky had not begun to lighten. Tel had only been able to cross half the distance from wakefulness to sleep, spending the night either lost in foggy thoughts or listening to his lover breathing. Vared had not slept much, either.

Their union the night before was gentle and unrushed but intense. Both were tearful—a fact neither acknowledged. When his tongue tasted the salt from Vared's eyes, Tel became preoccupied with what he might have done to prevent this temporary parting. Perhaps he could have long ago been more vigilant, more suspicious, as Caip had always urged. Maybe if he had stopped drinking sooner or had reached out to his brother more, something would have changed. Could he have worked harder and faster on the peace negotiations? Might the treaty have been signed four or six or eight seasons earlier? Would he have even met the songmaker in that case?

Tel wanted to ask Vared these questions, knowing he would comfort him, but could not bring himself to speak. He would not let him see his self-pity or burden him with useless thoughts. Instead, he asked, "Would you like to watch the sun come up?"

"Yes."

All but Vared's terquin and one outfit had been stowed on the ship the previous afternoon. He and the king dressed quietly, eyes on one another in the gloom.

Stepping out of the tent, Tel told one of his guards that he and Vared would be walking alone. He instructed her to make certain Ruitha and Ofya were brought to the wharf on time. They would stay in Omela for the duration of the war. Belo had written a note for them to give to his mother. They would be well looked after. Belo had offered passage to the foreigners and Feighans Tel had liberated from the dungeons of Fort Gontrahd, but they all chose to stay and join the fight.

A few minutes outside of the encampment, Tel asked, "Did you enjoy seeing some Omelan faces?"

"I did."

"And you met your crown prince. Were you impressed?"

"I've met his mother. And I'm her favorite. How impressed could I be?" He giggled.

"Do you find him handsome?"

"A prince? I only find kings handsome now." He cupped Tel's chin with a hand and kissed him. "Black-haired kings."

Tel adjusted the strap on the terquin case, which he insisted on carrying. "I can feel the autumn in the air this morning."

"It's not autumn yet, savage. All this time with me, and you haven't learned to mark the seasons correctly?" Vared brushed the king's fingers with his own. They clasped hands as they ambled down the empty road.

"I am willing," Tel said, giving a little squeeze, "to alternate years."

"I like that."

"I hope I can see Laich's Omelan drama one day. Belo says it is quite a tribute to your history and culture."

"I'll tell him that," said Vared.

"Sounds like he really loves the place."

"Seems one cannot spend much time in Omela without becoming a bit Omelan. I've found the same to be true of Feigh."

They did not speak for a long time but continued to hold hands, their legs dangling over the spray. They looked at one another more than they watched the sun as it breached the horizon to will itself skyward.

The town was coming to life around them, a sign Vared would be gone soon. Tel silently cursed his people, ordering them back to bed, demanding they stop the day. As unfair as it felt to have to see him leave—and to not know for how long—he knew he did not deserve to question the justice of the circumstance. Looking at him closely, he was sure of his own unbelievable and unmerited good fortune. That certainty was an odd pressure in his throat, chest, and gut. After all he had done and all he had failed to do, he still found Vared in his path. That the songmaker had noticed him and given him affection was kindness beyond measure.

Tel's composure broke apart and fell away. He saw through his tears the similar state of his man. He let go of Vared's hand for the first time in two hours. He took the Omelan's face and pulled him to his mouth, kissing him long enough and deeply enough to taste him. When his cock stirred, he withdrew. He wanted the contact for its sweetness, not its heat.

Vared fished Fyor's necklace from his clothes. "You're sure I may keep this?"

"Yes. You are Vared of Foghar now. Vared of my blood. Vared, my king." He saw that his words had moved and astonished the boy. He cleared his raspy throat, fighting through breathlessness brought on by crying. It

295

threatened to grow into sobbing. "I have so much to say but...to try...It would be fruitless. You cannot know..."

"But I *do*," Vared struggled to whisper.

"Oh?"

"Yes."

"I believe you." Tel vibrated, restless. "I do not think I can—"

"Me, neither," Vared said. "Let's say goodbye."

They stood, Vared swinging the terquin case Tel had chosen for him onto his back. Their embrace was short and bordering on violent. They shook in one another's arms.

When the hug broke, Vared showed the fire of his eyes to the king. "Get to your brother and uncle and do what needs to be done. Soon."

Tel realized he was nodding. "You can be certain I will."

Vared made an elegant turn, of course. Tel could not stand to watch the distance between them growing, so he turned, too. Head down, he began the walk back to camp. The day warmed slower than it had in months.

Thirty and One

The king, his general, the crown prince of Omela, and the newly promoted Rightmajor Dar sat in Tel's tent. On the makeshift Table was their best map of Feigh.

"Thinking about this in terms of a larger strategy at this stage is pointless," Caip said.

"Pointless," King Tel dully echoed.

"We mustn't get ahead of ourselves," she continued.

"We will have no plan," said Tel, almost to himself.

"I would not say th—"

"We are at war," said Tel. "Strategy is pointless?"

Dar cut in. "What Caip's saying, I think—"

Tel's eyes were fixed on Caip's face. "You do not think we can win."

Caip flattened her palms on the map. "That isn't what I said, and it's not what I believe. Even if we get as many soldiers as we dare hope to join us in Athair, your brother still has ten times as many across Feigh. Over fifty thousand. And half that number again fighting to the north. We are lucky in that respect because the ships being occupied with an island war may just let us sneak into Athair by sea. *May.*"

"If your intelligence is to be believed," Belo said, "near ten thousand of those fifty thousand lay siege to Athair. Just in that place, our first test, they will have us bested two to one." He stabbed his finger at the port city on the map and took Tel's eyes. "They have piled all those thousands down there with a stalemate to the north and you and your claim to the throne unchecked. They are not going to sit outside that city through winter."

Caip nodded. "We must focus on the first stage. And that's ending the siege. We don't have the luxury of tens of thousands of troops to plan with. We have a few thousand in Athair, but they're trapped. We have to see—if we can win at Athair—how many of us survive before we can think of what's next. I want total focus on breaking the siege."

Dar appeared to have been struck by realization, his face at once a lighted lamp. "And it's not just about the numbers."

"Go on," said Caip.

He looked at Tel, his lips crooked into a slight smirk. "The people loathe your brother. The further south we go, the truer this is. He's treated the southern half of the country like an unwelcome houseguest. Your mother was loved, so it galls them more. And they love you, too. You look like her. And they know you gave years of hard work to this kingdom. But…"

"Honesty," said Tel.

"But those years were given for peace. The peacemaker prince. Most Feighans appreciate that work, and they'd be proud to have you as king. But they also know Lag has a real army and you don't. Not to speak of. The people always know the lay of the land. And they think, *Am I going to risk my head because I hope the* peacemaker prince *and his few thousand are going to defeat the huge Feighan army?* They'll sit it out. Keep themselves and their families safe. But if you can give them reason to answer that question differently—"

"A victory. A victory when you should lose. When you should be crushed," said Belo.

"Yes. Exactly." Dar leaned over Table. "Kick their asses at Athair, send 'em running. Give people reason to support you openly. To join the fight. You may even attract some of Lag's ranks to your side."

"Many of them were conscripted. The others are doing a job. Most of those, if they have any loyalty, it is more to your kingdom than to Lag," said Belo.

Caip's expression was grave, her brown eyes on the map. "It's the only way we win. By attracting more soldiers. And a decisive win in the first battle is the best way to do that."

"And if we lose at Athair, it is done." Tel searched Dar's face.

"Yes."

When the king looked at him, Belo said, "Yes."

By the time Tel's eyes found Caip, she was nodding. He said, "Then, all my silver on this bet."

Belo put a hand on Tel's shoulder. "And ours."

Tel narrowed his eyes and let his tongue play between his teeth and cheek. "Wait. Wait." He saw he had their attention. "My uncle and brother know I have support concentrated in Athair. They rebelled in my name. They fly my colors. Lag and Aith know what we are about to do because it is simply…"

"Our only option," said Dar.

"Yes, to counterattack. To break the siege. To arrive by sea and consolidate my force. Increase our numbers." He stood, bent over the table, pulling the map toward himself as his fingers walked over it. His index finger tapped a spot. "What do you know about this town? About… Thasach?"

"Nothing," said Dar.

Caip turned her palms up.

"Dar, find someone who does. Quietly. Bring them here."

* * *

The king and his slapdash Table considered and debated for a few hours. In the afternoon, Tel started at one end of their village of tents and made his way to the other. He met all the new soldiers he could, shaking hands, clapping backs, and expressing his gratitude. Of those who did not know him yet, most were nervous. Their eyes seemed to register awe. Tel wondered whether they were struck with his stagsblood or his station.

"Relax," he told some of them, "I am yet only king of this camp and you sad, dirty piles of leavings." It won him laughter and apparent approval.

Remembering Vared's admonishment, he avoided loitering. He simply introduced himself and said a few words before moving on. The Omelan contingent was larger than the Feighan, and he was pleased by the absence of tension. He did not detect resentment from the black-haired soldiers about fighting alongside former enemies, nor from the blue-haired about being brought across the ocean to risk their lives for a foreign king.

His visits lasted into the night. Craning his neck to look at the stars, he realized how much his feet ached. His stomach protested, for he had not eaten all day. He shuffled to the largest structure on the site, his tent.

"Antlered god," he swore, seeing Caip sitting inside. "You startled me."

"Why are you not in bed? We sail early."

"I could ask you the same."

"I'm worried about my friend," said Caip. "Come. Sit. There's some food."

Wide-eyed, he thought he could kiss her, so he did, on the forehead. "It is as if you have heard my prayer. Remind me to give you a castle or estate or—"

"I would prefer a ship, honestly."

"Done." He allowed himself to fall into the chair. Before him was a plate of smoked fish and boiled vegetables.

"You did a good thing today. Meeting them." She flicked her chin at the tent's flap.

"They are—" He felt tears coming on, which irritated him. Using that frustration, he choked the sentiment back. "Impressive. I thought it might be helpful. To let them know me." He attacked the plate of food.

She smirked as she watched him. After a couple of mouthfuls, she leaned toward him. "But that's not all."

Tel took another bite. "Mm?"

"It was helpful to you, not only because your soldiers came to know you."

Tel stood and moved to a little table next to his bed, on which a pitcher of water sat. He poured a glass and took a drink. "How else was it helpful?"

"You've kept busy since the moment you returned from the wharf this morning. Now you're exhausted. You haven't had a chance to be with your thoughts. Since he left."

He returned to his chair and popped a small, pale starchroot into his mouth. He chewed, savoring the creaminess. After swallowing, he took another swig of water. "We will all be busy now. Not much time to be with our thoughts. We are at war." He had a bite of fish.

Caip tilted her head. "I know it feels good to be busy. But as you say, it's only going to get busier. And maybe it isn't beneficial. Maybe being with your thoughts is what will be most helpful."

Tel waved his hand. Mouth partly full, he said, "Pining for him—dwelling on it—is not going to end the war any faster. It is not going to get him back here. If he even wants to return after gods know how many seasons. Assuming we win. He is young. Young people are fickle. He will only be alone for so long. Someone else will take his eyes."

Caip crossed her arms in front of her body. "You're awful, sometimes."

He eyed her face, seeing how solemn she was. "What?"

"Vared's my friend. Don't talk about him like he's some fool you dipped your prick in."

"That is not what I said. Or meant."

She glared. "Did he say he would come back to you? Did he say he was your man?"

"Yes."

"Has he ever given you cause to doubt those things? Or anything he said?"

"No."

"Then don't spit on his word. You're trying to find ways to avoid grief. This is...what you *do*. Used to be with drink. Now you do it by trying to make what you have with him...less important." She uncrossed her arms and sighed, her face softening. "Don't jump over the sadness. It'll prowl after you and pounce at the wrong time. On the battlefield, perhaps."

"Just a few weeks. That is all we had. A few weeks of...honesty about wanting to be *near* one another. For one hundred seasons, I had not cared to have that with anyone. Then, there he was, in Omela. Then, I had to bring him here with his terquin and his hair and his talent and his haughty attitude—*the haughtiest orphan who ever lived*—and his godsdamned eyes. And behind all of it, this endless well of kindness and selflessness and wonder. People say I am lucky to have my mother's face. I am even luckier he has her heart."

"He's brought out your parents in you. Woken up their blood in your veins," said Caip. "You're likable again. I've always loved you. But there have been some seasons it's been difficult to like you."

He made a strangled sound of agreement before being carried away by laughter. It proved contagious. Soon they were both giggling.

Tel said, "I never would have guessed what the last four seasons have brought me. Terrible and pleasing, both. Never, ever." He finished his water. "How do you…cope with being away from Mor?"

"I make sure he's in my prayers. Make sure I think of him often. I don't want to avoid thoughts of him. I want him near the front of my mind."

"But is that not painful?"

"Yes," said Caip.

"And…that is *good*?"

She grew animated, throwing her hands in the air. "Where did you get the idea that life was supposed to be free of pain?"

"I—"

"This is how you fell in love with the drink. It's strange and self-centered—to think life's never going to assault you. So, when it did, you numbed yourself. And over time, you needed to deaden even the little hurts."

He remembered Craid.

Caip continued, "I can be in pain without suffering. Without letting it kill me. When you decided to let Vared know how you felt about him, did you know there was risk involved?"

"That I could be hurt? Of course. It was terrifying. Is terrifying."

"Not that you *could*. That you *would*. Vared will hurt you. He's just a man. You'll hurt him because you're just a man. And life could take him from you. It will take one of you from the other, even if you're together until the end. One of you will leave the other first. To the black."

Tel frowned but said with good humor, "You are not much of a best friend."

"Would you prefer you hadn't met hi—"

"No. Doe and Stag. Of course not."

"And I feel the same way about Mor. I'll miss him. I'll *pursue* the missing. There's happiness even in the missing—in the pain of it. Because he's Mor." Her eyes glistened in the lamplight.

"We are so old."

"Ancient," she agreed.

"Because he is Vared." He gulped.

"We need them. In the front of our minds. The thought of getting to them…may get us to them."

After a long silence, Tel let out a breath. He stood and stretched, twisting his upper body until his spine popped. Looking at the bed, he made a little sound of dread. "May I ask you a favor? Please say no if you like. But remember," he said, turning to cock his head at her, "I am your king."

"Yes. I will sleep here with you."

"Thank you."

Under her breath, she said, "At least now you don't reek of ale."

The king was breathless with laughter. "I deserve that."

"No argument from me."

"I think I have just enough energy," Tel said, "to try it."

"The tether? This ability…is new?"

"My powers are different since I stopped getting pissed."

"But you could always read people before if you touched them?"

"I never used the dynasty on you, Caip."

"Good thing for you, eh?" She whacked his shoulder with the back of her hand.

"I suppose so." He snickered. "I am glad you will be with me. On the *Crunadam*. Not only because we need to practice tethering."

"I'm glad, too. Besides, you need protection. Especially since you won't have a findo on your ship."

He lowered his mind, pulling from nothingness a spherical tangle of hissing, humming lightning. It hung about a half-meter in front of his sternum. "I am my own findo."

"You've made your point." The tent dimmed as the lightning disappeared.

"Now, how do we practice?"

Thirty and Two

An hour after sundown, King Tel and Corporal Bin ascended a tower on Athair's city wall.

"Antlered ones." Bin looked down at the besiegers through a crenel. "There are a lot of 'em."

"This is the fourth night in a row you have made the same remark," said Tel.

"No less true tonight than it was the first." Bin spat over the parapet.

"You cannot hit them from here."

"Maybe the wind'll take some to a face or two."

"We can hope," said Tel, grinning.

"Those trebuchets are frightening. Not sure how long this old wall would stand."

"With luck, we will not need to find out."

"I never asked why you wanted me in your boat. I'm not part of your guard."

Tel chuckled. "Firstly, you are a good fighter with a keen mind. Secondly, I like you."

"An' my mother said I'd never amount to anything. Liked by a reformed drunk of a king."

"I am not only a reformed drunk," said Tel. "Please do not forget I used to toss my seed at anything that moved."

"Why? I'm sure most of *them* did by the next evening."

"I see now the affection between us goes only in one direction," Tel replied with mock sadness.

"You think it'll be tonight?"

Tel squinted. "I know they have not been in any real danger. At least, I am almost sure. I do not let myself fumble around in her head for very long. It does not feel right. All I know for certain is they have not been in position yet."

"Should've been."

"Something has delayed them." Tel closed his eyes and started to bring his mind low.

"It's spooky. The look that comes over you."

"Quiet." Tel moved his breaths from his chest to his belly. As he did, his own thoughts slowed and thinned, like clouds giving way to fair sky at the fringes of a storm. His awareness spread, fingering out from him—in every direction but no direction at all. Free of his own internal noise, he could listen to the din of thoughts and feelings of others, pushing aside the ever-present, repeating worries and longings of the soldiers inside and outside the walls. *He'll never stay faithful...we are trapped here...disloyal scum... don't want to die...can't wait to redden my blade...I'm missing the harvest...*

He was lost in an ocean of chatter, more letting the current take him than swimming. Allowing the stagsblood to lead him was a challenge. Every instinct cried out for him to flail and search the dark and endless depths. Like seaweed brushing a night diver's skin, secrets tickled and startled him from the ink. *I need her...the baby should be talking by now...thirsty...Doe, please forgive me...*

Tel wondered how long he had been searching, trying to find something familiar onto which he could grab. It was challenging to let go of the question. He thought of Bin watching him, which caused his mind to lift. He found his breath and wrestled himself downward, letting the tide retake him. Time passed, his fatigue building.

Mor.

He thought he imagined it, so he was carried past.

Mor.

It was her. Hearing it again, he reached out.

Mor.

He had her. Gently, he beckoned her mind to come to him along the stagsblood tether. His search was careful. She was tired and needed to eat. Some soldier or other had irritated her earlier in the day with his laziness. Aith frightened her. She missed Vared. She loved Mor. Tel's best friend loved her man so much. Most importantly, they were ready. Tel opened his eyes.

"Anything?" asked Bin.

"You will want to stand back for this."

"I'm not sure why you have to do it."

"She cannot consistently hear me along the tether. It is my failing, not hers."

"They're in position?"

"Did you think I was kidding about standing back?"

The muscled, scar-covered soldier opened his mouth as if to speak, then closed it. After two rearward paces, he looked at Tel before taking two additional, larger steps toward the battlement.

Tel pushed his mind to return to a meditative state, gathering his strength. A bit of nervousness gnawed at the edges of his consciousness, slowing his progress. He became worried about the worry itself—about pushing it away—which only stoked it. Soon, nervousness swelled to fear.

At Coltach, he had said he could do what he was about to attempt as if he were talking about walking from one end of a room to the other. Now, he doubted. Would it kill him? Dread kept him from lowering his mind. He was tethered to trepidation as he had been tethered to Caip moments before.

"Majesty?"

"Sh." He needed to leap past the fear, to strain its leash until it snapped. He thought of Vared. His mind anchored to the memory of the orange eyes, the sweet way they had regarded him. He repeated his pet name for the Omelan silently. He felt a swell of amusement about how irksome Vared had found it. After a moment, all other thought sloughed away. Mind blank and low, he was soon speaking his mantra aloud. "Veery. Veery. Veery. Veery. Veery."

Tel raised his right arm above his head, turning the palm to the stars and gauzy strips of cloud. As his fingers spread, his chanting quieted to a whisper. His head snapped back. An eddy of salted wind curled around him. He felt the dust stirring about his legs. He stopped chanting.

An argent bolt of lightning screamed from his hand into the night above Athair, as brilliant as any summer squall's. Unlike the fulmination of an ordinary storm, however, it did not abate in less time than it took to blink. The silver tower of energy persisted. For five beats, it threw daylight and shadow over the city and its besiegers. When it finally stopped, the king was left nauseated. His hair and back were sopped.

"I don't think she could have missed that," said Bin.

Tel waved him over. "I have to rest. Can you help me?"

Deflated, he leaned on Bin until he was in the carriage at the base of the wall. As the horses pulled them through the heart of the city to the large home of Des's family, he collapsed into sleep. When they arrived, Bin supported him again as he walked from the carriage to his bed. Tel crawled across the covers in his leather armor and thin cloak. He did not even remove his boots.

Bin said, "Are you going to be—"

"Just need sleep. Thank you," muttered Tel. "Possible this creates a reaction outside the walls. Rouse me, if necessary."

"Of course."

"Bring a bucket of cold water."

Bin chuckled in the dim room. "Need anything else?"

"No."

"If I didn't know you, I'd be petrified of you."

"Good."

* * *

Mid-afternoon the next day, Tel scaled the tower again. It occurred to him he had not looked upon the army outside in the light. They appeared

308

even more formidable. It was a glorious day, warm but dry. If not for the continuous sea breeze, it would have been hot in the sun. Small, cheerful clouds crawled across the vault of sapphire.

Caip and Dar had argued against this next phase, but Belo had supported him. It would not have mattered to the king if he had found no one on his side. He would never enjoy another night's sleep if they did not try. Nik had the knack for politics of his late father, Craid, and had quickly risen to a position of importance in the besieged city. He had volunteered for the task without hesitation.

Tel could not see the massive portal open from his position, but he heard and felt it. A few beats passed, and the process reversed. The door was closed. Nik appeared below him, walking backward on the road, toward Lag's army. In his hands was a staff with Tel's banner, which he held perpendicular to his body, so the colors were on his left. Approaching a force in this manner—back shown to the enemy, banner displayed but with humility—had for centuries denoted a request for a peaceful discussion. No weapons, aside from personal dirks, were permitted.

Nik crossed half the distance between the gate and the earthen mounds and trenches protecting Lag's soldiers from counterassault, past the ramparts protecting the city. Straight as the pole he held, he stood waiting. The green and orange rode low on the light wind. After a painful pause, someone approached Nik's position, walking backward, bearing Lag's colors.

A meter separated them. Lag's soldier must have asked Nik if he would turn in peace because Nik spun to face him. After a brief discussion, the soldier scurried back to his side. Within a handful of minutes, another person walked to Nik, this time facing frontward and with less caution. The second emissary was likely of some significant rank.

Tel realized his breathing was shallow. The muscles of his body had tightened from jaw to calves. He strained to see. The talk lasted quite a bit longer than the first. When it ended, Nik strode to the city gate. The king scrambled down to the base of the wall.

Nik approached, shaking his head. He gave the ground his black eyes.

"I'm sorry."

"You have nothing to be sorry about. What happened?"

"He was third in command, he said. I told him our side wants peace in Feigh and peace on the world above all other things. I said this was an impossibility with Lag on the throne. That his actions have demonstrated this. I told him we didn't want to turn good Feighan dirt into mud with their blood or ours but were willing to do so to end his reign. I offered them the opportunity to surrender, after which they could return home or join us. As you requested, I asked him to take my word our side was not as outmatched as they believed, and we would very soon bring many of them to the black if they didn't take the wise course. I told him they have until sundown."

"His reaction?"

"He laughed and walked away."

"He said nothing?" The king saw an unhappy flicker in Nik's eyes. "What is it, Nik? I must know."

"He said they had no doubt about being able to take the city easily once the order came. They were not impressed with your display last night. One dynast does not intimidate them. He said a scout had seen the ships approaching from up the coast, and they knew it was you and your army. Word of your arrival is on the way to Affas. That this meant the order would come before too long."

"It does not sound as if they know all the ships but mine were empty. And? What else did he say?"

Nik hesitated, squeezing his eyes shut and sighing. He opened them and said, *"Emperor Lag's treacherous brother is behind that wall. We'll see his head separated from his body even sooner than we hoped.* He laughed and walked away."

"Thank you, Nik. I am sorry to say blood will hit the dirt soon after tomorrow swallows today. I hope the Stag looks upon our offer with some favor."

* * *

Dark came without word from the besiegers.

Although his mind chewed at the endless possible outcomes of the night ahead, Tel found himself able to nap for a short time. He was still drained from his recent output of magic, and he would need every shred of physical, mental, and dynast energy for what was before him.

Not long after midnight, just shy of three thousand Athairian fighters, more than he had ever dreamed, stood ready inside the main city gate, alert in proud columns. The king ruminated on the irony that the military placed such importance on crisp order in their preparations for the bringing of chaos. He and one hundred archers took positions atop the wall. What he could see of the enemy camp indicated a typical nighttime routine.

An eternity passed in what must have been a quarter of an hour or less. Tel thought he could hear the archers' breathing above the quiet chatter from the camp. He considered reaching out to find Caip's thoughts but decided against. It would be a foolish expenditure of the dynasty. He knew she was ready from his contact with her the previous night. They had reviewed the plan countless times before she and the bulk of the little original army had gone ashore at Thasach, a two-day march north of Athair. He had faith she would execute with perfection. The only question was whether the scheme would succeed, giving them a significant victory.

The racket popped out of the darkness beyond Lag's army. Twelve tremendous, clean cracks sounded, one after the other. Following the explosions, an unsettling silence seemed to stretch impossibly. The quiet below ended in a manner the king would not have guessed. Rather than being thrown into mayhem, the sound was of an enormous beast unhappily roused from its slumber. It moaned and griped as it stretched. Then came a clamor that conveyed something closer to fright.

Some of the archers shifted their weight, fidgeting. A few nocked and raised. "Not yet. Easy," said Tel.

The second set of findo reports came. This time, cries of panic and pain reached the battlements.

"Nock," called Tel. "Draw." One hundred bows were angled to send their missiles into the besiegers' ranks. He allowed his eyelids to fall. *Veery.* All the arrowheads were aflame. He heard a few archers gasp, no doubt startled at seeing their first use of magic. "Steady. It is only your reformed drunk of a king." He looked to his left and his right, waiting for calm to return. When it did, he gave the order. "Loose."

As the flames at the tips of the arrows had no real fuel, he had to maintain a lowered mind until they sailed through the air and landed. He was shocked how few of them caught fire when they found the army below. It did not alarm him, however. Accuracy was not the goal. Surprise and fear were the aims. What he heard from Lag's force told him they had succeeded. Minutes had passed since the initial loosing of the findos, and he discerned no organized response from the enemy.

For a third time, a dozen explosions split the night. The weapons were closer now, and the balls must have torn through the camp. From Lag's force rang sounds of terror and death.

"Nock. Draw." He whispered his man's pet name, bringing his consciousness low. On either side of him, an orange glow warmed the gloom. "Loose." Tel waited for the arrows to land. "Come," he said, leading the archers down to the gate. He ordered it open, and three thousand women and men flowed into the main road from Athair, fanning out when they were beyond the city's ramparts. They began to spill over the enemy's barriers. Soon, he heard swords striking swords as shadows met one another at the edge of the camp.

The king was alone, striding up the center of the road. Three soldiers entered the thoroughfare in front of him, smallswords raised. He lifted an arm and sent lighting into the woman in the middle. The others gaped at what was left of her sizzling corpse and dropped their weapons.

The besiegers had been unable to muster any order. Too many of them had started to move toward the walls, scrambling away from the awful findos. Those fleeing only met the focused Athairians, who had the advantage of knowing the time and shape of the attack. Tel and Bin ended up fighting not far from one another. Seeing the monster of a man to his right calmed him, even as he witnessed him chewing through nearly a dozen soldiers who made the unwise decision to challenge him.

Caip had just less than two thousand, but they were far more experienced than the city's force. The general's advance from the rear was rapid and disciplined, squeezing Lag's people to the middle. Tel's army gave them no opportunity to mount an organized retreat, although many fled along the coast to the northeast and southwest of the city, deserting.

As both sides of Tel's force pressed closer together, he found he had to use the stagsblood as a warning more than he needed to unleash it on people. For the most part, the women and men would see his frightening capabilities and cower or run. As Lag's thousands were pushed into a compact knot between the king and his general, it became apparent the seasoned, hardheaded core of officers could no longer spur the rank and file to mount a defense, let alone a counterattack.

Just a few hours after it had begun, Lag's banner guard emerged from the chaos, walking backward toward King Tel and the city. They carried the brown and white low. Tel called for Bin, who rushed to his side. The corporal's clothes and leather armor were slick and blood-darkened. "Take a banner and approach them in peace. Remind them we made an offer less than a day ago. Tell them each person may choose imprisonment here in Athair, where they will be cramped but well-treated, or enlistment in my army. Explain I will be able to read whether they are sincere about fighting for our side with the stagsblood touch. These are the terms, or the fight continues."

Thirty and Three

Between their triumph at Athair and the weeks leading up to the winter solstice, Tel's army tore northward. Lag sent wave after wave, trying to end his brother's upstart campaign safely in the south. Clever use of the stagsblood and the keen martial thinking of Caip, Dar, and Belo brought them one victory after another. They took a series of forts and towns, their ranks swelling with volunteers and turncoats. Many of Lag's women and men had no love for their leadership, fought like it, and chose to switch sides over imprisonment of indeterminate length. Some, however, preferred life in a cell to marching for a dynast, unaware they had already been doing so. To others, the stagsblood dynasty was immaterial. They simply refused to take orders from a *bluebell lover*.

The inhabitants of the town near Fort Falbra reported Lag's army had scrambled away. Tel's brother had ordered the army split in two. Their best intelligence and a bit of guesswork told the rebels Lag had about thirty thousand troops remaining. Tel now had nearly as many. Fifteen thousand loyalists melted back to protect Affas, while the others headed for Larotha, the largest city in the western third of the country. There, they would shelter behind the wall and under the rooves for the winter before resuming the fight.

Tel, Caip, Belo, and Dar agreed Lag hoped they would hunker down for the coldest weeks in and around Fort Falbra before heading north again. Come spring, as they engaged those defending the capital, the force from Larotha would swing up behind them. Tel's hopes would be choked to death just south of Affas before the air grew hot again.

King and Table had unanimity in believing they needed to make a play for Larotha. An unusual mildness had so far held the worst of the cold at bay this year, but the ice and snow could not be avoided forever. They hoped they had enough time to make it to the city and take it. A conventional assault would be costly in the best scenario. Larotha was a relatively young Feighan city with strong, sophisticated fortifications. Even with the siege weapons they had acquired, they could be held off for a long time, if not permanently.

As soon as Tel decided to bank the westward turn, he was almost overtaken by a tingling pleasure immediately under his skin. Finally, he was answering the mysterious inner goading toward the western mountains of Feigh. It had been with him since he had put down the drink.

The area of the country west of Larotha was wild and free of settlements. A vast forest tumbled down the Chreok Mountains. These peaks formed most of the boundary between Feigh and Sheruck. The enormous woodlands spread over the hills beneath the range and extended over flatter ground, deep into the kingdom. As the solstice approached, Tel veered the army south of Larotha into this wilderness. They marched northward until they were directly west of the city, as close to the edge of the forest as possible without risking detection of their fires.

"I will send Sitha back with word as soon as I can," King Tel told his general.

"This whole plan makes me uneasy," said Caip.

"Me, too. But we cannot fight our way in without too many losses. And we cannot chance facing the two halves of Lag's force in the open. We would be in a vice. One half now. We rest and recuperate until the ground thaws. Then, the rest."

"Very well," she said softly. "Be fast. I hate the cold."

King Tel led four hundred and fifty and five soldiers away to the north. All were Feighans from the southern half of the kingdom who had volunteered for the mission. He would have preferred a larger number, but that was as many as he thought would seem realistic.

They traveled light and pushed fast. When they were far enough north

315

of Larotha, they looped east, out of the forest, before banking south. It needed to appear as though they were traveling from the direction of Affas.

* * *

Tel, Bin, and Sitha sat at a table laden with a sumptuous feast in their honor in an equally lavish home. It belonged to a distant relative of King Tel. He had never met his lord cousin but knew he did not appreciate his taste in décor, thinking it was all garishness and pretension. The lord had been called to Affas.

"I hope you do not think it rude of me to ask you to please share the purpose of this surprise visit," said General Fen. He was one of the most well-known and respected leaders of the Feighan military. Tel's father had always liked him. He was fair-minded and sharp. His love of his nation was unimpeachable. Tel thought Fen's support of his brother and uncle must be based on an understandable belief that the younger brother was the rightful leader of Feigh.

"I hope it wasn't an unpleasant surprise," said Tel, in the higher voice he had, with the help of Caip's ear for impressions, practiced. He tinged it with a bit of menace.

"Of course not, Table Head Aith. I just want to know how I can best help you," Fen responded. Tel could see past his attempts to hide his fear. "Is the wine not to your satisfaction? You haven't had a drop."

"I fear my tongue's been spoiled by the fine reds of Andow served at the castle," said Tel, continuing his approximation of Aith's voice. "All else is swill."

"The lord of this house must have some of the good stuff," said Fen, flicking a hand over the table. "Paig!" Into the room stepped a slight servant girl with braided hair. She could have been as young as forty and four seasons or merely tiny at sixty. She would not raise her eyes from the carpet.

"Unnecessary. Thank you," said Tel, feeling sweat rising over his body.

"My throat is sore, at any rate. I'd prefer to skip niceties and get directly to the matter at hand."

"You still haven't told me what that is." Fen's perturbation was evident. He modulated his voice, adding some light and air when he said, "I'm eager to hear what you have to say."

Tel was confident in the cloak of disguise he had made using the southern fire magic of the stagsblood. He was less sure of the voice. Fen and Aith had never been close but had been casually acquainted for decades. Tel's head also swam intermittently, a kind of mild intoxication upon him now that he found himself near the Chreok Mountains. He said, "Emperor Lag dispatched me here with news, and to oversee the response to that news."

"News?"

"Yes, General Fen. Seems my traitorous nephew has decided to come west to attempt to take this city. We have information he and the fat Omelan queen's son should arrive in two or three weeks."

"Good luck to him." Fen scoffed. "This place is better fortified than Affas. An army twice the size would not breach these walls, even with the new Omelan weapons. And it's only going to get colder. A siege in the heart of the western winter will alone kill hundreds. I'll be happy to welcome them to Larotha."

Tel slapped the flat of his gloved hand on the table, causing dishes to jump. "Antlered ones! We won't underestimate him again. We thought we had laid a trap for him in Athair. He crushed us. We thought he was too ill-equipped and shorthanded to survive his march up the guts of the kingdom. Instead, he overwhelmed us in the open and in our strongholds. All the while, he grows his army, attracting our own soldiers and citizens to his treasonous cause, no doubt using the stagsblood for mind control. Your arrogance proves the need for my presence." He stood. "The rightcolonel and corporal here will take charge of your defenses and report directly to me." Bin and Sitha rose from their chairs, the corporal still chewing at a mouthful of food.

General Fen sprang to his feet. "Table Head Aith, please. Sit. Enjoy the meal. I understand your perspective, and I'm grateful for the assistance.

You and your people will have cooperation and anything you need."

"Good evening, Fen. I hope you understand my seriousness," said the king, wagging a finger. "This traitor, Tel, will plot and plan and scheme right under your nose—under this very roof if he could. And you'd be none the wiser. As for the food, sadly, it's not much better than the wine." He swept his vision across the tabletop and pulled a face.

When they were out of earshot, Bin said, "I thought the food was good."

From the corner of her mouth, Sitha said, "Putting a little extra crust on the pie with all that *under your nose, under this very roof* business, don't you think?"

"Swept away by my own performance," said King Tel.

* * *

A couple of evenings later, disguised as his uncle, Tel decided on a long stroll around the neighborhood where the rambling house stood. The food of the west really was both blander and heavier than the cuisine of the rest of Feigh, and he took the exercise to spark his digestion. The first serious cold of the season was threatening, filling him with worry.

The streets of Larotha—and the activity upon them—felt odd. Too many soldiers strutted about. It reminded Tel of his last weeks in Affas. Ordinary citizens seemed to scurry from one point to the next, eyes on gravel and cobbles.

When he turned down a little street to begin looping back to the property, he saw him, five meters or so ahead. The stranger was across the uneven road, walking in the opposite direction. Tel's breath hung dry in his throat. The lithe young man appeared to float down the pavement. His height was a match, as was the bouncing mass of curls. It was not Vared, of course. The lad was Feighan through and through. Even in the dying light of approaching dusk, it was easy to see the tresses were as black as Tel's own hair and beard.

He allowed the man to pass. Looking about to be sure no eyes were upon him, Tel pulled a cloak of invisibility over himself. He began to follow, watching. Unlike almost anyone else on the street, he was unrushed. His gait was graceful but lazy. Embarrassment heated Tel's skin, even though detection was impossible. He waited, unsure of what he anticipated. This was as close as he could be to Vared, and—silly as it was—he needed to take the opportunity. Indeed, the boy had the shape and the elegant manner of carrying it. The more he followed, however, the less like Vared he seemed. By the time the thin man ducked into an alehouse, Tel's embarrassment had turned to shame. Ambling down an empty street, he transformed from nothing to his uncle again.

When he returned to the house, he collapsed on the bed in what was meant to be Aith's guest room. The days of maintaining a cloak for hours at a time exacted a toll. Disguise magic brought a different kind of weariness than did anything else of which the stagsblood made him capable. Along with the mental fatigue, a vicious headache stabbed at his temples. All the discomfort was eclipsed, though, by the absence of Vared. The manifestation of the sad longing was as physical as tiredness or a screaming skull. A hollow, dull burning gripped him from his throat to his bowels. Even in his misery, a nap tugged him down.

A knock at the door pulled him back up to a confused consciousness. He was unsure how long he had been out. It would be Sitha and Bin. "Come in."

"We can come back, Table Head," offered Rightcolonel Sitha, for the benefit of anyone passing near.

He remembered to alter his pitch. "No. Of course not." He got to his feet. They entered, mouths agape.

Bin closed the door behind him. "Unlocked, majesty? And you can't just tell people to come in when you're not disguised."

"If I may, your majesty, you look exhausted," said Sitha.

Tel allowed his weight to fall onto the mattress. "Only because I *am* exhausted." He rubbed his eyes with the heels of his hands. "Now. Out with it. How will we do this?"

"I'm going to insist you sleep. We can share the details in the morning," said Sitha. "We have a plan, and we'll put it into action tomorrow night if you approve."

"Surely I can hear it now."

"No." Bin took a step toward the bed. "General Caip specifically talked to me about this. I'm to make sure you rest when you need it."

"But…"

"But nothing," said Sitha.

"You're using the blood a lot. We'll need you to use it more," said Bin. "Sleep."

"Breakfast. We will talk then." Tel forced himself to follow them to the door, so he could lock it behind them.

* * *

Tel doubted he had moved a finger once he had fallen asleep. He woke up famished and tore into his breakfast with more gusto than even giant Bin. Only a mug of hidybrew sat in front of Sitha on the shaky little table in Tel's room where the three of them sat. She declined food, saying she had eaten soon after rising, three hours before.

"The southwest gate. It's the least secure because the guard's a bit lighter. We've made it even lighter, reassigning people to other *vulnerabilities*," she said.

"And now that area's staffed mostly with our people," said Bin.

"That corner of the city is also regularly neglected by their patrols." The rightcolonel pushed her face over the table toward the king. "In a short time, we've seen a lot. Studied the routines here. Would we prefer to have longer? Of course. But we don't have that luxury, as you know, your majesty."

Tel nodded as he finished chewing on a hunk of toasted bread. "And we simply let our own army into the city?"

"At the right time," said Sitha, "we'll open the gate. Thirty thousand of us will stream in and take the city."

The king popped another piece of toast into his mouth. When he swallowed, he said, "This bread has a resistance to it. Chewy. I have never had anything like it in Affas or Foghar or anywhere abroad, for that matter. At least not all their food is rubbish."

"You'll go from lean prince to fat king." Bin chuckled. "It's always the way."

Sitha looked at the corporal with rounded eyes.

"I am using the dynasty more than ever. It is making me hungry." He enjoyed a few gulps of fruit juice. "There will be fighting. Here in the streets of Larotha. It will be bloody. The bloodiest thus far. And the people. They will be close to it."

Bin pushed his plate back and laid a hand on his stomach. "We'll surprise 'em. We get lucky and perform well, less blood'll hit the dirt."

"No avoiding it," Sitha said, "if we want to take Larotha this way. Our only other options are to lay siege or to fight the force defending Affas first."

"No," said Tel, fingering the worn edge of the table. "My mind is made up. The stagsblood has given us this advantage. Let us take it. You leave tonight?"

Sitha nodded. "I'll have a horse and head right out the southwest gate. It'll be much quicker than our trip here because I can take a direct route. In six nights, we'll return. The army will travel slower, but it'll still give us an extra day for unforeseen circumstances."

"May the Stag and Doe walk alongside your mount, Sitha. Thank you." Tel nodded at the rightcolonel.

Sitha and Bin left him alone in the guest room. In his veins, the dynasty bade him walk out of the southwest gate himself and disappear into the woods, where *something* waited.

Eyes closed, he wondered how much of his fatigue came not from his extensive magical works but from the tremendous burdens of war. He was not only now a fighter, but the person in whose name tens of thousands fought. Thousands of them had died already.

What would mother think today? Father? They could not have anticipated this. What about Vared? He only knew of this in abstraction. If he saw me killing—ordering others to kill? And he waits for me, not knowing this moment if I am on the world or in the black. Not knowing if I am the same man or if violence on this scale is rotting my heart in my chest like meat in the sun.

He had to tell himself he was stopping many more deaths by making war than he would by staying quiet. His brother's designs on empire would require much more blood, Feighan and foreign. Lag's strange obsessions with security and loyalty were making citizens into paranoid neighbors. On balance, doing what he needed to do to put himself under the rack crown would be better for Feigh and all the people on the world.

He had to tell himself these things but was haunted by the number of times his certainty had been proud folly. *I judged my brother backward but harmless. I believed I would never see another war in my lifetime. I knew more people than not would reject me because of the stagsblood. I was convinced I did not want to have a man again.*

Thirty and Four

A few moments before Tel planned to slip out of the house to head for the southwest gate, someone banged on his door. He was irritated to have to form the disguise just to answer the knock, knowing he would need every bit of magical energy for the battle ahead. Tel unlocked the door and yanked it open, revealing General Fen sweating in the hallway.

"Fen? What is it?" asked Tel with Aith's voice.

"Something you need to see."

"This cannot wait until morning?"

"It cannot." Fen's jaw was tight.

"Very well, then," said Tel, throat aching from days of impersonation. "Lead me to what it is I need to see."

Fen escorted him to the room his lord cousin used as his study. When the general's hand touched the hardware on the door, he hesitated. He turned his head to the side, enough so Tel saw his profile. "I know I've chosen the wrong side now. I was trying to serve Feigh." He pushed the door open.

"Tel of...what is it now, Omela? I'm so pleased to see you."

She had said it before the door had opened all the way. Tel had recognized the voice immediately. Before him, Gran stood next to a chair.

"General, have a seat. Tel, come in."

King Tel stepped into the room, stomach sour. Fen sat in the chair at Gran's side.

"I've never seen you so quiet." Lieutenant Gran waved her hand in his direction. "Perhaps because I didn't end up in Kamber, as you said I would. I think you can drop the costume now."

Tel wanted to wipe her off the world then and there. He could do so with little effort. His hatred—an intensity of ill will of which he did not believe himself capable eight seasons ago—beckoned him to violence. He strained to wrestle the sentiment downward, needing to find out what was happening here. With a subtle adjustment of his mind, he allowed the stagsblood disguise to fall away.

"At first," Gran said, picking at her coat under her smirk, "I merely thought I was the luckiest woman in all of Feigh. Can you believe I arrived a day and a half after you? And for the same reason you gave General Fen for your visit. Or Aith's visit. To look over the security of this place. To prepare for the arrival of the rebels." She gave a dry laugh, which struck Tel as forced. "Fen didn't even believe me. *A misunderstanding*, he said. *He was in Affas when I left*, I said. *I don't know you, Gran*, he said. Couldn't take my word for it. He'd just had dinner with Aith the night before. Do interrupt me if I leave anything out, Fen."

Her smirk grew. "*All it'll take*, I said, *is a little observation.* I suggested just listening from the next room. Sadly, though, this house is well-put-together. I'd need someone *in* the room. Impossible, of course. Unless we could get someone *between* the walls. Someone *small* enough, but smart enough to listen."

Blind and burning with rage, he knew she spoke of the servant girl, Paig. "Where is she?"

"Close, Tel. Close. And if anything happens to me tonight, she'll be killed. Most unpleasantly. An innocent. So, you're going to stay here with me for a while. There are other reasons you'll stay with me. I'll tell you those. But I need to do something first."

She moved to the side, so she was behind Fen's seat. His defeated eyes were locked on the lush rug. In smooth flashes of her wrist and elbow, Gran had her dirk out. With equal efficiency, she drew the edge across his throat and pushed him off the cushion into the already pooling crimson. She spat on him and watched the spasms weaken until they stopped. "This is what happens when you question the word of a true, pure Feighan. He worshipped too long at the altar of your traitor father's peace cult."

Tel had seen enough blood mix with the dirt now that his reaction was intellectual—not emotional—horror. He could not afford sentimentality. It would lead only to him curling into a ball on the battlefield and dying. This room was a battlefield now. He needed her to continue talking. Feeling wholly unmoored by the shock of finding himself in the same room as Gran, he tried to lower his mind.

Gran cleared her throat and walked around the chair. She stood with her right foot in Fen's blood. "In another year, maybe two, mushy-minded women and men like him will all be gone. The non-Feighans will be gone. Maybe most important of all, those who want to dilute the line from Stag and Doe to us, the ones who want to erase what it means to be a Feighan, will be gone. The Stag's lesson will be spread over the world. A third of this city's forces are on the streets, many outside this very house. You'll not get far, even with lighting and fire. I know because a close friend who understands these things told me your magic isn't endless. It's finite. If you leave, you'll be dead as this so-called general soon enough."

"You know he is a dynast?" asked Tel. "But I thought this was an abomination?"

"He was made a dynast by the Stag to oppose *you*. To keep Feigh safe from you and your power and your kind. Your *weakness*."

"As ever, Gran, you make no sense. If he was made as him, and you were made as you, then I was made as me."

She crossed most of the distance between them and pushed her face toward his, snarling. "*I* make no sense? You're engaged in a conflict you cannot win. A conflict that only removes more of you from the world. It ends within a day. Here. In Larotha." She looked around them, arms swept into a broad gesture. "All of it's over, Tel. There's another third of the army in the wilderness. And another third just outside the southwest gate. Five thousand in front of Caip and your little messenger, Sitha, and five thousand behind. With the advantage of surprise. Stay with me, and the prisoners we take will be spared. Leave, and they die. Along with Paig, who never raised a sword in her life. And you, of course."

"You do not even know." Now it was Tel who spread his arms wide.

325

"What?"

Tel fought to lower his mind and form a tether. He grasped for Gran's inner life. "That most of them are innocent. Always have been."

"What?"

"Paig *is* innocent. She never raised a sword, as you say. But those who have, in this fight and others? Those who have raised a sword since the beginning? Most of them were innocent. Doing what they did for queen and queendom. Doing what a king asked them. Doing what they needed to do to eat. Keep their families safe. Or escape from an unsafe family. A drunken father's fist. A sibling's advances. So many of them are innocent. And until we change the ways of the world, the ways of the queens and kings and ladies and lords, the innocent will keep dying with raised swords. *That* is the Stag's lesson. It is not to pay tribute to the goddesses and gods as we Feighans do. It is not to force the faith on others. It is to honor his grief by living in peace."

He knew by the tether Gran had lied. Young Paig had hours before been killed with even less ceremony than Fen. When the general had made the mistake of asking Gran a question about her plans, she had frightened him into compliance by murdering the girl.

King Tel ended Gran's life with lightning and made himself invisible.

* * *

The district in which Tel's lord cousin's house sat was the old heart of the city. Its streets were thick with the brown and white. King Tel noticed how relaxed they seemed. Although they had to know what had begun, their lack of concern was apparent. Tel meandered through them at a speed he found painful. Even invisible, he had to wait for opportunities to pass through them undetected. He needed to get to the southwestern corner of the city.

He reached less densely-packed roads and alleys after too long, allowing him to travel with some swiftness. He started to jog. Passing a rutted side street, he heard someone say, "Can you fuckin' believe this one?" Squawks of laughter, derisive and threatening, stopped him. With care, he peered around the corner, forgetting for an instant that no one could see him. In the little street stood a clump of soldiers.

One of them said, "Thinks he can just tuck the red hair up under a hood."

Straining his eyes and ears, the king began to move toward them. Even in the darkness, he could see peeks of red, bright as berries. He was a Kamb.

"Thousands of us in the streets, and this pile of leavings is out strolling," said another of the soldiers. More cruel laughter rang.

Tel found himself wondering what had happened to the innocence of these soldiers. How had their minds been molded into this perverse shape? They were Feighan girls and boys, just the same as those on his side of the fight. Kingship felt more burdensome than ever.

"And what about the young lady? You must like Kamb cock," said a third soldier. "Must like 'em little."

Tel said, "Step away from them, or you will die in this street."

"Who's that?" The speaker squinted in Tel's direction. "Show yourself, coward."

"Final warning." Tel heard himself growl. "Move away from them or die."

One of them stepped back a pace. With nakedly false boldness, he asked, "And who are you?"

He allowed himself to appear in the street. "I am the king of Feigh, and I warned you." They drew their smallswords. Six crackles pierced the cold, thin air as Tel cut them down, one by one. The clean smell of rain mingled with the rank odors of burning hair and clothing. "Get somewhere safe." The Kamb man and Feighan woman scrambled away, looking back at him, big-eyed.

Tel moved to continue toward the southwest gate, but nearby footfalls froze him. At the end of the street ahead of him, a woman bolted around the corner.

"There," she shouted, finger pointed.

At least two dozen spilled into the street, drawing their weapons. They each crouched a bit and started to move in his direction. At least as many again piled behind them. Almost fifty soldiers advanced on him in an open roadway. He eased himself backward, knowing he could eliminate them all if he needed to, but wanting to protect his rear. Something about the leisurely pace at which they moved made that desire more acute.

He was right to be concerned. More soldiers entered the street behind him. The sounds of swords leaving sheaths woke the hairs on the back of his neck.

"It'll be so much better for me if we can take you alive," a woman said, sword waving. "Give up, and we'll see how merciful your brother's feeling when we get to Affas. Or die here. I'm sure we'll still be heroes."

A low chuckle rumbled from one of the men. "Your friends are already dying outside the city, pretender."

Without thinking, Tel pushed his hands through the air, fingers splayed, in the direction of the lines of soldiers who had first entered the street. *Veery.* A wall of fire, tall as a man, walked toward them. The inferno hung, churning in the air above the road. The flames had no fuel to keep them alive, only the stagsblood, so he needed to move quickly. Thinking he could save some of his magic, he said to the smaller group at the other end of the street, "Drop your swords, and I will spare you. Keep them in your hands, and you will not live."

The demonstration of his magic did not deter them in the least. They strode much faster at him now, determined faces stroked by the shifting glow. Branches of lightning fanned from Tel's free hand, sending weapons clanging and bodies thumping to the ruts. Seeing five of their comrades die by stagsblood still gave the others no pause. They continued their advance, and the king killed seven more as he worked to hold the barrier of flame behind him. Four more separated from the pack and marched forward, infuriating him. A nasty tangle of energy screeched at them, cooking the front halves of their bodies. All but one of the rest raced from the street.

This last soldier dropped his sword, lowering himself to his knees. He shielded his face with quivering arms. "Surrender. I surrender."

"Give me your eyes," Tel boomed. The pretty boy he had followed a few evenings before looked at him through his lashes, wincing. Tel felt the wall of fire weaken behind him. He stabilized it with a thought. "You?"

"Surrender. I surrender."

"I am not going to hurt you," said Tel. "Why do you fight for my brother?"

"What?"

"Why do you fight for him?"

The boy began to whimper. "I don't have a choice. Me or my sister, they said."

Tel's eyes stung. "You can fight for me. Then you can go home."

"What's the difference?"

The fire behind the king wavered again. He turned and saw through the flickering orange, yellow, and white tongues that most of the soldiers on the other side had left the street. They could be upon him from the other side at any second. He jogged away, looking back at the young man with the black curls. As the stagsblood fire died, Tel saw the ink of night swallow him.

Nearing the southwest corner of the city, he encountered more evidence of fire. The smell of it filled his nose and mouth. He saw a few towers of smudged white smoke stretching into the dull sky. Whether the blazes had been set deliberately or were the result of an accident in the chaos, he could not be sure. The sound of warfare, unmistakable and familiar as a friend's voice now, skated off buildings and along streets. Somehow, Caip had pushed at least partly past the walls.

When he reached the fighting, the mayhem was so total, it was almost impossible to comprehend what was happening. What he saw was less two sides locked in battle than a mass of one-on-one fights and larger, vicious brawls. Many had lost their weapons, striking with fists, feet, and heads. He could not discern friend from foe until he was upon them. Both forces were lost in a confused orgy of violence. Soldiers wrestled and punched one another to death atop mounds of bodies. Boots splashed through crimson puddles.

The king pressed into the melee, saving his soldiers as he moved, eliminating his brother's. He brought his mind so low, he lost a swath of time. Coming out of his trance, drenched with blood and sweat, leather armor dripping, he only knew he had been using the dynasty to cut down his enemies because he was still alive and fighting. More and more of his people began to find him in the night, recognizing him because of the lightning. They rallied to him, restoring a cohesion that had dissolved in Gran's surprise, two-headed counterattack.

Yelling questions to this soldier and that, he began to form a sense of things. Caip had used the bulk of her force to defend from the rear, holding off the five thousand that swung on them from the wilderness, while a smaller group blasted the findos at those approaching from the city. As had happened so many times before, the Omelan weapons had terrified the opposing ranks, causing disorder. They had beaten a chaotic retreat into the city but had been unable to secure the gate. The findos had continued to loose. By the time Caip had the rest of her people within the walls, there had been no gate left to close. Sitha had died outside the city, swinging her sword even flat on her back.

Tel had many of his people reorganized near the western wall. Word came of another large group, pressed to the southern wall. The women and men held their ground for hours while he became increasingly frantic about reconnecting with Caip. Lag's side continued to come in waves. The king sent fresh personnel to relieve those along the force's edges, allowing the front to melt backward for rest. Over and over, he made these swaps. Only twice did he step back from the most active fighting for a handful of moments, asking himself how much longer it could continue—and how much longer he could.

As the sun rose high enough to spill over the top of the eastern wall, the battle's tenor shifted in a manner Tel failed to understand at first. Something more than the light and temperature had changed. After a time, a woman, features obscured by filth and blood, found him and made a report. Larothan civilians, by the hundreds or thousands, had taken up arms—swords, shovels, and sticks—against Lag's soldiers.

The other side was compressed into a tired knot, squeezed by Tel's fighters, those with Caip along the south wall, and the civilians arriving from the north and east. Lag's women and men began dropping their swords. Their banner was marched backward out of the fray, the white disk at its center stained pink. King Tel accepted the surrender personally. Voice bellowing but shaky, he made them the offer he always made. "Swear an oath, join our side and fight in good faith or be imprisoned until the end. Give it thought. I can know by the stagsblood if you dissemble."

Next, he expressed his gratitude to the civilians who had taken to the streets, telling them he now knew why the people of the west had earned their reputation for toughness. He asked them, too, to consider joining his army.

It took two hours to sort the details of where the prisoners would be brought and held, and who would bring them there. A sudden slap on the back almost knocked him to the ground. He knew before turning it was Bin. When he faced the corporal, the big man embraced him, squeezing hard enough to make him sputter. "I'm glad to see you alive, majesty."

"The same, my friend," said Tel, once his breath had returned. He regarded Bin's face. His friend was not smiling. Tel's stomach shifted sourly. "Caip?"

Bin looked at the Feighan blood spilled on the Feighan dirt.

Thirty and Five

Save the initial work of separating those new prisoners who would fight sincerely for him and those who merely wanted to escape confinement, for a long time, King Tel did not call upon the stagsblood. He slept away the better part of a month, sweating through dreams about climbing the city's walls to disappear into the great, howling western wilderness. The Battle of Larotha left him hollowed out. When he was up, it was for a few hours, and he ate like a beast as he took updates and gave orders.

He would return to bed, where he longed to have Vared against him, believing his presence would somehow make the rest more restorative. His strength was slow to return, and he could not spare the mental energy to fret about missing him. Instead, he simply allowed himself to ache.

The winter was as hesitant about blowing out as it had been about blowing in. Once it had taken hold, in the days following the battle, its grip had been merciless. Now, well beyond the equinox, a day hinting at the mild air to come was followed by one frigid enough to stiffen the muscles on the first step outside. A very light snow fell, too far into the spring even for the west.

"Will this weather ever break?" Bin entered the parlor Tel had been using as an office, little white flakes disappearing into his hair.

"That's what we were just discussing," said Dar.

"And I always thought Feighans did not complain about the weather," said Belo.

"My thinking is it will break all at once, and we'll be thrown quickly into summer." Relaxed in his chair, Tel laced his fingers on top of his head.

"Does have that sort o' feeling this year." Bin let his weight fall into a seat.

"I do not want to wait much longer. It is time to march for Affas. I am restless, and so is the army." Tel eyed Dar. "How much notice would you require?"

"We're more or less prepared. Two days."

"Consider this notice, then."

With a grin and a nod, Rightmajor Dar said, "Very well, majesty."

"How are your people holding up?" Tel asked Belo. His contingent had absorbed disproportionate losses in the fight for the city.

"We are ready," said Belo. "They love you as they love me."

"I doubt that very much."

"They would like to return home before they go gray, however." Belo tucked a tumble of blue hair behind his ear. "The sooner, the better."

Bin squinted at King Tel. "And you're really feeling strong enough?"

"It has been months."

"You didn't answer his question." Caip strode into the room. As usual, Tel tried and failed to prevent his eyes from finding the empty right sleeve of her jacket. "I'm sorry to be late. I was screaming at some sloppy Larothans making a butchery of a drill."

"Naturally." Wiggling a black eyebrow, Dar smirked.

Caip took Tel's eyes. "Answer."

"I am not quite totally myself, I admit." He shifted his weight forward in the chair. "But I need movement. Air. I must get out of these walls. Stretch my legs. March. Camp. Get back to the fight. If I keep sitting still, I will never have my full powers. Even two days feels like two days too long."

Bin stifled a laugh, which only caused his body to rattle with it.

Tel asked, "What?"

"You sound like one of us," said Bin. "A lifetime military man. Peacemaker prince, indeed."

Corporal Bin could not have known how much the comment stung, so Tel did not respond or—he hoped—let it show. He wrestled his features into a smile.

Caip's gaze had not shifted. "Two days."

333

"Excellent," said Tel. "Gentleman, may I have a word with Caip?"

"Come on, boys," Bin said, rising. "Mother and Father need to talk."

"He didn't mean anything by it," said Caip, once they were gone.

"We do bicker like a corded pair."

"You know very well I meant the *peacemaker prince* comment."

"Yes."

"Someone should cut out his tongue," said Caip, shaking her head.

"I think I will make him a lord, instead. It is good to have someone to remind me, king or not, I still piss with my cock in the wind."

"What's on your mind?"

By a reflex he did not understand, his eyes again flicked to where her right arm should be. Heat prickling the skin of his face, he looked at her. "We need to talk about it."

"About what?" The question had come out hotter than Tel's cheeks.

His mind returned to the moment Bin had led him to her after the battle. Her arm had been badly mangled in the fight. Trying to save her, a soldier had amputated above the elbow, but she was bleeding through the dirty bandages. Tel had told himself it was not as bad as it looked. *Some of it is not her blood. Some of it is not her blood.* Crying and nauseated, he had used the dynasty to seal the wound.

"Do you not understand I need to say I am sorry? You hesitated about my plan, and I did not listen. Perhaps if we had done it your way…"

"Goddess, Tel." She spoke through a tight jaw. "You'll even make my loss about yourself."

"But it *is* about me. How dare you?" He rose to his feet, huffing, and raked a hand through his hair. "How dare you? Firstly, you are my friend. Secondly, it is my responsibility. You are a warrior, and the hand with which you hold your sword is gone. It hurts me. It is very much about me."

"I wonder sometimes if you ever bother to listen to yourself. To hear yourself." She paused. It looked to Tel like she had turned inward. She reemerged after a handful of beats and took a breath. With a lower voice, she said, "It *is* your responsibility. Welcome to war, Tel." She shrugged. "How many people died or lost a hand or eye or leg because of a choice I have made these last few seasons? I'm a leader of women and men. *We* are leaders of women and men. If we dwell on that question, if we hold onto those thoughts, we'll be paralyzed. Unable to lead. Useless."

Sensing she was not done, King Tel sat and gave her his full attention.

"I was in bed healing for some long weeks. I had the chance to relive the whole experience again and again. Your choice was correct. We won the battle, we have the city, and we have taken half their army off the field. My arm was but one of the sacrifices. I'm not saying this to make you feel better, to take away your guilt. *You* will have to work at that."

The space under Tel's ribs ached. He could only manage an understanding grunt.

Caip allowed her head to fall back, so she was looking at the ceiling. "If we'd done it a different way, maybe we would've lost. Maybe we would have won with less loss of life. Maybe more. Maybe it would've been someone else's arm. It still would've been your choice. This is why you hate war. Why I hate it. Why we worked to avoid it for years. Maybe one day it won't be necessary, but I don't think it's that day yet. And I long ago swore to do what was necessary until that day. You entered this fight with your eyes open. You were willing to do what's necessary, too. *We* caused the loss of my arm. We live with it." She returned her eyes to Tel's face. "Living with it is the necessary thing if we want to see this through."

He gave a solemn nod. "And you are ready for that?"

Caip opened her mouth to answer, but a commotion in the house interrupted her. They froze in their chairs. Tel strained to hear, looking at his friend. A voice spoke excitedly, but he could not make out words.

"Your majesty," said Dar, stomping into the parlor. "I don't believe it."

* * *

Tel's uncle had arrived, sending an elaborate banner guard marching backward to the gate. King Tel sent Bin out to speak for him. The corporal's talk with Aith's officer went quickly. As nightfall was approaching, Aith

335

and his people would set up camp and sleep. In the way of formal peace discussions taking place on the field, Tel's uncle's side agreed to erect a large tent where both sides could negotiate comfortably, beginning at midday. Aith insisted he talk directly with Tel. Each of them could bring one person who would wait outside the tent. Only personal dirks would be permitted.

Tel did not sleep.

In the morning, he and his Table agreed chances were good Aith had no intention to surrender, although they acknowledged the possibility. They were confident they could take Affas with the troops they had. Perhaps Lag knew it was over.

As she had the day before, Caip asserted she did not like the idea of King Tel alone in the tent with his uncle. "It should be one of us. Your uncle can't be trusted."

"I know that. I am not afraid of him. I am more afraid of Bin. Because I have good sense. Speaking of which," he said, producing a scroll and flattening it on the surface in front of him, "does Table agree I am of sound mind?" He snatched a quill from the mess of papers, books, and mugs.

Caip, Dar, Bin, and Belo looked at one another and quietly indicated their agreement.

"Very well. I have no children and no heir named, which is reckless. It feels especially so today. Upon my death, Caip of Foghar will be the rightful queen of Feigh. Do I hear any objections?" Seeing her widened eyes, he raised a finger. "Not you, Caip." After searching their faces, he signed the document and rose. "Bin."

Tel ordered the others to stay behind and continue with preparations under the assumption they would still need to fight for Affas. He and Bin rode out to the eastern gate without saying a word.

Two hundred meters beyond the wall stood a tent under the high, strong sun. It looked tiny from the city. Aith's contingent of soldiers stood far enough behind the temporary structure to appear nonthreatening. All evidence of the previous day's dusting of snow was already gone. Knowing matters of solemnity demanded a humble bearing, Tel removed his doublet and cloak, revealing a plain ivory shirt. Eyes on the gate, they walked backward to the tent. Halfway there, Bin said, "If you need me, just call my name. I'll cut down the one outside the tent and come to you."

"Thank you." Tel's throat was dry. When they reached the tent, he asked, "Will you turn in peace?"

"We will, nephew."

The high pitch chilled the king. Memories of posing as Aith soured his stomach. His mind conjured an image of Paig, the little servant girl. He saw the black gleam of her braids.

Aith had brought a nondescript soldier, much smaller than Bin. "You look well, Tel."

"I prefer to dispense with the small talk, Aith, and begin a meaningful discussion."

"Fine. After you."

Tel slipped into the cool tent. A few oil lamps threw light onto the fabric panels and over a small, central table. Tradition dictated the king should negotiate from the side nearest his army. A shabby antique trunk, burnt honey in color, sat in Tel's place. Scratched and grimy, it was meant to be his uncomfortable perch. Aith's side, naturally, had a cushioned chair. When they were seated, the uncle was taller than the nephew. Before they began speaking, the king noticed a faint, familiar smell. *Has he been drinking?*

Tightlipped, Aith peered down at him.

Tel resented having to speak first, as he had not asked for this conversation. He forced his pride down. "Your representative indicated you wanted to discuss peace."

The old man clucked his tongue. "You don't wish to catch up? We're family."

"I have long hoped," said Tel, "to understand the purpose of this playacting you do."

"Purpose? Playacting?" Tel's uncle folded his hands on the table.

Aith was not wearing his gloves. The skin on his fingers and the back of his hand was scaly and inflamed. Tel felt uneasy at the sight of it. After clearing his throat, he looked at his uncle and said, "I am not prepared to offer many, but what are the conditions you propose? What are the terms of your surrender?"

"You're the very worst sort of person, nephew."

"I know your feelings about me. You have shared them before."

"What's so wrong about peoples who have always fought keeping to themselves?" asked Aith. "Centuries of war. Millenia. For ages, the different cultures simply have been unable to coexist quietly. Why cannot Feigh be only Feigh? Omela be only Omela? We look different because we are different. Why cannot we just stay in our homelands?"

The tangy odor menacing Tel's nostrils had grown more intense. Still, it did not turn his stomach as much as his uncle's words. "You and my brother started a war with Kamber almost immediately. Now you ask why the nations cannot let one another live in peace?"

"Because, Tel," Aith said, coming to his feet and gesturing with both diseased hands, "of people like you. Centuries of evidence to the contrary, and you think living amongst one another, trade, cultural exchange, and *mixing* will bring about an age of understanding. Peace. I don't think so. We have no reason to believe that's possible. Even if it were, so much would be destroyed. Feighanness. Omelanness. If these things mean nothing, why were we made so our differences were so obvious?"

"It is *hair*, Aith. All of us on the world live and die and love and hate and screw and work a—"

"You prove my point. Shaking his head, Aith retook his seat.

"So, you would have Feigh be all alone. Feighans only in Feigh. No outsiders." Tel squinted, his grasp for understanding genuine. "Then why invade another land?"

"Because people like you aren't just here. The naïve aren't just in Feigh. They're spread over the world. So, the world must be made Feighan."

"You would eliminate everyone from every oth—"

Aith smirked and tipped his head toward Tel a fraction. "We'd eliminate the Feighans like you first."

"Uncle, you understand most of the people in our kingdom think more like me than you and my brother, do you not? It is why you have no choice but to come here and negotiate your surrender. Your bent philosophy started dying off long ago. Before *your* brother's rule."

"I'm not here to negotiate our surrender. I'm here to ensure yours."

"You must see you are beaten. Continuing the fight only delays the inevitable and makes more mud of Feighan blood and dirt. It is a matter of time before I take my place in the capital. I am the rightful king of Feigh. I will be a good king. All your trying to muck about in my head with the tethers has not made me feel otherwise."

Aith gave Tel a strange look from the side of his eyes, forehead knitted into a jumble of creases. "You will surrender. Now or very soon."

King Tel laughed for a moment, then pushed his snarling face over the table. "On the dirt my parents are part of now, I will never surrender. Not if this war goes on for a hundred seasons. Two hundred. You are foul. I am here to send your ideas to the black. If you follow, I will not grieve. I will not honor you with the death rite. The Stag and Doe demand this."

"Very well." Aith sighed and drummed raw fingers on the table. "Maybe a gift will change your mind."

Tel's animal face was unchanged.

"Your songmaker." He tapped his fingers again. "The name escapes m—"

"Vared?"

"Ah, yes." Aith's lips twisted into an obscene grin. "*Vared.*"

"Vared is in Omela."

"No, nephew. No." Slowly, Aith shook his head. "That ship did not make it to Omela. It came upon a Feighan vessel. To think of the chances. We've had so few ships to spare to patrol the eastern coast, especially that far south."

Open-mouthed, dizzy, Tel found he could say nothing.

"The ship was boarded. A terrible mess. Bloody. But your *Vared* was among the prisoners taken back to Feigh. To Affas. Of course, it was not long before someone recognized him. So, we held onto him. Everyone else, we eliminated. But not your songmaker. And a Feighan child. Eight or so seasons when we found her."

"Ofya." He could not see.

"Yes. No sense in harming her. Her mind could still be saved. She's with good, pure Feighan people now, back in Affas. At the orphanage in which your mother showed such interest. Of course, it's more of a *school* now. Alongside other children who've been liberated from disloyal families, she'll learn the true faith and the superiority of her Feighan blood. But we did keep the Omelan housed in one of the cells of Affas Island all these months. Knowing I was coming to see you, I decided we should take him on this trip. So we could return him to you." Aith rose and walked behind his nephew, moving toward the tent flap.

King Tel felt like he was going to fall off the world. "Give him to me." He dropped his head. "Please."

"But you have him." Tel heard the tent flap open. "You're sitting on him." The flap closed.

Tel threw himself from the trunk, stumbling. He weaved a senseless, ragged circle around the tent. "Help me," he whispered. Knowing he needed to say it louder, he tried to scream but could not find the back of his throat. His stomach felt as if it was pierced by a blade, and his hand flew to cover the nonexistent wound. A memory came to him, disjointed—another tent. He tried to move his hand by breathing into his stomach.

"Bin," he shrieked, turning in time to see he was already walking in.

"Majesty," he said, wild-eyed.

Tel was unable to face the box upon which he had been carelessly sitting only a moment before. Is that him? Bin, is that him? You have to tell me. You have to look, Bin." His finger, awkwardly held to the side and back of his body, bounced in little jabs in the direction of the chest. "Is that him? Is that him? Is it?" It was difficult to see, but he realized the corporal was no longer in front of him.

Bin gasped. "Oh, my goddesses and gods."

A thud.

"It is him?" Tel screamed.

"Yes."

King Tel burst from the tent and ran after his uncle, who was not yet halfway back to his troops. His experience was that of watching himself, unconscious of choice or will, flying toward his target. Tel crossed the turf like a man half his age. He was upon Aith and his bodyguard in what seemed like an instant. Hearing him approach, they turned and froze. Tel did not even know the antler-handled dirk was in his hand until he drove the blade into the solar plexus of his uncle's escort. The man fell to the dirt on his back, scraping his boots on the ground as he rocked in pain.

Tel lunged at Aith, tackling him to the ground. At the edges of his awareness, he knew the other soldiers had to be moving in his direction.

"Peacemaker prince," spat his uncle. He snickered.

"What did you do? What did you do to him?"

"The stagsblood touch told us nothing. We didn't know if it was some magic of yours. So we had to try to make him talk. We did *so much*. He gave us nothing useful, and we really expended so much effort to...*encourage* him. He was completely broken by the time he joined us for our trip here."

"No." It was more primal grunt than word.

"Yes, Tel."

"What did you do?"

"Are you sure you want to know?" Aith's smile was a nasty taunt.

Tel responded with a punch to his uncle's mouth, the dirk's handle in his fist. His knuckles bled. "What. Did. You. Do?"

"Last night, we drowned him in a barrel of ale. In your honor. It was perfect." Even with a destroyed mouth, he looked to be in ecstatic reverie.

Before Aith had finished his confession, the stagsblood had shown Tel everything. *They had slowly poisoned his father. They had driven Craid mad and thirsty with the tethers. They had tried to do the same to Tel. They had tortured and killed Vared. And Lag—not Aith—was the dynast.* In just two beats, King Tel experienced all the fetidness—the many seasons of treachery and cruelty.

He made no decision but became aware he was stabbing his uncle's chest. Bin was on him, dragging him back in the direction of the tent and the city. He was not sure how many times he had sent the edge into ribs and flesh.

"Tel, Tel. They're coming," said Bin. "He's dead."

"No." Somehow, he found the strength to buck the giant corporal. He charged forward at the advancing soldiers, about twenty and five of them.

On the way, he sent lightning into his uncle's companion, still moving on the ground. Raising his red, dripping sleeves, he sent two bolts into the turf a short distance in front of the troops barreling at him. They were undeterred. He cut them down, one by one, with the dynasty, until a handful had the good sense to flee.

When the threat was eliminated, Tel held his bloody arms over his head, braying in wild, irrational triumph. He walked back to the tent, past a sputtering Bin.

Tel secured the lock on the chest and lifted one end of it off the ground. He began dragging it toward the gate.

"I'll help you." Bin walked to the other end of the box.

King Tel roared at him until he stepped back.

Thirty and Six

Once the king had pulled the box containing his dead man inside the wall, he asked the group of soldiers arrayed near the gatehouse, "Who is in charge of the gate?"

"I am, your majesty." Her voice quaked.

Tel saw only her feet as she stepped forward. "Do not collect their bodies. Do not burn them. Do not offer them a syllable of prayer. Give them to the scavengers. Kill anyone who tries to tend to them."

"Yes, your majesty."

He raised the end of the chest by the leather handle and began walking west. The people who had gathered near the gate, hoping to hear news of a war ended, melted from his path.

"Your majesty," Bin begged, "let me help. Tel. Please. We'll get a wagon and take him that way."

"No. He is my responsibility."

"It's too far."

"Ride home, then." He did not pause, pulling the chest over the street without looking up.

"I won't leave you."

Tel answered with a guttural rumble.

"If you'd let me take the other end so we can carry him properly." Bin made a move for the strap.

Tel dropped his end of the box. As it struck the cobbles, he saw Bin look at the container and wince. "Leave him alone." He lifted the chest again and, eyeing it, sobbed. "I am sorry I dropped you." He continued down the

343

street, dragging Vared behind him. "I am sorry. I am sorry. I am sorry." He shook his head, eyes burning. "I am sorry. I am sorry. I am sorry. I am sorry." The words shook apart and were replaced by tremulous humming.

A bubble of silence surrounded them as they progressed through the city. Tel had the sense—pressure on skin—of people watching. They dared not speak or move. The only sound Tel heard outside his own whimpering and rambling was the chest scraping over the stones. It was enduring thunder in his ears.

After a while, he heard something else, but from inside himself. Although his mind was not lowered, he seemed to be sending out grasping, undulating tethers. The connections were brief. He received fragments of thought and emotion from all directions as if the dynasty was at work independent of his will. He was barraged by shards of consciousness, animal and human. The stagsblood read everything and nothing at all—a maddening din.

He needed to switch arms frequently. His shoulders, forearms, wrists, and fingers were dull fire. After an hour or more, he stopped, lowering the box to the street with care. He craned his neck to look at the sun. "Of course. Now. Finally." He shed his bloody shirt, whipping it to the side.

The undershirt was thrown to the street a handful of blocks after that. Sweat dripped from his aching body. He smelled himself in the air as he panted and pulled. *Maybe this will kill me.* "Because I am not stopping. Not stopping."

When three-quarters of his procession was complete, one end of the leather strap by which he was dragging the chest detached from the wood. Tel's arm was twisted painfully as the box lurched over and downward. He had not thought of Bin in a long while but now noticed him visibly rein in his urge to assist. The reminder of his presence filled King Tel with a quiet rage.

He began to stagger and weave as he neared the end of the pathetic march. He stumbled to the ground a pair of times, moaning as he straightened and resumed dragging Vared to his absent lord cousin's house. When he finally pulled the box inside, he heard the voices of Caip, Dar, and Belo. He understood nothing save one word.

"No," Bin boomed.

Tripping and falling and grunting, he heaved the chest up the stairs, pulled it into his room, and slid it onto the bed. He crawled alongside the battered coffin and collapsed on his belly. For a long time, he was still and silent while his mind raced. The thoughts came so quickly they were incomprehensible—some his own, some pulled in by the tethers. Hours passed. All was a gale of meaningless noise. He slept.

* * *

His rest was not long. The indigo light told him it was early evening. He wondered how it was possible to wake up crying. Face still on the pillow, he folded his body, so he came to his knees.

He wailed into feathers and fabric and snot, hugging his abdomen. Tel keened so long and hard into the pillow he thought his throat might bleed. He hoped the blood would drown him. *Let them have the kingdom. Let them have the world. Let them create not mud of dirt and blood, not rivers of red, but oceans of it. Let them cover the whole of the world.* A dark liberation was upon his mind. He had lost.

Time passed. He was on his side in the nearly black room, hugging his knees, looking at the box, listening to all the tethers lure pieces of people into his mind. He heard nonsense.

Caip's voice followed some knocking behind him. Squeezing his eyes shut, he could make no sense of her words. She left. He waited as long as he could, then got to his feet because his bladder was full. When he reached the door, he froze.

I cannot leave him. Cannot leave him alone.

He pissed in the corner and returned to the bed.

Between twitching fits of sleep, he moaned.

* * *

The next morning, he opened the door and yelled for a servant. He asked her to bring him a hammer, nails, and blankets. When she returned, trembling, he began covering the windows.

Caip knocked when he had finished hanging the first blanket and opened the door. "My love."

"What?"

"I wanted to—I heard the banging."

Tel moved to the next window and hammered a nail through the luxurious blanket. "Made for the bed of a lord," he muttered. "Soft enough for the slumber of the antlered ones." He needed her to leave. She should not see him. His mind was slipping away. It was humiliating, but he could not stop.

"Would you eat something?"

"No."

"A drink? Juice?"

"Go."

"I...I'm so, so sorry."

In her voice, Tel heard the tears. He kept hammering. Moving to the third and final window, in his periphery, he saw her leave.

Tel got into the bed and pressed his back against the wooden thing holding Vared. He wanted to look at him—to open the box and see for himself.

Maybe he is not as bad as you think. Maybe he is not even d—

The fear was too strong.

If you loved him, you would look.

He thought of the summer day he had removed the stinger from the back of his neck.

If you loved him, you would not have put him on the ship. He begged to stay.

Tel covered his mouth with his hands and screamed into them. He could listen to himself no longer. Finding the tethers, he gave his attention to the inane buzz of humanity. Numb hours passed. He slept.

He woke in confusion, not understanding where and when he was until he felt the box next to him. Throwing himself out of bed, Tel began pacing around the bedroom, praying aloud as he wept.

"Please hear me. Please. I do not know what you expected me to do. What I should have done differently. I know you want peace. I know you do. Can you not see? Can you not see, with Lag, there will be no peace? What was I supposed to do? Let him make an empire? Let him murder the whole world until it is all Feigh? Is that what you made us for? Would you murder the beaked god? The finned goddess? Would you watch someone else do it?"

"I know I am a hypocrite. That I have thrilled in combat. I know. Maybe I should be punished. I drank my life away. I was careless with people. I know. I know. Selfish." The king began jabbing an index finger in the air violently as he walked in circles. *"But I was doing better. Trying. It is so hard to remember all the things. All the things we must do to be good. It is so much. You try it! No. You are perfect. We are so...we are people. I am a person. What do you want?"*

His gestures grew broad and wild. *"It was not enough punishment? My mother and Hod? Not cruel enough? I must be the worst person to ever live. Why else would you do this to me twice? It almost killed me. It almost killed me. Is that what you want? Then why not take me in the war? Give me a disease. Have them drown me. Give him back. Caip can rule. Lag. I do not care. Give him back. You punish him? You take him? Did you hear him? Why would you take that from the world? He made so many people happy, and he was so young.*

"What is wrong with you? You took his music from the world? And I am supposed to believe you are fair? That you are just? Who could believe that? You are abandoners in the first place. What is wrong with you? Life is not hard enough? You take good things from the world. You give us nothing. Nothing. And that is what you are. I hate you. Come here and give him back." Tel's open hands were at his sides. *"Prove you are not nothing. Come here and answer me. Show yourself. I. Am. King. A king speaks to you. Come here. Now!"*

From his right palm, a small bolt of lightning arced. It leapt to a chair and scorched the back cushion. A narrow column of flame jetted from his left hand into the air. About a dozen strange black crystals, the size of peas, materialized in the middle of the room, instantly falling to the rug with tiny, hushed thuds. Tel had not lowered his mind to ask for these conjurations. Frightened, he sat on crossed legs where he was, waiting for the Stag and Doe. He stayed still until he could remain upright no longer. He lay on the rug and slept, the black crystals cutting him in his fitfulness.

* * *

In the morning, eyes not yet open, he heard the slivers of people's lives on the other end of the tethers, one after the other, after the other, after the other. Once he pushed past the sea of noise, he realized he was not alone. He opened his eyes, rolled over, and seeing them there, closed his eyes with a short moan. Rolling his body again, he faced away.

"It's time," Caip said.

"Time?"

"We have—" Her sentence died in her throat.

"Tel, we have to take him," said Bin.

King Tel scrambled to his feet, putting his body between them and the chest on his bed. He backed up and sat on the mattress. "No."

"This isn't right," said Bin.

Tel looked at Caip. Her face was twisted with agony. She did not raise her eyes to him.

"It's not good for you," said Dar, softly.

"Everyone's worried. You need to eat. The people need to see you. Your people. This is the third day," said Bin.

"Your people are asking for their king," said Belo. "And, we need to move, while we have the advantage. We need to march on Affas now and take the capital."

"Move? More death," Tel said. "Eat? More flesh."

"Less." Dar leaned toward the king. "If your brother has to choose between Kamber and Affas, he'll choose Affas. Every day we sit is a day we risk reinforcements arriving by ship from the war up there. We have them vastly outnumbered and demoralized. If he puts more on the field, there will only be more death."

"More death."

Caip scooted to Tel's feet. The sight of her doing so with one arm made him swallow hard. She looked up at him, showing him her grief-carved face and swollen eyes. "Tel. We have to bury Vared. Deep, the Omelan way."

"Here?"

"It has to be done," she said.

"Not here."

She took his left hand in hers. "It's not good to keep him with you. He can't stay. We're doing it tomorrow. We've decided for you."

"Because I cannot decide."

Caip said, "Yes."

"Tomorrow?"

"Yes."

"Belo," Tel said, without looking at him.

"Yes, friend?"

"He should be home. Not here. He was so Omelan. He should be added to Omelan dirt. If we burn him. The ashes. They could be brought to Omela for burial…"

Belo said, "It is done. Sometimes. In war. But you must do something publicly."

"At the market cross, maybe," Caip said.

"Publicly? Market cross?"

"There will be no dealings," Caip said. "No sales. Your people know what's happened. Many will want to be there. They need to. For you."

King Tel squeezed his best friend's fingers. "Tomorrow." His scorched eyes again threw tears into his beard. "Not on a pile. I will burn him with the stagsblood. Clean on stone."

The bed moved under him. Dar and Bin were taking the box. His whole body twitched as instinct told him to fight them off. His friend did not let go of his hand. A groan, soft and pinched, escaped him. "Caip?"

"Yes?"

"May I rest one more day?"

"Yes."

* * *

Freshly bathed and dressed, Tel sat in a chair in the room that had been serving as his. Feeling a bit better to be clean, he had taken down the blankets he had hung over the windows. He could not manage to bring himself to open the shutters, even though it was a warm day. His chest and gut hurt. The vexation of the tethers was constant. A knock at the door caused the room to vibrate.

It took a few beats to gather his strength to make his voice loud enough. "Come in, Bin."

"You're dressed. Good."

Tel did not look up. "Yes."

"What will you use for the ashes?"

"One of the cooks said there was a plain box," answered Tel.

Corporal Bin took a couple steps toward him. "I have this."

Tel looked up to see Bin presenting a wooden container on his palms. "It is pretty."

"It is my woman's. Her mother used it for odds and ends. She cleaned it and painted it for me. For keepsakes. Some of her yellow hair. A few letters. Rocks and shells. I pack it up with my tent and have it with me wherever I pitch it."

"I cannot take your keepsake box."

"If you look at the picture she made, it's a little frog and a stag." He brought it closer for his king to see. The paint on the cover was primitively rendered but clear and colorful. "For the two of us. She's the Andowian frog, and I'm the Feighan stag. I know it's not perfect. Vared would be a bird. But the meaning's the same."

"It is too special for you to give up."

Bin squatted so he could be eye-to-eye with Tel. "That's exactly why I must give it up. Vared was my friend. And my woman would want the same. You would do us a great honor."

Tel felt a glimmer of gratitude for the first time since the people of Larotha had joined their fight for the city. He saw his friend's sad smile, and the flash of thankfulness sparked like steel hitting a flint. He appreciated the brief respite from the tide of baneful thoughts as much as the gift and sprang at Bin, embracing him.

"Thank you," Bin said.

Caip knocked and said it was time.

Crossing the distance from the bedroom to the front of the house was the most difficult walk of Tel's life. The open air and light of the day loomed and daunted. Outside was the brightness of the spring and the darkness of his new reality. Inside, he could pretend he was exempt from time itself. Outside, Vared was dead. Inside, Tel could, at least in part, deny it.

In the street in front of the house was a simple, flat wagon hitched to a horse. People, standing quiet, lined the road. Belo stood at attention next to the cart. On it was Vared's body, tightly shrouded in black. Tel had expected the chest. "Who wrapped him?"

"The three of us," said Dar, behind him. "We did not want anyone else to do it."

Vaguely, Tel considered how horrifying it must have been. He could only find a little of his voice. "Thank you." He turned to Caip. "The people. I do not want them to feel they have to be here. It is vulgar if they must be here just because I am highborn. None of them know him. Most of them do not know me. Or you. Many of them have lost just like we have. They will lose more."

Caip said, "That's exactly why they're here. We've all lost. And will lose. They believe you to be decent. They know a decent ruler bears a little bit of each loss."

King Tel took his place behind the wagon. Belo and the three others fell in behind him. Clutching the box Bin had given him, he let his vision dull and soften. Still, he could not miss the many Larothans who, as a sign of respect, held palmfuls of dirt—*Feighan* dirt—out for Vared as they passed. The procession lasted close to two hours.

At the market cross, the silence was utter, despite the presence of thousands. All the tents and stalls were gone. Even the wind did not dare to stir. Caip, Dar, Bin, and Belo lifted Vared from the wagon. Gingerly, they placed him down on one of the large slabs that formed the wide row dividing the usually bustling market in two.

The march had exhausted the king to numbness. He asked himself why he could not feel anything and realized it was a blessing. His steps to the slab were deliberate. In front of his lover's head, he stopped, still holding Bin's woman's piece of handicraft. He looked at the frog and stag. Bringing his eyelids down, he lowered his mind, which caused the noise of the tethers to swell in his head. He focused past the voices.

Veery.

It was not a fire, exactly. It was instantaneous. With the dynasty, Tel incinerated him. He was now ash and fine bone on the slab. Tel was paralyzed for a few moments. All the people watched and waited. "Thank you for being with me, Larotha. I should have said a prayer. I should have told you about him. I am sorry." He worried he had done everything the wrong way.

He squatted and, using his bare hands, put the ashes into the container. He hated that it was impossible to get it all into the box. Even in the stillness of the day, some drifted away. Some would not come off the slab, clinging. He wondered if he had part of his hair, his nose, the flat belly, the elegant fingers. Desperation and panic might have swept him away, but he remembered the eyes upon him.

King Tel and his friends made the long, silent walk back to the lord's house.

Thirty and Seven

Tel wanted to go up to sleep immediately, but Caip and the others forced him to eat. They shared a meal together in the enormous dining room. The king's gut both demanded food and grumbled about its arrival. He had never known such a combination of hunger and nausea and could only pick at some starchroot.

Caip, Dar, and Bin shared a few memories of Vared. Tel could have kissed and punched them all for it. Eyes damp, he stared at a dish on the table as his friends chatted and enjoyed respectful laughs.

When he thought they would let him leave, Tel excused himself.

"I have something for you." Caip pulled a fine handkerchief from her pocket. It was folded into a tidy square. Handing it to him, she said, "I was not sure if you would want it now or if I should hold it. Tell me if I should."

He unwrapped the little silk package. The chain and Doe pendant almost slipped off the fabric onto the floor, but he caught it. He felt sorry he had not even thought of it. "I am glad to have it," he said, beginning to weep. "Thank you. I will wear it." It was difficult to see through his tears, so he fumbled with the clasp.

"Here," Belo said, putting his hand out. "I will put it on for you."

Tel gave his friend the necklace that had belonged to Fyor and to Vared. He stared at his own fingers while Belo secured the chain around his neck. "Thank you," he choked out. "Goodnight." Behind him, he heard Belo clearing his throat.

"Friend," the Omelan said. "Tomorrow. We must talk about what comes next. We must leave soon for Affas."

Tel picked at his right thumbnail with his opposite index finger. "So soon?"

Belo's voice was firm. "Freezing you in place was the aim of…what they did. It is harsh. And I do not envy you. But yes."

"So soon? With Vared still under my fingernails?" He spun on the foursome. "Do you see this?" He threw his hands in front of himself. "He is still on my hands." A dancing ball of lightning appeared, encircling the end of his left arm. He wondered at it. "I seem to have trouble controlling it. Because I am not myself." His voice began to thunder. "Because the stuff of my man *is still stuck under my nails!* I know the war is important, but can I clean him—Fuck!"

A hundred or so tiny black gems materialized around Tel and fell to the table and floor. The tethers shouted their rubbish at him. A corner of a napkin caught fire in front of Dar. He smothered it by banging it with his hand and pushed himself back from the table, openmouthed.

Tel began to struggle to speak between stabbing breaths. "You want me to finish this. You want me to finish this war. How do I do that? How do I make war when all I want is to be tender? I have just now learned. I have just now learned to be tender. Vared has just now taught me. And I am to bring death? To bring that kind of hardness? How can I be hard when life is already short brutality? Where do I put the tenderness now?"

He fell to his bottom on the rug. As he hit the floor, orange sparks jumped from him in all directions, like pops from a fireplace. A bolt of lightning, originating a half-meter in front of his face, screeched under the table, blasting part of a wall away. It barely missed Dar's leg. The entirety of the house shook. Small objects crashed to the floor. Dust rained.

The others got to their feet and cowered in the archway between the hall and the room. "I am sorry. I do not kn—" He fell onto his back and heard a great commotion in the hallway. He was unable to make sense of it. Then, along one of the tethers, he heard a woman's voice, clear as an early autumn sky.

I'm a dynast. I'm here to help. I don't want to hurt them. Tell them to let me in.

Tel mustered all his strength to yell, "Let her help me!"

A few seconds later, he felt her and saw her shadow but could not focus. More obsidian beads fell on them.

He heard Caip say, "What is that? What are you doing?"

It felt like a yellow needle plunged its barb into his earlobe. He calmed.

* * *

Someone joined him on the mattress. A shadow hung. He felt a pressure on his ear for a pair of beats. Something changed. A veil had been pulled up and away. His senses began experiencing the world around him in the typical ways. Gone was the gauzy warmth and sense of pleasant detachment.

"I'm Icas," the figure sitting on the bed told him. She flicked her hand, and the lamp on the table beside the bed came to life. Gray-eyed and pale-lipped, she had a broad forehead and a small mouth. A bit of a wave appeared at her temples. Otherwise, her silver and black hair was straight. She looked to be between twenty and forty seasons older than him.

"You are the dynast."

"Yes."

"I am King Tel. I am also a dynast."

She rolled her eyes. "Really?"

"I do not like to presume people know who I am."

"Every reasonably trained, moderately gifted dynast knows you now. Intimately."

The king sat up against his pillows. "What does that mean?"

"Tell me about the last few days."

"I would rather not." He let his head fall back to the pillow.

"We all know you lost your Vared. You've been throwing out a thousand forceful, unwelcome tethers about it. It's why I came to you."

He turned a look of disgust to her. "I am sorry to hear I have inconvenienced you with my grief."

"I accept your apology," said Icas. "You'll have to ask the others."

"The others? What is wrong with you?" Getting out of the bed, he nearly knocked her over. "It was outside of my control."

"Precisely the problem. You were casting all kinds of undisciplined energy over all the nations. The unintentional fire and lightning and conjuring you saw was only the beginning. We call it the bleeding. Had it intensified, you could've torn the whole of the world."

"Ridiculous." He rubbed at his sore left ear.

She softened her face. "Yours is an extraordinary gift. Dynasts all have a bit of the stagsblood in us. You have more than most. Remember, it's the blood of the gods. The ones who made the world. If they had that power, they had the power to unmake it. That power is in us. In you, especially. But in you, it's raw and unshaped and dangerous. Because out there, they're ignorant and fearful. They expect us to let our gift die. But some of us are so strong, there is no dying. Like in your case. And it's a risk to the world itself."

"And in your case?"

"No. I ran away, west, as a child. I was called here. We all were. Some of us young, some of us older. You were called, but you ignored it."

"To the forest."

"Not far from here," said Icas.

"How many?"

"Just more than one hundred."

"Undiscovered? No one has ever come upon you?"

"If they did, I don't think they'd like it." She chuckled. "But, by combining our magic, we make it so no one can find us."

"Invisibility."

"No." Again, she gave a little laugh. "You can still walk into something invisible. It's more like tethering. We send out a dome of...emotion. Anyone without the blood who approached us would be overcome by fear. They wouldn't continue."

He was overwhelmed by the thought of a hundred dynasts living together. "Why are we pulled to the forest?"

"We don't know but suspect it's because of the bloodpines."

"Bloodpines?"

"A kind of tree. The wood has a strange effect, but only when it pierces the skin. It renders the stagsblood useless," said Icas. "More or less renders the whole dynast person useless. They can't do magic, and they can't do much else. I put a bloodpine pin through your ear to keep you from killing your friends."

"I..." Tel's mind raced. "Would you like some hidybrew?"

"It's my favorite," she said. "Gods know I'll need it if these questions keep up."

* * *

They talked all night over pot after pot of steaming hidybrew. The members of the king's miniature Table looked in on them frequently, foreheads wrinkled over narrowed eyes.

Icas explained the value of proximity to others with the stagsblood. It was not merely about the transmission of skills or knowledge. Pointing out Tel had taught himself how to lower his mind, she told him his lack of exposure to others with the gift was likely the reason his control over the magic had begun a perilous disintegration. Dynasts, like all humans, needed socialization to thrive and maintain their sanity. Their requirements in this realm were specialized. Some of the socialization must be with others with the stagsblood.

"So, I am stronger with the magic of the fire and dirt than any of you?" Tel turned his face to the pastel light beginning to show around the shutters.

"Yes. You're stronger—at least you have the potential to be—with the rain and wind, too. But they have been more difficult to master. They always are. The fact that you can work with them at all is unusual. Amazing. Except that—"

"Except that I was once *very* close to a dynast. Even if I did not know."

"Yes."

"When I killed Aith, I could not believe it. I had looked inside him before, but not deeply and not for long. I thought it was him. Thought he controlled

357

my brother with tethers. That he took advantage of my brother's stupidity and vanity."

"But Lag is the dynast."

Tel saw the smudge of his reflection in the polished tabletop. "It was he who took advantage. Of my uncle's cleverness and ambition."

Icas clucked her tongue, nodding. After a few beats, she wrinkled her nose. "Why did you hide your stagsblood, even as a child, from your family? Before recent seasons, not even the most backward feared the children."

King Tel frowned. "I told my mother. Only after the dynasty did not seem to be leaving me as it should have. She asked me the same question. And helped me answer it. I was the son of the king and queen. I had to be the perfect Feighan. She told me I was a damned fool, in the way only a loving mother…" He was stunned by how much he still missed her.

"Sweetheart." Icas moved her hand to cover his. "What if you'd been uncooperative when I arrived here? What if the bleeding had been so great there was no getting control back?"

"I am not sure."

"A cataclysm. An apocalypse. We would have two choices." She lifted her hand. "We would've had to kill you, against the faith. Or would've had to take your dynasty."

"That is possible?"

"At a great price. The one to draw another's stagsblood out along a tether destroys their own dynasty in the process." As if even speaking the thought aloud had troubled her, she pushed a breath out through her lips. "In your case, many of us would've had to make the sacrifice. And your brother?"

"Lag?" He was not certain what she was asking.

"What would happen to Lag if he were to feel an enormous loss? The loss of a kingdom."

He felt dizzy. "He is stronger than me. I can feel it."

Icas nodded. "We can feel it, too. More powerful even than you."

"I will have to…kill him? I will not do it. My own brother? And I am not going to create a martyr. I need to unite this kingdom. I will exile him."

"Then you'll need to take his power. Subdue him with the bloodpine and pull it from him." Icas's eyes drilled into his. "And in the process, you'll give away your own."

"But I do not want to do that." He had not meant for it to be heard. It had slipped out. "There is no guarantee. He is stronger."

Her small eyes glinted in the low morning light. "If you move fast after getting the bloodpine in his skin, we think you'll be able—"

"Think?" He looked at the ceiling, shaking his head. Icas stood and padded to the window, opening the shutter. The cold morning spilled into the room. "Think? You must help me. I cannot leave this thing undone. This war. I have to try to make him face this loss. And there is no guarantee we will win. You must help my army win, and then you must help me contain my brother. It is the only sure way."

She moved to him and placed a hand on his shoulder. She looked like she was about to cry. "We can't do that."

"Why?"

"The faith." Her exasperation was apparent. "We can't participate."

Tel's bitter laugh rattled through the whole house. "So, you will endorse me killing my own brother? Or at least me cutting a path of death to get to him so I can strip his stagsblood and give away my own? You will encourage me to march an army to his door? But you will not participate. You will not sacrifice. An...*apocalypse*, as you call it. But you will do nothing to stop it You will have others stop it for you."

Icas raised a finger. "Many in our community were willing to sacrifice the stagsblood to stop you from destroying the world."

"None of you will answer the call of your k—"

"We do not have kings in the Chreok Forest, Tel." The muscles of her jaw were rocks. "Our decisions are formed around what the majority wants. We didn't ask for this situation. We live outside your society because of the fear and prejudice of the non-dynasts."

"I live openly."

"You live openly *now*," said Icas. "And you're a royal. For centuries, for millennia, what's perfectly acceptable for one of you is disallowed for the rest of us. We must be with one another, openly, or else our powers become dangerous. In trying to keep themselves safe from us, this kingdom has made a much more precarious situation. A threat to the world the goddesses and gods made. To every living thing on it."

"But still not a profound enough threat to call you to action," said King Tel, under his breath. He worked at his lower lip with his teeth until it hurt. "I think the most threatening things of all are moral absolutes. Even the love of peace. I used to think it primitive that women and men solved problems with violence. Any problems. But keeping your hands at your sides while someone bloodies your face is madness. Nonviolence in the face of apocalypse is suicide. Lifting those arms to form fists—that might be violence. It is an affront to the antlered ones. But letting someone punch you to death—that is violence, too. To yourself. And an even bigger insult to the gods."

She met him with a wall of a face, immovable. They sat a long while, as the shadows were slowly chased from the room.

Icas ended the quiet. "You didn't want to drink when you lost him?"

"I...It did not even come into my mind. To think I used to need a slug or two just to get through a short meeting."

"Something was repeating in your mind while you bled. Over and over." She hummed part of the song Vared had written for him.

Tel was frustrated to the point of rage to be sobbing again, tears and snot running into his black whiskers. It was a flash of angry resistance before he allowed himself to surrender.

"Would you tell me about it?" asked Icas. "I only could discern a few words. But that melody..."

King Tel told her about the song and its maker before she returned to the wilderness.

* * *

Tel and Caip rode through the city to join the larger force waiting outside the walls. He was moved to see her in Kelseigh's saddle. She had brought

Pony for him. Nodding and waving to his people on the way, he told her about his long conversation with Icas. When he related the truth about Lag, the threat he represented, and how he must contain that threat, she became enraged. Caip wanted to charge into the forest and demand the dynasts help Tel. He explained it would be fruitless. Their decision was firm, and the dome of fear would prevent her from approaching. Inside a pocket of his doublet, he fingered the bloodpine pin.

The city guard raised the gate, and the thousands of soldiers outside roared upon seeing their king. Tel could not escape the air of anticipation and eagerness among the army. They had the advantage over Lag's force in every conceivable way. He would lead them to meet their foes outside of Affas. In about three weeks, the final battle would be joined.

That night, in his tent, Tel spoke to Vared. "Veery. Do not think I have forgotten about you. I never could. I am not trying to make what we had less important. But for the next weeks, I will have to ask my feelings to wait. I must be king and king only for a while. I will be back to my heart and to you soon. I will see my grief through."

He found sleep without trouble.

Thirty and Eight

The rigor of the march helped him continue to sleep easily for the next two nights. On the third, he fell asleep without trouble but was awakened in the middle of a terror. His brother had been working at his fears. It was not the dark nature of the dream that had launched him to wakefulness on his pallet. The drums were thundering alarm. Once it registered, he was outside, scrambling to Caip's nearby tent. She was already giving orders.

"What is it?"

She did not even face him. "They approach. Their whole force. From the north."

"All of them?"

"I think so," said Caip.

"They want to meet us in the open instead of defending Affas?" Tel could not believe his luck. "It's a blunder."

"Tel," she shouted at him, finally showing him her face. "They're marching presently. Tonight. They're almost upon us."

He swallowed. "Now, then."

"No. We retreat."

"Larotha."

"No," said Caip. "You don't understand. They are almost here. We wouldn't make it to Larotha. And even if we could, I have no taste left for turning those streets red. Those Larothans who still want to fight are with us. We couldn't put those people through more than they've already suffered."

"All right." He pulled on his beard. "To where do we retreat?"

"The road to the southeast. In that direction, it's hillier and rockier. We'll make it harder for them to maneuver. To flank or surround us. All these months, we've done better on irregular terrain. It flummoxes their side. And I'll not let them make all the choices about how this battle is fought."

"Very well. I trust you as ever," said Tel, eyes shimmering. "We withdraw to the southeast and pull them into the hills."

"This is…the first time…I don't know what to do," said Caip. "I can't fight with one arm."

Tel hugged her. Chin on her shoulder, he said, "I am no king without you, Caip. I am not sure I am a man without you."

Striking camp was a terrifying scramble, doom hanging about every sweating soldier and pack and tent stake. Tel only cared about keeping one possession near him. Carefully, he nestled the stag and frog box in a basket on a back board.

The king's general and her officers pushed them hard to the southeast through the darkness. Caip and Tel walked at the front of the snaking column, leaving their horses to others, as they often did. Tel found himself checking over his shoulder frequently, wondering just how close the enemy was. He considered trying to sense their proximity using the magics of the east and west, but he knew it would be wiser to hold his energy for the coming fight.

A fog materialized around their boots. They did not make it to the rocky hills.

Those hummocks had just begun to show themselves against the bluing predawn when the horrible sound came at them, seemingly from every direction. A rumble and clatter shook their bones, spooking person and beast. A mild sort of chaos seemed to swirl around Tel and Caip, everyone trying to discern what, exactly, was happening.

The sounds, of course, did not really hit them from all sides. When the screeching joined those lower noises, it became clear. Another force—not the one at their backs—approached from the northeast. By the time the realization had settled in Tel's mind, it had already begun.

They had not even tried to soften them up with archers first. Their cavalry simply charged, shearing their parade of thirty thousand neatly in two. Tel's soldiers fled in every direction, like rabid, drunken bats. The king found he was frozen in his place. His thinking was trapped in a useless cycle as he tried to understand from where all these enemies came. He stood dumb.

Caip yanked at his leather armor, but he turned and squinted in the gray-blue light as he shuffled backward, trying to see the enemy as they hacked away at his sisters and brothers in arms. He was convinced he would see Hebites swinging those swords, that Gawash had sent his emperor reinforcements. It was the only explanation. His gut twisted when he saw, to a person, they were black-haired. They were Feighan.

Tel said, "Where…"

"Come on!" Caip screamed at him.

It pulled him from his stupor. He remembered he was a dynast. "No." He ripped himself away from her. He raised his arms and lowered his mind.

She stepped in front of him. "We need to think. To regroup. Organize. Let's go."

Caip had uttered it as an order, and Tel obeyed it. They clamored away until they were walking uphill. None of Lag's women and men pursued them. Some of the troops retreating in the same direction, among them the banner guard, began to recognize their king and general and fell in behind them. When Caip told them to stop, they were five or six hundred.

From a lower slope at the beginning of the range of hills, they regarded the mayhem. Tel had vastly overestimated the number of his soldiers who had fled. The bulk of his army was engaged with the enemy still. Others, having scrambled away at first, appeared to be heading back to stand with their comrades.

"We cannot sit up here. Especially not me," said Tel, looking down at his feet, belly hot. "I am too strong to hide."

"Stag and Doe," a young member of the banner guard said, pointing.

Tel returned his attention to the battle below. Thousands more of the brown and white charged through the mist toward the fight. He understood. "Lag pulled the force from Kamber to destroy us. They came up behind us.

The ones from Affas..." He hung his head again, thinking of Vith, ashamed to imagine what the dead king would feel if he could see his land from the black.

It occurred to Tel his father was the most courageous person he had ever met. He had led a suspicious country to an understanding with their bitterest enemy, like a shepherd leading a skittery flock through hills like these. He had done this knowing the dirks would come out for him.

Tel's own lack of courage—his inability to face his easy, gilded life without numbing—had rendered him unable to shepherd the nation to an internal understanding. That was the second half of the journey. His father had left it to him to complete it.

He raised his head. "I am going."

"There's another way," Caip said. "Surrender. I'll take your colors to them now. You run. For Omela."

"I will not surrender. Not to Lag. Not to his lunatic ideology. I will not dishonor my father more than his sons already have."

"There's honor in surrender, Tel," said Caip. "When it's hopeless. It saves lives."

"I cannot. You will be queen when I am gone."

"*Queen of wha*—Tel. My friend. It *is* hopeless. They have the numbers. They timed it perfectly."

"Then this is the last weight I have for the scales." Tel began to trot downslope toward the violence, raging for the fight. His singleness of focus prevented him from noticing for a moment the sound of the people behind him. He turned. Every woman and man who had been perched with him marched at his back. "It is hopeless, even for me. All the lightning in the world cannot stop a sword from piercing my heart just like anyone else."

"You're our king," Caip said.

He could see clearly what would happen. His army had managed to regain some order. He watched them form a tight wedge, which they used not to hold ground, but to press forward, into the enemy lines. They had decided to refuse to yield or fall back, instead choosing a mad offense. The other side—as fresh and invested in the fight as he had seen the enemy since the war started—outnumbered them two to one. Lag's force would simply continue to send people forward, broadening their front until they could wrap around the sides of the wedge. He looked at his friend and knew instantly she had made an identical assessment.

They walked in tense silence for a few moments. "This is where the general stays," Tel said.

"I'm not staying anywhere."

"Caip. I have no doubt you will ably swing a sword with your left arm in a few years' time. If anyone can adapt, it is you. However, you are not able to fight today. He removed his back board, leaving it with her. Get to Omela. They will need you very soon. Lag will not stop. Get word to Mor. So he may join you."

She screamed—a frustrated, guttural, animal cry.

King Tel and the others continued toward the melee. "Caip of Foghar," Tel called, without turning, "you deserved better than me."

Tel ran in an easy arc at the battle, so he could charge the enemy's flank. Yelling with all his throat, he began to loose compact silver bolts of energy at them. "Veery! Veery! Veery!" He gave no concern to preserving his powers. Instead, he threw everything he could, delighting in the way they panicked when they saw him tearing their way. The satisfaction was perverse and deep, a sensation he felt in his balls.

It did not take long for them to adjust tactics. Maybe a thousand of them broke off to face him. His stagsblood would be depleted before he could cut them all down—*well before* at his reckless pace. He asked himself what would happen when he had no more left to send at them. He shouted, "My dear Stag and Doe, if you still listen to this warmaker king, let him collapse dead, spent on this Feighan dirt before they have the pleasure of seeing his hot blood on their blades. Veery! Veery! Veery!"

The sounds of lightning cooking the spring air stood out from the din of ordinary warfare as he pressed forward. Over the chaos, the sizzle and scream of his magic filled his ears. Something about the noises seemed strange. For a moment, he stopped sending the bolts out. He realized the sounds continued despite his stillness, distant. The whole irregular mass of enemies seemed to lurch in his direction.

He thought for a long stretch of beats that he was losing his mind. Then, he saw the wedge of his army push forward. It was a matter of a handful of meters, but it was progress. In front of them, Lag's lines seemed to fray. The spasmodic ripple of their troops sideward and in his direction continued. The pace of the bleeding of the force from its flank quickened. Soon, many women and men had caught up to the contingent that had begun advancing on Tel.

Resuming his assault, King Tel pressed forward. He sent out a tether, probing. Never had he heard and felt such a stew of fear and misery. It threatened to bring him to his knees, but he heard something else.

There. Icas was here. She and more from the forest had joined his fight.

Within an hour, it was over.

* * *

Icas and Este, a soft-bodied and soft-spoken old dynast woman, sat at the little round table in Tel's tent near noon the next day. He brought them each a mug of hidybrew and prepared his own. He took a seat. Even though it was morning and he had only been out of bed an hour, he was exhausted and relieved to be off his feet.

He asked, "What made the community decide to let you come?"

"The community did not decide. Nineteen of us chose to help you." Este eyed Icas darkly.

Tel took his first sip of hidybrew and set his mug down. "But what will happen? You have defied the will of the community."

Icas seemed to withdraw into herself, closing her eyes for a moment. "I don't think we'll be welcomed back home."

Este choked on a sob.

"My gods," said Tel. "This kingdom...is indebted."

"It was the right thing to do." Icas put her hand over Este's, stroking her fingers with a soothing thumb. "Our best chance of rejoining Feigh in our lifetime."

"And that is what you want?" asked Tel.

"It's what some of us want." Este lifted Icas's hand to her lips and kissed it. "At least, we do now that you've made it possible."

"It was my father who did that. His openness. His broad heart."

"Have you tried to tether your brother?" Icas looked from her lover's hand to Tel.

He fumbled to explain. "It is...*He* is too big...too loud. It is—He overwhelms. I cannot find him because he is everywhere."

A long time passed. The only sounds were from outside the tent. Tel drained his hidybrew and rose to refill his mug. "I will need your help to get to him. If I can, I will draw the blood from him and give away mine. Both things are necessary. Yesterday, I felt a lust for violence. It was so powerful. I did not experience the bleeding, but now that I have felt it, I know it is possible. And I understand we could be the end of everything. Him *or* me."

Thirty and Nine

About two days outside of Affas, the tremors started.

Walking alongside King Tel and General Caip, a male forest dynast named Hil closed his eyes and allowed his head to fall forward for a handful of beats. "Lag bleeds."

"He is panicking. Flailing," Tel said. "I can hear his thoughts and feel his—" His mouth flooded with saliva. He swallowed. "I can feel his despair. But I cannot communicate with him. I cannot get anything inside his mind. There is no way for me to exert influence. The feelings are too powerful. The thoughts are too repetitive."

"It's the same for me." Icas appeared strained.

When they were within a handful of hours of the city, they saw the ragged, smudged towers of black against the pastel softness of the early morning sky. Affas burned. The ground now shook with more vigor and frequency.

The families of Affas streamed out of the city. They headed south along the road as the army marched north, reporting that even his personal guard had abandoned Lag. Tel's brother now loosed the occasional bolt of lightning and ball of fire from the island's towers into the city on the mainland. White, sharp-edged crystals—most of them tiny, some as large as an adult's fist—fell intermittently from the sky. Sections of stone and wood were simply blinking out of existence, causing buildings to fall.

Tel stopped them outside the city wall. Without explaining himself, he asked for patience and walked a few dozen meters away from his people to find some peace. He sat on the turf and allowed his mind to fall.

Veery.

Using the tethers, he searched, listening. His consciousness veered to and fro, through a dense jungle of thought and emotion. Lag's output of magic was volcanic. Sensing a particularly overwhelming impulse of rage racing toward him along the stagsblood tethers, he braced himself. The ground shifted, rocking beneath him. He opened his eyes to see the southeast corner of the city wall crumble. White jewels the size of fat snowflakes pelted him. He saw the people of his army shielding their faces against them.

The tremors settled, and the dangerous precipitation abated. Again, Tel's mind descended. Within moments, ignoring his brother's eclipsing magic, he had found young Ofya's mind. She was still in his mother's orphanage, terrified. He severed the horrible connection. Recovering from the emotional onslaught, he shouted for Dar and Bin and gave them their instructions.

Rejoining his people, he said, "Only Dar, Bin, and the other dynasts are to enter this city. The rest of you remain here."

Caip, naturally, objected. Belo echoed her concerns.

"You are my heir," said Tel. "We need to minimize the danger to you in case I do not survive this."

The twenty and two of them entered the marred capital. King Tel estimated a quarter of the structures were burning or had collapsed. Smoke and areas of raining crystals made a haze through which he could see his childhood home, gray-green and jagged but beautiful.

The party trudged the north-south road through the heart of the city in utter silence. Three-quarters of the way to the causeway linking the island to the mainland, Bin and Dar headed east. Tel simply nodded at them. They returned the gesture. He walked on, the nineteen dynasts arrayed behind him.

"I am trying to keep my mind high until I need to lower it, but I cannot shut him out," Tel said, over more quaking. Before the round of tremors stopped, a three-story structure moaned and disintegrated thirty meters in front of him, spilling into the street. Another collapsed behind them. He and the dynasts were forced to climb over rubble.

Tel struggled to hold onto his own identity. His brother's presence overwhelmed him. He was the weakest of the group with the east and west dynasties, but he saw his companions' inner battles, too. The effort was naked on their faces. They were assaulted not by tethers—not by threads—but by a nest. He felt like he was walking against the most powerful of gales.

As they reached the bridge, a curtain of pure white fire appeared halfway between them and the island. It heated the skin of Tel's hands and face.

"A boat?" said Hil.

"It is almost impossible to scale the sides," said the king.

"Can't very well fight fire with fire. Or lightning," said Este.

"We don't need to," said Icas. "We can conjure water."

Another of the female dynasts said, "I've never created water."

"But you have made objects. You have called them from nothing onto the world," said Icas.

"Of course. This ring on my finger was once just space."

"Water is just another something to pull from nothing," said Este.

In a way he could not describe—a way that just *was*—Tel felt the minds of his sister and brother dynasts come low. It was not the same as perceiving through the tethers of east and west. Instead, the presence of focused, intense magical work in such proximity aroused a different sense in him. Those alongside him were united in purpose. He thrummed with it. The feeling girded his will.

Tel inhaled through his nose as he took his first step onto the causeway. His lungs, throat, and mouth filled with his burning city and the spitting Gray Sea. After his next step, his face was met with significantly warmer air. An energy shift, just at the fringes of his awareness, made him tilt his chin upward. Near the top of the bright wall of strange fire, what was dry air became a tinkling mist. The white flames seemed to pull the mist closer, creating a messy ring of steam like a crown at the fire's upper limit. What was fine spray became a shower, fat-dropped and falling from too low in the sky. Tel raised the hood of his filthy cloak. Lag's inferno roared in response to the magic of the forest dynasts, stretching upward and thickening outward, but the shower was now a steady rain. Flame and water hissed, announcing their union. Billows of steam were born, white as the flames themselves and thick as any of the dark plumes rising from the ruins behind them. King Tel did not pause or slow his march. His brother's dynasty did not weaken, but he strode forward, face hot and wet.

The rain screamed down in a torrent. A column of water crashed to the span and sea, massive as any falls on the Sheruckian side of the Chreok Mountains. Tel closed his eyes and walked. He was unsteady on his feet, for the whole of the bridge shook.

He had no idea how long the causeway could withstand the shaking before beginning to break into the ocean below. Although he had made peace with the possibility of his death at the start of this long journey, the notion he might die on this bridge, steps from home, terrified him. It did not matter if it was by magic fire, magic water, or a simple plunge to the Gray Sea. Still, he did not slow his pace and did not raise his eyelids.

He heard a sound, like the whole of Affas sighing. Then, all was silent except the waves at the base of the span. Even the shaking of the world had stopped. A dozen steps later, he finally opened his eyes. He found he had walked past where the unnatural fire had been. Turning, he saw the shapes of the dynasts through the churning steam. He raised both arms and showed them his palms. When they waved back, he uttered a small sound of amusement.

The causeway trembled again. Lasting only a few beats, it was stronger than any of the rumblings that had yet occurred. It knocked Tel onto his tailbone, painfully. As he recovered his senses and made his uneasy way back to his feet, he saw a crack appear, grow and split the bridge in two, lengthwise. The jagged fissure ran one hundred meters from the city side in his direction. Frozen, he watched the section to the east of the fracture detach and lean for a moment, suspended. Knowing he should run, he found himself unable to look away. The entirety of the world seemed to yawn and moan. The massive segment dropped to the waiting rocks and white caps.

The quaking resumed. Tel spun and ran, knees and elbows chugging in desperation. His ears told him more of the bridge detached. Upon reaching the other side, he saw to his right some of the island itself shearing off into the sea. The surface area that had fallen away was large enough to support a handful of merchants' homes. King Tel pulled the slack from his jaw, lowered his hood, and looked up at the castle, trying to reason where his brother might be.

* * *

Dust and debris fell on Tel as he walked through the convulsing castle. The seat of Feighan power was in a state of disarray approaching ruin. Little piles of the glimmering white stones sat here and there, on the furniture and floor. Tapestries and paintings had torn from their anchors. Entire stones had dropped from walls and ceilings. He heard an enormous racket, as what must have been a large portion of the castle—a wall or tower—shattered and collapsed. As he reached the hallway that would lead him to Lag, the tremors stopped. He knew his imminent arrival had been sensed by his brother—and that it had focused or even comforted the younger man. The bleeding had, for the moment, ceased.

A slate haze of smoke clung to the ceiling of the corridor. A pair of thickly cushioned chairs burned against a wall. Tel was hard-pressed to estimate the number of times he had sat in one or another of them. They had been, truthfully, a bit ratty looking. He had long ago decided he would have them replaced once he was king.

A memory came, vivid enough to make a statue of him. In this narrow stretch of gray-green stones, he had once raced his brother. Lag had elbowed him, causing him to split his head open on a wall. He felt an uneasy amusement, and a hollow chuckle crossed his lips. Hearing his own laugh reshaped humor into anxiety.

He took a few breaths deep into his belly, extending the exhalations as much as he could. With aching slowness, he walked down the stretching hall. He did not even quicken his pace as he reached the heat of the burning furniture. It threatened to scorch his clothes, but he kept his gradual tempo. So much planning and struggle had ferried him to this moment, but nothing, not even flames, could force him to rush to the conclusion. He paused, closing his eyes, and took three more breaths, just shy of the archway. Every muscle hard, he crossed the threshold.

Atop the throne, under the rack crown and the great stone antlers, lounged Vared.

All the work he had done to steady his respiration fled Tel. His breaths were ragged and no deeper than the bottom of his throat. The cavernous chamber bent and twisted around him. He widened the distance between his feet and rested his hands on his thighs as he tried to steady his vision and regain composure. Sweat surfaced over the entirety of his skin. The little choking gasps he heard were, he realized to his horror, his own. He could not get air. Thinking he might die, he welcomed it for a moment.

Only the desire to see his man again kept him from collapsing. He brought the entire might of his will to bear on flattening his breath and straightening his back. His vision cleared, revealing the beautiful, blue-haired creature, wrapped in the blinding white of the winter ermine. The fur cloak opened to show the perfect silk of his skin, from jutting collarbone to navel. Throat burning, Tel began to plod toward him. His starving eyes overflowed with tears. They seemed to instantly turn to steam on his cheeks. Vared was all he remembered, pretty as morning, thin as the branch of a winter tree, delicate as the finest Omelan lace. The songmaker opened his legs, showing Tel his nakedness.

The king more fell to the throne than walked. He was drawn toward the splendid chair of his father—and all the mothers and fathers of Feigh before him—like water is drawn downslope. Two meters in front of the throne, he slowed, his right hand flying to his heart. "I love you."

Vared's elegant hand flashed to the cushion beneath him and produced a dirk, but Tel was on him, clamping his own left hand over the spindle of a wrist.

"You always were slower than me," said Tel through grinding teeth. "And you always were a cheat."

He could manage no delicacy with his right hand, so he stabbed the bloodpine pin into the place the long column of the neck met the clavicle. He watched the stagsblood disguise fall away from his brother, who slumped forward, sending dirk and rack crown clattering to the floor.

Tel fell to all fours on the rug before the throne. He croaked and moaned as if he had lost Vared all over again. This time it felt like he had caused the losing. Wailing, he realized this was not true. He had felt responsible the first time, too. *I sent him away to keep him safe.* On the floor, he wept a long while until he realized Lag was speaking.

"Will...you...kill...me?" His speech was labored, the sounds wet.

Tel pushed his upper body off the floor and sat on his haunches, "I thought not, because you would be a martyr. But no one truly loves you, brother. No one will follow. Not when they know you are weakened. There is in this kingdom a minority of people who see the world your way. A sizable minority, but a minority, nonetheless. They will die off as people with yellow and white and red hair come to walk among us, and we among them. So, I will banish you. To Hebe. I do not believe anywhere else will have you. Gawash will be your king."

"Too...soft..."

"I started with an army of one hundred and sixty and four and crushed an army of nearly eighty thousand. Quite hard enough, I would say. And I spare your life not out of softness. I spare your life mostly because I know you want to die now but lack the courage to rid the world of yourself."

Lag sputtered. It might have been a laugh.

Tel looked around. He coughed. "You have destroyed our home."

"Couldn't...help...it."

"I am about to draw the blood from you," said Tel. "You will lose your gift. You will feel a fraction of the pain you have caused."

"So...will...you."

"I will gladly suffer to watch you do the same. And to make Feigh safe from you."

"You're...not...Feighan..."

King Tel brought himself to his feet. He crossed to his brother and grabbed him by the underarms. "I said that I would knock you from the throne. Seems I will have to settle for dragging you from it." He yanked Lag out of the seat. "How is it we had the same parents?"

"Brightest...boy," said Lag. He sputtered again. This time, there was no mistaking it for anything other than laughter.

Tel let his brother's upper body fall to the floor from higher than necessary. He straddled him, laying his hands on either side of his face. Frightened, he pushed his mind low.

It was agony.

Forty

King Tel had neither the time nor the inclination to leave his wounded Feigh until more than five seasons had passed. The work of repair and healing was endless. Still, he set about it with fervor, driving himself to the physical and mental brink. In his first days back in Affas, he decided he could only preserve his sanity by minimizing complaint. The brutal schedule saved him in the handful of months following his confrontation with Lag. During this time, the main symptom of losing the stagsblood was a black mood always looming at the edge of his awareness. He knew if he gave that void his attention, a part of him would find it seductive, and he might be lost to a dark courtship. Instead, to avoid the wiles of the demon suitor, he asked himself: *What else can I do?*

Tel knew the many thousands of Feighans who most fiercely supported his brother had simply shrunk back, melting into the populace. Forgiveness was his policy for all but the most egregious crimes. That grace, he decided, must be coupled with vigilance. Goodwill alone could not defeat their hateful notions of Feighan purity. The king favored imprisonment over execution. During the fortnight following the evening he had pierced Lag with the bloodpine, the people of Affas flowed into the streets, demanding his head. Tel resisted the temptation to buy their favor by giving them a spectacle of vengeance. Before his brother was put on the *Crunadam,* Tel proclaimed the penalty *would* be death if he ever put another toe on Feigh. He swore an oath to carry out the sentence personally.

The object of their rage gone, the populace calmed. They turned to rebuilding their homes and the places of commerce and assembly. Tel made Icas and Este in charge of forming a proper school for child dynasts in the city. Within weeks, more than a dozen adults with the blood, dynasts who had not heeded their inner demands to drift westward, trickled into the capital, asking for an education, too. They were welcomed. Women and men with the gift were not as rare as had been long believed. Superstitious stories had pinned the sorcerers to the shadows.

Some young Feighans, children removed from households Lag and Aith had deemed disloyal, had no close relatives left. Bin and Dar had rescued Ofya and the other parentless ones from the orphanage Tel's uncle had perverted—the same one his mother once administered. Corporal Bin took a special interest in locating more distant kin or generous families with room in their hearts and homes. These little ones had been left to fend for themselves when Lag's people had withdrawn from the city. Seeing Bin's passion for the orphans, King Tel had asked Caip to discharge him from military service so he might oversee the welfare of the children. Bin was elated.

Caip remained, as ever, Tel's rock. She checked his worst tendencies and shepherded him to the realization that healing the kingdom would be a project that would outlive them both. As Table Head, she continued to tell him when she disagreed with his thinking. She debated him sharply, as she always had. However, when a decision was made, she carried out his orders with her usual fire and excellence. Mor came to Affas to live in the castle with her. King Tel blubbered with joy at his arrival more than she.

Early on, he had left it to Caip to decide when it was safe for him to sail to Omela. Near the first day of the Feighan autumn—the very middle of the Omelan summer—she told him to go.

* * *

Some weeks later, the king of Feigh stood in a hole nearly as deep as he was tall, shoveling Omelan dirt over his shoulder. The sun was growing gentler in the sky above him. The hole was in the corner of a meadow, near a handsome tree.

"How was Cessa?" asked Turo. The former athlete leaned on his own shovel, looking into the hole.

"Sweet and round as always."

Turo snickered. "I shouldn't laugh at my queen."

"She wouldn't mind. She adores you." Tel returned to his digging.

"You're thin."

Tel opened his mouth to disagree but changed his mind. "I know."

"I'm not careful, I'll get roly-poly," said Turo, patting his abdomen.

"I wouldn't say that. The life of a farmer is not exactly sedentary."

Turo made a visor of his hand. "Isn't it beautiful here?"

Tel smiled at him. "Truly it is. As you told me. And I thank you and your parents. For letting me do this here. Cessa didn't understand. *He will not rest in the palace of Omela? He will not rest with you in Feigh?*" He chuckled at his own impersonation. "But he deserves to be in the dirt of Omela. And he never cared for palaces or castles. Or kings and queens."

"He cared for *you*."

Tel wiped the back of a filthy hand across his damp forehead. "He was the one who convinced me I was a king. But he never once looked at a king when he looked at me. Not really. Not once."

"Hm."

"And now, at least, he will be with an Omelan family who will look after him," said Tel.

"He will. This is deep enough." Turo let his shovel fall and walked to the hole, offering Tel his arm. The limp was mild but noticeable. Bending his body, he pulled Tel out.

"I know a high one should start this, but…"

"The high ones do their part and then leave the family," said Turo. "This part's for you."

Tel looked at Turo's painted face and asked, "What do we do?" His nerves fluttered.

"We can just sit. And you say the kindnesses Vared gave you in the mystery."

Tel turned to the tree. "Ofya, my love, will you come to me, please? I think I need you to hold my hand."

The girl, now sixteen seasons old, had been chucking pebbles at the trunk. She bounced to him, giggling. "I will hold your hand." When she reached him, he scooped her up and placed a kiss on the tangerine ribbon in her black hair. "You are dirty."

"And you're heavy, little one." Tel pulled a face. She mirrored it.

The three of them sat in the sable dirt near the grave. Tel's hand surrounded Ofya's. The box with the painted stag and frog rested in his lap. He looked at his companions and took a breath.

"Vared's kindnesses to me were uncountable. He didn't want to love me, but he let himself. He made me a song once. I'll always have it. It's about grief and almost as lovely as he was…"

About the Author

Gideon E. Wood writes gay fantasy fiction. He has been proudly clean and sober since 2011. Second chances and transformation are at the heart of his work. Gideon lives in New England with his cat but thinks it's important you know he isn't a cat person.

You can connect with me on:

🌐 http://gideonewood.com
🐦 http://twitter.com/gideonewood
🔗 http://author.to/GideonEWood

Subscribe to my newsletter:

✉ http://gideonewood.com

Also by Gideon E. Wood

Book Two of the trilogy, *The Stagsblood King*, will be available October 2021. Book Three, *The Stagsblood Brother*, will be released June 2022.

"Songmaker," a 12,000-word story about Vared, is out now, free to subscribers to Gideon's newsletter.

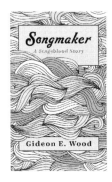

"Songmaker"
http://gideonewood.com
FREE NOW TO GIDEON'S NEWSLETTER SUB-SCRIBERS!

Vared is not only the most beautiful young man in Omela. He is also its finest tenor and most promising songmaker. Forced by his wealthy adoptive father into a yearlong contract to entertain the queen and her palace guests, he looks forward to setting out on his own. The contract is nearing its end and Vared will soon be free from the whims of the rich.

But the highborn have other ideas. He will now be sent to Feigh, a strange kingdom an ocean away, to serve as a cultural emissary. Vared is to join the household of the Feighan prince, Tel, for an additional year.

At first, it seems older, charming, handsome Tel might inspire Vared to scuttle his plans to run away from it all. But the songmaker quickly judges the prince to be just as bad as the rest of the elite.

"Songmaker" offers Vared's perspective on the opening days of *The Stagsblood Prince*. The beginning of his personal adventure also marks the start of an epic tale of love, magic, war, faith, loss, myth, and redemption.

Printed in Great Britain
by Amazon

'To describe the 356 as a spec
Volkswagen is not to co
it for its humble origi

Porsche 356 Pre-A p56

Contents

66

76

150

244

242

20

170

26

124

192

98

198

Editorial

THE GREATNESS OF PORSCHE

How we love Porsche. There's no other company that has stuck to its principles and inherent quirkiness as steadfastly as Porsche, sometimes getting it wrong, but usually getting it so very right.

In this celebration of all things Porsche, we give you over 200 pages of the greatest road and race Porsches of all time, from the very first Porsche – the Type 64 – to the most recent Porsche that we'd count as a classic, the early 1990s 993.

What's so great about classic Porsches is that there really is one for every budget, which certainly isn't the case for many other marques of this pedigree. For just £1500 you'll pick up a perfectly reasonable 924; or for £150,000 you could stretch to a 911 2.7 RS Carrera. The latter might attract bigger crowds and be eligible for more events, but who's to say it will give more pleasure?

> ## What's so great about classic Porsches is that there really is one for every budget

This publication should give you the rare chance to compare and contrast your favourite models, with the help of some of the world's best motoring writers. Want to know which version of the 356 or the 911 is best for you? There are great comparisons here to guide you. Or would you like to know the finest 911 RS? We have a superb track test by seasoned Porsche racer Tony Dron, covering all the RS models from 1973-on. And there's plenty more like that.

So I hope you'll enjoy this publication, and I hope you'll continue to enjoy Porsches, whether you're simply an admirer of the marque or an enthusiastic owner.

David Lillywhite editor
david@octane-magazine.com

INFORMATION

Editorial office
Octane, 4 Tower Court, Irchester Road, Wollaston, Northants, NN29 7PJ, UK
Tel: +44 (0)20 7907 6585. Fax: +44 (0)1933 667309
Email: info@octane-magazine.com

Advertising office
Octane Media Advertising Dept,
19 Highfield Lane. Maidenhead SL6 3AN. UK
Tel: +44 (0)1628 510080. Fax: +44 (0)1628 510090
Email: ads@octane-magazine.com

Editor	David Lillywhite
International editor	Robert Coucher
Deputy editor	Mark Dixon
Production editor	Glen Waddington
Assistant editor	Keith Adams
Art editor	Rob Gould
Designer	Robert Hefferon
Test drivers	Tony Dron, Mark Hales
Website contributor	Matthew Hayward
Publishing assistant	Alex Lowit
Advertising sales	Rob Schulp
Advertising director	Sanjay Seetanah
Advertising production	Kerem Kolcak
Publishing director	Geoff Love
Managing director	Ian Westwood
COO	Brett Reynolds
Group finance director	Ian Leggett
CEO	James Tye
Chairman	Felix Dennis

Porsche Classics is published under a licence from Octane Media Ltd, a subsidiary company of Dennis Publishing Limited, UK. All rights in the licensed material belong to Felix Dennis, Octane Media or Dennis Publishing and may not be reproduced, whether in whole or in part, without their prior written consent.

Repro by Octane Repro
Printed by BGP, Bicester, Oxfordshire
Distribution by Seymour, 2 East Poultry Avenue, London EC1A 9PT. Tel: +44 (0)20 7429 400

Periodicals Postage paid @ Emigsville, PA. Postmaster: send address corrections to Octane Media c/o 3330 Pacific Ave, Suite 404, Virginia Beach, VA 23451

CONTENT LICENSING

Editorial content in *Porsche Classics* is available for international licensing and syndication. Please call Winnie Liesenfeld on +44 (0)20 7907 6134 or email winnie_liesenfeld@dennis.co.uk

SUBSCRIPTIONS AND BACK ISSUES

UK subscriptions 0844 844 0382
Overseas subscriptions +44 (0)1795 414972
US subscriptions 866-622-5138
Subscribe online www.octane-magazine.com
Email helpline octane@servicehelpline.co.uk
Manage your subscription at www.subsinfo.co.uk

ALSO FROM OCTANE
Other publications and useful resources...

Octane magazine
The features in this publication are from *Octane*, a monthly magazine on the greatest classic and performance cars. It's available at retailers and by subscription.

Other publications
Octane has 'magbooks' on *Sir Stirling Moss*; *Aston Martin*; *MG*; *Jaguar*; *Ferrari*; and *The Classic Car Price Guide*. To buy, visit www.octane-magazine.com and click on 'shop'.

Online price guide
Ever wondered what a particular model of Porsche is worth? All the model varieties are listed and valued on the *Octane* magazine website, www.octane-magazine.com.

Octane prints
A selection of the best *Octane* pictures and Felix Petrol illustrations is available, framed or unframed (or printed on canvas), starting from £15 on www.octaneprints.com.

Porsche recommends **Mobil ⚑**

Call **08457 911 911** or visit **porsche.co.uk** for more information.

Porsche Intelligent Performance.

Uniting the track and the road.

At Porsche, we take a more intelligent approach to the delivery of power. From track supremacy to on-road capability, the concept of Porsche Intelligent Performance applies. This thinking delivers efficient and responsive performance, notably in our hybrid technology, evidenced in our new 911 GT3 R Hybrid race car. It features two additional electric motors which recover energy under braking to deliver more performance without using power from the engine. Our innovative thinking also applies to the road. The new Cayenne S Hybrid integrates our new parallel full hybrid system for the performance you would expect from a Porsche and the capability to drive for short distances up to 37 mph without calling on its V6 supercharged engine. A 22% reduction in fuel consumption and CO_2 emissions is the remarkable result*.

*Compared to Cayenne S

A BRIEF HISTORY OF PORSCHE

It's 62 years since the first Porsche rolled out of
a shed in Austria. And all this has happened since

Words: Ben Field

Dr Ferdinand Porsche couldn't have had much of a home life in the 1930s. As the most in-demand engineer of his generation he spent the bulk of his time developing extraordinary cars for other people. Zündapp, NSU, Auto Union and Austro Daimler all benefited from his genius. Oh, and he designed the KDF-Wagen (that would later become the Beetle), building the prototype in the garage of his Stuttgart home.

But in 1939, as the German industrial machine was turning its tools to war, Dr Porsche and his equally gifted son, Ferry, designed and built three racing cars for the planned Berlin-to-Rome endurance race. The Type 64 sported fully-enclosed aerodynamic bodywork, wheel spats and a 32bhp air-cooled flat-four engine, mid-mounted just forward of the rear axle. The only thing missing was a Porsche badge, but it's hard to dispute that this slippery take on race car design was anything but the very first Porsche.

The start of the Second World War put a stop to the Type 64's racing debut and Porsche's Zuffenhausen factory went from building sports cars to assembling armoured cars. When Allied bombing wrecked the factory in 1944, remnants of the Porsche concern were evacuated to Austria, with the company's top men →

Left and far left
Ferdinand Porsche shows off a model of the first Porsche to grandsons Butzi (left) and Ferdinand Piech; father and son: Ferdinand and Ferry.

Left, far left and below left
Butzi Porsche with his masterpiece; the Gmünd 'factory'; Porsche no1 sees the light of day.

'It's hard to dispute that this slippery take on race car design was anything but the very first Porsche'

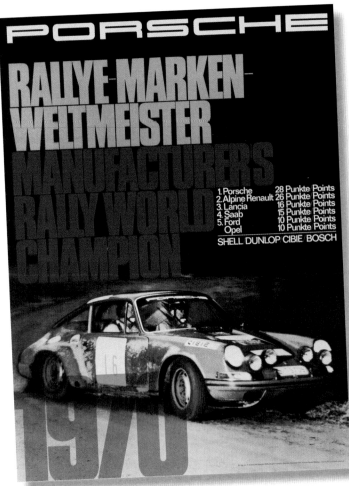

PORSCHE

RALLYE-MARKEN-WELTMEISTER

MANUFACTURERS RALLY WORLD CHAMPION

1. Porsche	28	Punkte	Points
2. Alpine Renault	26	Punkte	Points
3. Lancia	16	Punkte	Points
4. Saab	15	Punkte	Points
5. Ford	10	Punkte	Points
Opel	10	Punkte	Points

SHELL DUNLOP CIBIE BOSCH

1970

Left and below
911's rally prowess featured in advertising; 550 Spyder was a major competition success.

reduced to working in the less-than-salubrious surroundings of a former sawmill in Gmünd.

After the war, Dr Porsche, like many German engineers and industrialists, was arrested and interrogated by the Allies a number of times. During one long period of his father's detention, Ferry got to work on the car that would bear the Porsche name for the first time – the 356. This open car didn't look much different from the production 356 that we're used to, but its feeble, mid-mounted engine, weak brakes and cramped cockpit would need serious development if the model were going to succeed.

The return of many of Porsche's designers, engineers and body men who had been displaced by the war gave the 356 project a huge boost. And by the time production began back in Zuffenhausen in 1950, the 356 had a range of bodies from Coupé to Speedster and a more powerful engine behind the rear axle – a position that has come to typify the brand. Ferdinand Porsche died a year after his company's return to Zuffenhausen but, by way of honouring his name, a 356 SL took a class victory at the Le Mans 24 Hours in June that year. In the same year, a pair of 356s took speed records at Montlhéry.

Porsche's experiments with the mid-engine layout didn't end with the prototype 356. The 550 Spyder of 1953 used a four-cam, 1488cc flat-four in front of the rear axle. Capable of nearly 140mph, it secured Porsche's position as a racing car manufacturer with wins at Le Mans, the Nürburgring and in the Targa Florio. It's unfortunate that this landmark Porsche is also remembered as the car that 'killed' movie idol and racer James Dean in 1955.

Meanwhile, the 356 was selling in the tens of thousands and had developed from a steady performer to something of a road burner with 140bhp in Carrera 2 trim by 1962. But the competition hadn't stood still. The car world was still agog from the launch of the Jaguar E-type in 1961, the 356 was showing its age, and Porsche needed something bigger and faster to show it still had sports car muscle. Ferry's son, Ferdinand Alexander 'Butzi' Porsche came up with a shape, Hans Mezger designed a 2.0-litre flat six to sit behind the rear

axle, and the concept took shape. The car was launched at the Frankfurt Motor Show in 1963 as the 901, but it didn't stay that way for long. Peugeot had rights on numbers with zero in the middle, so Porsche added a '1' and the 911 was born.

The heavier engine hanging out back tested both the car's dynamics and drivers of the early 911 in equal measure. The solution to get them both out of a spin? A cast iron weight in the outer corners of the front bumper – crude, but effective.

Motor sport continued to be a major part of Porsche's gameplan. The late 1960s and early 1970s were awash with victories for the marque's endurance racing 906, 910 and 907/8 in the Targa Florio, the 24 Hours of Daytona and the Nürburgring 1000km. The new 917 took overall wins at Le Mans in 1970 and 1971. Away from the circuit, the 911 proved its rally mettle coming top in the Monte Carlo Rally for three years in a row from 1968 to 1970.

While the push-me-pull-you looks of the first 'cheaper Porsche', the mid-engined 914 of 1969, failed to make much of an impression, the same can't be said for the 911 Carrera RS that arrived in 1972. This was the ultimate first-generation 911; stripped out and with 210bhp it sold double the necessary 500 for racing homologation and remains one of the most revered Porsches to this day.

Impact bumpers adorned the second generation of 911s to comply with new US legislation. They took away some of the delicacy of styling that had helped popularise the 911, but there was no suggestion that Porsche was about to tow the industry line. In 1974, with the world in the grip of a fuel crisis, Porsche launched the 260bhp 911 Turbo (930), the first turbocharged production sports car. The penchant for snap oversteer that had been gradually engineered to a safe level in the 911 came back with ferocious alacrity to terrify anyone foolish enough to invoke the 930's giant KKK turbocharger mid-corner.

Porsche quickly became recognised as an expert in turbocharged engines and by the mid-1980s it was designing and building units for Formula 1. The Tag Turbo engines designed by 911 engine man Hans →

'Motor sport continued to be a major part of Porsche's gameplan. The late 1960s and early 1970s were awash with victories'

Mezger developed up to 960bhp from just 1.5 litres, and went on to power three Formula 1 World Championship-winning cars.

Always the innovator, Porsche was the first car manufacturer to use double-sided galvanising for its steel bodies from 1975. The company introduced its first front-engined car, the 924, in the same year. Another front-engined car, the 928, was introduced in 1977 as a would-be successor to the 911. As a concept it couldn't have been more different to the car it planned to usurp – the 928 was a fast and complex grand tourer with a 4.4-litre aluminium V8. It would go on to be built in conjunction with the 911 until 1995. Porsche may not have found its 911 replacement, but 1977 was still a success with the 936 winning at Le Mans. The 936 won at Le Mans again in 1981, celebrating the company's 50th anniversary, and the 944 was launched the same year. Whereas the 924 had been deemed too modest for a Porsche, the tough-looking 2.5-litre 944 was far better received.

Porsche had played with four-wheel drive for years and showed the 911 Group B (as the concept 959 was called) at the 1983 Frankfurt Motor Show. It boasted not just four-wheel drive but 400bhp and the real possibility of 200mph. The necessary 200 orders were taken at the show for the car to be built and homologated and the 959 was launched in 1986. Not everyone noticed that the new car had a very significant change – for the first time a rear-engined Porsche featured water cooling, albeit just to the cylinder heads. And it wasn't long before the 959's four-wheel drive tech dripped down the model range. In 1988 the 911 Carrera 4 arrived with all wheels driven.

Attempts to replace the 911 had already failed and creating a car to complement it had proved difficult, too. The 944 and its ultimate evolution the 968 were fine cars but by the early 1990s they were looking a bit old – while the 911, in 964 and 993 guises, was constantly improving. The discerning sports car market of the time expected a lot from Porsche and it delivered with the Boxster in 1997. This mid-engined roadster went from concept to production in three-and-a-half years. The fact it used a water-cooled flat six didn't bother a new generation of buyers who were getting their Porsche kicks for £20,000 less than a 911 buyer. Hardly surprising, then, that more than 55,000 Boxsters were sold in the first three years of production.

A quest for ever-more performance and the need to get the 911 through drive-by noise regulations brought water cooling to the flat-six engine for the first time in 1998. For some this was the motoring equivalent of Dylan going electric and they clung to their air-cooled 911s. But far from being the end of the line, as many predicted, the 911 has continued to improve through the 996 and 997 variants.

If water-cooling the 911 was a departure for Porsche, the lifestyling of the brand that came with the Cayenne in 2002 was an astonishing move – but a very profitable one. The Cayenne shares a platform with the Volkswagen Touareg and the Audi Q7 and that kept development costs under control. With a Porsche badge on the bonnet, the Cayenne soon started to replace other 4x4s on posher drives. The Panamera, Porsche's recently-launched four-door model, puts the brand into yet another market, lining up against established luxury-sector cars from Mercedes-Benz and Bentley.

As the Boxster approached its second generation, a long-held plan to develop a coupé version of the car to sell alongside it started to take shape. Designer Pinky Lai was tasked with the difficult job of making a coupé out of a convertible. The resulting Cayman, that first appeared at Frankfurt in 2005, shows just how right he got the shape. In S spec the Cayman will match a 911 for performance and can be driven faster by the average person at the wheel, thanks to the car's more predictable handling. For some, Porsche has unwittingly found its fabled 911 replacement in the Cayman.

Wondering where Porsche finds itself in the market today? Turn the page.

'The 924 was modest for a Porsche, but the tough-looking 2.5-litre 944 was far better received'

PORSCHE
TODAY

It's not just 911s any more. Now SUVs and limos are
as important to Porsche as hardcore sports cars –
and there are more surprises around the corner

Words: Glen Waddington   Photography: Porsche/Rex Features

If it hadn't been for Wendelin Wiedeking, Porsche probably wouldn't exist today. He saved the company from almost certain doom, and turned it into the world's most profitable car maker. In return, he became Germany's most highly paid captain of industry. And then last year he was sacked.

There have been turbulent times in the boardrooms of Zuffenhausen. Porsche is still, at heart, a family business but Wiedeking followed the succession of Dr Ernst Fuhrmann (the 356 Carrera engine designer), Peter Schutz, Arno Bohn and Heinz Branitzki as CEO – members of the Porsche family having set up a supervisory board in 1972 to oversee the appointment of non-family directors to the executive board. It's complicated stuff, but not as complicated as the company's ownership situation became.

Ever since founder Ferdinand Porsche designed the Volkswagen Beetle, there has remained a link between the two companies. During 2009, after a series of dramatic moves, it looked as though Porsche would take over Volkswagen. But before the year was out, the situation was reversed, and Wiedeking paid the price.

Under Wiedeking's direction, Porsche had been buying increasing shares in the VW group since 2005 but the crunch came as Porsche stock dwindled in early 2009, leaving the company crippled with debt and unable to buy the final controlling share in VW. Yet VW's profits were soaring, enough for it to see off any potential Porsche backers. The result? The two companies will 'merge' in 2011.

The real irony here is that the VW Group was led by Ferdinand Piech from 1993 to 2002, before he ended up on Porsche's supervisory board – from where he deposed Wiedeking. Piech just happens to be Ferdinand Porsche's grandson, and a man whose career highlights include helping to create the original 911 and the 917 racer, then inventing the Quattro for Audi .

The fact is that Wiedeking's business methods reaped huge financial rewards for Porsche. When he became CEO, aged 40, Porsche built 14,000 cars per year and was worth £500m. He left it building 100,000 cars and worth £30bn – but servicing £10bn of debts.

His methods were controversial. In the early 1990s, Porsche had an ageing model range: the air-cooled 911; the big, fat 928; and the 968, that traced its roots to a design commissioned by Audi in the early 1970s. Wiedeking's plan was radical: two new model ranges spun off shared architecture, so the company could afford to replace the 911 and produce a junior sibling worthy of the Porsche name. The 928 was canned in 1995, while the Boxster and the 996-generation 911 arrived in 1997 and 1998 respectively. With *water*-cooled flat-sixes. Heresy!

But Wiedeking's real money-spinner is even more controversial. There's shared architecture again, this time that of VW's Touareg off-roader, which underpins the Porsche Cayenne, introduced in 2002. It instantly took Porsche into a new, fashionable market – and away from one obsessed with the arcanery of rear-engined folklore. Still, it was only Porsche's *second*-best selling car, still beaten by the 911.

But as Wiedeking always excused himself, without the Cayenne spewing euros into Porsche's coffers, there'd have been no money with which to develop the 911. And develop it has, along with the Boxster, which spawned the hardtop Cayman. Even the Cayenne had a spin-off, another controversial one, as Porsche now fights in the luxury saloon car market with the recently-launched Panamera.

You can read more about these cars over the page. →

Above
On the left, Ferdinand Piech, grandson of Ferdinand Porsche, and the man who deposed Wendelin Wiedeking (right) – Porsche's most successful CEO.

Boxster

Power 306bhp **Torque** 265lb ft **Weight** 1355kg
Top speed 170mph **0-60mph** 5.3sec (Boxster S)

Forget the old 924. *This* is how you do an entry-level Porsche. The Boxster arrived to a rapturous welcome in 1997, priced in upper-ranking Audi TT/BMW Z3 territory, with a flat six of only 2.5 litres but 201bhp. It quickly became clear that the mid-engined chassis could easily handle more power so, in a 911-like move, 228bhp 2.7-litre and 249bhp 3.2 S versions turned up in 2000.

Those flat sixes all shared their design with the 911's 3.4-litre engine, and much of the car's structure was common too – even down to the controversial 'fried egg' headlamps for the first three years. Yet the Boxster cost half as much as a 911, a situation that continues today.

The second generation arrived in 2005, lightly facelifted to the current spec for 2009, these days with a standard 2.9 and a 306bhp 3.4-litre S. Drive that and you'll wonder why you'd ever need any more power, while the mid-engined balance makes your mind boggle that Porsche insists on continuing with rear-engined cars. Soul is in abundance, and the folding roof is a bonus.

Talking of which, there's now a Spyder rag-top (pictured), probably best for Californians and Cote d'Azurians. Like the old 356 Speedster, it's really meant for blasting along roof-down, with little more than an umbrella for emergencies. Thankfully, the standard car's electric roof is perfect for northern Europeans.

Cayman

Power 316bhp **Torque** 273lb ft **Weight** 1350kg
Top speed 172mph **0-60mph** 5.2sec (Cayman S)

Boxster just a bit, well, soft for you? Here's the Cayman. For many, it's much more the modern equivalent of the original 911 than the current 911 is. It was derived from the second-generation Boxster, arrived in 2006 and followed that car's subsequent upgrades. But in line with the Cayman's role as a harder-edged sports car, it's always pumped out 10bhp more model for model, and features uprated suspension – something it can easily cope with because the closed-coupé body is more rigid than the soft-top Boxster's.

You'd need to compare Boxster and Cayman back-to-back really to feel those upgrades, but instantly you'll notice that it's lighter and nimbler than the 911, with the kind of steering response and feedback that puts you in mind of cars from the 1960s – cars rather like the original 911, in fact. And take a look at the performance figures. If you were thinking of buying a 1973 Carrera RS 2.7 purely on the basis of acceleration, top speed and handling, save yourself a quick £100,000 and buy one of these instead.

Of course, those aren't the sole reasons why anybody would buy a 911 RS. It has the kind of racing provenance, heritage and relative rarity that are well byond the Cayman's reach. But can you think of a more appealing modern sports car for the money than the £45k Cayman S on today's market? No, neither can we.

Cayenne

Power 493bhp **Torque** 516lb ft **Weight** 2170kg
Top speed 173mph **0-60mph** 4.7sec (Turbo)

It's never going to challenge a Land Rover on the Karakorum Pass, but then no Land Rover is going to match the Cayenne's performance figures. Look at that acceleration figure! In a car that weighs more than two tonnes!

Until the Panamera showed up last year, the Cayenne was Porsche's only practical family car and, with its underpinnings pilfered from the Volkswagen Touareg, many derided it for not being a pure Porsche. But it's survived into a second generation, just launched, and those headline figures are for the quickest of the lot. Yet Porsche has even made an attempt to appease the green lobby, by launching not only a diesel-powered Cayenne but a hybrid too. Don't expect Prius-style parsimony though. This thing mates a 3.0-litre supercharged Audi V6 to a mid-mounted electric motor, for a total of 375bhp and 428lb ft.

As if to underline its confidence in Porsche's off-roader, Volkswagen is launching its new Touareg after the Cayenne; finally, the group's trio will be complete in 2013, when the next Audi Q7 rolls out.

Being a Porsche, this car handles like no other SUV, so you can actually make use of its performance on real roads without making your rear-seat passengers queasy. And it will handle modest terrain easily enough, too. Not that you'd want to get it dirty, mind.

911

Power 612bhp **Torque** 516lb ft **Weight** 1370kg
Top speed 205mph **0-60mph** 3.5sec (GT2 RS)

Think back to 1962: a modest 2.0-litre flat six, with an undemanding 130bhp for a top speed of 130mph: quick but not brutal. Then take a peek at those figures above. Yep, the 911's come a long way in its near-half century.

Of course, we're talking here about the range-topping £164,107 GT2 RS, the twin-turbocharged 911 on steroids for those mad enough to believe that the standard four-wheel drive Turbo just ain't so quick, or that the naturally-aspirated GT3 isn't quite hardcore enough for them. *This* is quick. Brutally so. And with all that power – 90bhp more than before, while weighing 70kg less – coursing through the rear wheels only, quite a handful. It's the most powerful street-legal Porsche of all time, and it's just posted a 7min 18sec lap at the Nürburgring Nordschleife. That's phenomenal stuff for a production car.

Yet it's the 911's breadth of ability that matters as much today – with this, the second series of the second generation of water-cooled cars – as it did nearly five decades ago. It's got a usable boot. Room for a couple of young kids in the back. And even the cheapest one (the £64,256 Carrera 3.6) posts 180mph and 4.9sec. Our pick? The Carrera S 3.8 for turning the wick up just enough to make life interesting every day. Or maybe the GT3 if you can do without those rear seats: sufficiently civilised on-road and an absolute storm on-track. But never, ever brutal.

Panamera

Power 493bhp **Torque** 516lb ft **Weight** 1970kg
Top speed 188mph **0-60mph** 4.2sec (Turbo)

A few years ago, if you wanted a business saloon you bought a Mercedes S-class, maybe a BMW 7-series, perhaps even a Jag XJ. Now there's more choice. Want gorgeous looks? Aston Rapide or Maserati Quattroporte. Space and luxury that even the S-class can't match? Bentley Flying Spur. A four-door sports car? Here comes the Panamera.

In fact, it was launched in 2009, loosely based on the Cayenne SUV. The Panamera makes little pretence at spaciousness: four full-size adults will fit, and there's even a tailgate to make loading luggage easier, but the ambience within is about intimacy rather than volume. And the low driving position with near-vertical steering wheel is pure 911. Granted, it's challenging enough in the looks department even to put off its own mother, but if your idea of a luxury car is more about driving than being driven, this is your top choice.

Even so, for some, the Panamera is an unwelcome stretch of the Porsche brand, and whether or not there will be another generation depends on this car's sales success: Volkswagen is reported to be keen to quell any notion of a replacement in order to protect Audi and Bentley from in-house competition. So if you fancy a luxury car with the Stuttgart crest on the nose, best get down to your local Porsche dealership soon.

→

'Limited production is expected by 2014,
and reckon on little change from £400,000'

What happens next

The 918 hypercar is on its way. So's a new 911, a
new Boxster – and a baby Porsche is coming too

You could say the future's already here.
Porsche makes sports cars, right? Even the
Cayenne puts the emphasis on the 'S' in SUV.
Except a *diesel* version arrived last year, and
there's now a hybrid version of the new Cayenne.

But there's a much more exciting hybrid to
come. Porsche recently announced the green light for its
918 Spyder, a petrol/electric supercar with headline figures
of 200mph, 0-60mph in 3.2sec, emissions (important, this, in
today's climate) of just 70g/km and claimed fuel economy of
94mpg. Yes, you read that right.

All that comes thanks to a 493bhp 5.0-litre V8 developed
from the RS Spyder Le Mans Prototype racer's, and an
additional 215bhp from the electric motor. Yes, we all know
you won't achieve those eco-figures if you floor it everywhere,
but cars like this give Porsche a green conscience so the rest
of us can carry on enjoying ourselves. No official dates or

Above
5.0-litre V8 + electric
motor = 708bhp for
forthcoming 918
Spyder. It promises an
amazing 94mpg too.

prices yet, but limited production is expected by
2014, and reckon on little change from £400,000.

For mere mortals, the next 911 generation is
due next year. Unlike the current 997, it will be
more than simply a heavy facelift of what's gone
before, with a new structure and refreshed styling
– but still the classic rear-engined layout, with more power
than ever from Porsche's now-legendary (even in water-
cooled format) flat six. As for a hybrid version, it's unlikely,
thanks to that rear engine position.

As before, the next 911 will share front-end underpinnings
with the next Boxster, due in 2013. But the real news is a new,
smaller sports car, to slot below the Boxster as an entry-
level Porsche. It will have a mid-mounted four-cylinder
engine and is expected to share its structure with that of
Audi's forthcoming R5. Don't expect to see it before 2012. Do
expect everybody to refer to it as 'Porsche's new 356'. △

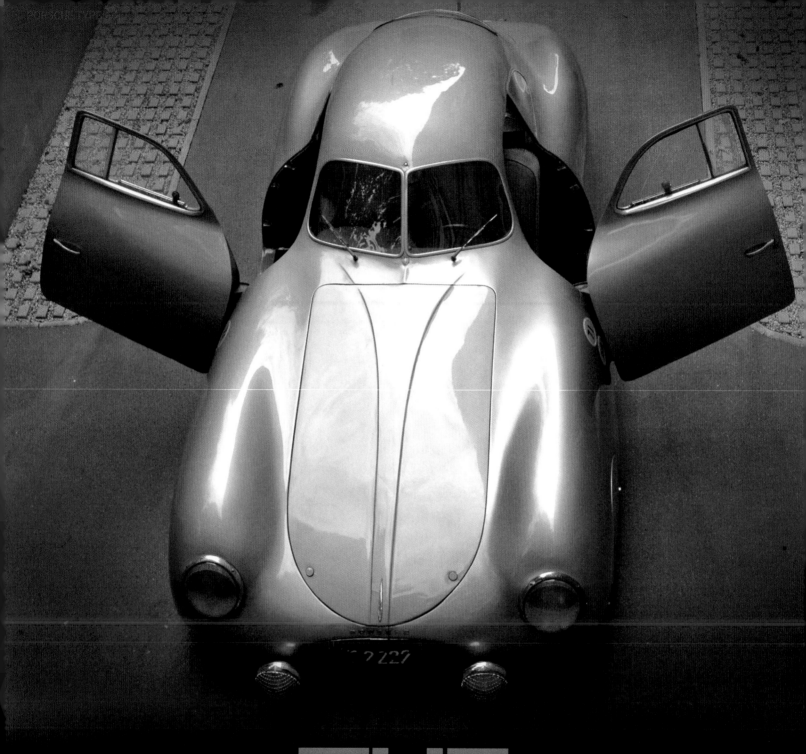

THE FORGOTTEN PORSCHE

This sublime streamliner pre-dated the original Porsche 356 by nine years. Ferdinand and Ferry Porsche used it as personal transport to evaluate solutions for their subsequent sports car; its first private owner then kept it for almost five decades. Now it has returned to the public eye

Words: Hans-Karl Lange Photography: Mark Kucera, Rob Box and The Porsche Archives

A Porsche before the first Porsche?

We've been used to thinking that the Type 356.001 mid-engined roadster, followed by the rear-engined Type 356.002 alloy coupé, was the origin of the species. Both were built in 1948 near Gmünd in Austria, where the Porsche engineering company designed the Cisitalia GP car.

After the war Ferry Porsche drove a supercharged Volkswagen convertible. When the first batch of 356s was in the making his father passed on to him the car he had previously been using, a slim coupé known as project number 64. British occupation authorities registered it on 26 April, 1946, under the company title of Porsche Konstruktionen, with a K-prefix for the Carinthia province (Kärnten in German) on the number plates. While the mid-engined 356 was to remain a one-off, three examples of the Type 64 were built, dispelling any doubts about which car should really be considered the first Porsche.

Ferry himself placed the raised letters spelling out PORSCHE on the nose of the single Type 64 that had survived the war. Chris Barber's book *Birth of the Beetle*, written with the support of Professor Ferdinand Porsche's nephew and secretary, as well as with unlimited access to the Porsche and Volkswagen archives, underlines how this streamlined grand touring sports car is the link between the people's car and the Porsche 356. And it's no mere missing link, as we found out when *Octane* tried the sole survivor on the outskirts of Vienna, where it shares garage space with a 911 Carrera RS 2.7 of 1972 vintage.

The Porsche Type 64 is not simply a streamlined Volkswagen special, as it might appear at first glance. Under the light alloy skin it shares drivetrain and suspension with the early Beetle, just as the majority of early 356s do, but when the third (and current) owner had the car dismantled for the first bottom-up restoration in five decades it turned out that the chassis was a far cry from a →

Above
Alloy body of Porsche Type 64 has welded outer skin, held together with 2000 rivets underneath – like a WW2 aircraft.

Volkswagen central backbone with flat floor sections to both sides. The pressed-steel backbone had been retained, but altered in several areas. Either side of it are rectangular tubular structures made from aircraft-gauge duralumin. These frames are sandwiched between an aluminium alloy underbody and floor. Not your usual Beetle chassis!

Boasting spats over front and rear wheels, the streamlined body is made from alloy panels, welded on the outer skin and held together by some 2000 rivets underneath. 'WW2 aircraft technology', as the Hungarian aircraft builder involved in the restoration pointed out. It was styled by Erwin Kommenda, an Austrian who worked on the Auto Union and Cisitalia GP cars in the Porsche design offices, as well as on the VW, the Porsche 356 and the 550 Spyder. The shape was inspired by the 1938 Type 114 F-Wagen, a stillborn sports car that was to have been powered by a mid-mounted V10.

The Reutter coachworks, across the road from the Porsche premises of Zuffenhausen on the northern edge of Stuttgart, built three Type 64 bodies in 1939/'40. Ten years later Porsche would rent space in the Reutter plant to gear up 356 production in steel, as his own works were still occupied by American troops. By 1963/'64 Porsche had taken over the coachbuilder's premises, while the car seat-making branch of Reutter went on to set up at another site under the name of Recaro, and would supply Porsche for years to come.

The original VW air-cooled flat-four of 985cc and 23.5bhp was tuned to 32bhp; later the alloy cylinders were bored out to 1131cc but after the war a 1085cc unit enabled the surviving Type 64 to compete in the 1100cc class. The second owner then had a 1.3-litre engine of 60bhp installed and claimed a top speed of 112mph.

With his chauffeur at the wheel, Professor Porsche timed one evening trip of 125 miles on the Reichsautobahn from Berlin to the Volkswagen plant near Fallersleben (named KdF-Stadt in those dark days and Wolfsburg since the end of the war) at an average of 83mph. Not bad for a 1.0-litre road car. This, possibly the least powerful car ever to be featured in *Octane*, is every inch a thoroughbred. A kerbweight of 1346lb, a slippery shape and the unsurpassed traction of the rear-engined layout make you feel every single one of the 40 or so horses propelling you from behind. Before pushing the starter you need to play with a brace of levers to reduce the air supply to each of the two carburettors, enriching the mixture during warm-up. Take-off is brisk. This is not a silent motor car, nor a comfortable one as the torsion bar suspension is jarringly stiff.

That narrow cockpit with close-mounted seats in staggered positions is reminiscent of the 1952 Fiat 8V's. The plain-painted dash, simple wheel and central speedometer hint at the earliest Volkswagens. The dark cabin is a nightmare for the claustrophobic and not entirely watertight, so it will mist up in the rain. Imagine an impatient and choleric character like Professor Ferdinand Porsche in here, being chauffeured on the German Reichsautobahn on a dark, rainy night...

Clockwise from right
Type 64 in 1939; on the 1952 Coppa d'Oro; Korneuburg 1952; Innsbruck 1977.

'In one event, the right-hand door flew open and Otto Mathé managed to get it closed again only by driving along a rock face'

A long-distance road race was the original reason for the birth of this Beetle-based sports car. This was to be a propaganda event to applaud the glorious axis powers of Germany and Italy, covering over 940 miles from Berlin via Austria down to Rome. Several car manufacturers, including BMW and Lancia, prepared streamlined specials for the event.

Professor Porsche took the chance to convince the Government of what he had been refused earlier – a sports machine based on the people's car he had designed and seen through to production. To get his sports car paid for by the German national labour organisation, Porsche re-named his Type 64 the Type 60 K10, standing for the 10th body version of the Type 60 Volkswagen which was by then called the KdF-Wagen.

The race never took place. One month after the first of the three Type 64 sports cars was ready and two weeks before the Berlin-Rome race was to start, German troops swept into Poland, forcing France and England to declare war. The finished

Type 64 became the company car of the head of the German labour front – try to imagine a union boss driving around in a Porsche!

Ferry had just turned 30 on 19 September, 1939, when he proposed in a board meeting to finish the other two sports cars and use them as experimental models. The second was ready in December 1939, the third by June 1940. These two were driven by the Porsche and VW management, including Anton Piech, an Austrian lawyer who had married the Professor's daughter.

Plenty of mileage was clocked up by the two Porsche-operated Type 64 sports cars – experience that would prove valuable for the design of the Type 356. But just one of the cars was to survive the war.

The labour-union boss crashed the first Type 64 in about 1941 and its chassis was supposedly incorporated into the third car, although in what respect is not clear. The second model survived the joyrides of the young Ferdinand Alexander Porsche and Ferdinand Piech (aged ten and eight by the end of the war) around the glider airfield of

Zell am See, but not the driving habits of the American soldiers who liberated it in the last days of war, cut off its roof to make space for more passengers and drove it until the engine seized. The car was eventually scrapped.

Model number three had its bodywork in tatters after the war. In 1947 Porsche entrusted the restoration to none other than Pinin Farina. Much later, around 1969, Pininfarina would supply Porsche with the body of a stretched 911 four-seat prototype.

Porsche demonstrated the 356.001 roadster to the public on 11 July, 1948, at Innsbruck, with his private Type 64 in pursuit. Most books list this Hofgarten race as Porsche's first victory, but this is quite an overstatement: on the photos that exist, both driver and passenger are wearing hats... There were just a few demo laps before the real race of three pre-war cars was started, a Fiat special beating a Fiat Balilla and an Austro-Daimler.

The man in the Balilla was rather unusual: apparently lacking his right arm, he changed →

PORSCHE TYPE 64
ENGINE
985cc, later 1131cc and 1086cc VW-based fan-cooled OHV flat-four, two single-choke carburettors
POWER
32-40bhp @ 3500-4200rpm
TORQUE
52lb ft @ 2800rpm
TRANSMISSION
Four-speed manual in unit with engine, rear-wheel drive
SUSPENSION
Front: independent via double transverse torsion bars, trailing links. Rear: independent via transverse torsion bars, radius arms and swing axles
BRAKES
Outboard drums, servoed from late-1940s on
WEIGHT
545kg (1193lb) dry
PERFORMANCE
Top speed 88mph (32bhp)

Left and below
Type 64 on recent historic
events, including the
Ennstal- Classic and the
Kaiserstrassenrallye.

'The second car survived the joyrides of the young Ferdinand Alexander Porsche and Ferdinand Piech, but not the driving habits of the American soldiers who liberated it in the last days of the war'

gear with the left, squeezing the wheel between hip, belly and chest in the process.

He was local hero Otto Mathé, who had lost the use of his right arm in a speedway accident. He fell in love with the Type 64, bought it the following year and would keep it to his last day 46 years later. To get to grips with the gearchange he converted the car to right-hand drive and had a tuned engine of 1.3 litres and 60bhp installed. Mathé beat 55 competitors in the 1950 Alpenfahrt; class victories in the Italian Coppa d'Oro delle Dolomiti followed, plus eight overall victories in Austria. In one event the right-hand door flew open, and Mathé managed to get it closed again only by driving along a rock face.

He won the 22 races he entered in 1952, but mostly with one of his two alloy-bodied Porsche 356s. From 1953 the single-armed competitor took on the establishment with a Porsche-powered special of his own design. The Ahnherr (for 'the ancestor' of all Porsches), as Mathé used to call the Type 64, was restored again and became the central piece of his private collection.

Why does Porsche tend to neglect the first sports car it ever made? The official line is that the carmaker was born in June 1948 when the original 356 was type-approved. The very same Austrian authorities – by then under British occupation – registered the Type 64 in April 1946; in fact, its body was made in June 1940, while the chassis dates from August 1939.

But then consider the climate after the war. The Porsche Type 64 (or Volkswagen

Type 60 K10 for that matter) was born under patronage of the National Socialist regime to serve as a propaganda tool. Its link to Hitler's pet project KdF-Wagen (re-named Volkswagen) was just too obvious in the body shape. After the imprisonment of his father in France for war crimes, Ferry was desperate to cut all links with the regime. The Type 64 was a relic from a financially and technically rewarding but socially unhappy past. The 356, by contrast, was a new beginning, born from the determination of Ferry Porsche alone.

Unlike the mid-engined 356.001 that was sold to one of Porsche's financial backers in 1949 and bought back later for the marque's museum, the factory was never too keen to get the Type 64 back. One story goes that Otto Mathé once trailered The Ancestor to Zuffenhausen behind his Range Rover. When the doorman at the factory gate told him the Professor was not available Otto returned to Innsbruck on the spot.

Substantial offers were made when the Type 64 turned up at Laguna Seca and Monterey in 1983, but Mathé refused to part

with it. As it was his ambition to display all his cars, bikes, boats, trophies and inventions to the public in a museum, the 83-year-old widower was receptive to proposals of an Austrian oil trader and signed a contract in 1990, without reading the small print. The oil trader then offered the car to Porsche for a considerable sum, which did not go down well at Zuffenhausen. It took the lawyers four years to get The Ancestor back to Innsbruck.

Things got complicated again after Otto Mathé passed away at age 88, late in 1995. This unassuming and notoriously under-dressed man left behind a considerable fortune; he had promised donations to several persons and organisations, from a classic car club to the animal care league. It took two years to settle the case.

The third owner of the surviving Type 64 is no stranger to Porsche enthusiasts (he's the author of the definitive volume on the 1972/73 Carrera RS 2.7). He found the ancestor of all Porsches was in a desperate condition, its chassis partly collapsed at the engine mounts, but after a restoration that preserves as much of its delightful historic patina as possible the car took part in the Austrian Ennstal-Classic event, as well as in the Goodwood Festival of Speed.

Only the Mille Miglia organisers refused it – for a lack of historic relevance... To date the Berlin-Rome Porsche has never actually made it to Rome. △

Thanks to Dr Georg Konradsheim (www.rsr.at) and to Klaus Parr in the Porsche AG historic archives.

PORSCHE. A word synonymous with engineering excellence and purity as well as motor sport and victory. Porsche is the most recognised sports car name besides Ferrari. Amazingly, even today, when you combine 356 with Porsche, people tend to smile and nod in response, although the last new 356 was manufactured some 47 years ago.

Porsche had been involved in design and engineering work with Volkswagen prior to World War Two and, following an introduction from fellow Austrian Karl (before he became Carlo) Abarth, Porsche teamed up with Italian industrialist Piero Dusio from Turin to begin the development of an affordable sports car. Dusio had made his fortune selling boots to the Italian Army during WW2 and was doing very well with his Cisitalia racing cars. Cleverly based on proven and inexpensive Fiat underpinnings, these cars were effective and profitable: a notion not lost on Porsche.

Late in 1947, as Ferry put it simply: 'We decided to build cars with the people we had, some very good engineers and mechanics.' Porsche followed Dusio's lead and turned to Volkswagen as a foundation for a less costly sports car. After the war, with the help of enthusiastic British Army officers, →

The Cult of the
PORSCHE 356

From early Pre-A models to the last of the line 356C, there's something special about the first Porsches – even though each is very different in character

Words: Robert Coucher   Photography: Paul Harmer

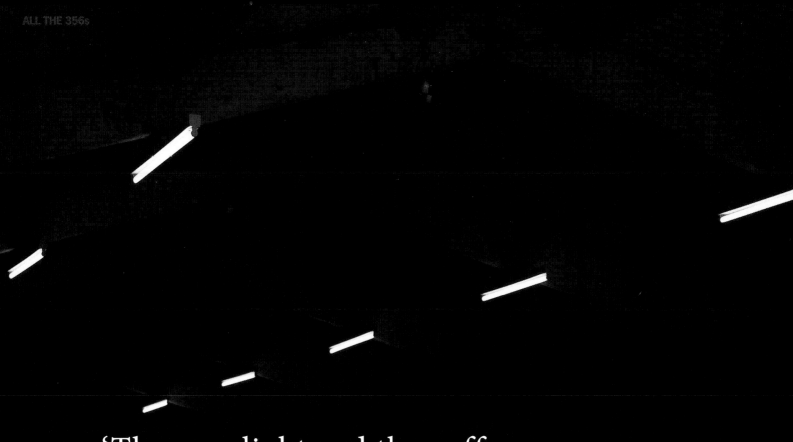

'They are light and they offer
simplicity, purity and function.
And they remain great to use today'

Volkswagens began rolling off the line. By 1946 some 10,000 VWs had been produced. Their engineering effectiveness had been proven and Porsche saw a pragmatic opportunity. In 1947 Porsche and Karl Rabe began planning an open two-seater around VW components. On June 11 the project officially began as 'Type 356'.

Based at the Gmünd Porsche works in Austria, the first 356 roadsters consisted of a light and stiff spaceframe with a VW-based engine mounted behind the passenger compartment and driving the rear wheels. This was a true mid-engine configuration, with the engine ahead of the driveshafts and the gearbox behind. The VW 1311cc flat-four pushrod engine produced a measly 25bhp but Porsche soon upped that to 40bhp.

In 1948 the 356/2 coupé saw the engine swung around and hung out over the rear wheels à la Volkswagen Beetle because of handling problems and the need for more space in the coupé body. In 1948 an order was placed for 50 of the 356/2 chassis and the first ten coupés by two Swiss enthusiasts, R von Senger and B Blank. Porsche was in business.

Porsche cars trickled out of Gmünd in small numbers and by 1951 it had delivered only about 60 cars, not the 150 projected. The aluminium bodies were constructed by men who had previously handbuilt Porsche prototypes with hammers and artistry. As Ferry Porsche explained: 'We had one real artist, Friedrich Weber, who could make every part of the body in half the time the others could. But he would often fail to come in on Monday because he'd been so drunk over the weekend. Nevertheless, he more than caught up with the others during the rest of the week!'

Obviously this could not continue and Porsche soon established its operation in Zuffenhausen, a suburb of Stuttgart, and by the end of 1950 the total output was 298 cars, some 33 per month. These steel-bodied cars differed from those built in Gmünd: they were smoother and rounder and beginning to bear the quintessential Porsche look. Motor racing was very much part of the ethos and in 1951 a streamlined 356 won its class and placed 20th overall at Le Mans. But the real Porsche 356, as we know it today, was launched at the Paris Salon in 1951, offering a 100mph top speed.

So from the salons of Paris and the German automotive Mecca of Stuttgart we travel to the unlikely village of Halstead, set deep in the rural heartland of Essex, England. Lost down interminable hedge-lined country roads you come across Maxted-Page & Prill Limited, which looks more like a horse stud than a specialist Porsche operation. Within the green barns tucked away on the six acres of property you will find some of the most important classic and exotic Porsches in the land, from sports prototype racers to this ensemble of exquisite 356s.

With Lee Maxted-Page controlling the sales operation, Andrew Prill is the Porsche engineering specialist renowned throughout the world as a leader in his field. A Porsche perfectionist, Prill restores, develops, maintains and races a wide selection of Porsches. Talking to Maxted-Page and Prill you soon learn how the classic Porsche scene has changed since *Octane* contributor Delwyn Mallett bought his first Porsche in 1969 (see following →

Below
Early Pre-A is the purest 356 shape, with curvaceous lines and minimal adornments.

feature). As with most classic cars in the 1960s and '70s, early Porsches were simply old cars and usually rusty to boot. They were very expensive when new (more than Jaguars) but soon became ravaged by the weather, the drivers and mechanical decline. Bought by enthusiasts, they were cheaply restored and kept running on a shoestring. But things started to change when their beauty, engineering and ability began to shine through.

'The name Porsche ranks up there with Ferrari,' says Lee Maxted-Page. 'Think of the values of 1950s and '60s Ferraris compared with those of Porsches. To my mind Porsches are undervalued. Certainly they are smaller cars, but they are light and they offer simplicity, purity and function. In their day they were highly competent machines with great motor racing successes, including Le Mans, the Mille Miglia, the tough Liège-Rome-Liège and the Carrera Panamericana. And they remain great to use in today's motoring conditions.'

Andy Prill adds: 'Denis Jenkinson drove his Porsche 356 all over Europe when following and reporting on the Grands Prix and he loved it. On one trip the engine fell out, so he tied it up with rope and got the car home.'

Looking at the quartet of 356s assembled here it is clear that standards have risen dramatically since the days when they were cheap cars. Now every Porsche 356 is regarded as an icon.

A beautiful engineering statement to be cherished. 'These cars are bought with the heart, not the head,' says Maxted-Page – which probably means they're more expensive than you'd think.

And that's the reality check. Porsche 356s rust with more enthusiasm than elderly Alfasuds. The intricate monocoque is clothed in coachbuilt steel body panels and all those lovely compound curves are hand-fettled and filled with lead. In the 1950s and '60s rust protection was not really something to get in the way of production.

'Yes, 356s are expensive to restore and in many cases we have to take a step back with a car, unpick the bad bodges of the past and start again. Parts are available but they are expensive and restoration is labour-intensive,' says Maxted-Page.

And with his usual forthrightness Prill adds: 'Porsche Classic in Germany is not what it once was. It does not encourage the production of spares and parts and seems to be more concerned with controlling supply and prices. But the upshot of this is that specialists in America, German and Italy remanufacture parts and continue engineering development. Just don't buy anything from China. In our experience it's rubbish!'

Not surprisingly, the purest and most 356-looking Porsche featured here is the 1953 Pre-A. Finished in German racing silver, the minimal and curvaceous little car is gorgeous. It appears

Below
Convertible D is effectively a 356A with a soft top and roadster-type front screen.

dinky, with its industrial minimalism softened by its rounded coachwork so redolent of the 1950s. Small on the outside, the Pre-A fits the brief of offering space for two ample Germans and their luggage. While it has fairly crude front trailing arm and swing axle rear suspension it does offer independent springing, allied to a light weight of just 850kg and 60bhp of power from the Super spec pushrod engine.

The Pre-A was the 356 that really put Porsche on the automotive map in Europe and America. This was the model that separated Porsche from its Volkswagen roots, with the Porsche-designed three-piece crankcase, alloy barrels and semi-hemispherical cylinder heads. Porsche was evolving into a future icon.

Some mutter that Porsche enthusiasts are a bit retentive and get all strung out about their car's originality, matching engine numbers and the ticking of the Kardex boxes. So we are very comfortable bringing you this race-proven Pre-A example to explode that myth. Road legal and a total blast on the country lanes, this little 356 is indicative of what the Porsche historic racing fraternity is capable of. This is a highly competitive racing car but it meets strict FIA standards so it is period correct, the sort of racer Porsche would have constructed in the 1950s.

In fact, this example was supplied new to a Mr Abouchakra in Beirut and was raced by Robert Nagar in Haifa in 1955-56, so its current guise as an historic racer is fully justified.

Apart from being stripped of its bumpers (they are probably somewhere in Jerusalem) and riding a bit lower on its Avon CR6ZZ tyres, the Pre-A's exterior appearance is standard. Climb inside and you are impeded by the firm racing seat, while an ample roll hoop is behind you. The engine remains the correct 1488cc but with development Prill has upped the power to 130bhp!

On the lanes it's a rush. The 356 feels like a limpet stuck to the road. It does not corner, it darts. It seems to shrink as forward vision becomes a computer game. Linking it through the corners, Prill does his best to leave stomachs behind at every twist and squirt. No wonder this 356 was in the team that won the Index of Performance and overall team prize at the 2006 Le Mans Classic.

The 1959 Convertible D is the next 356 in chronological order. This is effectively a 356A convertible as opposed to a Speedster. The Convertible D, the D standing for Drauz the coachbuilder, was built only in 1959 (the Speedster ran from 1956 to '58) and just 1300 or so were constructed, so it's worth around £75,000. Although running on wider tyres, with stripped bumpers and a rear luggage rack, it is no Outlaw (see next-but-one feature) and is indicative of a standard 356A.

In comparison with the fast and furious Pre-A racer, this Convertible D is gentler and more relaxed. Start it up and the unmistakable sound emanating from its twin exhausts is pure Volkswagen Beetle. The *chugga-chugga* idle does not match its →

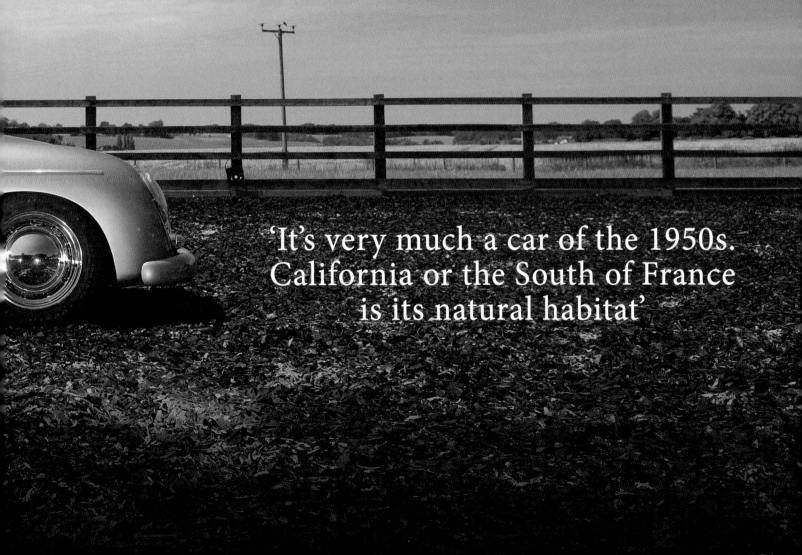

'It's very much a car of the 1950s. California or the South of France is its natural habitat'

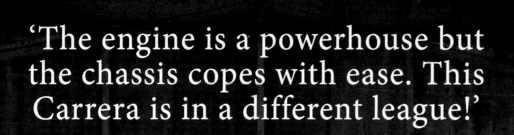

'The engine is a powerhouse but the chassis copes with ease. This Carrera is in a different league!'

elegant looks but rev the engine and things quickly smooth out. On the move it reveals those early Porsche delights of a butter-soft clutch, light gearshift and fingertip steering via that lovely wheel. Brakes are not of any great consequence because this car feels best when driven gently. Through the lanes you notice its gutsy torque delivery and easy nature but it also strikes you as being very much a car of the 1950s. California or the South of France is its natural habitat, even though the owner has fitted sporting bucket seats.

But turn up the wick and let the D carry some speed and the Porsche nature shines through. The pliant suspension allows some roll but not too much. The low-revving engine disguises its output because it has low-end torque and, helped by the light weight, you are soon whizzing along and maximising the 1582cc's 60bhp to the full. A glance at the speedometer belies the sensation of easy movement. With an extra 40bhp – readily available from Prill's workshop – this little convertible could join the ranks of giant-killer.

And that bring us to the burgundy red example, the

Below
Business end of this Carrera 2 GT normally houses a 2.0-litre four-cam lump producing 165bhp.

356 Carrera 2 GT. This 356 really deserves that giant-killer soubriquet. Built in 1963 using a T-6 356B bodyshell, this fabulous Porsche is a factory road racer. With aluminium bonnet, doors and rear lid, minimal bumpers, Perspex side and rear screens, stripped interior, roll hoop and Porsche-designed annular disc brakes, this lean Carrera weighs just 849kg ready for the road, making it lighter than the Pre-A racer.

This is amazing because stuffed under its rear lid is a more technically advanced, bigger and much heavier two-litre, four-cam engine designed initially for pure racing application by Ernst Fuhrmann. Only 310 were constructed and this is just one of 14 right-hand-drive factory-built racers, so it is valued at over £350,000. The Carrera lump in GT specification pushes out a claimed 170bhp when fitted with the virtually open sports exhaust so it should be quick.

On its first racing outing at the Targa Florio in 1961 a Carrera almost won, with another placed second. The Carrera photographed here is a works car with a racing history that includes the Spa 1000km. Today it is enthusiastically campaigned by its owner in historic →

rallies and events. But because Carreras are so rare and valuable it is true to say they are very different to pushrod-engined Porsche 356s. Among Porscheophiles the four-cam Carrera engine is regarded as a fragile and temperamental hand grenade, ready to go bang at any opportunity.

'Not necessarily so,' says Prill. 'They do take a lot of time to set up and to get the ignition timed correctly but once done we check the valves at every major service and they run just fine. Sadly, they got a bad reputation when the cars were cheap and not maintained properly.'

But the engines alone are worth between £50,000 and £90,000 each, so most well-heeled owners take the view it is prudent to leave the original on the bench and run a substitute for events where FIA regs are not required.

Although Prill thinks Carrera owners worry too much about the delicacy of their four-cams, he has developed a substitute engine for general running: a two-litre twin-spark pushrod 356 unit. This is not as out of order as it initially might seem because Porsche itself supplied a number of Carreras with pushrod engines: the Speedster and 1600GTs, for club racers and other impecunious types. Purists might not like the idea but the owners want a knocking-about engine and the 150bhp twin-spark special that Prill provides for around £16,000 seems reasonable insurance. Which is why one has been fitted to this car.

Time to give the Carrera a run. The car is immaculate but low key. It doesn't really look like a racing car, although the large exposed filler cap slap in the middle of the bonnet is a clue. As are the beautifully wrought wheels with exposed lug nuts. The bucket seats with corduroy inserts are snug and the wood-rimmed steering wheel looks odd in a racing car but it is the same as fitted to a 904, so there! Ensure both coil switches are pulled on and start the engine. It springs into life in half a swing of the crank and settles at a busy idle. The throttle response is cracking and the gearshift linkage is taut. The Carrera moves off on its ample torque as this engine is set up for rallying, where low-end shove is required.

Keep the throttle down and hang onto the gear and the 356 takes off. Snatch second and it winds up again, so it's straight into third, then top. The engine is a powerhouse but the chassis copes with ease. This Carrera is in a different league. While its road-rallying spec suspension is softer than the

Right
SC Cabriolet is the final 356 iteration. It's easily the most refined and the best to drive.

Pre-A racer's, the Carrera is significantly faster on real roads. This is because of the amazing engine that produces 100bhp at just 3000 revs and tops out with a fat 150bhp at just over 5500rpm. This low-end grunt means the little car reacts instantaneously to the throttle.

As soon as 3000rpm is breached the gruff and noisy engine – all 356s are noisy, this one and the stripped-out racer especially so – starts to get serious. The open Sebring exhaust starts to sing and you can hear the air being sucked down the velocity stacks start to go supersonic. Over four thou' the sound is loud and hearty. At five thou' it is fantastic! Running on sticky Avons the Carrera attacks the bends, feeling more planted and pliant than the Pre-A racer; and with more power and torque in hand, with effective disc brakes and road-tuned suspension, it would eventually pull away.

As is typical of a good 356, the Carrera GT feels tight and hard. Nothing rattles and the car feels all of a piece. The suspension is fairly pliant but the car's industrial design does not countenance any softness. Porsche's single-mindedness is illustrated by the deletion of the glovebox lid for lightness, for goodness' sake.

Sure, this Carrera GT has its original, valuable four-cam sitting under a bench, but the daily-driving two-litre twin-spark is a fine substitute that can be revved to the limit and enjoyed to the full without concern.

The last in our line-up is the 356C. This was the final iteration, the ultimate evolution of the air-cooled flat-four →

'It's not the fastest, not the most evocative, but the best in real driving conditions'

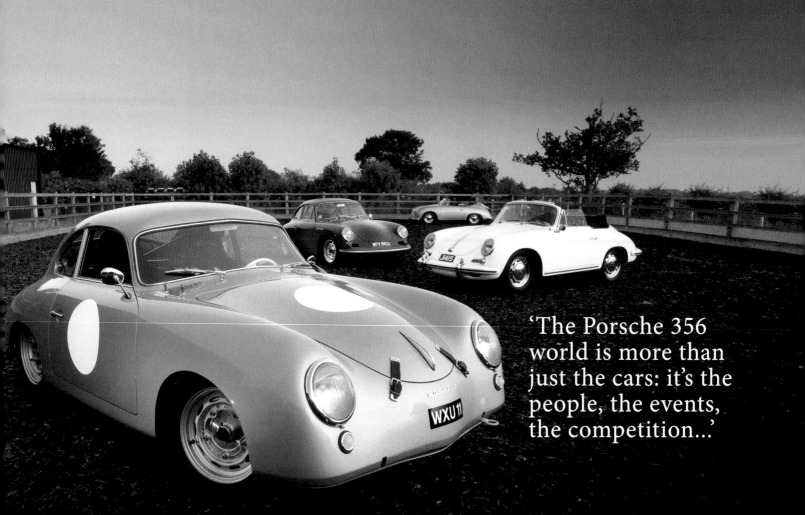

'The Porsche 356 world is more than just the cars: it's the people, the events, the competition...'

pushrod-engined car that was to be replaced by the 911. And the 356SC Cabriolet here is the ultimate C. It has the hotter SC engine, up from 75bhp to 95bhp thanks to uprated cams and carbs, and the Cabriolet soft top adds hugely to its desirability. This Porsche is a California import and has clearly led a cosseted life. Looking perfect, it will sell for the asking price of £75,500, a sum to give 356 enthusiasts of the past palpitations.

These later cars are not as pretty as the curvy early A models. They have higher lights, bigger bumpers and larger glass areas to meet American legislation of the period. But they also have the most powerful (standard) engine options and disc brakes all round, as well as 15 years of Porsche development and evolution behind them.

This ivory and tan-upholstered SC Cab looks fabulous. Almost too fabulous, in fact, and it's probably in the camp of being a girl's car (can one write that these days?), along with the Mercedes 230SL. It was the car of choice for Jacqueline Bisset in *Bullitt* so maybe that's where the idea springs from. The SC's interior is luxurious by 356 standards, with plump chairs and a fully stocked dashboard. The double-lined proper hood is neatly hidden under a tight-fitting tonneau and the big steering wheel gleams with chrome and busy detail.

The Cab romps off down the lanes and you are immediately struck by its feeling of real development. It is much more finessed than the previous cars. The controls remain light but seem more oiled and refined in

movement. The early cars do have a bit of a VW feel to them but the SC is more Mercedes. The engine is quiet, the steering is fluid and free of kickback. The disc brakes are firm, the suspension is wonderfully absorbing and damped and the handling is friendly and benign.

This last-of-the-line 356 is a super roadgoing tourer. Less sporting than the earlier car, perhaps, but certainly an indication of its manufacturer's effective development and evolution. Amazingly it is the most accomplished car of this line-up. Not the fastest, not the most evocative but the best in real driving conditions and the ultimate expression of the 356 genre.

The Porsche 356 is a cult car. The 356 world is more than just the cars: it's the people, the events, the competition, the racing. Owning a 356, you join an international group of individuals who appreciate engineering excellence in single-minded sports cars. With this selection of 356s, ranging from a highly developed historic racer to a rally weapon and two gorgeous road cars, we have at least sketched over the wide Porsche 356 canvas.

Which is the most desirable? Fortunately these four are so entirely different the choice has to be yours, depending on what you want to do. The *Octane* choice would be the slightly tired, ordinary-looking 356A coupé neglected at the side of Prill's workshop. With a T-Cut and one of his feisty 2.0-litre twin-spark engines slotted in, it would make a sensational road rocket.

Above
Porsche 356s for all reasons. They make great road, rally or racing cars, depending on your preference.

Porsche 356 Pre-A

These early cars are desired for their pure looks and delicate feel. Best when tuned because they are slow as original.

Porsche 356 Convertible D

Think of a minimalist 356 Speedster with a lined soft top and wind-up windows and this is what you have.

Porsche 356 Carrera 2 GT

One of the most desirable 356s in the world, this Carrera 2 is a thinly disguised out-and-out road racer.

Porsche 356 SC Cabriolet

Last of the 356 line, the SC has more upright lights, bigger bumpers and fewer curves.

Painted metal dashboard featuring green VDO instruments is beautifully designed and the thin ivory steering wheel is a joy. Interior is sparsely trimmed but surprisingly capacious.

Instruments look more recognisably 356 but the Convertible D still has a VW feel. Controls are light but rubbery so get the car into top gear and enjoy the supple ride and open motoring.

Wood-rimmed steering wheel might look out of place but it is the correct fitting. Glovebox lid was deleted for lightness. Bucket seats are superb and rubber floor matting functional.

Interior is more lavishly equipped. Seats are very comfortable and the dash has all the VDO gauges you would want. The hood is superb and allows for quiet closed motoring.

This 1500 engine meets FIA standards so it is legal and of correct capacity. It is tuned to produce 130 reliable horsepower, which it has used to good effect at the Le Mans Classic.

Drauz was the coachbuilder that constructed the body for this 356, hence it is known as a Convertible D. This is one of just 1000 made during 1959, making it rare and desirable.

Carrera badge is only fitted to very special 356s. Four-cam engines started as 1.5-litre, went to 1.6 and then 2.0-litre. This car is running a 2.0-litre twin-plug pushrod engine.

Thanks to a hotter cam and bigger Solex carbs, the SC's 1600 cranks out 95bhp. Not a lot but it gives the SC more energy than earlier 356s. This model is superb to drive on the road.

Simplicity of the details of the early 356, such as these tiny twin individual rear lights (as fitted to post-October 1952 cars), is what the purists pay so much extra for.

Wider rims look cool but blunt steering feel. 356 suspension is rudimentary – trailing arms at the front and swing axles at the rear – but with little power the suspension isn't taxed.

Lightweight wheels are mounted on Porsche-designed annular disc brakes. Apparently Porsche was too tight to pay for Dunlop discs so he made his own. Dunlop discs are better.

It's best to leave convertible 356s in original tune as they are all about relaxed open motoring. Coupés can handle more power and can be made to go incredibly quickly.

Thanks to the car owners and to Maxted-Page & Prill, +44 (0)1787 476338, www.maxted-pageandprill.com.

40 years in the BATHTUB

Octane contributor **Delwyn Mallett** bought his first Porsche Speedster in 1969 – for £300. Here he recalls the realities of living with an old Porsche in the pre-classic car days of the late '60s and early '70s

Above
Delwyn at the wheel of Speedster no2, reputedly bought new by Gloria Swanson, with his streamliner 'replica' behind.

A lot happened in 1969. Man landed on the moon. The beautiful people headed to Woodstock. Brian Jones, founder member of the Rolling Stones, died. The Beatles gave their last public performance. Monty Python's Circus and the Boeing 747 'Jumbo' jet made their maiden flights. The old halfpenny ceased to be legal tender. And I bought my first Porsche Speedster. It's still my first Porsche Speedster because I still own it, and I still own my second Porsche Speedster, bought a few years later.

As a callow youth what I originally desired was something Early English and perpendicular, but four years at art school studying graphic design opened my eyes, changed my direction and expanded my horizons. A passion for the Bauhaus pointed me towards form and function, modernism and 1930s streamlining. I'd also grown addicted to the magnificent *Shell History of Motor Sport* films assembled by Bill Mason, father of *Octane* contributor and occasional Auto Union pilot, Nick. The episodes chronicling the epic struggle between Mercedes and Auto Union, the 'Battle of the Titans', imprinted me like a baby duckling, to the extent that for years I was a bar-room bore on the merits of the rear-engined car as propounded by Professor Ferdinand Porsche. I've mellowed now. A little.

Having fallen off my 'modded', as in Mod, Lambretta too many times for comfort, a Mini soon followed but it was a Porsche that I had set my heart on. In 1967 I chanced upon a copy of the American magazine *Car and Driver* (great graphics, terrific illustrations by Ken Dallison), which featured a gorgeous black, slightly tricked Speedster in an article entitled *Love Affair With a Bathtub*. The yearning was irresistible. I just had to have one.

Remember, back then Porsches were not common, for fewer than 1000 right-hand-drive 356s had been sold in the UK in ten years. I lived not too far from the importer, A Frazer-Nash Ltd of Isleworth, so I had seen more than the average Joe – but I'd never seen a Speedster in the metal. Not surprising, since years later I discovered that AFN had sold just four.

Incredibly, *Exchange & Mart* (there were no Porsche magazines and no classic car magazines back then) almost immediately turned up a Speedster for sale. I should have bought it – it was black, just like the one in *Car and Driver* – I drove it, loved it, but an 'AA inspection' produced a list of faults that put me off; that and the fact that it was a left-hooker. The following week *E&M* produced another, right-hand-drive but in Cornwall, too far to travel so I didn't bother! Then, within weeks, a third. Again, a left-hooker, so guess what, I passed. With three in almost as many weeks I thought I could afford to be choosy. If only I'd known.

No more Speedsters appeared in the *Mart* in the next year, perhaps ever again. It began to dawn on me that they might be rare. Finally, impatient to be Porsched-up, I succumbed to a 356A Coupé. My elation began to dissipate even as I drove it home. Almost from day one of my custodianship bits began to fall off. I had discovered, the hard way, the curse of the northern European-delivered 356. 'Rust never sleeps', the saying goes, but my colony

of tin-worms must have been permanently on amphetamines because they had devoured about a quarter of the Stuttgart-steel in my little treasure. Remarkably the doors still shut with that lovely Porsche 'thunk'; the roof was sound but there was not much left on the ground floor.

Sod's law being what it is, almost the minute I became the possessor of a now-immobilised Coupé, a Speedster came over the horizon. With no money to spare I persuaded a chum to buy it by guaranteeing him that when he eventually wanted to sell it I would buy it from him for what he had paid. This offer was far better than it now sounds, as we were still living in the age when the cost of old bangers, even interesting ones, went down, not up.

So, 1969 arrived and I bought my Speedster – for £305. That *huuuuge* amount also included an aluminium hardtop made in period by Peel's of Kingston! What bliss. It wasn't an Auto Union, but I was more than happy and the Riviera beckoned. Oh, how I piled on the miles. Ray-Banned, linen flying helmet-clad and foot hard to the metal, I was the kiddy.

The Speedster was of course my everyday car, come rain, snow and the very occasional shine. After several miserable winters it wasn't difficult to see why AFN only sold four. Wilfully ignoring the worsening scuttle-shake and other signs of metal fatigue, I ploughed on until the inevitable happened – the proportion of oxide to ferrous went critical, the seat gave a lurch and I found my seat runners tobogganing along the road.

Enter Speedster number two, serendipitously found languishing shabbily roadside in a Chiswick backstreet. Prejudice against French number plates and left-hand-drive was suppressed, as the intention was to cannibalise number one and number two to make number →

Below and right
Pre-war VW Type 64 that inspired Delwyn's 356 streamliner (see next page); racing Speedster no1 in late-'70s HSCC events – pre-crash!

'Number one Speedster was pressed into HSCC racing – until I peeled it off the Armco, and retired'

Above and left
With 356 streamliner rep and Tatra T87; and 30 years earlier, en route to Le Mans in 1979.

Right and below
Porsche ownership was inspired by US mags; a very hip 1967-spec Delwyn with girlfriend (now wife) Carol and 356A.

'In the early '70s it was almost impossible to give a split-window 356 away. Nobody was interested'

three. It never happened. Astonishingly, number two wasn't rusty! A low kilometrage and an early life in Nice as the runaround of Hollywood legend Gloria Swanson had been kind to the chassis, whereas hot sun and, later, Parisian parking habits had not been kind to the exterior. Another 300-ish smackers and it was mine. A bare-metal repaint and a red leather re-trim later and it was gorgeous. Still is.

Number one was resurrected with a very non-standard floor. Nobody would touch an old Porsche in the '70s. Even AFN refused to get involved with welding a 356: it was just too complicated. Body panels were getting scarce. Floor panels were unobtainable but I did buy the last 'front clip' that the factory had. This consisted of a complete nose and both front wings, welded as one, and was delivered in a box almost large enough to park a car in. Well, half a car.

With its boiler-plate floor and a rollover bar, number one was soon pressed into a bit of HSCC racing, in the then (but not for long) bog-standard Road Sports category. After a couple of seasons thrashing around Silverstone and Donington I was, I thought, getting the hang of this racing business when, at Brands Hatch, I chose a non-standard line through Clearways. After peeling my car off the Armco I decided that perhaps my exuberance outweighed my talent and retired. Everything you have heard about 356 handling is true. Slow in, fast out, is the mantra. Whatever you do, don't lift in a corner.

In the late '60s and early '70s a 356 could still outperform or hold its own with most everyday cars and it was easy to stay ahead of the pack, but gradually and inevitably they had to give way to progress. Today you venture into the outside lane at your peril, for pretty soon white van man will be driving up your *auspuff*.

What attracted me to the 356 was that it is really a 1930s streamliner whose introduction was delayed by the Second World War. The 1939 Berlin-Rome Type 64 Volkswagen streamliner (see *Octane* issue 42) is a prototype for the 356. Take out WW2 and we are talking about three or four years' development. After my two Speedsters, I bought an early split-window 356 and proceeded to build my own streamliner, inspired by the Berlin-Rome cars and the first 356 Le Mans cars of 1951 and '52. Was this the first outlaw Porsche in the UK?

At that time it was almost impossible to give a split-window car away. They were considered crude compared with the 356A and nobody was interested. Today their scarcity has seen the prices of well-restored versions reach £200,000. Despite its radical look there are only six small fixing holes in the bodywork that weren't put there by the factory. Not a lot of restoration work for the next owner!

When I bought my first Porsche, the great unwashed still considered 'Porches' to be souped-up VWs and most had no idea what a Speedster was. Little kids loved mine because it was red with yellow wheels and looked like a Noddy Car. I patiently forgave their parents for thinking it was a VW Karmann-Ghia but I couldn't forgive them when later they started to proclaim: 'It's one of those kit cars, innit?'

Forty years watching the world speed by from my bathtub(s) has inevitably left me wrinkled. One of my Speedsters, the red car, has aged with me ungracefully, looking even more ravaged by time than I do. The other, although not quite 'factory fresh', still provides as much satisfaction as it would have given its first owner in 1957. Now with 120 horses under its deck-lid, maybe even more.

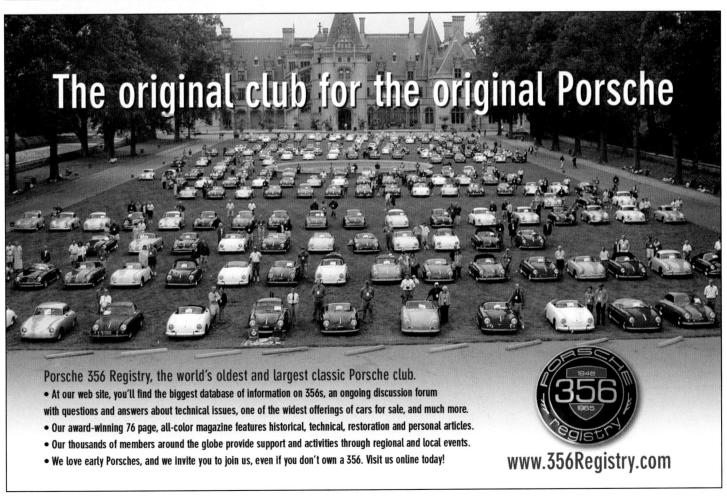

SMOOTH CRIMINALS

Of all thoroughbred classics, it's the early Porsche that attracts by far the most attention from customisers – and never more so than in California, home of the 'Outlaw' 356

Words: Nigel Grimshaw   Photography: Matthew Howell

In the turbulent years preceding the Second World War, little could Ferdinand Porsche have realised the appeal his work would later hold for the free-thinking, avant-garde world of the customiser and hot rodder.

With hindsight, the swooping lines and charismatic design style of his Volkswagen were always going to catch the eye of the world's car modifiers, in much the same way the 1932 Ford or 1941 Willys had already done. No surprise then that by the mid-1960s men of a certain mindset were tackling the Beetle with their angle grinders and welding torches. As with many a fledgling scene, various approaches were unsuccessfully inflicted on the Volkswagen until finally a blueprint emerged and the California look was born.

Clearly the availability and affordability of the Beetle made it a favourite among customisers but, inevitably, the similarly swooping lines and charismatic style of the sibling 356 also caught the eye of the planet's modifying community. So began the evolution of the Outlaw Porsche...

Outlaw: the word is suffused with excitement and mystique. Which is why it's appropriate to talk of an Outlaw Porsche. Like the hot rods of the 1930s and '40s, the Outlaw Porsche was born of a desire to go fast, be fun and look good doing it. And just as it was with the hot rods, when mensuch as Alex Xydias, Ed Iskenderian and Vic Edelbrock unwittingly established templates that have lasted to this day, the Outlaw Porsche too had its pioneers.

Arguably the first to take the leap was Dean Jeffries. Like his contemporaries such as George Barris, Ed Roth and Von Dutch, Jeffries is a legendary car designer, builder and painter. He has had an incredible career in hot rods, TV and movie cars, most notable among which is the Monkeemobile. However, unlike many of his contemporaries, Jeffries prefers to let his work do the talking, so he is generally less well known. One of the most incredible things about Jeffries' Outlaw is that he customised a four-cam Carrera. Work included extending and recontouring the nose, which housed frenched headlights and driving lamps. Jeffries then built louvres into the roof à la Mercedes race car and engine-turned the interior surfaces and door jambs. The car was eventually sold to a less-than-desirable purchaser who turned out to be a murderer. Outlaw indeed!

→

Another prominent player in the world of the Outlaw Porsche is Gary Emory. Friends of Emory get to call him 'The Outlaw' and with good reason. To Gary there are two kinds of classic Porsche owners: those who polish and those who drive. But there is more to it than that. Emory grew up in California's San Fernando Valley during the 1950s. Son of custom car builder Neil Emory, of the Valley Custom Shop, young Gary had a head full of Los Angeles custom car culture, of an aesthetic that had to marry with driving, having fun and Porsches.

In 1960 Emory went to work as a parts boy at the Porsche dealership of Chick Iverson in Newport Beach, California. Here he watched as 356 customer after 356 customer drove from the workshops, their cars freshly fitted with Nardi or Derrington laminated wooden steering wheels, decambered suspension to lower the ride height and improve handling, reversed wheels to gain offset, nerf bars instead of bumpers and Bursch stingers to replace the factory exhaust. These Iverson cars hinted at the Outlaws to come. They looked better and went faster, but the world had yet to see the full-on collision between Teutonic cool and California custom culture that was spinning in Gary Emory's mind.

Gary spent the 1970s at Iverson's, helping Porsche owners tweak their cars into something that little bit different. This, of course, was at a time when the concours movement was shifting into high gear, restoring cars to better than original condition. As the '70s gave way to the '80s, Gary bought the parts business from Iverson and set about making even bigger waves. During that much maligned and underrated decade, Emory developed his own style of Porsche and caused apoplexy among purists, while attracting an alternative following all of his own. The Outlaw Porsche had finally become a movement and to celebrate the fact Emory created a badge, a badge handed out only to true Outlaws. Unsurprisingly, these badges now change hands for impressive sums of money, but true devotees hold onto theirs.

So what exactly does an Outlaw Porsche look like? Well, like Mark Motshagen's wonderful orange 1964 356C. Built at Willhoit Auto Restoration, Long Beach, Mark's Outlaw is no gaudy Kustom. Far from

Left and below
Mark Motshagen's 356 is pure Outlaw: subtly modified but with tough 1925cc twin-plug engine and striking paint.

'Like the hot rods of the '30s and '40s, the Outlaw Porsche was born of a desire to go fast, be fun and look good doing it'

Above and right
Chris Toy's 356 is Outlaw in looks and concept, but Porsche 930 turbo engine has raised un-Outlaw-like handling issues.

it. There is a vintage feel to go with the 'look'. In essence the cars are close to stock, but look more like a GT – as if the factory might have done the work, had Porsche decided to further develop the model.

Motshagen's Outlaw also respects the importance of racing heritage in all things Porsche: that a race car should always have arrogant dazzle. Consequently the colour is a tangerine from the 911 chart called Blut Orange (Blood Orange). Combined with the 1925cc twin-plug motor, lowered suspension, black 15x6in Panasport alloy wheels and spartan interior, Motshagen's 356 is archetypal Outlaw.

Or consider Chris Toy's black 1964 356, which has all the tricks you expect from an Outlaw 356 but with one enormous exception: Toy has shoehorned in a turbocharged 3.3-litre six-cylinder motor from a 1979 Porsche 930 – over triple the power, and ten times the fear factor. Ironically, Toy's hot rod has many a traditional 'Outlaw' scratching his head in bewilderment: especially those fortunate, or unfortunate, enough to have taken a ride. Suffice it to say that corners are not a speciality.

And then there's the Silver Bullet shown on the previous pages: based on a 1955 356 Continental, this 356 subscribes to the Outlaw philosophy... if a little loosely. The body is recognisable up to the B-pillar, despite the roof having been chopped by several inches. From the rear edge of the doors back flows a striking fastback that helps enhance a hatful of fabulous details. Power comes from a mid-mounted 3.0-litre 911 motor mated to a 915 five-speed gearbox. You can't say it's not striking.

Thanks to John Willhoit, Mark Motshagen, Gary Emory, Rod Emory; www.partsobsolete.com, www.willhoitautorestoration.com, www.fantasyjunction.com.

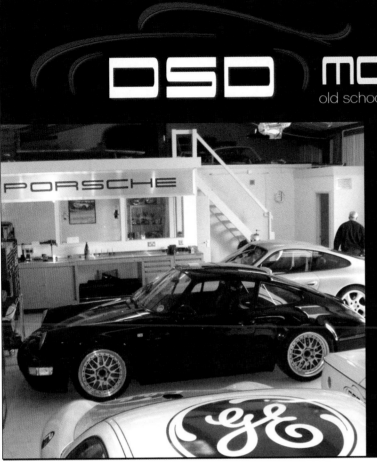

THE
SOUND OF
flat-four
MUSIC

To mark 60 years of Porsche, *Octane* took several versions of
the 356 back to the company's home territory, deep in the
Austrian Alps. They may look similar, but what a difference
there is between the early and late models

Words: John Simister   Photography: Andy Morgan

Every new driver should learn in an early Porsche 356 on ageing crossplies. Here's another mountain bend: feel the nose drift wide, back off, *wa-hey*! Round comes the tail, and up it goes too as the swing axle tucks itself under. This is one interactive car, a crash course in throttle-steerability. And I'm only going about 40mph.

Here's a car that calls for commitment or else the tail will be flailing all over. Maybe BF Goodrich's interpretation of the 1950s tyre-making art (it's called the 'Silvertown') isn't the optimum footwear, but it certainly gives a window into the forces unleashed in a moving car. And now I must hunt for that second gear again. I couldn't find it last time, but I know it's under the dashboard somewhere.

The early 356, what aficionados call a 'pre-A' from 1954 (so it's the same age as me), was developed on roads like these. Mountain routes between Gmünd, where the first Porsches were made, and Zell am See near the Porsche family seat at Schüttgut. As these roads are deep in Porsche ancestral territory they continued to be used even after the company returned to Stuttgart, where Dr Ferdinand Porsche the elder had his consultancy pre-war.

This particular route, the first part of our journey to Gmünd to mark Porsche's

Below
Steel-bodied pre-A proved a handful on the twisting Alpine roads to Gmünd.

'As these roads are deep in Porsche ancestral territory they continued to be used even after the company returned to Stuttgart'

60th anniversary, takes us from the Gaisberg hillclimb, a broken con-rod bolt's throw from the Salzburgring race circuit, to Zell am See. Our 356 is the oldest of a pack of precious Porsches parked at the bottom of the Gaisberg, where RS60s and 356 Abarths and flat-eight RS Spyders once rent the air with their air-cooled aural edge. It's small and silver, but steel-bodied because only the first 52 cars, the Gmünd production, wore aluminium panels. With its low arches concealing wheels buried deep within, it looks like a cartoon version of more familiar later 356 models.

Is it, then, the shape of a Gmünd car reproduced in steel? There's a rather legendary Porsche figure here who can answer that question: Herbert Linge, just turned 80, whose name I remember from many 1960s race reports. He seemed to get a lot out of cars whose engines were much smaller than those of Ferrari or Ford. The Targa Florio was a particular Linge favourite.

Linge was also the Porsche company's first new employee when it returned to Stuttgart in 1949. 'It was Dr Porsche and his secretary to begin with,' he says, 'and then they took me on.'

First, though, we need to go back a couple of years.

In Gmünd the company had been doing small-scale engineering and manufacture under contract while US forces occupied its old buildings in Zuffenhausen, near Stuttgart. But Ferdinand 'Ferry' Porsche, son of the man who founded the company and invented the Volkswagen and the rear-engined

Below
Porsche's original Gmünd factory, a former sawmill, has been restored by the Austrian Porsche Club.

'You'd never trust
this 356, unfailingly
predictable in its
unpredictability,
in a really quick
corner'

1954 PRE-A

ENGINE
1488cc air-cooled
flat-four, pushrod
OHV, two Solex 32
PBI carburettors,
compression 7:1
POWER
55bhp @ 4400rpm
TORQUE
78lb ft @ 2800rpm
TRANSMISSION
Four-speed
all-synchro transaxle
in unit with rear
engine
SUSPENSION
Front: torsion leaves,
parallel paired trailing
links, telescopic
dampers
Rear: torsion bars,
swing axles,
telescopic dampers
BRAKES
Ate-Lockheed
aluminium drums,
finned at front
WEIGHT
830kg
PERFORMANCE
0-60mph 17sec.
Top speed 99mph,
allegedly

Auto Union Grand Prix cars, had a dream of making a sports car using parts from the more prosaic of his father's inventions – a creation for which the Porsche company would later be able to claim intellectual copyright and be paid a royalty.

Porsche set up its Gmünd base during the war to escape from Allied bombing raids, but it took a while to get going again once the war was over, not least because Dr Porsche senior was detained in Baden-Baden by the French forces, who wanted to check out (unfounded) allegations of Nazi collaboration. And while there, he had the Renault 4CV to help refine. Anyway, in 1948 the company's first own-badged car took to the road, a roadster with an obvious 356 look derived from Dr Porsche's three streamlined, special-bodied Volkswagens (the Porsche Type 60K10) built for the September 1939 Berlin-to-Rome race that never happened, but mid-engined and mounted on a tubular chassis.

This car, styled by Erwin Komenda and dubbed 356/1 even though it was actually Porsche's 349th design project, came to nothing, although it still exists. (Dr Porsche had started his design and engineering consultancy back in 1931, and its first project was numbered seven to give the first client, Wanderer, the impression of an established company.) The next attempt reverted to the rear engine position of its Volkswagen donor, and most of the other mechanicals were similarly Beetle-sourced. It was a coupé, and the definitive 356 profile was born.

So, Herr Linge, is this 356 before us effectively a Gmünd re-make in steel? 'Oh no,' says Porsche's most senior employee, 'every panel is different. And all the aluminium cars were different from each other anyway.'

The scale of the Gmünd/Stuttgart differences will become clear

Below
Mementoes at the
Porsche family home in
Zell am See, a place of
happiness but also tough
Allied occupation.

'Dr Wolfgang Porsche,
the youngest of Ferry's
four sons and chairman
of Porsche's
supervisory board,
is here to meet us'

as our journey develops, but for now let's get to know the oldest Porsche I have yet encountered in person. It's so old it doesn't even have the Porsche crest on the nose, a crest whose central prancing-horse motif is the symbol of the city of Stuttgart.

The horse is the same as Ferrari's, by the way. According to Ferry Porsche's autobiography, an Italian airman shot down a German aeroplane in World War One, and the aeroplane bore the Stuttgart crest. The Italian kept it and later suggested his friend Enzo Ferrari might like it as an emblem for his new racing team. 'Ferrari accepted the suggestion gratefully,' wrote Ferry in his dry, pragmatic way, 'and so the coat of arms of the City of Stuttgart appears twice as an automobile trademark.'

This 356 has already evolved from the first Stuttgart cars, though. Its bumpers are moved slightly away from the body, but like all 356 bumpers they are still painted in body colour with bright metal trim strips. It has gained horn grilles below the headlights, and the windscreen is made in one piece with curved edges. Curiously, it still has a bend in the middle where earlier cars had a divider between the two panes.

With 55bhp from its 1488cc, a capacity achieved by endowing the Beetle-based engine with a longer-stroke crankshaft and larger, chromium-plated bores in new aluminium cylinder barrels, the 356 is not fast despite its twin carburettors. It's still quicker than the earlier 1086cc and 1286cc engines, though, if less rapid than the optional 72bhp version of the 1500, which uses a roller-bearing crankshaft and was intended for motor sport. There was also a 1290cc version of this engine.

Above
Dr Wolfgang Porsche,
son of Ferry, grew up
surrounded by 356s and
still exhibits a strong
passion for the classics.

The sound is as Beetlish as you would expect, although no 1954 Beetle would come near even this car's modest pace. There's a red sector on the tachometer (it's hooded, like the adjacent speedo) which starts at 5000rpm, but really it's all over by 4800.

Other niceties about the facia include an oil temperature gauge – vital for an air-cooled engine – with Celsius and Fahrenheit scales and a double-ended needle, as well as a plethora of unlabelled knobs and switches seemingly made from soapstone. And there's a big fabric speaker grille in the middle, for one of those new-fangled radios.

Nothing else feels quite like a 356, especially an early one on crossplies and bereft of an anti-roll bar. The tyres climb cambers and ridges as the nose gently wanders, and it's best to let them find their own way. Allied to this is steering that feels vague at first, calling for big movements to make things happen – and then they do, quickly, as the yaw moment rises.

You take fast corners like facets of a threepenny-bit until you learn to stop over-correcting; and the knowledge of what lurks in the darkness of uncertainty, should you back off, inspires little confidence. You'd never trust this 356, unfailingly predictable in its unpredictability, in a really quick corner unless you knew exactly where the corner went.

Meanwhile, the clunky gearchange is getting more obstructive as the temperature rises, the drum brakes are calling for an ever-harder push and now the handbrake has stopped working, joining the indicators and brake lights on strike.

Is this the stuff of which a future legend would be made? Engaging as this 1954 car is, it's hard to imagine it so.

→

Above
Cabriolet version of the 356B Carrera 2 is seriously rare, and highly-strung with its four-cam engine.

WE'VE ARRIVED at Zell am See, well south of Salzburg. From here it's mere minutes to Schüttgut, the Porsche family house and estate that Ferry Porsche bought in the late 1930s. Dr Wolfgang Porsche, the youngest of Ferry's four sons and today the chairman of Porsche's supervisory board, took it over in 2004 and he's here to meet us now in his traditional Austrian collarless jacket in green.

He likes green. There's a 911 Turbo cabriolet in dark green parked outside, plus a Cayenne Turbo in Bentley Brewster Green (Dr Porsche is on Volkswagen's board, too, given that, at time of writing, Porsche controls Volkswagen – and therefore Bentley – in a delicious historical irony.) A pearlescent white 959, pleasingly travel-stained, is also in the line-up, while a Porsche tractor and a Porsche Schwimmwagen are under the converted stable nearby.

Beyond the house, an abode stuffed with stags' heads, giant decorated cowbells and family memorabilia, stands a small chapel to mark the graves of the Porsche and Piëch families. It's a place full of poignancy. Ferry Porsche talks in his book of how the American 'occupying forces' came to the house as war ended, and how they discovered one of the Berlin-Rome cars at the nearby flying school. They were racing it on the airfield.

'It was such a beautiful hot summer,' wrote Ferry, 'that the soldiers eventually used metal cutters to remove the coupé's roof, turning it into a "roadster". They had great fun with it, but they did not think of

filling it up with oil and one day it ran dry, and the dream came to an end. The wreck ended up on a dungheap.'

And what's this? It's a 1949 Gmünd-built 356, beautifully restored in a shiny red-orange oxide hue. It has a bench seat and an ultra-simple dashboard inside, a high floor, intriguing curved front quarterlights and a tiny single exhaust pipe. There are trafficators in the front wings and tiny rear lights, and two bright strips traverse the nose above the bumper. If the 1954 car is slow, then this 1086cc car must be very leisurely; despite its twin carburettors the otherwise-VW engine manages just 40bhp. That said, this primordial 356 is very light and aerodynamically slippery, and is reckoned to be able to reach 87mph. Eventually.

HERBERT LINGE is looking at this 356, too. 'We used to test on the Stuttgart to Leonberg autobahn,' he tells me. 'One side was still closed after it was built and we used it twice a week for six months, testing the 356 and the 550 Spyder for Le Mans. There was nowhere else to use the time. We discovered the wheel spats helped a lot.

'Dr Fuhrmann [Ernst Fuhrmann, Porsche's engine designer] had designed a four-cam motor for racing, and we put it in an aluminium Gmünd car. Professor [Helmut] Bott, the chief of the experimental department, thought it had too much power and there was an argument between him and Fuhrmann.

Right and below
Chapel at Zell am See marks the graves of Porsche family members; gorgeous coupé is 1949 alloy-bodied model.

'Professor Bott and I thought we should try it with an anti-roll bar. So I tested it without one, then with it, all night. The first time I drove, I was spinning everywhere. It was definitely overpowered. With the anti-roll bar it was much better and I could go faster. We showed the results to Dr Fuhrmann the next day, and he had to change his mind.' Bott and Linge were right, and the whole 356 range later got an anti-roll bar.

Back in the hotel at Zell am See, Wolfgang Porsche is joining us for dinner. He tells us how important it is for Porsche to remain a family business, how it has gone from being almost broke to being one of the world's biggest car makers, if you include the Volkswagen connection. But even Porsche itself now builds over 100,000 cars a year, compared with 11,353 in the 356's best year, 1963.

'Cars will become smaller and lighter again,' Dr Porsche is saying, 'and people will get used to that. Today people want gadgets, which need motors and add weight, but they will return to a more purist outlook. They might even open the boot themselves!'

'We had a big advantage at the start. We made our small, exclusive car in small numbers but we had the Volkswagen organisation behind us. Other manufacturers said it was a hazardous thing for us to do, but too many men had lost their youth and it was a dream to fulfil. Today people point to Porsche and say cars like ours spoil the environment, but they produce just 0.01% of all cars' carbon dioxide.'

1962 356B CARRERA 2 CABRIOLET

ENGINE
1966cc air-cooled flat-four, DOHC per bank, two Solex 40 PII-4 twin-choke carburettors, compression 9.5:1

POWER
130bhp @ 6200rpm

TORQUE
119lb ft @ 4600rpm

TRANSMISSION
Four-speed all-synchro transaxle in unit with rear engine

SUSPENSION
Similar to 1954 Pre-A but with addition of front anti-roll bar

BRAKES
Ate discs all round

WEIGHT
1012kg

PERFORMANCE
0-60mph under 10sec.
Top speed 124mph

'The occupying forces came to the house as war ended, and discovered one of the Berlin-Rome cars at the nearby flying school'

→

'It's cruising at 90mph as if it had been built one year ago, not 45. This is why people held these Porsches in such high regard'

Above
Coupé 356B proved a delight, a clear step on from the earlier cars, with surefooted handling and high-speed stability.

NEXT MORNING it's time to try out the ultimate roadgoing version of Fuhrmann's four-cam engine, installed in one of just 34 356B Cabriolets thus powered and dubbed Carrera 2, to denote the engine's stretch from 1498cc via 1587cc to 1966cc (that is, 2.0 litres).

A louvred valance under the rear bumper, home to a pair of fat tailpipes, gives the external clue along with the badging and, hiding behind wheels mercifully shod with radial rubber, Porsche's first roadgoing use of all-round disc brakes (by Ate, pronounced *a-tay*, not to be confused with ATE).

I drove an earlier incarnation of the Carrera engine a few years ago in an ultra-lightweight Mathé Porsche special, and it was a mighty energetic beast. In this Carrera 2 it's handicapped by extra weight but counters with 130bhp at 6200rpm. Two twin-choke Solex 40 PII-4s meter the fuel and air.

This is a complex engine, with bevel gears and vertical shafts taking the drive from each lower, exhaust camshaft to each upper, inlet camshaft. Setting the backlash in the gears is the time-consuming part when building one. But it sounds great, the Beetlish flat-four beat 'n' clatter overlaid with a crisp-edged blare, and it has the throttle response you'd expect from a choke per cylinder.

Today we'll drive to Gmünd via the Grossglockner pass. It's a route often travelled by Ferry Porsche, sometimes with the young Wolfi, as the family called him, in the passenger seat. Straight away the Carrera 2 feels a generation removed from its ancestor of yesterday, and not just because its exhaust barks so inspirationally through the crisp morning air. It's quick, if not bombastic, and its steering has a precision and certainty absent in the pre-A 356.

Tyres and a front anti-roll bar are why, helping accuracy and progression respectively. Much else has happened between 1954 and this car's 1962 year of birth. The bumpers and headlamps are higher, the hubcaps are flatter, the windscreen forms a continuous curve, and the dashboard, although still of painted steel, is entirely different. The tachometer takes almost centre stage ahead of a steering wheel now made with three knurled aluminium spokes, presaging the 911's instrument layout.

1963 356B
ENGINE
1582cc air-cooled flat-four, pushrod OHV, two Solex 32 NDIX carburettors, compression 8.5:1
POWER
75bhp @ 5500rpm
TORQUE
86lb ft @ 3700rpm
TRANSMISSION
Four-speed all-synchro transaxle in unit with rear engine
SUSPENSION
Similar to 1962 Carrera 2 cabriolet
BRAKES
Ate-Lockheed aluminium drums, finned at front
WEIGHT
934kg
PERFORMANCE
0-60mph 13.5sec. Top speed 109mph

Left and below
Porsche museum,
just down the road
from the original
factory, boasts a
wonderful selection
of artefacts.

And the gearlever is mounted further back, making it easier to find the ratios – although this remains one aspect of Porsche driving that's deprived of the precision you'd expect. A double-declutch helps. It's reassuring to feel solid, responsive brakes under the middle pedal, and the stage is set for a spirited blast up the pass. Into a hairpin, power round, feel the traction as the rear torsion bars twist and the tail squats; it's still very throttle-steerable but you, rather than wayward camber changes, control the rate at which it happens.

There's snow now, and the air is getting thinner. I can tell because the power's edge has dropped away and the hills have become a struggle. But now we're at the top of the pass, and gravity will henceforth be on our side.

Which throws up an unexpected snag. The brakes are working hard. We stop at some roadworks and, expecting the lights to change at any second, no handbrake is applied. The next application of the brakes sees the pedal heading straight to the floor because the fluid has boiled. So much for disc-brake technology. Staying in a low gear, not touching the brakes for a few miles and trying not to think of precipices cools them off, and once down in the valley they're fine again.

AT GMÜND there's a fine Porsche museum. Here you'll find an original 356 wooden body buck, early 356s and a military Beetle, a 906 (Carrera 6) GT racer complete with blue-tinted rear window, a 911 Carrera RSR, a plethora of engines and much more. It's an essential pilgrimage point, but it's not the old factory. That's a couple of kilometres up the road, where all that remains of the former converted sawmill is the wooden office building, restored by the Austrian Porsche club, complete with engineering diagrams – one for the four-wheel-drive Cisitalia – on their drawing boards.

This is where Porsche started as an independent car maker, a company we think of as German but with as much claim to being Austrian. From here back to Gaisberg we'll drive a 356B coupé, in red like the Carrera 2, via the faster Katschberg pass, the old road running next to the modern autobahn. It's a 1963 car with 75bhp from its 1582cc. That's the middle of three outputs, the others being 60bhp for the gentle *Damen* version (you'd never get away with that today) and 90bhp for the Super 90.

We're back on drum brakes here but this is one delightful car. It's brisk rather than quick, with a torque delivery more akin to the pre-A's, but the engine has that unstressed, unburstable feel that was always a Beetle's trademark. This 356 feels absolutely solid, with not a rattle to be heard nor a shake to be felt, and if you close your mind to tales of a swing-axle's wilder habits you can have a great time.

Here's a long, fast, downhill bend, the sort to make any of your cheeks clench. Slowish in, fast out and stay committed is the mantra here, but the 356B stays flat and responds to every input with copious, perfectly proportional real-time feedback entirely alien to the driver of a typical modern car. It feels more benign than I'd have ever guessed. Look at how people used to race these things. The handling can't be that savage unless you really upset it.

Now on the autobahn, the 356B is cruising at 90mph as if it had been built one year ago, not 45. This is why people held these Porsches in such high regard. They work properly, no excuses. They are practical, usable sports cars. Sixty years on, nothing has changed. △

Thanks to Porsche AG, and especially to Porsche Museum director Klaus Bischof and his team.

Riding with Linge in the 356 Abarth

HERE'S the most intriguing 356 of all. Just 20 356B 1600GS Carrera GTL Abarths were made, the product of a meeting between Ferry Porsche and Carlo Abarth (formerly an Austrian called Karl). The production 356's weight was hampering its racing ability so Porsche commissioned Abarth to make this lightweight, with an aluminium body designed by Franco Scaglione, which saved 90kg.

And here's Fuhrmann's four-cam, 1588cc and 135bhp, in full cry, as Herbert Linge takes me for a blast up the Gaisberg hillclimb. This is one of two cars he raced in the early 1960s, winning the 1963 German GT Championship having come sixth, and winning the class, on the GTL's 1962 race debut in the Targa Florio. The engine is utterly dyspeptic below 5000rpm, then explodes into life all the way to 8000rpm.

Some cyclists aren't impressed as Linge gets in the groove, but the GTL was here before they were. It's colossally loud and a proper racer with its crackle-finish dashboard and chronometric tachometer. Next to these the vast steering wheel and sloppy gearchange seem incongruous.

'I last drove it 40 years ago,' Linge is shouting. 'I'm an old man but the car is the same, maybe better than I remembered.' His favourite, though, is the beautiful 904. Linge came second in a 904 in the 1964 Targa Florio: 'I was leading up to the last lap, and then the rear suspension broke.'

Time traveller

Porsche's 356 was way ahead of its time in many ways. We drove what
is reckoned to be the world's best of the early split-windscreen
models to see what all the fuss was about

Words & photography: Delwyn Mallett   Archive pictures: Porsche AG

'It's probably fair to say there isn't another soul

For Porsche as a manufacturer, the immediate post-war years were inextricably linked to the success of Volkswagen. If VW had not continued in production it is virtually certain that the Porsche concern would have remained a design consultancy to the auto industry at large and, without its magnificent line of sports and racing cars, wouldn't have become a household name.

When in 1945 the British Army restarted VW production at Wolfsburg it was more of a morale-building exercise to provide jobs for the vanquished and demoralised German workforce than a commercial venture. By 1948, however, under the direction of the extraordinarily energetic and ambitious Heinz Nordhoff, the miracle of the Beetle was beginning to win the hearts and minds of the world. Ferry Porsche, son of Ferdinand and – due to his father's deteriorating health – now effectively head of the company, negotiated with Nordhoff to honour a pre-war agreement and pay a royalty of 5DM per car for his father's design. In addition, a contract for further consultancy work, the appointment of Porsche KG as the sole importer of VWs into Austria and an agreement to supply parts to allow Porsche to build a sports car of its own were also agreed. In those difficult early years ever-increasing VW production provided Porsche with a vital cash flow.

From the beginning Ferdinand Porsche and Ferry had envisaged spin-offs from the basic VW design, including a sports car bearing their name, but these pre-war ambitions had been thwarted by the political implications of a state-sponsored project providing parts through which a private company could profit. It was only with the announcement in 1938 of the Berlin to Rome

Above
Cockpit Spartan but seats are leather and deeply padded. Door cappings were wood on early cars; engine just 1086cc initially.

race, a propaganda stunt linking the two Axis powers, that Porsche had the opportunity to build a 'hot' VW-based sports car. As war approached, the race was cancelled but three highly streamlined KdF (VW) Rekordwagens were eventually built, and were clearly the progenitors of the 356.

Towards the end of the war the Porsche design bureau was relocated to the village of Gmünd in Austria, close to the Porsche family home. There between 1948 and 1951, working from a converted sawmill, Porsche managed to hand-build around 50 coupés and cabriolets. Designated 356, these cars abandoned the VW chassis in favour of a strong box-section platform made from simple, folded sheet steel panels. The running gear, suspension, wheels, brakes, steering and gearbox were purely VW, while Porsche tweaked the engine with redesigned heads and a Solex carburettor above each bank of cylinders, on twin-port manifolds.

It quickly became evident that Porsche's ambition to become a sports car manufacturer would require better facilities; a return to its old premises in the Stuttgart suburb of Zuffenhausen presented the most feasible option. With money in short supply, a mutually beneficial deal was struck with the Reutter Coachworks to supply an initial run of 500 steel bodies. Ferry considered that this was the total the world market could absorb, spread over several years. Perhaps one of the few things that he got wrong!

In March 1950 production started at the Zuffenhausen works. Demand for the new Porsche was far greater than expected, with the original quota of 500 cars being reached almost exactly one year later, in March 1951. By

who knows more about the first 500 Porsches'

March 1954 Porsche had built ten times Ferry's estimate! Over 77,000 356 variants would be made by the time the model was finally replaced in 1965 by the 911.

It's taken Oslo-domiciled Paul Rui an absurd amount of time, research, dedication and a massive bundle of kroner to defy time and turn the clock back to zero on his stunning example of a 356 from Porsche's first year of Stuttgart production. For Paul, already an expert in the renovation of early VWs, restoring an early Porsche was a natural progression, if a much more difficult proposition. Paul is a graphic designer and typographer with an uncompromising eye for detail, so once he had decided to restore his Porsche nothing short of perfection would do. Not content with 'received' knowledge gleaned from books or other restorers, he embarked on a series of pilgrimages to Stuttgart and the Porsche factory archives to research exactly when and what changes were made in the first year of production. After half-a-dozen visits and hours spent poring over Porsche internal memorandi, it would be fair to say that there probably isn't another soul who knows more about the first 500 Porsches than Paul.

When *Octane* was invited for a drive in his Porsche the (rebuilt, and reset to zero) odometer showed a mere 62km, and as chassis 5355 sat shimmering and breathtakingly beautiful in its pale Radium Green metallic paint, it was hard, for a moment, not to believe that we had been transported back to Verk 1, Augustenstrasse 82, on the day that it was wheeled out. In 1950 there was little that could be compared with it; almost totally without embellishment, the 356 depends on the harmony of wind-cheating curves for its impact.

Above
One of just 500 cars built in 1950, this example is widely thought in the Porsche world to be the best survivor.

Despite its inherent mechanical and dynamic limitations, you can easily see why the first Porsche so quickly endeared itself to the cognoscenti. The doors produce a satisfying thunk as they close and wind noise is virtually absent at speed due to the combination of excellent aerodynamics, good sealing and Porsche's almost fetishistic obsession with the accuracy of its panel gaps. The 356 was built for comfort and long journeys, with wide, deeply padded, leather-covered seats set low in the extraordinarily roomy cabin.

A new sensation for the period was the lack of bonnet ahead. With no engine to cover, the lid drops from sight and the front aspect starts, and stops, at the base of the screen, much like the view from a modern car. The dash can only be described as Spartan, albeit in a Bauhaus kind of way. A speedo and matching clock make up the two main dials, with a smaller oil temperature gauge alongside. No revcounter and no fuel gauge! The clock would be replaced by a revcounter in 1951, but owners had to rely on the reserve fuel-cock and a wooden dipstick for several years to come. It took a long time for the Brits to warm to the Porsche. In an age when the sporting motorist aspired to a dial-laden dash hewn from a mahogany plank, it is easy to see why.

As always with a 356 the six-volt starter 'hangs' for a moment before the engine catches and springs into surprisingly loud life. The single-pipe Eberspächer silencer met with much criticism from owners, as silencing was not one of its better features, but from the cabin the exhaust note is not particularly intrusive and the motor's thrum is pleasingly light aircraft-like. Depress the cable-operated clutch, reach out for the slightly-too-far-away →

Clockwise
from far left:
First steel-bodied
car off the line;
each early engine
built by one man;
drying booth; wooden
body buck at Reutter.

'To describe the 356 as a special-bodied Volkswagen is not to condemn it for its humble origins'

gearlever and prepare yourself for the weakest link in the VW ancestry – the crash gearbox. With no synchromesh on any of the ratios the transmission is a disappointment both in respect of gear-whine and embarrassing, not-quite-got-it-right-that-time grating. Although a certain amount of satisfaction can be gained from mastering noiseless up and down changes, contemporary reviewers, and customers, were unanimous in saying that the new Porsche deserved a better 'box. The marque's own groundbreaking and much-copied synchro unit arrived in late '52. As compensation, the light steering is a delight and the ride is as smooth as a modern's.

The only area where Paul was forced to deviate from the as-delivered 1950 spec is with a slight upgrade to the engine capacity, where the original 1086cc has grown to 1286cc. Porsche announced the larger-capacity motor in 1951 and, as the increase was achieved simply by fitting bigger-bore Mahle alloy barrels and pistons, many owners opted to have their engines reworked.

This move not only boosted performance but also saved weight where it mattered most – behind the back axle. A combination of rear weight bias, skinny 16in wheels and tyres, no anti-roll bars, lever-action back shocks and swing-axles resulted in dramatic and often terminal lift-off oversteer. German drivers coined the word *wischen* to describe the approved cornering style. Phonetically, this suggests that one made a wish before approaching a difficult corner but in fact it translates as 'wiping' – hanging the tail out, accompanied by a lot of compensatory sawing at the steering wheel! Enter a bend too fast, and you'll certainly be wishing as you *wischen*.

To describe the Porsche 356 as a special-bodied Volkswagen is not to condemn it for its humble origins but rather to emphasise what an exceptional design Professor Porsche's KdF car was, and the potential that was waiting to be unleashed from its basic components. In every respect the 356 is the model that, if circumstances had allowed, Porsche could have built and sold in 1939. If this car had hit the road then it would have been nothing short of sensational. As it was, in 1950 it was still remarkable.

In September '50 Professor Ferdinand Porsche celebrated his 75th birthday at a ceremony in Solitude, close to Stuttgart. New Porsches from across Europe converged to mark the occasion. In November of the same year Ferdinand, with Ferry, visited the by-then-thriving VW factory, the construction of which he had overseen before the war. On the night of his return the Professor suffered a stroke. He died a month after Paul's car was completed, on January 30, 1951. △

Paul's project wouldn't have been possible without the following: Richard King of Karmann Konnection, Bruce Cooper of Sportwagen, Rob O'Rourke, Christer Rye, Kobus Cantraine, Jens Thorner of Porsche and Nadine Katz of Porsche Museum.

The pre-A 356

Long neglected in favour of the later, more developed and more user-friendly versions, the much rarer, so-called pre-A 356 has caught collectors' attention in recent years, with a 1950 model recently selling in the UK for a cool £200,000.

Twelve hundred of these distinctive split-windscreen cars were made between March 1950 and March 1952, when the single-piece, so called 'bent screen' 356 was introduced.

These early 356s are referred to as 'pre-A' to distinguish them from the A-, B- and C-series 356s that were built from 1955.

The split-screen models marked the return of Porsche from wartime exile in Austria to its premises in the Zuffenhausen suburb of Stuttgart, and the fulfilment of the family's ambition to be an independent auto maker.

Few cars survive from the period. Paul Rui's restored 356 featured here is one of the best, and possibly the best.

Above and right
Eclectic entries ranged from Stratos and Daytona to 2CV, plus, of course, the Faure/Mallett 356.

Tour de farce
CONFESSIONS OF A RALLY VIRGIN

It may have just 60bhp, but when it's driven by Le Mans racer Nick Faure a Porsche 356 cabrio can still do the business on the Tour Auto. If only the same were true of its navigator, *Octane*'s Delwyn Mallett

Words: Delwyn Mallett Photography: Patrick Payany, Mathieu Heurtault & Delwyn Mallett

It was on day four of the 2005 Lissac Tour Auto that, as we entered a vicious downhill chicane on the Circuit de Nogaro, one of our hubcaps decided it had finally had enough and jumped ship. I think it was also on this circuit that I decided the racer's mantra of 'slow in, fast out' was a relative concept, as our 'slow in' seemed to be frighteningly faster than anyone else's. I say 'think', because, after 1500km of twisting roads, mountain passes, four racing circuits and five hillclimbs, it is difficult to be precise about the actual moment that this fact dawned upon me. But, like our hubcap, I get ahead of myself.

Coincidences are fascinating. I was just re-reading Denis Jenkinson's stirring account of his historic ride to victory with Moss in the 1955 Mille Miglia when the phone rang. It was old chum and long-time Porsche-pusher, Nick Faure, asking me if I would accompany him on the Tour Auto – the start of which was only a couple of days away. Now, I must confess, I had always cast myself in the role of Moss rather than the hairy-gnome navigator. And France in the Noughties is not Italy in the Fifties. But then, life is never perfect.

The gap between fact and fantasy widened a little more when Nick explained that we'd be in his bog-standard 60bhp 1958 Porsche 356 cabriolet. Nick's racing E-type had expired that morning, and his wife felt that the Porsche was too tame for her and had ducked out! One woman's loss is another man's gain.

Monday morning found the three of us – Nick, the Porsche and me – easing into the parking area that had been created on the Esplanade des Invalides (celebrations to commemorate VE Day having displaced the start from its traditional spot opposite the Eiffel Tower on the ramp of the Trocadero).

The event is split into 'competition' and 'regularity' classes and, with his racer out of action, Nick had switched our little Damen to regularity. Secretly, I felt that this might be the category for wimps. I mean, there was even a Citroën 2CV in our group! Although Nick had successfully changed his entry, the programme failed to note that he had also changed passenger, so I remained 'Mary' for the duration of the rally, garnering puzzled looks and predictable jokes on the way.

Tuesday morning was grey, cold and wet as we were despatched, at 30-second intervals, into the Paris rush hour. After only 200 metres and one instruction on the route map, I was thrown into confusion as the car in front turned in the opposite direction to that which I had just indicated to Nick. After a few moments of tetchy consultation, we decided that I was right and he was wrong.

Once clear of the city, we headed towards Vichy via the twisty bits, and the rally proper. The prevailing weather conditions had persuaded us that, despite a slightly premature earlier agreement to make this a 'roof-down' trip, we would be much more comfortable with the top up.

In the next five days some of the most gorgeous and picturesque parts of France whistled by. Vichy, Clermont-Ferrand, Toulouse, Pau and hundreds of small villages came and went, spectacular mountain cols were negotiated, wonderful local gastronomic delights were savoured, the weather and our speed picked up, and the roof came down. Gradually we became blasé at the sight of Ferrari 250GTs sailing past, or stopping at some isolated petrol station and queuing behind a clutch of exquisite 1950s sports racers, and our arms ached from waving at the thousands of enthusiastic spectators lining the roads.

But there were also frustrations: having to rush through wonderful lunches in order to meet the allotted departure time; missing the racing at the tracks because we were always getting back on the road just as the racers, who were travelling behind us, were about to start their events; being presented with a massive box of chocolates, only to find it welded into an inedible mega-lump by the time we opened it.

Four circuits were included in the rally: Magny-Cours, Charade, Nogaro and Pau. The idea for the regularity competitors is to attempt to complete three consecutive laps in identical times. Each group circulates together and it is all too easy to be seduced into 'racing' with others in your group and to screw up the lap times. Only stop-watches are allowed in the car and, to this end, Nick had brought along his kitchen egg-timer and I had brought a large Russian stop-watch that I use in my photographic darkroom. The battery was flat in Nick's egg-timer and the Russian clockwork seemed reluctant either to start or stop predictably so, even if I had been capable of recording a lap time accurately, repeating it was clearly beyond our means. I had been reduced to nothing more than ballast.

However, what our team lacked in navigational expertise was more than compensated for by driving skill. Every gear change was exactly on the start of the red line. The brakes were applied at exactly the same point each lap, the turn-in was always smooth, and power was always on throughout the entire radius of a curve. 'In a 356 you never, ever lift in a bend,' advised Nick.

I protested to him that the line between 'slow in' and 'Oh my God!' →

Right and below
Rural France has
been the Tour Auto's
preferred territory
since 1899.

I'll never get around there at this ridiculous speed!' is extremely fine indeed. Even as a Frazer Nash viciously slammed the door on us, Nick didn't lift but flattened his line, launched the little 356 over the kerb and powered on. Such was the metronome precision of his mental timepiece that, on the second day, we – OK, he – won a prize for completing four successive laps within a fifth of a second of each other!

Somewhere in the Auvergne we were dropping out of the mountains over a torturously twisting road, just the sort of country where a 356 comes into its own: lots of relatively slow bends where the weight over the rear wheels can really be used to advantage to power the car out of the turns. Ahead we spotted a Mini-Cooper S. Almost imperceptibly at first our speed through the corners started to pick up and gradually we began to reel in the Mini. Pretty soon we were right on the tail of the car, which had noticeably raised its own speed, but after a kilometre of pushing through the bends the driver eased a little and waved us through. However, the snarl from the Mini's exhaust and the scream from its gears indicated that its pilot had every intention of sticking with us.

Our descent may have been aided by the gravitational attraction of over 32 stone of prime manhood but, overall, this equated to a very poor power-to-weight ratio for our equipe. Gradually we eased away from the Mini as the little Porsche dug its rear tyres into the tarmac. And then we were in the valley, the road straightened and Nick eased off the pace.

Within minutes we had entered the Parc Fermé, where two race-suited, sweating and adrenalin-soaked Frenchmen decanted from their Mini and approached Nick. 'That was fan-tas-teek – your lines through zee corners woz amazing!' gasped the driver. 'Av you got a 120 'orsepower engine in zere? We 'ava a 110 and could not catch you!' Both men visibly slumped as Nick announced that he had no more than the 60bhp that the factory had issued. He even had to lift the deck-lid to prove it.

By the last day we had abandoned all pretence of gaining a sensible position in the results and, as we lined up for the final hillclimb, event organiser Patrick Peter whispered to Nick: 'Thees is a good 'ill. Just go for it.' So he did. The regularity competitor's aim is to climb the hill in an allotted time, fast but not flat-out. We went flat. Once again I had to marvel at what an astonishingly grippy machine a 356 can be – as long as you don't bottle out! The newly fitted Avons were pushed to the limit as they scrabbled for traction on bend after bend.

On the way up the six-minute climb we passed the E-type that had departed 30 seconds before us, then the Ferrari that had left 30 seconds before that, and we arrived at the finish line just as the car in front of that was clocking in! This caused much confusion for the timekeepers and a heap of penalty points for us, but failed to erase the smiles of satisfaction from our faces. We were still grinning as we arrived in Biarritz. Despite our transgressions we finished 40th overall. I dread to think what the 50-odd cars below us were up to. △

'As a Frazer Nash viciously slammed the door on us, Nick didn't lift but launched the little 356 over the kerb and powered on'

Tour Auto

The name Tour de France Automobile was first used in 1899, at a time when the great French road-races set off from Paris and thundered to some distant city. As an even more challenging trial, the 1899 race took a 2000km route around France, including the mountainous and punishing Auvergne.

The original Tour lapsed in the 1930s but it was revived in 1951 by The Automobile Club of Nice and *l'Equipe* magazine, with a formula that proved immensely popular with spectators and competitors alike. Competitors travelled 5000km around France, visiting and competing on virtually every circuit and hillclimb.

The Tour ran over a week, with overnight stops in hotels. With the odd break it continued until 1986, by which time the public could thrill to the sight and sound of full-blown sports prototypes frightening the livestock in rural France.

In 1992 The Tour de France was revived as a 'classic' event, run over a slightly shorter distance and restricted to cars that competed in the Tour between 1951 and 1973. To avoid confusion with the cycle race, the name was changed in 1998 to Tour Auto.

Nick Faure

Nick started his racing career by winning the Mini 7 Championship in 1965, but soon 'changed ends' and campaigned the 1968 British Saloon Car Championship in a Porsche 911. Sixteen wins in a Carrera 2.7RS run by Porsche Cars GB secured him the 1973 STP Production title. During the 1970s and '80s Nick competed in 11 Le Mans 24-Hours in Porsches, Ferraris, a De Cadenet, Lola and Dome, among others.

From the start he has regularly driven classic racers, too, winning in everything from a Birdcage Maserati to a D-type Jaguar.

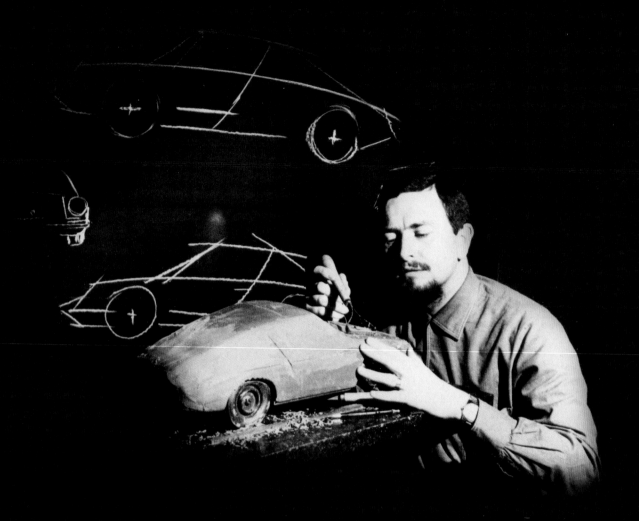

THERE
IS NO
SUBSTITUTE

Some argue that the aircooled 911s are the
best Porsches of all – which means they are
some of the best cars ever. **Robert Coucher**
introduces our guide to the 'classic' 911

Photographs: John Colley, Porsche archives, Paul Harmer, Rex Features

Love or loathe...

It is true to say that drivers either love or loathe the Porsche 911. The supporters agree that it offers one of the purest and most thrilling driving experiences available. The detractors shout that 911s are dangerous and feel strange, with their six-cylinder engines slung out over the back wheels. And those who have not actually driven one often dismiss the cars as 'leaving them cold'.

A lot of this opinion has to do with social values. When the first 2-litre 911 was announced at the Frankfurt Motor Show in September 1963, there were some pretty spectacular sports cars on the market: the Jaguar E-type, Aston Martin DB6, Corvette Sting Ray and Ferrari 275GTB. Against this backdrop the comparatively expensive 130bhp 911 was never going to be snapped up by the mainstream; instead, it was bought by drivers who wanted a quick and unobtrusive car.

Today, driving an historic car is a statement – and a 911 is a very strong statement. But it depends where you are.

In America, a 911 is a small sports car driven by single-minded enthusiasts. When you see a classic 911 pounding along a wide-open highway from the comfort of a large American sedan, you know that the Porsche driver is enduring rather severe conditions in order to indulge in his driving enjoyment.

On the Continent, 911s are used as fast and efficient tools, flat-out down the fast lane to get to the next meeting 100 miles away. Come the weekend the European 911 is enjoyed up and down the twisting mountain passes, with skis strapped to the rear grille. It is considered a sharp and effective instrument.

But then we come to Britain. Ah, the eternal British diseases of envy and class. Initially in Britain 911s were appreciated by focused types, and through the years the cars' amazing performance and practicality made them the choice of every young man in a hurry. The urban myth of the time was that there were more 911s in central London than anywhere else. And when the financial markets really took off in the Eighties, it seemed that every barrow boy who had made a few quid in the City bought a red 911 to match his braces. But the bewinged and spoilered 'retail red' Porsches were crashed early and sold quickly once the Filofax brigade realised that a 911 was not a status symbol, but a hard and uncompromising driving machine.

Within the Porsche world, 911s are now loosely divided into four categories. The early cars are the short-wheelbase 2-litre models built from 1965 to 1969, which are the race-eligible machines in great demand among the hard-core historic race and rally competitors. Then there are the pre-impact bumper 911s built from 1970 until 1973. These are probably the most desirable road-going classic 911s, with engines ranging from 2.2 to 2.4 litres. In 1974 the impact-bumper 911s were introduced; these are some of the least desirable models, but the later (post-1978) 911SC and 3.2 Carreras make excellent usable classic drivers.

The 'modern' classics, if you like, begin with the 964, first launched in 1989. This is a very different machine to past 911s, with coil-spring suspension and dual-mass flywheels, and it was generally not well received by Porsche purists. The 964 marked the arrival of the tamer 911, aimed at the broader motoring market. The last aircooled Porsche, the 993, was launched in 1994 and is an eminently usable daily classic with real character. That's why it commands higher secondhand prices than the later, watercooled 996.

Over the following pages, we analyse and appraise each iteration of the aircooled 911. →

Stephen Bayley on Nine Eleven

An Aberdare trolleybus was the first Porsche-designed vehicle in Britain. Today there are many more, but for most people Porsche will mean one thing. Nine eleven. They even did research after the Manhattan atrocity and decided the numbers meant so much it was worth preserving them. That says a lot about what a car means.

Dr Porsche's original design consultancy went under the name of the Konstruktionsbau-fur-Motoren-Fahrzeug-Luftfahrzeug-und-Wasser-fahrzeugbau. So snappy titles played no part in effective branding. A very odd sports car was revealed outside some wooden huts in Gmünd in 1948. It had been given the drawing office number 356. The 356 used Volkswagen components (including a 40hp 1131cc engine) but its most interesting feature was its appearance. A genetic pattern was set.

When it came to replacing the 356 with the 1963 car we now know as the 911, Ferry Porsche's brief to the engineers was to offer a sensation that was 'driving in its purest form' (although it has to be admitted that an additional part of the brief was room to stow golf clubs, so perhaps impure forms were allowed as well). The car was originally a 901, but the designation was changed to 911 when Peugeot's lawyers laid claim to all three-digit appellations with a zero in the middle.

It was drawn by Ferdinand-Alexander 'Butzi' Porsche (on left in picture above, with father Ferry), who later went on to establish the quite separate Porsche Design business to specialise

in sunglasses and document wallets. The model began as Porsche Type 695 in 1959. Early on, Butzi had said: 'The headlamps play a great part in the face.' And while the new car paid semantic attention to what was already a rich Porsche heritage, it was also the first one to be considered artistically, and not as a wholly technical exercise. Ferdinand-Alexander said of his father: 'He has taste, but is not a stylist.' So a stylist was brought in.

There are rather blurred black-and-white photographs of early versions of what became known as T-7 – a car with a distinctively Porsche nose, but with a strangely capacious and airy glasshouse with a forward-sloping B-pillar. Prototypes were on the road in the early-'60s. Screen, bonnet, doors, DLO (daylight openings) and general arrangement are all immediately identifiable, but are visually muffled by a weird

front air intake and a split rear glass with tail fins that locate the concept in the past with Ledwinka's Tatras, not in the future.

The first productionised, athletic, sculpted 911 appeared at Frankfurt in 1963, the same year as the architectural and monumental Mercedes-Benz 600. Against the Benz's portentousness, there was something in the lascivious austerity and quirky rationality of the 911 that appealed very strongly: its shape was inimitable, yet laid claim to history. It had upholstery in racy Prince of Wales check.

The wonderful thing about the 911 is that the engineers satisfied the brief and so too did the designers, making the 911 perhaps the single greatest example of automobile art of them all. Substance and style are as one. Just as the specification improved from a gawky, wheezy thing on spindly tyres, so too did the body semantics evolve from cutely sharp to thumpingly meaningful.

If machines have life, they must also have genes, and the 911's go back to the 1930s when aerodynamics pioneer Erwin Kommenda sketched a body for the first Dr Porsche's People's Car. Ghosts of that unique shape still haunt the modern Porsche. Of course, there are no actual radii in common, but you could line up everything from a 1936 Volkswagen to a modern-day 997 and there would be a visually seamless morphology that is heartbreakingly beautiful.

The Porsche 911 is both evolution... and intelligent design.

'You could line up everything from a 1936 Volkswagen to a modern-day 997 and there would be a visually seamless morphology that is heartbreakingly beautiful'

Left
Purists love the original 911 for its ultra-clean shape, though SWB cars can be a handful.

The hard core

1965-1969

911S model introduced in 1967, producing 160bhp (later 170bhp with fuel injection). In 1968, softer T (Touring) and base L models introduced, and the E (*Einspritzung*, or Injection) in 1969. 911 Targa available 1967-69. Weight: from 1080kg

Choice model: 1967 911S, 160bhp
Prices: £25,000+
Watch out for bodged restos and hidden rust. Cars need to be very carefully set up.

'Early 911s are the more fragile cars and not as user-friendly as later models. You need to rev the nuts off them and they are noisy, twitchy and hard'

Early 911s are the cars chosen by competitive historic racers because they are light – in racing trim the weight usually has to be kept up to the homologation weight of around 1000kg – and they are fast. The standard 2-litre produces 130bhp and the hotter 'S' 160bhp, with plenty more available to a skilled engine builder.

Just a few years ago these small-displacement, peaky and difficult-to-tune, generally worn out and rusty old dogs were the runt of the litter. Thanks to the resurgence of historic racing and rallying, and the veritable army of specialists who now really understand these cars, early 911s can be made to run obediently and are regarded by the hard core as the cream.

But early 911s are the more fragile cars and not as user friendly as later examples. You need to rev the nuts off them and they are noisy, twitchy and hard. When the model was first released, experienced drivers were perturbed by the 911's wayward handling. Its six-cylinder engine weighed about 200lb more than the outgoing flat-four, hung out over the rear wheels, and the cars still wore 356-sized 4 1/2-inch wheel rims. All this conspired to induce immediate and severe oversteer when lifting off through a corner. Porsche tried to rectify this by adding 22kg of weight to the front bumpers, which was hardly the ideal solution.

In 1969 the wheelbase was lengthened by 2 1/2 inches and the wheel rims widened to six inches, which helped the weight distribution and the previously hedge-busting handling.

But drivers such as 'Quick' Vic Elford had soon got to grips with early 911s, and Monte Carlo Rallies and circuit races were vanquished. Many historic racers actually prefer the pre-'69 short-wheelbase cars, now that the chassis can be properly sorted by swapping tyres, dampers, roll bars, torsion bars, suspension pick-up points and so on.

An early 911 is an adrenalin pump to drive. The car feels small and light, and the joy of the flat-six is that it gets smoother and more eager as the revs rise. From the driver's seat you feel the vehicle swivelling from your hips. You need to allow the lightly laden front wheels to squirm about and keep a loose grip on the steering wheel.

Once you accept that the sensation of driving a 911 is different from conventional cars, you will be hooked. The Porsche is so responsive, clean and quick-witted you soon find yourself covering ground at serious speed and exiting bends ahead of the pack. Just never, ever lift off while going into a corner... →

Road-going rockets

With sales taking off in the late-'60s (particularly in the USA), Porsche knew there was scope to widen the 911's appeal even further. A bigger powerplant and a spread of models were called for. In 1970 engine capacity was enlarged to 2195cc and T, E and S states of tune were made available, along with the semi-auto Sportomatic gearbox and Targa top.

These 911s remained lightweight driver-focused sports cars, with their slimline look, minimal trim and vocal engines. Of the 2.2-litre engines the 'S' is again regarded as the one to have, because of its rev-happy nature and full quotient of 180bhp.

In 1972 the capacity was further enlarged to 2341cc, and fuel injection was used across the range. The 2.4S of '73 pumped out 190bhp, which meant a 0-60mph sprint time of 6.6 seconds and a top speed of 145mph. In the real world, the less-cammy 2.4E is probably the most usable road car of this group while still having real driver appeal.

But in 1973 arguably the greatest 911 of them all was launched: the 2.7 Carrera RS. Just 1580 examples of this magnificent 911 were manufactured in Touring, Sport and Race trim.

1970-1973
2.2-2.4-litre engines plus the 2.7RS in 1973
Power: 125-190bhp (210bhp RS)
Weight: 1100kg (940kg for RS Lightweight)
Choice model:
2.4E for road use, 2.4S for a bit more.
Prices: £30,000+; £40K for 2.4S; £150K+
for RS. Beware of fakes; provenance is
all, so check all numbers. Watch out
for rust and crash damage.

With its distinctive and effective ducktail spoiler, front air dam, lurid Carrera script down each side and tyres that were wider at the rear than up front, the RS quickly became a sensation. The 210bhp model had an enlarged engine, up to 2.7 litres, which gave it a lovely dose of free-revving power. Allied to a low weight of just 940kg in Lightweight trim, the Carrera proved to be a fast and flexible race winner.

An RS feels just as light and pointy as an early 2-litre car, but it has the added full-fat wham of 188lb ft of torque, 18% more than the 2.4S. Yet a 2.7RS will happily spin to its 7300rpm maximum with unabated enthusiasm. These 150mph machines are extremely quick on the road, as well as on historic race or rally events. With mechanical fuel injection, the RS copes well with modern traffic, too.

But now that the Lightweight version of the 2.7RS commands over £150,000, the lesser 2.4S at around £40K begins to look like good value. As mentioned, for driving enjoyment on the road, the smoother and torquier 2.4E provides almost all the sensation if not quite the out-and-out speed. A 0-60mph time of 6.8 seconds and top speed of 143mph are not too shabby.

> 'If you want an excellent, tough, reliable, rustproofed 911 to leave outside and drive on a daily basis, the 911SC from 1978 is for you'

From fright pig to daily driver

In order to meet American safety standards, Porsche fitted its 1974 models with large, impact-absorbing bumpers. These mid-'70s 911s are the least loved because they have all the problems of the 1970s cars – engines prone to breaking head studs, body rot, etc – without the light weight of earlier models. 911s of this period are cheap and have usually suffered years of neglect and abuse. European 2.7- and 3.0-litre models are rare, and the post-

1974-1989
2.7-3.2-litre engines
Power: 150-231bhp
Weight: from 1130kg

Choice model: SC for solid simplicity,
3.2 Carrera is easier to drive.
Prices: from £6000 for unloved 2.7;
£12,000 for clean SC and £18,000 for best
3.2-litre Carrera. Ensure SC has
had camchain tensioners
modified to hydraulic type.

'78 cars are simply a much better bet when it comes to using them regularly.

The first glimmer of hope that Porsche was sorting itself out was the mad, bad and dangerous-to-know 911 Turbo, launched on an unsuspecting world in 1975. We'll not go into early Turbos here because they are monstrously expensive to maintain (they have 917 front brakes) and don't offer any real benefits over the normally aspirated cars for regular use.

If you want an excellent, tough, reliable, rustproofed 911 to leave parked outside and drive on a daily basis, the 911SC from 1978 is for you. The cars were fully galvanised (a feature first introduced in 1976), so they have modern levels of protection against the ravages of rust. From 1981 power was up to 204bhp, and in this form an SC will dash from 0-60mph in 5.9 seconds, carry on to 150mph and nothing will drop off along the way!

The SC is also the last of the 911 range you can fix with a socket set, a screwdriver and a hammer – and every time you shut the vault safe-style door with a solid thunk, you will smile, knowing that this is one of the most carefully constructed cars ever.

Classics for the modern era

The very different Porsche 964 was launched in 1989, initially in four-wheel-drive guise. It replaced the previous 3.2 Carrera and was claimed by Porsche to be 87% new. The suspension was totally different, with McPherson struts and lower wishbones up front and semi-trailing arms with coils at the rear. Engine power was up to a strong 250bhp, so performance was excellent (0-60mph in 5.5 seconds, 161mph top speed).

When initially road tested, the 4WD 964 was felt to be a bit numb and unexciting, as it was prone to understeer. Sure, the hard over-centre clutch of the past had been replaced and the gearshift was more conventional in action, while there was also unobtrusive power steering. But it met with a lukewarm response. The two-wheel-drive 964 was launched in 1990, and was so safe and predictable it almost made the 4WD car redundant. Lift-off oversteer had finally been tamed, but the overall results were, er, dull. Not a word normally associated with a Porsche 911.

We have not gone into limited-edition offshoots here but the 964RS is worth a special mention. The car is just 'stonking', to use track day parlance. First seen in 1991, the RS was criticised for its harsh ride. But what a machine. Stripped down to 1229kg and producing 260bhp, the 964RS combines a 2.7RS's deftness with modern levels of grip and braking.

Porsche tried hard with this car to make it a focused driving machine. Weight was shed by ditching the air-con, power steering, electric seats (for heaven's sake...), central locking and rear seats. Glass was thinned and an ally bonnet fitted, along with Recaro composite buckets, Turbo-spec front brakes and 17-inch magnesium alloys. And the body was seam welded. This is one special Porsche, so no surprise that prices are rising fast. Expect to pay over £35,000 for one of only 2364 RSs manufactured.

But 964 sales began to plummet, in part due to the economic problems of the time. Japanese consultants were brought in – Mein Gott! But it worked. In 1993 the company built just 8292 964s. By the end of 1994 it had turned out 16,643 examples of the new 993.

The 993 was again 80% changed. It ushered in fresh organic styling as well as cutting-edge multi-link rear suspension. It was great to drive, thanks to its superb 272bhp aircooled flat-six, and in 1995 Varioram induction was added (upping the power to 285bhp) to coincide with the launch of the very sexy, wide-bodied Carrera S. Available first in 4WD configuration, then with more desirable 2WD a year later, the Carrera S (0-60 mph in 5.3 seconds with a top speed of 168mph) is a joy to drive. It's probably one of the most exciting and best-rounded 911s of the lot. →

1989-1998
3.6-litre engines
Power: 250-285bhp
Weight: 1380-1400kg

Choice models: 964RS; pretty much any post-'95 Varioram 993 depending upon how you want to drive.
Prices: 964 from £14,000 to over £35,000 for RS; 993 from £20,000 to Carrera S at £35,000; RS over £40,000. Important to go for a desirable colour and ensure RSs have the correct magnesium wheels and other lightweight fittings.

'The two-wheel-drive 964 was so safe and predictable it almost made the 4wd car redundant. Lift-off oversteer had finally been tamed'

Left
Modern classics:
from far left, 1990
964 Turbo, 1993
Carrera 2 and Turbo
3.6, 1995 993 Turbo.

Driving a 911
Porsche racer Tony Dron on the best driver's cars

The feel of a good 911, pressed to the limit, is one of those special things in life. Yet there's no denying that those very first 911s did prove a bit of a handful. Works driver Vic Elford had no problem driving them at ten-tenths, on ice and snow, as his spectacular outright win in the 1968 Monte Carlo Rally proved. He had the confidence, the sense of balance, plus the lightning reactions required to put the car sideways when travelling downhill at high speed on ice. Frankly, Vic was some kind of Superman.

The ideal way to drive Porsches had been established with the previous model, the 356, in which it was relatively easy to use the weight of the rear-mounted engine as a kind of pendulum. Many 356 owners regularly hung the tail out on opposite lock as they entered corners; then, opening the throttle held the slide. It was even fairly simple to flick between left and right corners. Lifting off completely would, of course, make the car spin. And finding enough front-end grip for downhill braking without locking up was always an issue calling for extra caution.

That sideways stuff was all fine in the little 356 but it was harder in the bigger 911 with its heavier six-cylinder engine. The same principles, however, applied if the early 911 was to be driven really fast and ordinary 911 owners did tend to come to grief until the factory lengthened the wheelbase by that small but critical amount. The standard roadgoing 911s of the early 1970s were

never totally confidence-inspiring. The steering felt wonderfully 'live' and informative but they were not cars to be thrown casually sideways on any corner. The model for that was the 2.7RS of 1973. It was the greatest driver's car ever – utterly predictable when driven on the limit in traditional Porsche, slightly sideways style.

After that, despite the impact-absorbing bumpers and other safety features which made cars bigger and heavier, Porsche's consistent brilliance was to retain the 911's integrity while pressing ahead with the latest technology.

Throughout the 1970s and 1980s, that rock-steady, predictable 911 feel stayed with all the normally aspirated models, making each of them great and reassuring to drive, especially with a touch of deliberately induced opposite

lock. Early Turbos, on the other hand, were a much hairier proposition. On a circuit they could be exploited to the full, but they had to be driven with caution on the road. Ignore that and, for sure, one day you'll spin it. Given a few corners, most drivers found themselves much quicker in a non-turbo 911.

It is true that the 1988 4WD Carrera 4 understeered excessively under power, and there was simply no way round that in terms of driving technique. The driver had an amazing sensation of easy control but the only sensible thing was to swap it for a later model – the viscous coupling used in the transmission from 1994 made Carrera 4s far better balanced and satisfying to drive.

Despite the desired looks and performance, early Carrera 2s were as dull as people say. Again there's no way to drive around that, but you can introduce a sports car-style hard edge by fitting a much stiffer sprung-blade trailing arm in the rear suspension. We did that to the new Carrera 2 that I raced around 1990 and it really did the trick.

The new 993 brought a return to the pure pleasure of driving. These 911s respond in the traditional Porsche manner mentioned above, but generally at much less lairy angles than in the models of 40 years ago. They are faster, safer and much easier to drive – and that's probably no bad thing because, let's face it, there are lots of us but there was only ever one Vic Elford!

'The sideways stuff was all fine in the little 356 but it was harder in the bigger 911 with its heavier six-cylinder engine'

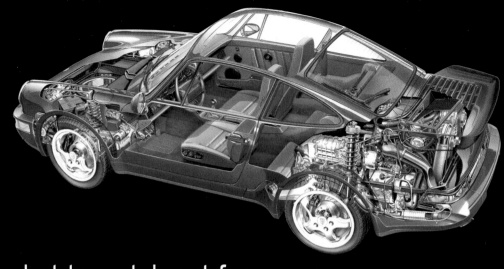

Buying a 911
Basic checks, and what to watch out for...

Words: Paul Hardman

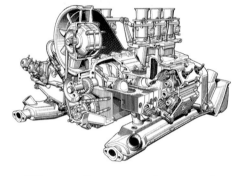

Aircooled 911s are tough old things, but mistreat one for too long and eventually someone is going to cop a big bill. A few basic rules hold good for the entire aircooled range.

Regular care is everything, so first check the service record – your prospect doesn't have to have visited an official Porsche Centre all its life, but on-time service stamps from specialists are what you want to see. Service intervals are usually 12,000 miles.

All 911s rust, but it's slower on post-'76 cars, when the factory began to galvanise the bodies. Typical rot spots are at the roof-to-wing joint at the rear, and scuttle-to-wing joint at the front. Overspray on the windscreen rubber is a giveaway that scuttle rust has been dealt with – but pull back the rubber and make sure the screen surrounds, front and rear, are not corroding. This is more common on 964s and 993s than earlier cars. On the latter, rust in the back corners of the door shuts may have spread into the sills, and if it has affected the 'kidney bowl' reinforcements behind the door pillars, the fix is around £1500 per side.

At the front, stone chips under the headlights aren't serious, and you might find star-dents in the bonnet if the owner has slammed the lid over too-bulky luggage. Inside the boot, pull out the carpet, spare wheel (a space-saver from 1974: check the compressor is present) and tools, and look at the floor. If it's rippled or uneven, the car has probably had a shunt.

If the wings have been off, it'll be obvious from spanner marks on the mounting-bolt heads. 'If the chassis rails are the same finish as the body, that's a sign the car has been shunted and repaired,' says Tom Firman of 911virgin.com.

The chassis plate is riveted to the right-hand inner wing and will reveal the type, year of manufacture and original market (www.911uk.com is useful for decoding later cars. In the US, www.pelicanparts.com is an invaluable source of information). The engine number is vertically stamped into the right-hand fan

> 'Cost of ownership isn't down to the age of the car – it's about how that particular model has been treated, and they're all different'

support. Under the rear end, few 911s are completely dry. Oil return pipes between the cylinder heads and crankcase can corrode through and leak, but can be replaced without having to pull off the heads.

Firman says 964s tend to leak from the cylinder base gaskets – and that's an engine-out job because the barrels have to come off: 'And it's expensive because you're going to do the piston rings and bearings while you're in there.' Detecting these leaks is difficult because there's a foam-lined undertray that catches the oil – and some owners pressure wash it before sale to mask the problem.

With their self-adjusting tappets, 993s tend to leak from the cam cover gaskets with age because these don't have to be replaced for tappet adjustment, as was the case on earlier cars. And oil pipes usually corrode in the right-hand rear wheelarch in front of the tyre, but ensure you check their entire length – they run under the right-hand sill to meet the cooler behind the right-hand headlight. Rear exhaust boxes cost about £200 to replace, but many cars wear stainless systems now.

Porsche 911s need using, says Josh Sadler of Autofarm, which specialises in early and rare 911s: 'Brake calipers tend to seize on cars that have been standing.' Gearchanges aren't the smoothest, and they all have a different feel, with the G50 'box (post-'86) generally favoured over the earlier 915; if the change is excessively baulky it might be that the clutch is on the way out – they last as little as 80,000 miles, so check if it has been changed. This job costs as much as £1200 on late cars; £500-600 up to the end of the 3.2 Carrera.

Camchain tensioners weren't very good on early cars, and many have been retro-fitted with the later oil-pressurised tensioners used from 1984. If there's a nasty big-end-type rattle that disappears at 2500rpm, says Sadler, chances are the chain is flailing about and needs attention before it does expensive damage.

Because these cars are dry-sumped, the oil level gauge won't give an accurate reading until the engine is hot and the oil thermostat has opened. This is when you should check the level in the dry-sump oil tank in the right-hand rear wing, with the engine running. Oil pressure should read 4 bar or above at anything over 3000-4000rpm.

Sadler also reports that the magnesium-cased engines, 1968-'74, are prone to snapping head and barrel studs due to the differing expansion rates between the cylinders, cases and studs. If one is broken, you might hear a 'chuffing' under acceleration when the engine is cold: 'But the only sure-fire way is to remove the lower rocker covers and see if a stud falls out.'

Engine-management systems fitted to the electronically injected cars are becoming more sensitive to poor connections as the cars get older. And if any of the heater fans aren't working, it might just be a fuse – but don't bank on it.

Tom Firman says you should budget £1500-2500 a year running costs for a 3.2 or later 911: 'Cost of ownership isn't down to the age of the car any more. It's more about how that particular model has been treated, and they're all different.' △

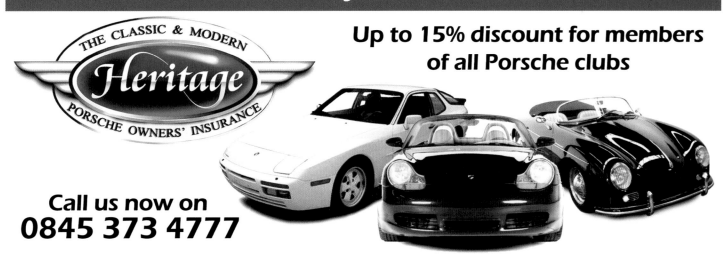

An RS version of the Porsche 911 has been available for most of the last 25 years. **Tony Dron**, who has raced and road tested them from the very start, compares every model

Photography: Stuart Collins

Every PORSCHE

No other car stirs up debate quite like the Porsche 911

It has its fanatical followers and, cards on the table, I am one of them but it also has its enemies. Oddly enough, most of them turn out never to have driven one.

They don't know that it's ridiculous to discuss the 911 as one car anyway. Since its launch in 1963, the 911 has been a whole series of different models with a wide range of performance and abilities. Of course, all 911s are united in having a six-cylinder boxer engine mounted in the rear and their shape is instantly recognisable.

The 911, however, is an idea which has evolved, fending off every threat to its existence; whether it was fears about crash legislation, noise tests or anything else. Defying its critics, it always came through with flying colours. Even so, back in the 1970s we all assumed in some strange way that Porsche would have to make something completely different for the future, so along came the 928 and other front-engined models, including some extremely quick ones.

The 911 survived them too and thanks to its unique magic and Porsche's engineering ingenuity it remains with us today. It has changed again and again but the wonderful thing is that the essential character remains intact.

Some say that for everyday use the best 911 in any age has always been the standard model. That's a respectable view but, come on, there just has to be a special excitement about the ultimate performers, the RS models which have formed the basis of the race and rally cars.

Every schoolboy knows that the icon here is the very first of them, the 911 2.7 RS of 1973. Thanks to Josh Sadler of Autofarm, we gathered at Bruntingthorpe test track with examples of every RS road car, from 1973 to date, plus for good measure the 1980s Clubsport, to see how they compared. It's one thing to have driven these models extensively down the years, but this unique opportunity was revealing and occasionally surprising.

Above
Pert ducktail spoiler on 1973 2.7 RSL reduces aerodynamic lift and helps car stay planted at speed.

1973 Carrera 2.7 RSL (white)

In just one day we shall experience 35 years of excellence, starting at the beginning with the 1973 911 Carrera 2.7 RSL. We know very well that this represented a peak of development for the 911, ten years after it first appeared and just before the onset of international legislation concerning safety and emissions.

Long recognised as one of the all-time greats, it started as a pure homologation special, which seemed a gamble then. The sales and marketing departments were not confident that they could sell the 500 cars required by the motor sporting authorities but, within days of its unveiling at the 1972 Paris Salon, the order book was full and production plans were increased.

With 210bhp from 2687cc, the RS was capable of 152mph and 0-60mph in 5.5sec. All the RS models were light, weighing around 1000kg depending on the specification. The factory says that there were 1308 RS Tourings made, plus 200 RS Sports and 17 special homologation cars. The Sports model, the lightweight at 960-1036kg, became known universally as the RSL.

Mike Jopp, the enthusiastic owner of this left-hand-drive RSL, bought his car two years ago. With just one German previous owner from new, its condition is superb. Generally, these machines feel light at the controls and are sublime to drive. Contrary to uninformed opinion, they are not at all scary. The curious little ducktail spoiler reduced high-speed lift at the rear from 320lb to a mere 93lb, keeping it stable. That, combined with suspension development, low weight and the latest Pirelli rubber then available, made it by far the most predictable and controllable 911 known up to that point.

It had 15in wheels, 6J at the front and 7J at the rear, and it was predictable on power oversteer. Dithering or lifting off once you had it sideways could cause problems but a competent driver should never, ever lose control of one of these things.

Mike's car is fitted with relatively wide Michelin Pilot Cup Sport tyres which are ideal for dry track day use. As he pointed out, they were hardly the best rubber in the wet conditions at the start of our test day. Even so, his car remained perfectly stable and forgiving, but the cornering power was modest and it did want to understeer quite strongly. However, there was still just enough grip for it to lift an inside front wheel through the twisty bits.

Even today, this is still a very fast car. You have to remind yourself that when it was new it ventured out onto roads thronging with Vauxhall Vivas, Morris Marinas and MGBs. By today's standards, the old 2.7 RS suffers from wind and road noise and one feels unexpectedly exposed, sitting relatively high up with plenty of glass to look through. But it remains magnificently engaging, and that engine noise is just fabulous.

'Even today, the 911 Carrera RSL is still a very fast car. You have to remind yourself that when it was new it ventured out onto roads thronging with Vauxhall Vivas, Morris Marinas and MGBs'

'Only six right-hand drive 1974 models are said to exist – we had to insure this one for £300,000 for this track outing'

1974 3.0 Carrera RS ('Black')

Porsche maintained the RS theme into 1974, bringing out a three-litre successor, the 911 Carrera RS; but with just some 110 made, and half of them RSR racers, this was always an extremely rare car. Only six right-hand-drive examples are said to exist, so this machine commands a premium. We had to insure it for £300,000 for this track outing.

For the 1974 Model Year, the entire 911 range was given a revised body, known as the G Series, to meet new US laws demanding impact absorption at 5mph. Hence the big bumpers which seemed somewhat grotesque at the time. It's odd how such perceptions shift. If we notice them at all today, which is unlikely, they don't look remotely incongruous. The visual effect of the design, in fact, is one of a slightly less delicate machine than its predecessor. To my mind, somehow it looks better now than it did in its day, but I can't quite put my finger on why that should be.

The 1974 Carrera RS also had markedly widened rear wings and, not really noticed on this black car, black window frames and doorhandles. Although the new RS shared the same wheel diameter with the previous 2.7, they were wider at 8J and 9J. The suspension was beefed up with stiffer anti-roll resistance, possibly

Below
1974 was the first year of the US-spec impact bumpers, which actually suit the 911 shape remarkably well.

'The most incredible thing about this Clubsport is that it's done 400,000 miles. It still felt absolutely superb'

to cope with a slight increase in weight to at least 1060kg. Bigger ventilated discs, drilled and almost identical to those developed for the 917, were used for the same reason. The increase in engine capacity, to 2994cc, produced a rise in power and torque of about 10%. The 0-60mph time dropped to 5.3sec but, subjectively, performance was similar to that of the 2.7 RS.

On track, with a rapidly drying surface and more suitable tyres for these conditions, it was considerably quicker than the 2.7 in corners. Oddly enough, this car also wanted to understeer just a little more than I expected and I began to wonder whether this is how the owners prefer them to be set up these days. Were it mine, I would certainly want to adjust it to get a bit more bite from the steering.

Or was it something to do with the track conditions on that day? I can't be sure there but it was certainly quick through the bends and the beefier engine made the predictably wonderful noise of a great old Porsche. In this case, it was even harder to keep remembering that this machine dates back 34 years. Apart from the old-fashioned and rather wobbly gearshift lever, which does give its age away, the 1974 Carrera RS still feels extraordinarily modern when pressed.

The owner, who shuns publicity, is a very lucky man to have acquired such a rare gem.

1988 3.2-litre CS (white)

Apart from 20 911 SC/RS competition cars for 1984, the RS name then lapsed for some years but we felt it was essential to include the 911 Carrera Clubsport Coupé of 1987-'89. Despite its relatively normal looks there was much of the RS spirit in this 3164cc sporting model, with its wind-up windows and lack of rear seats, hi-fi system, soundproofing and so on. We were fortunate that two were found for our Bruntingthorpe test, both of them 1988 models.

The weight-saving exercise cut 100kg from the standard figure, not massive but enough to make a difference to the feel of the Clubsport. Although the power quoted was unchanged at 231bhp, lighter inlet valves gave easier revving and raised the red line from 6520rpm to 6840rpm. On the face of it, the performance of the 152mph Carrera 3.2 and the Clubsport looked the same but closer examination reveals that the latter's acceleration between 60mph and 120mph was far quicker than the standard car's.

Fifteen-inch wheels were fitted to the Clubsport at first in Germany, with a 16in option for 1989. Our first car (not pictured), owned by Nigel Wright, was fitted with 16in wheels from new, which it seems was the UK specification at the time.

This beautifully maintained 911 was brought along by two

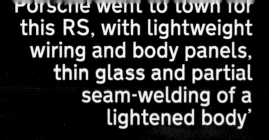

Porsche went to town for this RS, with lightweight wiring and body panels, thin glass and partial seam-welding of a lightened body'

friends of the owner, David Royce and Michael Harrington, and I reported my thoughts to them. The performance was terrific and the enjoyable sound of the engine within the cabin was the best so far that day but, yet again, understeer was very evident. In fact, it was quite pronounced and I also found the steering unacceptably heavy. For that reason, it would be tiring to drive on twisting roads for any time – not something you expect to find of a 911.

Both David and Michael assured me that Nigel Wright is happy with the steering but I would not be and I did wonder if it was something to do with the 16in wheels, or whether some change has been made to this car. Something seems wrong to me, anyway.

The second Clubsport, owned by Andrew Morris and shown on the previous page, felt much better. Converted to 15in wheels when it was almost new, the steering was lighter and there was no tendency towards excessive understeer. Both these cars had been fitted with non-standard, thick-rimmed and smaller steering wheels which were not to my taste at all. I'd junk them and put the originals back on, improving the steering feel and enabling me to see the instruments properly again. As both cars had them, however, the small wheel was obviously not what made Nigel's steering feel heavy.

Below
964 RS is too extreme to be really enjoyable as a road car, but is now increasingly sought-after for track days.

The most incredible thing about Andrew's Clubsport is that it has done 400,000 miles. The engine was rebuilt by Dick Lovett Porsche 200,000 miles ago but apart from that it has had only regular servicing. Even the gearbox is completely original. The fact that the entire machine still felt absolutely superb says much about Porsche engineering. With only about 50 such Clubsports in the UK this is another collectors' item. As for the total number made, different respected authorities claim 189, 312 and 340. Somebody's got it wrong but, whatever the truth, these are rare cars.

1992 964 RS (yellow)

When the RS name returned to the 911 for 1992, it was applied to the next generation, the Type 964, and every Porsche nut knows all about these monsters. They had excellent roadholding and handling on a smooth surface and, with 261bhp from a 3.6-litre engine, they were certainly quick (161mph), but they were too extreme for normal road use.

Porsche went to town for this RS, with lightweight wiring and body panels, thin glass and partial seam-welding of a lightened body. It had stiff rubber engine mounts, with no hydraulic damping, there were special gear ratios and a limited-slip diff as standard.

This RS gave a totally different driving experience, quite unlike the relatively soft contemporary Carrera 2 on which it was based. The standard road car looked like a 911 but it was a radical change from the 911s that went before it, even having power steering and almost idiot-proof handling. The 964 RS, with all its extreme changes, should have been the business and in some ways it is but, away from a billiard-table surface, it darts about alarmingly. On bumpy B-roads, especially in the wet, even the most devoted 911 expert is inclined to back off in terror. As for road noise and the harshness of the ride, they are, in a word, appalling.

Nevertheless, the 964 RS has enjoyed a resurgence recently, pushing up values, and it's all because of the track-day driving boom, for which it is just perfect.

'Yes, it's a horrible road car,' agrees owner John Powell, with a laugh, 'but I knew that. I bought it 18 months ago from Germany. I don't think the original owner, an old boy of 72, could stand it any longer!' John has done the right thing and turned it into an all-out track-day car, complete with rollcage. →

He has even gone from 17in to 18in wheels which, as you'd expect, make the ride even worse.

Do not be dismayed. Out on track in this beast, I had my best fun of the day so far. It's fast, it felt like a racer, its handling was impeccable in that environment, the big gutsy engine really goes and the complete machine is obviously tough as old boots. I wouldn't like to drive home in it but I started grinning at Bruntingthorpe's first corner. Extreme satisfaction for hard nuts; enough said!

If I had to choose one model to convince a doubter about the whole 911 idea, the last car I would pick is Andrew's 964 RS, fun as it was. The one to go for, I think, is the next RS, based on the Type 993 body and produced in the 1995-96 Model Years. Partly thanks to its new multi-link rear suspension, which improved the roadholding and sense of balance in the chassis, the 993 was a big improvement on the 964 generally. It also had a six-speed gearbox with a better gearchange mechanism.

1995 993 RS (blue)

The RS version of the 993 enjoyed all these benefits but it was still air-cooled, the pedals still sprouted from the floor and, also following tradition, unnecessary weight was pared away – even the door releases are webbing straps that weigh almost nothing.

What's more the engine, increased to 3746cc, gave 300bhp at 6500rpm. Top speed, at 172mph, was close to supercar stuff.

Matthew Cyzer, owner of this superb low-mileage, left-hand-drive example, was not present at Bruntingthorpe but, thanks to German specialist Thomas Schmitz, Josh Sadler got permission for us to have it there. Schmitz also located John Powell and his 964 for Josh, so our special thanks must go to him.

Despite such modern touches as power steering, the 993 RS was a car that any traditionally minded 911 enthusiast would love immediately. When I first drove one, in Germany in 1996, I found it irresistible and this one brought all that back.

The hard, lightweight sports seats are comfortable for hours on end – in 1996 I spent a whole day giving passengers rides around Donington circuit in one and I felt no discomfort whatsoever. In short, the 993 has the true classic 911 feel, especially in its steering, but it's also accessible in that anybody could drive it to the shops. The gearchange and other main controls are easy to operate at low speeds and then, when you really press on, its finer qualities of poise and balance are immediately obvious. It's a wonderful combination of tradition and relatively modern engineering. It's also, I think, one of the best-looking 911s.

It's hard to fault the 993 RS and the condition of this as-new example was stunning.

'The 993 has the true classic 911 feel, especially in its steering, but it's also accessible in that anybody could drive it to the shops'

→

Left and below
Chasing 3.0 RS in the
993; Dron reckons the
2004 GT3 isn't quite
as predictable as
most 911s, but is
still easy to control.

'The 997 GT3 does everything you'd expect of a modern 911 but it's just so civilised and, with a stunning 409bhp, so very, very quick'

Below
Latest 997 GT3 RS comes with sports seats and a rollcage, ready for track-day use while still being road-legal.

2004 996 GT3 RS (white)

Now we're getting into the really modern stuff, starting with Nick Knight's 2004 GT3 RS, based on the Type 996, which John Powell refers to, disparagingly but with kindly laughter, as 'a kettle'. Yes, it's water-cooled, partly to meet noise reduction requirements. These cars are bigger, heavier and much more powerful than earlier 911 road cars. The top speed here is 190mph, and 0-200km/h (124mph) takes a mere 14.0sec. It's a different world of performance but it's still a 911. It looks like one, the design details are better than ever inside and out, and it feels like one – up to a point.

Reservations about the 996 GT3 RS have been lodged by some diehards and I would agree with them. Although the roadholding is outstanding, it has a reluctance to sit on predictable, slight oversteer in the classic 911 style. Oddly enough, it feels almost like a normal car in its handling and, near the limit in really fast corners, it's hard to tell precisely what oversteer/understeer balance it's going to adopt. I found this for myself a few years ago when I spent an afternoon giving passenger rides round Spa circuit in a 996 GT3 to members of the Goodwood Road Racing Club.

In truth, this is a fine point which only the driver is likely to notice. At Bruntingthorpe, Nick's car behaved itself perfectly and when I hit the occasional damp patch, cornering at speed, the tail would flick out but it was so easy to catch every time. It was never a drama. The GT3 may not be perfection in its handling but the sheer grunt, in a magnificent, bullet-proof and superbly styled piece of engineering, is pleasing. You can't help liking it.

2007 997 GT3 RS (orange)

It's only when you drive the 2007 GT3 RS, still just a current model, that you appreciate what the 996 RS should have been. This car was registered last November and sourced for us via track-day specialists RMA. Belonging to David Fitzsimons, it's utterly superb. In these more recent cars, the RS badge basically means that it's stripped of a few luxury items and fitted with →

'Values have been changing so rapidly recently that things might have shifted again before this magbook is even printed'

top-quality sports seats plus a rollcage, ready for demanding track-days but still road-legal.

The 997 GT3 does everything you'd expect of a modern 911 interpretation but it's just so civilised and, with a stunning 409bhp from its naturally aspirated 3600cc engine, so very, very quick – 0-60mph in a little over four seconds and a top speed of 192mph.

It will be most interesting to see what Porsche produces next in this line. Some of us are beginning to feel that the exquisite, mid-engined Cayman range offers very much what the traditional 911 enthusiast is looking for, but the 997 GT3 models have shown that the high-performance 911 idea remains very much alive and a force to be reckoned with.

Thanks to Josh Sadler of Autofarm who, with help from Thomas Schmitz and RMA Track Days, assembled the cars; and to the owners who responded to their call. Josh was one of the founders of Autofarm (www.autofarm.co.uk) in 1973, and the company grew up with the 2.7 RS. Over the past 40 years Tony Dron has driven well over 1000 911s on road and track.

What are they worth?

Values have been changing so rapidly recently that things might have shifted again before this magbook is even printed. But let's have a go: a good 1973 Carrera 2.7 RS is probably worth £150-250,000 and its immediate successor (the 3.0-litre), partly because it's that much rarer, over £300,000.

That makes a late-1980s Carrera Clubsport look like an incredible bargain at something approaching £40,000. Until recently the 964 Carrera RS of 1992 really was cheap but the track-day market demand has whacked values sharply up to a firm £60-80,000. That's right, we should all have bought one for £20k just three years ago.

The long-term prospects of the mid-1990s 993 RS are surely good enough to make it a safe bet financially. Values have been creeping up from around £65,000 to £100,000 and the example we tested here must be worth all of that or more.

The bargain of bargains here must be the 996 GT3, which I am told is worth from around £40,000. Now, these are far from old cars and that's not a lot to pay for a reliable machine that can get close to 200mph. Find a good one for that money and I think your investment will be more than safe.

The trouble is that everyone in the know wants a 997 and even the earliest versions of them will still be close to their new list price and fetching around £80,000. In this exotic end of the market, they were tremendous value for money as new cars. Look at what the opposition was asking.

Sparring
partners

While BMW battled with Ford in the Touring Car championship, Porsche prepared to take on the victor – and the competition gave life to two fantastic homologation specials

Words: Robert Coucher | Photography: Paul Harmer

The rain is coming down hard. The black clouds billow over the Spa-Francorchamps circuit, a sinuous gleaming grey snake of tarmac ducking and diving through the Belgian forest. This is typical of Spa, of course, where the rain, now lashing sideways, is a near-constant feature.

The idea of driving this 1973 BMW CSL 'Batmobile' and 1973 Porsche 911 Carrera RS 2.7 seemed a good one when it was hatched over a long lunch. BMW owner Philip Kantor rightly asserts (over another glass of red) that Spa is the true home of the Batmobile, a machine engineered to contend the Touring Car Championship, which it dominated in '74, '75 and '76.

So what to pit it against? The Batmobile's natural prey would have been a Ford Capri RS3100, the car from which BMW finally wrestled the European Touring Car mantle. But Kantor has recently returned from driving this CSL on the Tour Auto Lissac through France, doing battle with numerous Porsche 911s. On today's historic rally and racing scene, cars of the 1970s are all

the rage and we thought it would be interesting to see how the BMW stacks up against a benchmark machine: a Porsche 911 Carrera RS 2.7. So here we are in the rain...

As has been well recorded, Ford was creaming BMW in the European Touring Car Championship of the early '70s. BMW decided to get serious in 1971 and introduced the BMW CSL (Coupé Sports Lightweight), a homologation special spawned from the unsuspecting and rather timid BMW CS coupé. Drastic weight paring was exacted: the monocoque was formed from thinner-gauge steel and aluminium was deployed for the door skins, bonnet and, originally, the bootlid. Luxury items were ruthlessly deleted, including the power-assisted steering, electric windows, thick carpets, comfortable seats and sound deadening. The front bumper was left off and the rear was made of glassfibre. A substantial 250kg was shaved off.

Despite all this, Ford managed to keep the Capri ahead of the CSL on the track, thanks to the efforts of inspired engineers →

Right
Scheel seats in BMW
are set low; fuel
injection aids 206bhp
output; rear wing
was originally
supplied in the boot.

BMW CSL BATMOBILE

ENGINE
3153cc straight six,
OHC, Bosch fuel
injection

POWER
206bhp @ 5600rpm

TORQUE
195lb ft @ 4000rpm

TRANSMISSION
Four-speed manual
(five-speed fitted),
rear-wheel drive

SUSPENSION
Front: independent via
Macpherson struts,
coil springs,
anti-roll bar.
Rear: independent via
semi-trailing arms, coil
springs, telescopic
dampers, anti-roll bar

PERFORMANCE
0-60mph 6.8sec.
Top speed 138mph

WEIGHT
1250kg (2750lb)

VALUE
£80,000-plus

Jochen Neerpasch and Martin Braungart, so BMW did the sensible thing in 1972 and 'bought' their services. This formidable duo were the catalyst for the formation of the highly successful BMW Motorsport GmbH.

The engineers set about the BMW with the aim of reducing the big coupé's drag and lift. The already lightened CSL was subjected to the full Batmobile treatment, with the addition of a deep front airdam, pronounced air guides over the front wings, roof-mounted deflector and huge rear wing. These spoilers were illegal in Germany at the time and were delivered in the boot, to be fitted by owners. A steel bootlid was standard on these Batmobiles, to withstand the downforce of the rear wing. This aerodynamic treatment reduced drag by 16 percent, the equivalent of a 50bhp hike in power!

The straight-six engine was enlarged to 3153cc; the roadgoing cars produced 206bhp at 5600rpm (racers achieved 360-plus). Just 110 road cars were produced in this 3.2-litre form in 1973, with a mere 57 built before production stopped in December '75. As a result of these improvements, BMW beat the Capris in the '73 European Touring Car Championship, in what has become one of the most legendary racing battles in Touring Car lore.

The Porsche 911 Carrera RS 2.7 is similarly a homologation special, an engineering-led solution to racetrack success. Since the launch of the 911 in 1965, the Porsche racing department continuously developed hot race and rally weapons. In 1966 the Porsche 911S produced a lusty 160bhp from its 2.0-litre flat-six engine, the model that Vic Elford drove to victory in the 1967 European Rally Championship. In 1968 the car won the GT World Championship, and the 911 was also the first car to win the Monte Carlo Rally three times (1968-1970).

The true forerunner to the Carrera RS was Ferdinand Piech's lightweight 911R, which weighed just 800kg and produced 210bhp thanks to its use of the Carrera 6 engine. Porsche continued to increase the capacity of its roadgoing engines, first to 2.2 litres, then 2.4 litres in '71 when a 911 placed sixth overall at Le Mans and won the GT World Championship once again.

But in 1972, at Hockenheim, a 911 suffered the ignominy of being lapped by a BMW and a Ford! The solution was greater engine capacity and lower weight, though engineering supremo Ernst Fuhrmann had real problems convincing the sceptical marketing department that 500 stripped-out, thinly disguised racing cars would sell, especially as Porsche was focused on the American market – a place where weighty creature comforts were de rigeur.

The engineers prevailed and the car was named Carrera, the appellation used since the 356 for sports-oriented road models, as well as RS for Rennsport ('motorsport' in German). Designer Anatole Lapine placed the distinctive Carrera logos down each side and Grand Prix white became the official RS colour. The first roadgoing Carrera RS was delivered in the winter of 1972 and was known officially as the 911SC, to make it apparent that this was not an entirely new model but a variant of the then-current 911S model.

The 911 Carrera RS's engine was stretched to 2687cc by increasing the bore size from 84mm to 90mm. This was made possible by using Nikasil coating on the aluminium bores, eliminating the need for liners. Power increased from the 911S's 190bhp at 6500rpm to 210bhp at 6300rpm and torque rose by 31lb ft to 182lb ft at 5100rpm. (Full-race RSRs produced 330bhp prior to the mad Turbo era.)

As with the CSL, weight reduction was paramount and all luxuries were excluded from the cars. But from its inception the RS was offered in a number of derivations: the RS Sport or 'Lightweight', code M471; the RSL or 'Touring', code M472; and the all-out racing car, the RSR, code M491. The car you see here, generously brought along from Germany by Wilfried Holzenthal, President of the Carrera RS Owners Club and Registry, is the ➔

'In 1972 a 911 suffered the ignominy of being lapped by a BMW and a Ford! The solution was greater engine capacity and lower weight'

Right
Porsche interior features aftermarket wheel in place of plasticky original, and pedals less offset than in RHD version; fan dominates engine; glassfibre bumpers distinguish Lightweight.

PORSCHE 911 CARRERA RS LIGHTWEIGHT

ENGINE
2687cc flat six, single SOHC per bank, air-cooled, dry sump, Bosch fuel injection

POWER
210bhp @ 6300rpm

TORQUE
188lb ft @ 5100rpm

TRANSMISSION
Five-speed manual, rear-wheel drive

SUSPENSION
Front: independent via MacPherson struts, torsion bars, anti-roll bar. Rear: independent via trailing arms, torsion bars and telescopic dampers, anti-roll bar

PERFORMANCE
0-60mph 5.6sec. Top speed 149mph

WEIGHT
960kg (2112lh)

VALUE
£200,000

ever-so-desirable Lightweight M471, chassis number 911 3600573. As an export car it was waxed for shipping and it is one of just 200 Lightweights out of a total of 1580 Carrera RSs (including the M472 Touring) produced.

As such it has lightweight body panels, lightweight Glaverbel glass, lightweight bumpers, a glassfibre rear 'ducktail' and a simple interior with even the passenger sun visor deleted! The RS was the first roadgoing 911 to have wider rear 8x15-inch wheels fitted – 7x15s at the front – shod with 215- and 185-section tyres respectively. Porsche's wind tunnel tests indicated that these changes, in conjunction with the deep front airdam and rear ducktail, increased the car's top speed by just 4.5km/h. But the axle lift was massively reduced and the typical 911 nervousness at high speed was effectively banished.

After a botched attempt at the Tour de Corse on 3 November 1972, Porsche went testing at Paul Ricard, which proved a great success. Gérard Larrousse and Mark Donohue managed a lap time of 2:10 in the Porsche whereas the BMW CSL could not better 2:11, and Fuhrmann – with his eye firmly on the production-car class – commented: 'First we'll let Neerpasch (by then with BMW) beat Ford. And then we'll get them both.'

At the 24-hour Daytona race in 1973, Porsche was forced to race in the sports car class, but Peter Gregg and Hurley Haywood's Porsche 911RSR beat the favoured Ferrari Daytona into second place by 22 laps. David had comprehensively vanquished Goliath. At Spa in May the Touring Car race was won by Niki Lauda in a BMW Alpina. He then entered the 1000km race; the Porsche took fifth place and Lauda's BMW finished seventh. At Le Mans in the same year a Porsche RSR finished fourth in class (tenth overall), one place up on the BMW.

Sitting in the pitlane at Spa, the Porsche looks small and neat. It weighs 960kg and produces 210bhp – by comparison, a 1964 Porsche 356SC weighs 940kg and produces 95bhp. You can tell it's a Lightweight by the glassfibre bumpers (the Touring has chrome) and the rubber clips on the ducktail rear lid.

Entry into the cockpit is unimpeded and the bucket seat is very comfortable. Each of the simple door panels houses a door pull from a Fiat 600, a small plastic handle and a manual window winder. This simplicity continues with rubber mats, minimal trim and a set of large VDO instruments directly ahead, with a flash of war paint at 7300rpm on the rev counter and the speedo reading to 300 klicks.

Fire the engine and it catches immediately, emitting a hard snarl. This relatively unsilenced, air-cooled flat-six engine produces one of the best-ever automotive sounds. It responds to the throttle, via mechanical fuel injection, with alacrity. The clutch is soft and smooth, exhibiting that well-oiled Porsche finesse, but the gearshift is long of throw, if unobstructive.

The initial impression is of a docile and willing car. It is much torquier than the 2.4S of the same year; you feel the difference immediately. While the S musters only 115bhp at 4000rpm, and needs to be kept boiling at over 5000rpm to be at its best, the RS churns out 140bhp at 4000rpm, a huge difference. Yet it is happy to spin to 7000rpm without effort.

Wind the RS up and you feel its racing pedigree come through. The wider rear wheels do an effective job of keeping the rear weight bias under control and the aerodynamic aids start to hunker the otherwise organically shaped Porsche down onto the tarmac as the speed climbs past 80mph. The brakes do without servo assistance and need a firm shove.

You can get into trouble with the rear-engine layout, but the Porsche is so nimble you just brake firmly into the bends, drop a gear, nudge the apex with the millimetre-sharp steering and nail the throttle early on the exit. With its strong torque the engine lays down the power, aided by the excellent rear traction, and the RS slingshots out of corners at ludicrous speed. The front remains light and darts about in typical 911 fashion, while the ride is very firm. The car will understeer, but less so than most 911s because the steering is so sharp and there's less weight that needs to change direction.

➔

'The Porsche might get away on the first lap, but the Bimmer will reel it in, thanks to its speed, stability and benign handling'

Above
In the Spa pitlane, the circuit at which BMW battled first with Ford, then with Porsche. The result of the racing was these homologation specials.

The BMW CSL, chassis number 2275512, is a much more substantial machine although it weighs a relatively lean 1250kg. Finished in Chamonix white with all the stripes, wings and windsplitters it had when new in 1973, it's an impressive sight. And being one of just 167 examples, it is actually rarer than the RS, even the sought-after Lightweight version. You can check if a CSL is original: press down on the roof and the panel will concave alarmingly because of its thin gauge. The interior is workmanlike but more plush than the Porsche's, with wood cappings in evidence. The comfortable Scheel bucket seat is set low, making the rare original steering wheel seem too high. The VDO instruments are neat and the Halda distance recorder indicates that this CSL is used properly.

The straight six fires, accompanied by a fulsome growl thanks to its trick free-breathing exhaust manifold. CSLs had four-speed gearboxes as standard but Kantor has fitted a five-speed close-ratio Getrag 'box, with first on a dogleg towards you and back, and kept the original four-speed with the car's spares. The shift is heavy and mechanical and will not be rushed from first to second. From there on it is co-operative.

On the road the Batmobile looks outrageous but behaves like a BMW should: it's supple, smooth and fairly precise, the strong engine spooling out torque with no need to rev above 5500rpm. But at 100mph the Batmobile morphs from a Sunday jogger into an athlete. The steering sharpens and the smooth ride firms as the car squats onto the road. You feel confident but not aggressive, safe but not isolated. This big GT car is on your side and, as its quick-driving race preparer Gerald Smet of SG Motorsport explains, out-and-out sports cars like the Porsche

'The BMW is worth around £80,000, if you can find one, while the legendary, if slightly less rare, Carrera RS commands more than double that'

might get away on the first lap, but soon the Bimmer will reel them in thanks to its speed, stability and benign handling.

Both of these cars are homologation-special factory racers. They are pioneers in aerodynamics that look great and are effective in use. The Porsche 911 Carrera RS is a sharp and nimble sports car; the BMW CSL Batmobile is more of an effectively improved grand tourer. Both are a joy to drive quickly on the road and both are eligible for historic track events. The rarer car, the BMW CSL is worth around £80,000, if you can find one for sale, while the legendary, if slightly less rare, Carrera RS now commands more than double that.

A bonus with the BMW is that you can carry your tuxedo and black tie outfit in the boot for the gala dinner at the end of the Tour Auto... △

Thanks to Philip Kantor; Porsche specialist and restorer Wilfried Holzenthal (+49 171 773 2662) who has this RS for sale; and BMW CSL specialist Gerald Smet of SG Motorsport (+32 81 61 64 67 or www.sgmotorsport.be).

911 Turbo

Once an expensive must-have for 1980s City bankers,
the whale-tail 911 Turbo is now half the price of an early 911 –
and it's a much better car than legend suggests

Words: Robert Coucher   Photography: George Bamford

THE AWESOME prototype Porsche 911 Turbo was first seen at the Paris Motor Show in 1973. It was an almost unbelievable monster of a car, with hugely flared wheelarches, deep front spoiler and massive 'whale-tail' rear wing. It was bred out of the pure racing 2.1-litre Martini RSR Turbo which was launched at the same time. With lurid '70s *Turbo* script written down its fat flanks, the Turbo instantly captured the attention of every sports car driver with its naked intent: speed.

At the time the world was in the depths of the oil crisis, which effectively killed the BMW 2002 Turbo and delayed the launch of the Mercedes-Benz 6.9 by a few years. In Germany a blanket 60mph speed limit was imposed everywhere, including the Nürburgring and Porsche's own test track. But Porsche was run by engineer Ernst Fuhrmann and the Turbo was his idea, developed from Porsche's almost total dominance of the CanAm racing →

series, with its outrageous 1100bhp blown 917/30 sports racers. Fuhrmann was supported by his finance director Heinz Branditzki (unusual for a bean counter!) who stated flatly: 'If we are not in a position to sell such a superb product, then it's time for us to get out of the sports car business.' Amen.

There had been a good deal of infighting at Porsche about where to position the 911 Turbo. The marketing department wanted a stripped-out, bare bones and therefore cheap Turbo that would sell on price. But Fuhrmann's idea of a fully loaded, top-flight flagship for the entire Porsche range won over.

At the 1974 Paris Motor Show Porsche unveiled its first supercar, the production 911 Turbo – known as the Type 930 in-house, and sold in some export markets as the 930 Turbo. The outrageous Turbo, with a promise of

260bhp and a 180mph speedometer, was an immediate hit and demand outstripped supply. Fitted with lurid plaid and leather interior, deep cut-pile carpeting, electric windows and optional air conditioning, as well as that wild-sounding KKK turbocharger bolted to the engine, this latest supercar was snapped up by the likes of Steve McQueen and Princess Antoinette zu Furstenberg, who was so excited at the prospect of her Turbo she flew directly to the factory in her private helicopter to pick it up. The supercar for the Jet Set had arrived.

The 911 Turbo was extremely expensive when launched, costing twice the price of a regular 911. Fuhrmann's desire to sell about 500 was trounced when 1000 were sold in short order. When the British press finally got behind the fat three-spoke steering wheel

of the Turbo they were, quite literally, blown away. *Autocar* wrote: 'An outstandingly exciting motor car...' and *Motor* added that it was 'the finest driving machine you can buy'. When the Turbo was launched in America in 1975, *Car and Driver* called it: 'A Panzer among Porsches, a street racer that will guarantee you a place at the top of the pecking order in a way that not even a Ferrari or Lamborghini can.'

So why is it, up until now, that Porsche's amazing 911 Turbo has been disregarded by classic 911 fanatics? Today you cannot find a half-decent pre-impact 911 for less than £50k, whereas a superb Turbo commands less than half of that – the car in our photos, a Porsche Club (GB) concours winner with 69,000 miles from new, was on offer from specialist Cridfords at £20,000.

Basically it comes down to fashion, mis-information and ignorance.

Armchair Porsche racers now all clamour for the early short-wheelbase 911 and 911S models because they are eligible for historic racing. True, specialists have figured out how to sort out their near-lethal handling – these cars were originally shod with skinny 165/15 tyres and Porsche had to fit lead weights in the bumpers in an attempt to quell the snap oversteer – and real historic racers know how to pedal them. But the fashionisti still hang on to the belief that the only classic Porsche worth having is a pre-1973 example of the lightweight variety.

Certainly, if you are going historic racing or rallying then, yes, a 2.0-litre or 2.4S is a fabulous, lithe, lightweight driving machine (we'll leave the stratospherically priced 2.7RS out of this discussion). But to insist that these classics are a better proposition than a Turbo as a fast and effective road car is ill-advised.

A recent drive from London to Devon and back in an early Turbo was a revelation. In town the car felt heavy and slightly numb, due to its fat low-profile tyres and lazy off-boost engine. But on the motorway it instantly spooled up to the speed limit and loafed along in the most relaxed manner. The firm ride smoothed out and the most impressive aspect was how quiet the Turbo is at speed. Most elderly 911s induce ear-ache on the motorway. The turbocharger, as well as adding a good deal of wham, also quietens the normally loud air-cooled engine.

Come fast country roads, the Turbo proved immense. Powering up to a bend, the car was then easily reeled in by the vented disc brakes (yes, they are plenty powerful enough on public roads!), cornered quickly, then whooshed along to the next corner with consummate ease. What a great Gran Turismo the Turbo turned out to be.

Of course, you do have to drive the car while bearing in mind its turbocharged characteristics. Be in the right gear and allow the boost to build, don't get the boost on in the middle of a corner and stick religiously to the slow-in-fast-out maxim, and the Turbo behaves.

Roger Bell was the first British journalist to try out the 911 Turbo and he too enjoyed the combination of 'peace and power'.

'To be shoved so hard in the back that you need high-back seats to keep your head on, yet neither to feel nor hear anything more →

'The car in our photos, a concours winner with 69,000 miles from new, was on offer from a specialist for £20k'

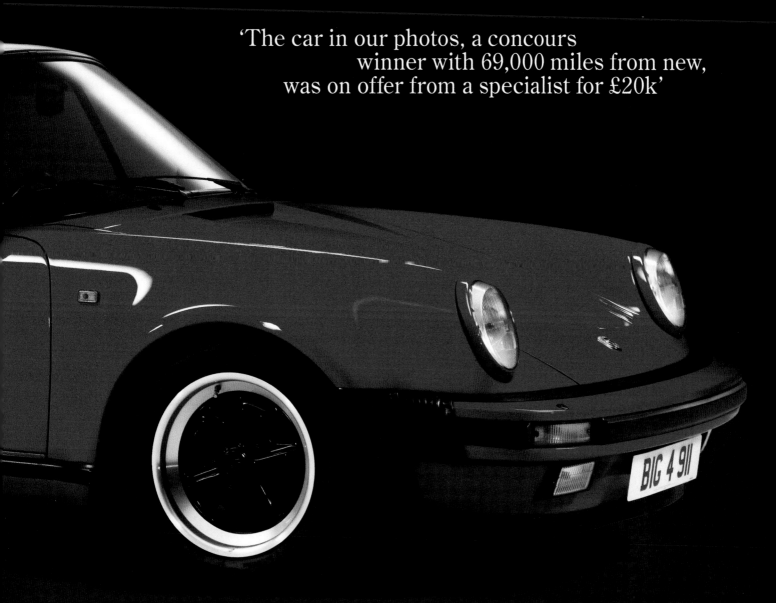

'The 911 Turbo is just as reliable as any other
Porsche of the period. If well maintained
and looked afer, they are no problem'

than a muffled hum, is a very odd sensation indeed in a car.'

The first-series 911 Turbos from 1974 to 1978 were of 3.0-litre capacity (up from the prototype's 2.7 litres to increase off-boost torque) and the horsepower was capped at 260bhp at a lowly 5500rpm (with 253lb ft of torque at 4000) by reducing the boost pressure and running a modest 6.5:1 compression ratio. Ernst Fuhrmann insisted the Kuhnle, Kopp & Kausch-supplied turbocharger be made to work with the well-proven Bosch K-Jetronic fuel injection.

The compact, turbocharged engine weighed in at 456lb, some 70lb more than the normally aspirated 2.7-litre six. Pistons were strengthened and the cylinderhead walls thickened, and exhaust valves sodium-filled

to help cool them. The standard forged steel conrods and rugged crankshaft were well up to the job. A very strong four-speed gearbox with widely spaced ratios was developed to handle the power and ventilated discs fitted all round.

Porsche 911 Turbo racer and specialist Josh Sadler of Autofarm is a Turbo enthusiast. 'The 911 Turbo is a real sleeper,' he says. 'They are just as reliable as any other Porsches of the period but some of the components like brakes are more expensive. If well-maintained and looked after they are no problem.

'Driven really hard, they will wear out a bit faster but that's what you would expect with all the additional power from the turbo,' Sadler continues. 'Porsche continued to develop and improve the 930-series Turbo up →

Below
Those vulnerable flanks are made of galvanised steel, used for all 911 models since 1976.

'The 911 Turbo evolved out of Porsche's all-conquering racing cars and was a usable supercar in an era when many over-promised and under-delivered'

until 1990, so my advice is to buy as late an example as possible.

'I raced one in the Porsche Club Modified Series in 1978. Sure, you need to get on top of the car and you have to adapt your style to the power delivery. Tony Dron raced my car – it was effectively a tweaked road car – at Donington and won the race against a couple of 935s! So don't believe anyone who tells you Turbos are no good.'

The immaculate Guards Red 911 Turbo you see here is a 1985 3.3-litre example. Introduced in 1977, the 3.3-litre Turbo was a marked improvement over the 3-litre. With added capacity and an effective intercooler, the engine develops 300bhp and 303lb ft at the same modest revs, allowing a 0-60mph dash in 5.3 seconds and an honest 160mph top speed.

The bigger engine capacity and revised clutch mean there is a 30mm greater overhang at the rear of this car but suspension revisions and the fitment of Pirelli P7 16in tyres on 7- and 8-inch Fuchs alloys keep the 3.3 well planted. Larger cross-drilled and vented disc brakes with four-pot calipers and servo assistance (developed from the 917 racer) deal with the task of shedding the Turbo's speed. Development continued and by 1989 the Turbo had received a five-speed gearbox and boasted a 0-60mph time of 4.9 seconds.

The 911 Turbo is a car of the '70s, even though it remained in

Left
Rear wheels are an inch wider than the fronts – but then they have a lot more work to do...

production until 1990. For so long the '70s were the decade that style forgot. But they are now very much in vogue again, and that includes automotive hardware. Steve McQueen's slate-grey 930 Turbo (as the model is known in America), which in 2008 for $137,500, now looks as desirable as a late-'60s 911.

Look at the photographs of this muscular, bewinged, Pirelli P7-shod Turbo and you cannot fail to be captivated. It must be one of the best-looking 911 derivatives, a car just waiting to ease down to the south of France, the long way around via the German autobahns, where you know you can run it at 150mph for as long as the open road allows.

The 911 Turbo evolved out of Porsche's all-conquering turbocharged racing cars and was a usable supercar in an era when many other supercars over-promised and under-delivered. Most certainly, it has to be driven with respect and within the driver's limits. But hey, take things gently through the bends and catch up on the straights.

As Josh Sadler points out, 'The 911 Turbo is a huge amount of supercar for ordinary money.' The one-time sleeper is now very much wide-awake. △

Thanks to Cridfords, Porsche specialists since 1987, for the loan of this 911 Turbo. See www.cridfords.co.uk.

DRIVING THE 911 TURBO

Everyone knows the Turbo's
fearsome reputation. But is it justified?
Tony Dron, a one-time instructor for
Porsche, has opinions based
on first-hand experience

Photographs courtesy AutoExpress

There's no getting around it: those early
911 Turbos were tricky beasts. They were out-and-out
homologation specials, of course, intended for a very limited
customer base, but then some bright spark in the marketing
department had the customer road cars luxuriously fitted
out, even with electric windows, and everybody wanted one.

Around 30 years ago, as a regular instructor at official
Porsche Customer Driving Days, I got to drive plenty of them.
I well remember taking one owner, a cheerful and likeable
Geordie, for a ride round Donington circuit in his new 3.0-litre
Turbo. He asked to be driven as fast as possible and I duly
obliged. On the second lap, through the sweeping downhill
Craner Curves, I fed in the power as the car was teetering on
opposite lock. He started laughing: 'Good God, man, it's
fantastic!' he said. 'I never knew my car could do this.'

'Hold on, my friend,' I was thinking. 'We haven't established
that it will yet...'

But I kept quiet. The car was behaving well enough,
cornering smoothly with just a trace of oversteer, and it was
going very fast, but it felt extremely edgy and nervous. The
slightest error on my part would have sent it flying off the
track in one of several possible directions. It demanded too

'The only trick, if there was one,
was to drive extremely smoothly,
with an almost superhuman
sense of pace'

much skill, making serious driving hard work instead of fun.

When taking corners progressively faster, building towards a quick lap time, the old Turbo would understeer predictably on turning in. As corner entry speeds were steadily increased, the change to oversteer was too rapid and the notorious turbo lag made the precise application of the required torque almost impossible to achieve. I never did spin one, but those cars sure made you sweat. I always carried plenty of clean shirts. They were a bit better when the optional limited-slip diff was fitted, but even then they were monsters. Respect them; and concentrate hard.

The only trick, if there was one at all, was to drive by the book, extremely smoothly and with an almost superhuman sense of pace. One false step, at real speed, and you'd be off. With one exception, all of our customers were wise enough not to approach the limit through the really fast bends, feathering them through instead.

One owner had developed the strange trick of sliding sideways into the very slow corners, without opening the throttle until the car had virtually stopped. It worked, but what was the point? Mr Trotter's three-wheeler could have sailed past that chap. The one owner who did

not show the proper respect ended up reversing fast into the concrete at Redgate Corner and wrecking his rear-engined car – expensive!

For the pure pleasure of driving on the road I found the normally-aspirated models infinitely preferable, and I haven't changed my mind. They feel so secure, so beautifully stable when travelling sideways and they give the classic 911 driving experience. Try to drive an early Turbo on the road like that and you're looking for big trouble. When they oversteer, they mean it.

In 1976, the original 3.0-litre seemed incredibly quick but times have changed: today's Boxster (the 2.7, Porsche's entry-level model at time of writing), is almost identical in the 0-60mph stakes and is actually 2mph faster. To be fair, the road Turbos were rapidly uprated, especially after the 3.3-litre engine was introduced. Used properly, the acceleration for overtaking became breathtaking.

Properly prepared for racing, they were very different. Years later, I had a one-off race at Donington in Josh Sadler's 930 and my luck was right in, thanks to unusual weather. This was a nearly standard road car except for its racing tyres and stiffer suspension set-up. With a couple of 935s and other hot machinery

in that all-Porsche race, we were expected to run well down the field, going for a modest class win. Despite a very fine drizzle, slick tyres were still the right choice: Josh's car felt beautifully balanced, the 935s and all the rest were hamstrung with appalling understeer, and I won outright quite easily. The weather, as I say, was on my side.

The quickest production-based 3.0-litre Turbo was probably the 1976 934 we raced at Le Mans in 1982. With 625bhp by then, it was clocked at 205mph on the straight. Five years of development had eliminated turbo lag and it handled beautifully – if you enjoy sliding slightly sideways at 150mph-plus, anyway.

Those old rear-wheel-drive Turbos were wild, they were exciting and they gave a novel, hefty shove in the back when their turbos started spinning. Their roadholding and braking ability were outstanding but ultimately they were out to get you.

Collectors' items? Yes, without doubt, but the true roadgoing destiny of this flagship performer in Porsche's range emerged later with the 4WD Turbo, and that *did* lead to an outstanding line of real drivers' cars.

For a longer personal appraisal of the 911 Turbo, see Tony's recent book *Porsche – Engineering for Excellence*, published by Haynes at £19.99.

turbo
chargers

Wild machines set for terminal oversteer?
Heath Robinson lash-ups on the verge of
catastrophic implosion? Or simply great period
giantkillers that you can't help but love?

Words: Robert Coucher Photography: Matthew Howell

Those of you

who have been reading motoring magazines for as long as all of us in the *Octane* editorial office will remember the great excitement of the turbo years. During the mid- to late-1970s, motor manufacturers suddenly stumbled upon the massively exciting and seemingly free extra power provided by newfangled whizz-bang turbochargers. Overnight a whole plethora of otherwise boring hatchbacks and lacklustre coupés were set alight by the addition of exhaust-driven turbines with additional pop-off valves, wastegates and other mechanical delights to enliven every schoolboy's boring study period.

This was soon followed by a burgeoning of aftermarket turbocharging specialists who promised to be able to bolt a turbo onto your mum's shopping hatch and turn it into an urban racer capable of blowing sports cars into the weeds. An early experience in a Renault 5 that had been subjected to this magical turbo upgrade cemented the astonishment and awe. That feeling of rapid acceleration actually accelerating itself, after the usual linear (and weedy) acceleration offered by most classic cars, was astonishing. Of course, the little Renault suffered from ridiculous torque steer, the brakes were not up to the task and it soon exploded and burnt out, but what a blast!

Turbocharging was the way forward and soon every proper manufacturer was on the case – as the examples here from BMW, Porsche and Lotus testify. As it happened, the whole turbo thing went off the boil come the late-'80s but those of you scholars who follow the modern motor industry will have seen how turbo technology revolutionised the nasty old diesel engine and how it is bursting back onto the scene once again, enabling smaller, more efficient and cleaner petrol engines to maintain decent power outputs. Cue the imminent McLaren MP4-12C, Rolls-Royce Ghost and the performance-focused M-series BMWs.

At a recent monthly editorial meeting, where the cerebral might and combined intellect of the *Octane* editorial team was engaged in sober and thoughtful discussion about this issue, some bright spark suddenly suggested a turbo feature and the meeting instantly descended into excited chaos.

Below
Esprit, 911 and BMW: each a very different take on the turbo theme, with surprising outcomes.

> '0vernight a whole plethora of otherwise boring hatchbacks and lacklustre coupés were set alight by the addition of exhaust-driven turbines'

mid-sized saloon to appeal to the middle classes. The 1800 TI/SA boasting 130bhp could only be bought by drivers with competition licences and it is right to suggest that the very attractively styled and feisty little 2002 model really brought this new BMW way of thinking into focus.

Here was a compact, entry-level BM that was thrilling to drive, especially in 2.0-litre, twin-carb ti and fuel-injected tii versions. The motoring press and lucky owners revelled in the saloons' ability to best more overt sports cars, though the semi-trailing arm rear suspension always allowed plenty of lurid oversteer. Soon 2002s were being enjoyed by aficionados and sporting drivers, supported by plenty of racing and rallying success in Europe.

The 2002 Turbo upped the game again. Engine designer Alex von Falkenhausen eschewed the option of a larger engine shoe-horned into the lightweight 2002 and instead developed the successful Group Five turbocharging idea for a fast road car. By using a KKK turbo coupled to the tii's Kugelfischer fuel injection he created a 170bhp engine that offered Porsche 911-beating performance: 0-60mph in seven seconds, with a top speed of 131mph.

Unfortunately the Turbo was launched into the jaws of the oil crisis of 1973 and its overt and aggressive appearance got the goat of the safety and speed lobbyists in Germany at the time. Some things just don't change.

BMW collector and racer Mark Ayton brought along this immaculate 1974 example finished in Chamonix White; Polaris Silver was the other option. Slim, neat and trim, the BMW 2002 Turbo looks incredibly small and typically German in that Bauhaus school of design mien. It is unashamedly a saloon – boxy with a large glasshouse area. But no matter: with the fat little Mahle alloys, de-bumpered and with a deep chin spoiler →

Yes! The crazy cars of an unloved era of motoring. The raw, untamed and downright dangerous machines that we have largely forgotten. These wild rocket ships that cannot safely be let loose on Her Majesty's public highways. We will have to secure a test track with a full medical trauma unit.

And so we find ourselves at the secretive and secure Millbrook Proving Grounds, hidden somewhere in Bedfordshire. The undulating Alpine Hill Route and High Speed Test Bowl are booked and we wait for the turbo weapons to arrive.

BMW claims the first European turbo road car with its 2002 Turbo, launched in 1973. The Turbo was only manufactured for a year and just 1672 examples were produced. All were left-hand drive, because the location of the turbocharger would not allow for right-hand-drive steering. The Turbo was a homologation special: read factory hot rod.

BMW changed its previous engineering strategy with a shift to the *Neue Klasse* in 1961, which was pivotal to the company's sporting success. The BMW 1500 replaced the rather sedate (boring) old BMWs with a light, compact, sharply styled,

1974 BMW 2002 TURBO
ENGINE 1990cc in-line four, OHC, 6.9:1 compression ratio, Bosch mechanical fuel injection with KKK turbocharger
POWER 170bhp @ 5800rpm **TORQUE** 179lb ft @ 4000rpm **TRANSMISSION** Five-speed close-ratio manual,
rear-wheel drive, limited-slip diff **SUSPENSION** Front: independent, MacPherson struts, coil springs, anti-roll bar.
Rear: independent, semi-trailing arms, coil springs, telescopic dampers, anti-roll bar **BRAKES** Vented discs front,
drums rear **WEIGHT** 1035kg **PERFORMANCE** Top speed 131mph. 0-60mph 7sec

and matt black front grille, and wearing the daring red-and-blue war paint, the BM looks like a proper saloon racer.

Climb in and the left-hand driving position is upright when you're squeezed into the tight bucket seat, with panoramic visibility aided by thin A-pillars. Ergonomics are a delight, from the meaty steering wheel to the clear and legible instruments. The colourful boost gauge adds drama.

Ayton has advised not to touch the throttle on starting, otherwise it overfuels the engine. But the '02 starts easily. Right off, you feel the turbo effect because the throttle pedal is soft and slow and needs constant tickling to keep the idle steady. The dog-leg five-speed gearbox is also a little inexact as you pull the lever towards you and back. The clutch takes up fine and the '02 ambles off feeling docile.

The Alpine Hill Route at Millbrook is a narrow and undulating two-lane road that dips and turns alarmingly. At least it is one-way only. The BM feels light and responsive, helped by absolutely sharp 12.8:1 worm-and-roller steering, which turns the snub nose in with precision. The 2.0-litre engine is smooth for a four-cylinder and, as you do a few exploratory laps to find out where the course goes, it behaves impeccably.

The 2002 is obedient and relaxed and plays along with the gentle driving. But owner Ayton in the passenger seat is soon bored and insists I nail it. So I drop the gearbox down a few gears and the taut little four picks up revs: 2000, then 3000rpm. The needle on the VDO boost gauge starts to flicker and an audible whine begins to build under the bonnet. With the accelerator pedal pushed hard to the carpet, the rev counter hits 4000rpm and the boost arrives with a wham. The boxy four-seater saloon suddenly transforms into a racing hot rod as it spears off down the road. The KKK turbo screams and you snatch another gear and the acceleration continues undiminished until you reach fifth gear and have to back off.

God, what a rush! What fun. The sensation of acceleration, accelerating is amazing. It's as if the car is attached to a huge rubber band. In reality the 2002 Turbo is not that fast by modern hot hatch standards but it is the way that the power is →

Right
BMW engine has long inlet tract (the black metal tube and rubber hose) from turbo right over the top of engine.

'The rev counter hits 4000rpm and the boost arrives with a wham. The boxy four-seater saloon suddenly transforms into a racing hot rod as it spears down the road'

'Its big slab of turbo power is so refined and effortless that you don't realise quite how quickly the speed builds up'

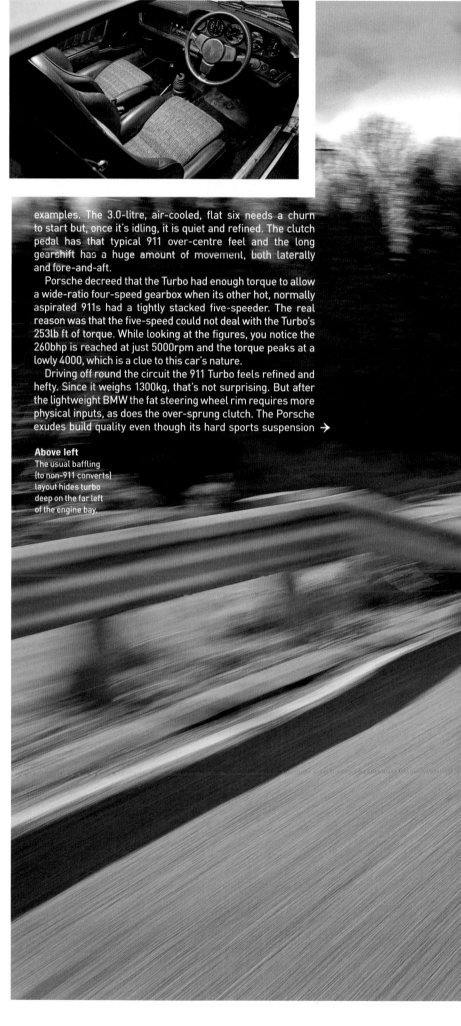

examples. The 3.0-litre, air-cooled, flat six needs a churn to start but, once it's idling, it is quiet and refined. The clutch pedal has that typical 911 over-centre feel and the long gearshift has a huge amount of movement, both laterally and fore-and-aft.

Porsche decreed that the Turbo had enough torque to allow a wide-ratio four-speed gearbox when its other hot, normally aspirated 911s had a tightly stacked five-speeder. The real reason was that the five-speed could not deal with the Turbo's 253lb ft of torque. While looking at the figures, you notice the 260bhp is reached at just 5000rpm and the torque peaks at a lowly 4000, which is a clue to this car's nature.

Driving off round the circuit the 911 Turbo feels refined and hefty. Since it weighs 1300kg, that's not surprising. But after the lightweight BMW the fat steering wheel rim requires more physical inputs, as does the over-sprung clutch. The Porsche exudes build quality even though its hard sports suspension →

Above left
The usual baffling (to non-911 converts) layout hides turbo deep on the far left of the engine bay.

delivered that gets your attention. This is proper old-tech turbo power: on or off.

Becoming comfortable around the circuit, you begin to push the 2002 Turbo harder. It has ventilated discs up front from the larger 3.0CS, larger drum brakes at the rear and a limited-slip differential. This allows you to pile the BM into the bends, its lithe 1035kg weight helping the car to react instantly to the superb steering. As you learn where the turbo cuts in you begin to judge braking points and where to downchange. If you play it safe, like me, you want the car on the boil as you go into bends, otherwise turbo-wham halfway through will make things unexpectedly exciting.

Held firmly in place by the bucket seat you slew the BM around the circuit, enjoying the blat of seamless power thanks to the wide-open throttle. Off the gas and off boost the car is a little lethargic but not as switched-off as you might think. The gearshift action is somewhat vague and you must remember the dog-leg layout, but this 37-year-old sports saloon is every inch a BMW, an ultimate driving machine.

The next turbo in chronological order is the Porsche. The original 3.0-litre 911 Turbo was first seen at the Paris Motor Show in 1973 and finally launched in 1975. The 911 Turbo was bred out of the pure racing 2.1-litre Martini RSR Turbo, which produced 333bhp.

Ernst Fuhrmann's racing turbos had totally dominated the Can Am series in America with weapons like the 1000bhp 917/30. It would have been silly if Porsche had not used this triumphant engineering for a road car. So at the '74 Paris Motor Show the first roadgoing 911 Turbo, code-named the 930, was unveiled. Its 3.0-litre KKK-fed engine promised 260bhp and a top speed of 180mph. The first year's production of just 540 were hand-made alongside the normal cooking 911s and all sold out. Steve McQueen was on the short list, as were other members of the high-speed motoring aristocracy.

This is an extremely rare 1976 model, distinguished by the simpler rear whaletail. Finished in white, it looks clean and organic and typically 911. Its Fuchs alloy wheels are shod with more modern rubber, which must be a good thing, because we have all heard the tales of the 911 Turbo's lethal handling.

The high-backed, houndstooth-checked bucket seat is comfortable but you immediately notice how offset the pedals are. Worse in right-hand-drive cars than left-hand-drive

1976 PORSCHE 911 TURBO

ENGINE 2993cc flat six, air-cooled, SOHC per bank, 6.5:1 compression ratio, Bosch mechanical fuel injection, KKK turbocharger **POWER** 260bhp @ 5000rpm **TORQUE** 245lb ft @ 4000rpm **TRANSMISSION** Four-speed manual, rear-wheel drive **SUSPENSION** Front: independent by MacPherson struts, torsion bars, anti-roll bar. Rear: independent by trailing wishbones, torsion bars, telescopic dampers **BRAKES** Ventilated discs all-round **WEIGHT** 1300kg **PERFORMANCE** Top speed 154mph, 0-60mph 5.8sec

1981 LOTUS TURBO ESPRIT
ENGINE 2174cc, 16-valve in-line four, DOHC, 7.5:1 compression ratio, twin Dell'Orto carburettors,
Garrett AiResearch turbocharger **POWER** 210bhp @ 6000rpm **TORQUE** 200lb ft @ 4000rpm
TRANSMISSION Five-speed manual transaxle, rear-wheel drive **SUSPENSION** Front: independent, upper
A-arms, lower lateral links, coil springs,telescopic dampers, anti-roll bar. Rear: independent, unequal-length
upper lateral links, lower lateral links and angled trailing arms, coil springs, telescopic dampers
BRAKES Solid discs all-round **WEIGHT** 1200kg **PERFORMANCE** Top speed 150mph. 0-60mph 5.6sec

means it thumps and bumps over the track irregularities. Point it onto the straight and drop down to second gear. There is no boost gauge so you wait for the rev counter to reach four thou. On the way up the power begins to swell and grow. At 4000rpm it really comes together and soon you are revving at just over five and changing up. No drama, no turbo whoosh, just a lovely linear progression of speed.

Come to the first sharp corner that the BMW went around as if on rails, you suddenly realise that the 911 Turbo is really shifting. The bend is upon you and you have to jump heavily on the brakes. Thank goodness they are one of the best features of the 911. Gulp. Hold on. Shove the brake pedal harder still and then understeer around the bend. Oh dear. Messy.

Calming down, you realise the Porsche is a real Jekyll and Hyde. Its big slab of turbo power is so refined and effortless that you don't realise quite how quickly the speed builds up.

Below
Porsche vs Lotus, a truly epic battle. The 911 feels less wieldy and less racy than the Esprit.

In this configuration the turbo effectively masks the engine's noise so it is quieter than a normal 911 but much, much faster.

Treating the 911 Turbo with more respect you have a go at the twisty bits. Carefully. With the more modern wide rubber, the 911 feels planted. The powerful brakes allow you to whoosh up to the next bend at speed, then reel it all in. Cornering at sane speeds, the car understeers safely. Allow it through the apex than boot it. The engine hung over the rear wheels provides good traction and, if you have the revs pinned at four thou, the wide 911 Turbo squats and then leaps off to the next bend.

The Porsche is best enjoyed at about seven-tenths through the bends, where real speed can be made up on the straights. It is heavy and physical to throw about and you have to factor the turbo cutting in, as with the BMW, but the 911 will throw you off the road if you get it wrong. Being solid, quiet and refined, the 911 Turbo is better suited for high-speed blasts along autobahns than it is being flung around an Alpine circuit. It is set up as a fast ground coverer with all the luxury accoutrements like air-conditioning, electric windows and so on. On the day, the 911 Turbo behaves when driven intelligently and does not actually bite any of us. But you can tell it is just waiting to have a good old nip...

The 1981 Lotus Turbo Esprit looks pretty radical when compared with the hot rod BMW saloon and evergreen Porsche silhouette. Designed by Giorgetto Giugiaro, it is the back-to-the-future old school of folded paper design. Finished in bright white with lurid red decals, Trevor Skedge's Esprit is a pure 1980s sports car. In today's world, where car design is dictated by the wind tunnel, this efficient Lotus looks really striking.

Shod with bronze Compomotive split-rims, the Lotus is low and rakish. The glassfibre body is mounted on a galvanised steel backbone with the DOHC 16-valve, slant-four all-alloy engine mounted longitudinally amidships, mated to a Citroën-Maserati sourced five-speed gearbox. All-up weight is just 1200kg. Being an early car, this engine features a dry sump and, unusually, the Garrett AiResearch T03 turbocharger blows through the sealed Dell'Orto carbs.

Open the driver's door and you are met by a chocolate brown leather-swathed interior. The chairs look like trendy, squashed →

'It is refined, gutsy, easy to drive fast and flatters the driver. It will hit 60mph in 5.6 seconds and top out at 150mph'

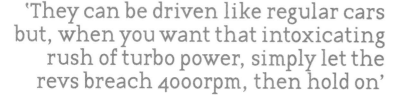

'They can be driven like regular cars but, when you want that intoxicating rush of turbo power, simply let the revs breach 4000rpm, then hold on'

Above
Three early European turbos on the twisty test track – and not a single accident or breakdown.

beanbags but once you're ensconced the driving position is comfortable. The absolutely flat front screen is up close and rear visibility is not great; you feel seated down very low, with a high waistline all around.

The gruff engine, this being the longer-stroke 2.2-litre, starts easily and settles immediately to a rock-solid idle. Testing the throttle reaction you are amazed at how sharp it feels. No indication of a turbocharger softening the response. The high-mounted gearshift has to be pushed firmly over and up to engage first gear. Let the clutch out and the Lotus eases off. The car is totally relaxed and astonishingly tractable, going up through the gearbox like a normally aspirated 3.0-litre.

Never having driven a Lotus Esprit before I am amazed. This is absolutely not what I expected at all. The Esprit is quiet and torquey. The steering is light and it seemingly pulls more strongly than the bigger-capacity Porsche. Swinging out onto the test track and dropping a few cogs, the Lotus comes alive. The power delivery is smooth and steady. Again at 4000rpm the 200lb ft of torque peaks as the turbo begins to whine. The carburettor throttle butterflies are placed as close to the inlet valves as possible and this effectively

eliminates all turbo lag. This overt sports car remains refined and the power comes on beautifully.

Snicking up through the gearbox, the Lotus slices through the bends. The steering is light and totally accurate. The suspension is soft! But the car turns in and can be placed with millimetre accuracy and the handling is pure joy. It is easier than the other two to keep on the boil, as the engine response is so sweet. The disc brakes do without ventilation but are more than up to the job of retarding the lightweight Lotus.

The Esprit is a completely unexpected surprise. One might imagine a Lotus to feel flimsy, lightweight and nervous. The Esprit is not like that at all. It is refined, gutsy, easy to drive fast and flatters the driver. It will hit 60mph in 5.6 seconds and top out at 150mph. It really is a thoroughbred sports car that more than lives with the other two very well-respected German marques.

This back-to-back test of three wild early turbo cars has not turned out quite as we expected. The precaution of taking them to a test track was not necessary. Each of these fast machines is entirely well behaved and not as scary as you might imagine. Certainly, since they are classic cars without modern electronic driver aids and controls, and all booting out considerable power, it is very possible to get things horribly wrong. But driven firmly within their limits, the BMW 2002 Turbo, Porsche 911 Turbo and Lotus Turbo Esprit have each turned out to be well-sorted, fast and entertaining drivers' cars. The BM is a factory hot rod, the Porsche is a refined mile-eater, and the Lotus is a superbly balanced sports car. They can be driven like regular cars but, when you want that intoxicating rush of turbo power, simply let the revs breach 4000rpm, then hold on...

Thanks to Mark Ayton for the BMW 2002 Turbo (www.munichlegends. co.uk); Trevor Skedge and the Lotus Forums (www.thelotusforums.com) for the Esprit; and Eclectic Cars and John Ward for the 911 (www.eclecticcars.co.uk).

A. BÜCHI. WINTERTHUR.

A brief history of

TURBOCHARGING

and how it changed the motoring world

Like most automotive inventions, turbocharging was patented in the early years of the 20th century. But it would take another 50 years and two World Wars before it began to revolutionise the car industry

Words: Mark Dixon

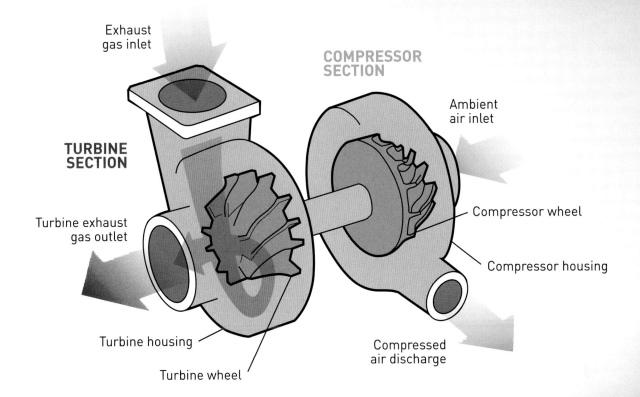

Exhaust
gas inlet

COMPRESSOR
SECTION

Ambient
air inlet

TURBINE
SECTION

Compressor wheel

Turbine exhaust
gas outlet

Compressor housing

Turbine housing

Compressed
air discharge

Turbine wheel

Turbochargers – they're great, aren't they? Since the 1970s we've been conditioned to accept that anything with a turbo on it has to be faster, and therefore better. The turbo is certainly a remarkable invention, which makes it all the more surprising that turbochargers were not widely used in cars until the decade of flared trousers and glam rock, even though the concept had been proven long before WW2.

First things first. What is a turbo, how does it work, and how does it differ from a supercharger?

The basic function of a turbocharger is to force more air into an engine, to produce more power. A small amount of petrol can generate an awful lot of energy. Getting enough air into an engine to make use of that potential is another matter, and that's where the turbocharger and supercharger come in. Driven by the engine they're attached to, either will push air into the engine at higher-than-atmospheric pressure.

The difference between a supercharger and a turbocharger is that the supercharger is mechanically driven by the engine, usually from the crankshaft, while the turbo uses exhaust energy – a combination of gas velocity, pressure and heat – to spin a turbine wheel that in turn drives a compressor. This is where the turbo has a huge advantage over the supercharger, because the mechanically driven supercharger diverts some power from the engine. It's a loss that is easily

outweighed by the gain delivered by the compressed air, but a loss all the same.

Otherwise both turbocharger and supercharger work on a similar principle, and in fact turbocharging was referred to as turbine-supercharging for the first half-century of its existence.

The man who started it all was a Swiss engineer called Alfred Büchi, who filed his first turbocharger patent in 1905 and had effectively designed the modern turbo by 1911. Büchi recognised one of the most important turbo applications from the start: it can be used to force-feed an aeroplane engine with air at high altitude, where the low atmospheric pressure would otherwise drastically reduce its efficiency.

American pilot Major Rudolph Schroeder flew a turbocharged Liberty V12-engined open-cockpit biplane to an altitude record of 33,114 feet in 1920; it was so cold up there that when he removed his goggles to change oxygen tanks, his eyeballs froze. He passed out from lack of oxygen and only regained consciousness just before the plane plummeted into the ground. Still almost blind, he landed safely.

Büchi's early tests with aircraft weren't hugely successful, however, and he focused his attentions instead on turbocharging diesel engines. The diesel is especially suitable for turbocharging for various reasons. One is that there's no throttle to stall the air →

Above and facing page
How a centrifugal turbocharger works: exhaust gases spin the turbine wheel, which drives a shaft to the compressor; father of the turbo, Alfred Büchi.

CUMMINS DIESEL Special

POLE POSITION WINNER

First of its kind...

and full of surprises!

JETFIRE
an exclusive from
OLDSMOBILE

Left and below
'Full of surprises' claimed
Oldsmobile about turbo
Jetfire; German SVT 137
155 railcar with 600bhp
Maybach turbodiesel
reached 134mph in 1939.

Above, right and below
B-29 bomber took turbo
engines to new heights;
Cummins Diesel Special ran at
Indy; Porsche 911 Turbo was a
pioneering 1970s turbo car.

'Development of turbochargers for aircraft was rapidly accelerated in WW2, when there was suddenly a pressing need for bombers to fly at very high altitudes'

compressor that's driven off the turbine, and because there's no throttle a diesel running on a small amount of fuel still produces more exhaust flow than a petrol engine does with the throttle closed.

That – and the fact that a diesel works over a narrower speed band than a petrol unit, so there is less speed differential for the turbo to deal with – is important because a turbo needs to be spinning at pretty high revs before it even begins to work properly. If it's set up to deal with high engine revs it won't be spinning fast enough at low revs, while if it's matched to low revs it will go absolutely ballistic at higher engine speeds. The former situation results in what's popularly known as 'turbo lag', as the turbo struggles to pick up speed.

Turbocharging was therefore mainly used on diesels for a remarkably long time. The German navy launched two ships powered by ten-cylinder MAN turbodiesels in 1925. In the 1930s, turbocharged Maybach V12 diesels were tried out in German railcars, eventually setting a 134mph speed record. And Swiss firm Saurer brought out a turbodiesel truck in 1938. Petrol engines were generally ignored, with the exception of the big motors used to power aircraft.

Development of turbochargers for aircraft was rapidly accelerated in WW2, when there was suddenly a pressing need for bombers to fly at very high altitudes to avoid flak and

fighters. Exotic metal alloys were devised that could cope with the incredible heat and stress imposed on turbo blades – a spinning half-ounce blade can be subjected to a ton of centrifugal force. The USA led the way and it was a turbocharged B-29 bomber that ended WW2 by dropping atomic bombs on Japan.

Post-war, the big turbo manufacturers turned their attentions either to jet engines or turbodiesels for lorries; turbos were still too expensive and difficult to make for small-capacity car engines. In the early post-war years, the first really successful turbo car actually had a diesel engine. The 1952 Indy racer, the *Cummins Diesel Special*, qualified on pole and completed 71 laps before retiring with a blocked air intake – the turbocharger had acted like a giant vacuum cleaner and sucked debris in from all over the track.

By the late '50s, however, American car engineers were confident enough to start experimenting with turbocharged petrol engines, and the first production turbo cars appeared within months of each other in 1962: the Oldsmobile F-85 Jetfire and the Chevrolet Corvair Monza Spyder (which, despite its name, was available as a coupé or convertible). The Olds was notable in using a water/methanol mixture, which Oldsmobile's marketing people dubbed 'Rocket Fluid', to control engine knock under hard acceleration. Owners had to keep the reservoir for this

Rocket Fluid topped up, which is one reason why the car was never a big seller.

After this brief flurry of activity, it wasn't until the 1970s that turbo cars really came of age, helped by the widespread introduction of Bosch K-Jetronic fuel injection. Early examples such as the BMW 2002 Turbo and the Porsche 911 Turbo were pretty lairy but in 1978 came the car that did more than any other to popularise turbocharging, the Saab 99 Turbo. The Saab's turbo was optimised for low-down torque, which made it more attractive for everyday driving and opened up a whole new market of keen drivers who also had families.

Across the pond, also in 1978, Buick brought out a turbo version of its long-running V6 that would prove very successful, and in 1979 Ford followed suit with a (carburettored) turbo 2.3-litre Mustang. The floodgates had been opened: within five or six years virtually every manufacturer had a turbo in its range, and soon turbos were being fitted to relatively small-capacity engines – especially in Japan.

Fitting a turbocharger to an engine brings all kinds of challenges as well as benefits. One is the heat generated within the turbo housing: switch an early turbo car off after a fast run

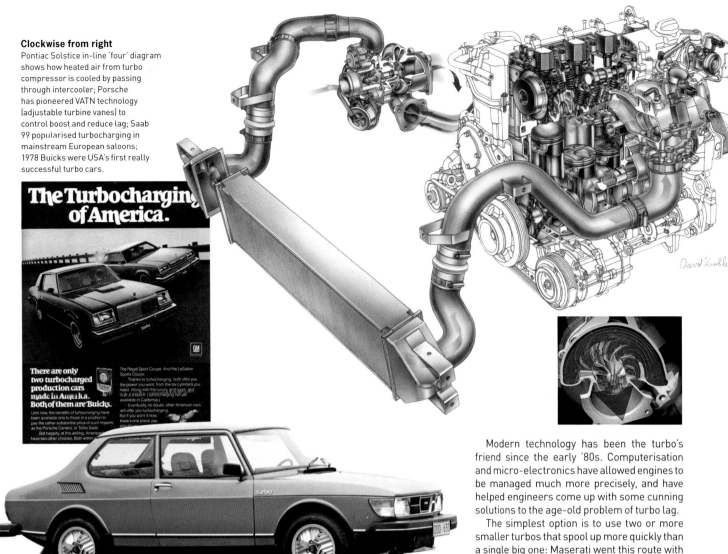

and the resulting heat soak could carbonise the lubricating oil, leading to ruined bearings. There's the problem of turbo lag, already mentioned; and the question of how to stop the turbo 'overboosting' the engine at high revs.

The simplest ways to control boost are either to fit a wastegate upstream of the turbo, which diverts exhaust gas around the turbo rather than through it, or to fit a 'dump valve' downstream of the compressor that vents excess air to the atmosphere with that characteristic 'pschoo' sound beloved of boy racers. Engineers frown on that kind of dump valve because it wastes air that's already been compressed, but marketing people love it.

Turbocharged engines can also suffer from pinking, also known as 'knock' or detonation, as they come on boost. That's exacerbated if the fuel/air mixture is still hot from being compressed by the turbo, which is why turbocharged cars are sometimes fitted with an intercooler – a heat exchanger – that reduces the temperature of the charge. Detonation can also be reduced by retarding the ignition – except that doing this reduces performance. That's why Oldsmobile went for the 'Rocket Fluid' option instead, back in 1962.

Saab addressed the problem rather more elegantly in the 1980s with its Automatic

> **'Switch an early turbo car off after a fast run and the resulting heat soak could carbonise the lubricating oil, ruining the bearings'**

Pressure Control (APC) system, which used a knock sensor and control unit to adjust the boost to suit variations in fuel, engine tune, ambient temperature and so on.

In other words, there's more than one way to skin a turbo cat, and in the 1980s there was still much to learn. As part of this learning process, several aftermarket tuning companies got involved in offering turbo conversions. In the UK we had Janspeed (who did a twin-turbo Rover SD1 V8), Turbo Technics and Brodie Brittain Racing, to name but three. Turbo Technics is still a major player in the turbo business, having moved on from the days of hotted-up XR2s to become a world-class specialist – their turbo balancing rigs are the bee's knees, and balancing is important given that a turbo may spin at 250,000rpm.

Modern technology has been the turbo's friend since the early '80s. Computerisation and micro-electronics have allowed engines to be managed much more precisely, and have helped engineers come up with some cunning solutions to the age-old problem of turbo lag.

The simplest option is to use two or more smaller turbos that spool up more quickly than a single big one: Maserati went this route with the twin-turbo 1981 Biturbo, a car that still causes older magazine road testers to break out into a cold sweat at memories of its infamously unpredictable handling.

A slightly more sophisticated solution is sequential turbos, which operate over different bands in the engine's rev range so that boost is always on hand. Another is to combine a supercharger with a turbocharger for a similar result – VW has done this very successfully in its recent 'twincharged' 1.4-litre Golf, which squeezes 160bhp and nearly 40mpg out of the same petrol engine. And yet *another* idea is the variable area turbine nozzle (VATN), where the turbine vanes are moved to increase or decrease the area exposed to the exhaust gases. Step forward, Porsche.

But the boffins are still coming up with ever more inventive ways to get more of the turbo's power delivered low down. Latest bright idea (from British company Controlled Power Technologies, by the way) is to add an electric motor to the twincharge system, which zips the supercharger up to 70,000rpm from idle in less than a third of a second, yet doesn't need the heavy-duty electrical systems demanded by conventional hybrids.

Combining an electric supercharger with a turbo, says CPT, is an ideal way to extract high performance from small petrol engines, which is the way the world is going. It seems the turbocharger will be thrilling new generations of drivers for some time to come.

THE
thinking man's
911s
PORSCHE 911 2.4S & 993

Convention has it that the 1973 2.7 Carrera RS is the best driver's car Porsche ever made. But what about the 2.4S or the later 993? Time to find out

Words: Mark Dixon Photography: Matthew Howell

Of course, we'd all like a 2.7 Carrera RS. It goes without saying – I'll take mine in Tangerine, please – but prices for these cars have effectively doubled in the last few years. That's what happens when a car is repeatedly acclaimed as one of the best driver's machines ever made. People start to take notice, and the values go up.

So, whereas a few years ago you could have bought a nice RS for maybe £70,000, you're now looking at £150,000 or more – a right-hand-drive Lightweight version made a cool £220,000 at H&H's Buxton sale in February this year (and it was finished in Tangerine, too). That puts them out of the reach of all but a few lucky individuals; the rest of us have to cut our cloth to suit our pocket. Which is how the *Octane* editorial team – forever on the look-out for today's top buys – came up with this month's cover feature.

What, we argued over a few drinks in the Wollaston Arms, was the best 911 after the 2.7RS? And which was the best value? Two candidates immediately sprang to mind. Of the classic pre-'74 911s, the 2.4S is the nearest in performance, its 190bhp fuel-injected engine giving away just 20bhp to the 2.7RS. But if you cast a wider net to include all the air-cooled 911s ever made, then the last-of-line 993 represents fantastic value for money and is reputedly a great drive, too.

With the help of two enthusiastic 911 owners, we headed to the wide open spaces of Wales – and the bright lights of Cardiff – to put our theories to the test. →

To be honest, I didn't care very much about how Paul Madden's Metallic Green 2.4S would drive. I just knew that I coveted it because it looked so utterly fabulous. The so-'70s Porsche colour of Metallic Green is original, and it suits the 911 perfectly.

Paint aside, the 2.4S is desirable for several reasons. But first, as Jennifer Aniston used to say in those TV ads, the science bit.

The 'S' model had been introduced in 1966 – 'S' standing for Super – as the hot version of the 911, upping the standard 2.0-litre engine's 130bhp to 160 by means of bigger valves, a higher compression ratio and two Weber 40IDS carburettors. A good start.

Over the next few years, Porsche made it even better, by switching to Bosch fuel injection in 1968, and then progressively enlarging the engine to 2.2 litres in 1969, and 2.4 litres – actually 2341cc – in 1972. The 2.4S developed 190bhp at 6500rpm, which is just 20bhp less than the 2.7RS; although the RS did have rather more torque, at 188lb ft compared with the 160lb ft of the S.

Enough facts and figures. Paul Madden's car is a 1972 2.4S, instantly recognisable to Porsche aficionados by the oil tank filler cap located in the wing behind the driver's door – a feature unique to this model year. Porsche had relocated the engine's oil tank in its never ending quest to improve weight distribution, but since the filler cap was now easily mistaken for a petrol cap – with predictable, if not hilarious, results – they moved it back under the engine lid for 1973.

Another giveaway that this is a 1972 car is its discreet chin spoiler. The 911 had a relatively slippery shape but it also acted like a wing: air passing over the top had further to travel than it did underneath, giving rise to negative pressure, particularly at the rear. At this stage, Porsche didn't worry about the rear end – you had to be cornering really fast for it to be a problem – but adding the little chin spoiler reduced front-end lift by almost 40 percent.

The lack of a rear spoiler certainly gives the 2.4S the edge over the RS in appearance

terms. The Carrera's 'duck tail' was added for a very good reason but it did nothing aesthetically for the 911's shape. Unadorned, its simplicity means you appreciate the details all the more, from the tiny slatted horn grilles inboard of the front side lights, to the beautifully curved and polished door latches, to the super-slim anodised alloy window frames. It all looks so delicate.

That impression is carried through inside the car, where a slender gearlever sprouts from an almost-flat floor. The four-spoke steering wheel is thin-rimmed, and narrow screen pillars mean the cabin feels light. The car is compact by modern standards but it seems spacious inside, helped by the absence of a transmission tunnel and a general lack of fripperies. You do get electric windows and a sunroof in this RHD car – remember when an opening sunroof was considered the height of luxury? – but the one place Porsche really went to town was the instrument display, which comprises five big dials right in front of the driver. →

Below
1972 2.4S leads 1995 Carrera: can either rival the iconic 2.7RS, regardless of age or current value?

'The 993 was a resounding success. It looked good and those laid-back headlamps emphasised the simplicity of the 911's shape once again'

fitted to this car when new – and twist the key. It's an interesting experience. You expect fuel-injected cars to run perfectly smoothly from cold but the 2.4S is a little ragged first thing, and there's even a hand thottle down beside the handbrake so you can keep the revs up until it warms through. The soundtrack is complex: a mixture of fan whine, mechanical clatter and thrum, and a wet plishy-plashy sound that's curiously reminiscent of a big, low-compression sidevalve. One thing it's not is quiet; 993 owner Paul Truckle is amazed how noisy the 2.4S seems in comparison with his own car.

morning after a night of 'guerilla photography' outside the Welsh Assembly Building – fortunately, the local CCTV operators must have decided terrorists wouldn't roll up in a brace of 911s – the 2.4S is untemperamental; although most of the power comes in high up the rev band, there's enough torque to trickle the car through city traffic without rowing it along on the gearlever.

In fact, if the 2.4S has a flaw, it's that the gearchange has a rather springy feel. It has a conventional H-gate, with fifth out on a limb to the right, but – on this car at least – you need to give the lever a little sideways twitch as you snick it from third to fourth. Once learned, no problem: but attempting to force the lever into a slot is doomed to failure. Like any precision instrument, this 911 requires a sympathetic touch.

Travelling in convoy to our photo location in the hills above Crickhowell, there's not much chance to extend the 911 so Paul and

the potted history of his car: sold new to a Greek shipping magnate in central London, it later suffered the indignity of being painted Guards Red, like so many ageing 911s in the 1980s, before being bought and restored on Paul's behalf by a then-young restoration outfit, Early 911. The car required extensive metalwork but the quality of the rebuild was superb and it still looks and feels in concours condition, five years and 15,000 miles later. Paul even uses it on track days – 'it only really comes alive above 5000rpm,' he says.

This healthy attitude extends towards urging me to take the car off and play with it for a while on the fast moorland roads around us. I don't need much encouraging. As Paul has already suggested, you really have to wind up the flat-six to extract its real performance – and to enjoy the unique sound of that Porsche motor howling and wailing through the Welsh hills, the low-speed clatter now transformed into a zinging snarl. From 3000rpm it feels merely brisk and it's not until you broach 5000, 5500, 6000rpm that the engine finds its second wind and starts to pull fiercely.

It's not just the engine that's working hard; the driver must do so, too, for driving the 2.4S quickly is as much a physical challenge →

Below
993's pumped-up rear wheelarches aren't just for show: they cover an all-new, wider suspension.

'Perhaps the 993 doesn't ultimately have the involving feel of the 1970s car, but the truth is that it's far less tiring to drive quickly'

1995 PORSCHE 993 CARRERA

ENGINE 3600cc all-alloy flat-six, air cooled, SOHC per bank, Bosch Motronic sequential fuel injection **POWER** 272bhp @ 6100rpm **TORQUE** 252lb ft @ 5000rpm
TRANSMISSION Six-speed manual, rear-wheel drive; four-speed Tiptronic optional **SUSPENSION** Front: MacPherson struts, lower wishbones, coil springs, anti-roll bar.
Rear: double wishbones, coil springs, telescopic dampers, anti-roll bar **BRAKES** Vented and drilled discs front and rear, ABS
WEIGHT 1370kg **PERFORMANCE** Top speed 160mph. 0-60mph 5.2sec

as a mental one. The non-assisted steering is fabulously communicative but loads up significantly in tight corners, and you start to feel the effort in your shoulders after a while. Slow in, fast out is the mantra; these early cars run on comparatively skinny 185-section tyres all-round, demanding a high degree of anticipation when you're pressing on in unfamiliar territory. But then, that's how you should drive any car, not just a 911, and the Porsche never feels the slightest bit tail-happy on these dry roads.

More of a worry are the grazing sheep that dot the roadside for miles in each direction, oblivious to traffic. Fortunately the 2.4S has disc brakes all round: an emergency stop caused by one such errant ruminant proves that the 2.4S pulls up quickly and neatly without locking the front wheels – which is more than can be said for a Toyota MR2 travelling in the opposite direction. The sheep was quite unconcerned, of course.

Thrumming into the hilltop car park in front of a waiting photographer and rapidly chilling pair of Porsche owners, I've rarely wanted to hang on to a car so much. But it's

time to skip forward a couple of decades and try a very different 911, the 993 Carrera.

Self-employed software engineer Paul Truckle owned a Porsche Boxster and (briefly) a 930 Turbo before he bought this 993 four years ago. It's not an everyday driver and he occasionally wonders whether he should sell it, but says he thinks he'd come to regret doing that. I think he's right.

Porsche had been going through a tough time when the 993 was introduced in, logically enough, 1993. Sales had been plummeting since the late '80s and there was even talk of a takeover by Volkswagen or Daimler-Benz. The revival started when Dr Wendelin Wiedeking was appointed as chief executive in September 1992. By adopting Japanese *haiken* practices to reduce costs and improve quality, he got it back on an upward slope – and the new 993 marked the start of a revival in Porsche's fortunes.

It was always considered a stop-gap, however. Porsche had taken the air-cooled flat-six as far as it could go in terms of juggling power output with increasingly stringent emissions legislation, and knew

that the only solution was to adopt liquid cooling; the air-cooled engine was simply becoming too hot. The plan was to introduce the all-new, water-cooled 996 in 1996. Meanwhile it needed a replacement for the 964 of the late-'80s, which had been criticised for its uninspiring handling and NVH issues.

For a stop-gap, the 993 was a resounding success. Styled by Briton Tony Hatter, it looked elegant, with headlights faired back into the wings; paradoxically, those laid-back headlamps increased the resemblance to early 911s by emphasising the simplicity of the overall shape once again.

A little drama was introduced at the back with wheelarches that swelled over the rear wheels in the manner of an old-style 911 Turbo. In fact, those swellings were necessary to accommodate the wider track that was a corollary of an all-new rear suspension. For the first time ever, the evil spectre of lift-off oversteer had been effectively exorcised.

The solution was deceptively simple. Porsche's engineers devised a new light-alloy subframe with coil-and-wishbone →

'The 3.6-litre was carried over from the 964 but was heavily reworked so it revved more easily, gave more power – 272bhp – and was easier to service'

Above
993 flat-six took air cooling to the max: emissions legislation meant engines were running ever hotter.

'The 911's soundtrack is complex: a mixture of fan whine, mechanical clatter and thrum, and a wet plishy-plashy sound'

Right
2.4S uses bored and stroked version of original 911 2.0-litre to produce 190bhp – up 60bhp since '64.

1972 PORSCHE 911 2.4S

ENGINE 2341cc all-alloy flat-six, SOHC per bank, Bosch mechanical fuel injection **POWER** 190bhp @ 6500rpm **TORQUE** 159lb ft @ 5200rpm **TRANSMISSION** Five-speed manual, rear-wheel drive **SUSPENSION** Front: MacPherson struts, lower wishbones, torsion bars, telescopic dampers, anti-roll bar. Rear: semi-trailing arms, torsion bars, telescopic dampers, anti-roll bar **BRAKES** Vented discs front and rear **WEIGHT** 1075kg **PERFORMANCE** Top speed 143mph. 0-62mph 7.0sec

suspension; cleverly, the wishbone mounts were set up to reduce squat and dive under heavy braking, and to allow a little wheel toe-in when drive torque was reduced – in other words, to lessen a tendency to oversteer if the driver lifted off mid-corner. The double-wishbone set-up also virtually eliminated wheel camber changes in the same situation.

Mechanically, the 3.6-litre engine was carried over from the 964 but heavily reworked – every part was new, said Porsche – so it revved more easily, gave more power (272bhp) and was easier to service; while a new six-speed manual gearbox was made standard alongside the optional Tiptronic four-speed auto.

Paul Truckle's car has the manual 'box and two-wheel drive; the four-wheel-drive Carrera 4 was introduced in 1994. 1995-on cars had 'Varioram' engines, with variable inlet tracts to improve mid-range torque, but Paul's 993 pre-dates that – 'I test-drove a couple of Varioram Carrera 4s but this pre-Varioram 2 just felt more spritely,' he says. After driving it, I can believe him.

First impressions aren't great, however. The car is so understated that it almost seems bland, a look that's emphasised by the chunky Cup alloys. Things go further downhill when you discover an interior in a dark blue shade strongly reminiscent of a mid-'80s 928, seemingly intended to make plastic trim look even more like plastic. It's comfortable inside but also noticeably cluttered when compared with the 2.4S, having grown a centre console over the intervening years. The dash has an identical layout to the '70s car's, which is rather appealing, but curiously the steering wheel seems to be offset an inch to the left.

That's all the carping you're going to hear from now on, however. To put it simply, this is just a great car in every respect. Start it up and you're greeted with a discreet, smooth-sounding, bassy engine note with just a hint of a sporting edge to its fuel-injected purr. The gearchange is short and positive without being in the least heavy; the steering power-assisted but only enough to be comfortable.

In fact, the greatest compliment you can pay the 993 is that nothing stands out to interrupt the harmony of the car as a whole. You don't particularly notice anything about the steering, brakes, gearchange, ride or handling because they all work beautifully together, leaving you to get on with your driving. Whether you're pottering along on autopilot or feeling in the groove and really flying, the 993 fits in with your mood. It is a Porsche for everyman, every day.

That doesn't mean it's not exciting. The power-to-weight ratio is not hugely different from that of the 2.4S – 190bhp and 1075kg of the early car plays 272bhp and 1370kg of the 993 – but the bigger engine is much more torquey. It feels the genuinely quick car it is, and, while it sounds comparatively subdued in normal driving, it develops a character of its own when being worked hard, reminding you that you are, after all, driving a Porsche.

OK, so perhaps it doesn't ultimately have the involving feel of the 1970s car, but the truth is that it's also far less tiring to drive quickly. The ride is firm without being crashy and this 89,000-mile car feels as solid as it did when it left the factory. German cars are sometimes criticised for being too efficient →

but the flipside of that perfectionist approach is that they encourage the serious driver to concentrate on driving as smoothly as possible. And that can't be a bad thing.

We haven't so far mentioned money. As you'd expect, the more modern car is now far more affordable than the classic. You can find decent, average-mileage examples of the two-wheel-drive 993 privately from £17,000, and even paying the extra for peace of mind from a dealer shouldn't cost you more than £24,000-28,000.

Such as, for example, the well-respected Yorkshire outfit Specialist Cars of Malton. 'Lots of people call the 993 the last "proper" Porsche,' says SC's Mark Mullen. 'They were really well built, and made in fewer numbers than the 996, which was more of a mass-market car.

'Mechanically they're very strong and there's little to worry about in terms of corrosion. I always check the panels below the front and rear screens, the wheelarch lips and the stays for the rear bumpers – if

these rust, the bumper goes floppy – but that's about it. Mileage is fairly irrelevant, although suspension bushes and shocks may need replacing after 60,000-70,000 miles.

'The most desirable non-turbo 993 is a Varioram manual coupé, but colour doesn't seem to affect value particularly – I recently sold a Carrera 4S very easily that was painted Viola, a lurid purple shade!'

Having his 2.4S repainted in its original Metallic Green seemed a brave choice on Paul Madden's part five years ago but has paid off since: 'Back then everyone wanted metallic silver,' says Nick Moss, who restored the car. 'Now, they are are going for the bright period colours.'

In fact, Paul's car has proved a sound investment all round. Nick values it at £75,000-80,000, which reflects the fact that the S models are rare: only 1750 coupés and 989 Targas were made in the 1972 model year, and slightly fewer for 1973.

'UK buyers always want the "fastest" version, hence the 2.4S,' explains Nick,

'although I personally prefer the free-revving nature of the 2.2S and its dog-leg 'change. Either way, it's a fact that the S is the only 911 that makes financial sense to restore at present. But there aren't many about.'

The main problem with old 911s, of course, is rust – as Nick says, 'anyone who tells you there is no rust in their 911 just hasn't found it yet'. So, while it is perfectly possible to buy a nice-looking S for less than the cost of a properly restored car, chances are you will simply be deferring expenditure.

If I had the resources, I wouldn't begrudge for a moment paying the money for a car like Paul's. But I've realised I would probably get more real-world driving pleasure from a 993 at one-third the price. And it's not often that you'll catch me saying that about a 'modern' – the 993 is *that* good.

Thanks to car owners Paul Madden and Paul Truckle; to Nick Moss at Early 911, www.early911.co.uk; and to Mark Mullen at Specialist Cars of Malton, www.specialistcarsltd.co.uk.

'As you'd expect, the more modern car is now far more affordable than the classic'

Below
Two decades apart, yet these 911s are both fantastic to drive – and they look remarkably similar.

WWW.HISTORIKA.COM

Specialising in Early Road/Race 911's and prototypes

Tel: 07836 384 999

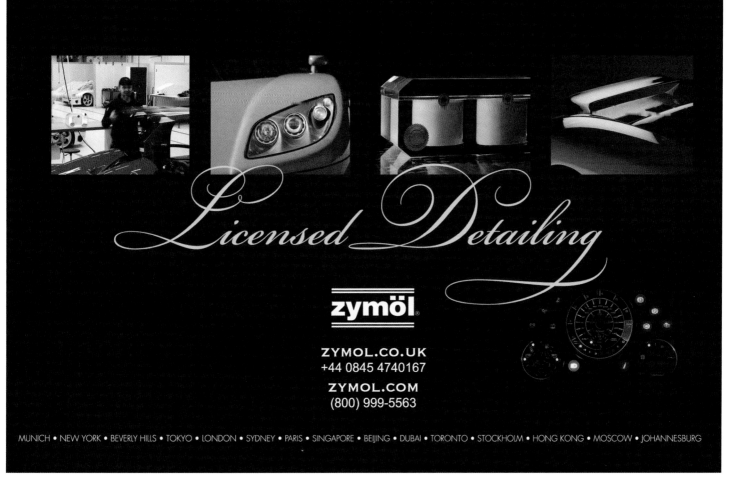

Licensed Detailing

zymöl

ZYMOL.CO.UK
+44 0845 4740167

ZYMOL.COM
(800) 999-5563

MUNICH • NEW YORK • BEVERLY HILLS • TOKYO • LONDON • SYDNEY • PARIS • SINGAPORE • BEIJING • DUBAI • TORONTO • STOCKHOLM • HONG KONG • MOSCOW • JOHANNESBURG

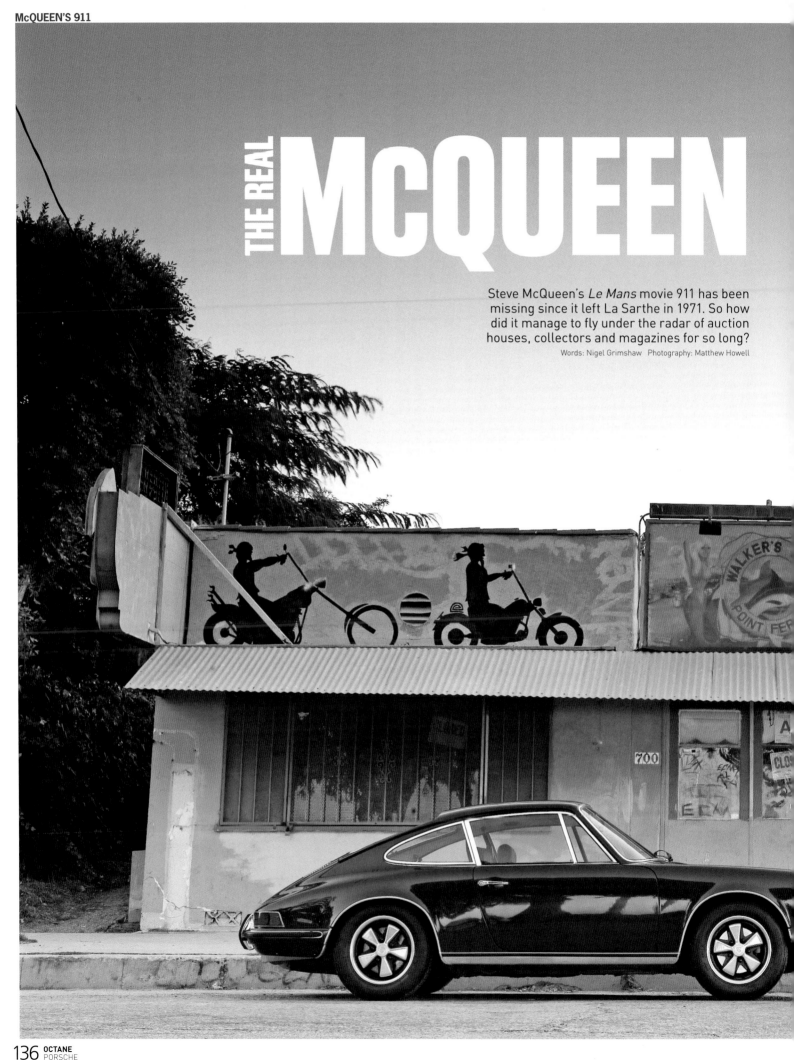

THE REAL McQUEEN

Steve McQueen's *Le Mans* movie 911 has been missing since it left La Sarthe in 1971. So how did it manage to fly under the radar of auction houses, collectors and magazines for so long?

Words: Nigel Grimshaw   Photography: Matthew Howell

The road unravels, turning first to the right and then to the left. The grey 911 bobbles as it crosses a tiny bridge. Climbing now, up a gentle rise, before dropping down into the still of a tree-lined avenue. Across a single-span bridge and into town. Easing past a pretty little restaurant with flower-filled window boxes for decoration. A long-shot as driver and Porsche enter the cathedral square. He eases to a stop and watches as a pretty woman buys flowers.

On the move again, out of town and back into the countryside. The land is flat and the road takes a hard right, the location now revealed by a sign that reads 'Le Mans'. Armco takes the place of trees at tarmac's edge. The car pulls over and the driver steps out: suede jacket, watch, bracelet. The camera circles the driver. Slowly but surely we recognise him, as the face of Steve McQueen fills the screen.

It's autumn 2007, and the scene shifts from early 1970s →

'To make his stay in France more agreeable McQueen bought a 911S, which he would use both in the movie and as personal transport'

La Sarthe to Los Angeles, California. Sitting at the wheel of the car that so famously filled the first four minutes of *Le Mans*, I see the tree-lined avenue and that beautiful woman buying flowers, but only in my mind's eye. Through the tinted glass there are burger joints instead of cathedrals, signs that read Long Beach rather than Le Mans. Check the mirrors: not a 917 or Ferrari 512 in sight. I pull Steve McQueen's 'lost' 911 out into the LA traffic.

It's early Sunday morning and there are more joggers out than cars, but the situation is no less surreal. This is STEVE McQUEEN'S car: the man who put out a *Towering Inferno*; the man who jumped barbed-wire fences as he rode to win his *Great Escape*; *Bullitt*, *Papillon* and, of course, *Le Mans*. Jesse Rodrigues, the car's third owner, sits at my side. 'Give it some more power,' he yells as we head for Highway 110.

Back in the spring of 1970, Solar Productions descended on Le Mans to start work on the film. To make his stay in France even more agreeable McQueen bought a 911S, which he would use both in the movie and as personal transport. He was so happy with his Porsche that at the end of filming he decided to keep it, once it had been sent to Stuttgart for different gear ratios to be fitted. The car was then shipped to McQueen's home in California.

The problem was, Steve already owned a 1969 911 and had gone to some expense installing a state-of-the-art stereo system. The *Le Mans* 911 was surplus to requirements and was advertised for sale in the *LA Times*. Jesse laughs as he recounts the story.

'The guy I bought the car from, the second owner, is a real 911 enthusiast. He bought a Targa S in 1969, but unfortunately the car was stolen in early 1971. He wanted to buy another S so he went to the *LA Times* and found an ad for a 911S. He called up the number and arranged to go and see the car, and guess who opened the door? Steve McQueen. The McQueen family owns the 911 "stereo" car to this day.'

McQueen's *Le Mans* 911 stayed in the hands of its second owner for the next 34 years, 20 of which it was used as a daily driver. Then, in 2005, Jesse attended an office luncheon.

'It's a once-a-month affair,' he recalls. 'And just like any other group of colleagues we talk about work and hobbies. On this particular day I mentioned I like old Porsches and one of the ladies said her husband owned one, but didn't go on to say whether it was a 911, 912 or 356. At the next luncheon she mentioned it again and I said I'd like to see it; I have four 356s so I was interested. It went no further, until one day I met her in Starbucks and she said her husband was thinking about selling the car. At no point had there been any mention of McQueen or *Le Mans*.'

In truth, Jesse was not really interested in the car. He had discovered it was a 911 but his passion is for the 356. The two of them continued to talk over a number of weeks, until finally a meeting was arranged. 'I went up to the owner's house,' remembers Jesse. 'The car was sitting, pretty much in the condition we see it today. It was in the open, in the driveway next to the garage. There were dusty cat paw marks over the hood and roof. Not being into early 911s at this point, it just looked like any number of other cars to me. We talked for a while, and then I left.'

A few weeks later Jesse returned to look at the car, this time with his wife. 'Again we stood talking in the driveway, which is when the owner told me the vehicle was Steve McQueen's 911. Obviously I know who McQueen is, but it was almost of no consequence to me. Because I have other commitments I wasn't sure I could afford the car anyway, and we hadn't even spoken about a price yet.'

Jesse and his wife headed home and nothing happened for another week. During this time Jesse talked to his automotive mentor, who has owned Porsches since 1960. Once again the significance of the first owner was sidelined as more practical matters came into focus. At this time the car had covered 116,000 miles, and concerns over engine and transmission rebuilds troubled the deal. However, on hearing about the McQueen connection, another of Jesse's contacts implored him to buy.

Encouraged and discouraged by his advisors in equal measure, →

Above, from top
McQueen pauses during intro to *Le Mans*; McQueen at wheel; Chad McQueen and Porsches at Solar Village: is one of them 'our' feature car?

Jesse decided to show his hand and told the owner he wanted to buy, but the response came as a surprise.

'The owner felt it was only right to offer the car to the McQueen family, which I totally agreed with. In hindsight, if I'd known then what I know today I would have been far more concerned.' Jesse laughs at the thought now, but in early 2005 it was a problem – and not the only one. A third party had expressed an interest, and Jesse was told whoever sealed the deal first got the car. He needed no further encouragement.

On the drive over Jesse revisited his concerns about the engine and transmission – in relation to the price asked for the car, rebuilding the motor or gearbox would be a huge issue. He had a mechanic who was willing to look over the 911, but the guy wasn't available for three days. 'I told the owner about my concerns,' recalls Jesse, 'and that my mechanic couldn't look at the car for a little while. Incredibly, the seller handed me the keys and said, "Take it."'

After three long days the mechanic was able to give the all-clear, and Jesse headed back to the owner's house. 'Until then all our conversations had been held out on the driveway, next to the car. It's better not to negotiate business like this in someone's home. When I finally walked into the house there was a poster on the wall of Steve McQueen and he's doing the "V" for victory sign. The owner looked at me and said, "Yes, that's a movie poster." I didn't know which film until he told me it was *Le Mans*. Can you believe I had never seen the movie?'

At this point the now ex-owner started bringing out file after file of documentation to go with the car. 'I really didn't know what I had,' admits Jesse. McQueen had kept every piece of correspondence, every detail of his ownership, every step of the 911's trip to the US, its registration... no part of the Porsche's life that could be documented had escaped archiving.

Little has changed on the car since it left La Sarthe. It has certainly been

repainted at some time and Jesse has restored the wheels, fitted new tyres and a fresh windscreen, which is why the stickers that can be seen in the film are not present on the car's glass today. But the McQueen-ordered air-conditioning, leather, tinted windows, muffler skirt, electric sunroof, aluminium wheel mouldings, Blaupunkt AM/FM US-band radio with manual antenna and driving lights are all present and correct.

'I've now bought the movie,' says Jesse as we drive the quiet Sunday morning Los Angeles streets in McQueen's 911. 'Some people say this is the most iconic 911. They could be right, but this is Steve's car, not mine, and that is how it should stay. The person who owns it now should be of no consequence. The funny thing is, though, I recently ran into the guy who sold me the car and he said to me, "What would you think if I gave you back the money you paid for the Porsche and the expenses you have incurred, and took the car back?" We laughed about it and I said, "I respectfully decline your offer, but will bear it in mind".'

Of course, the daily-driving days for McQueen's *Le Mans* 911 are well and truly over. While the car has spent its entire life in Los Angeles following its departure from Europe, today's Californian traffic chaos makes driving it seven days a week too risky. But every Sunday morning, before sun-up, Jesse pulls the grey 911 out of its garage and heads for the freeway and a 20-mile blast.

I glance to the right as we drive past another burger joint, Jesse still at my side. The early-morning LA roads remain mercifully quiet as the plate-glass restaurant window throws back the Porsche's reflection clear and true. My eyes rest for a moment on the surface of the glass. I see the car, myself at the wheel, a French restaurant with a flower box for decoration. Is that a cathedral too, and a pretty woman buying flowers? Finally, I notice the road sign: it's pointing east, and in my mind's eye it reads: Le Mans 5627 miles. △

'McQueen had kept every piece of correspondence, every detail of his ownership, every step of the car's trip to the US'

McQUEEN'S
MACHINES

Steve McQueen was a lifelong petrolhead who surrounded himself with an eclectic mix of cars, bikes and planes.
Here his son **Chad McQueen** introduces a selection of rare photos of the film star's collection
Research: Matt Stone

EVAN KLEIN

The photos and information in this feature are from *McQueen's Machines: The Cars and Bikes of a Hollywood Icon*, by Matt Stone with an introduction by Chad McQueen (above), ISBN 978 0 7603 2866 8, published by MBI at £16.99. Our article concentrates on Steve McQueen's road cars, but the book also covers his motorbikes, his racing, and the cars and bikes he drove and rode in his movies.

Ever since I was a kid, there were always cars and motorcycles around. Why did my dad have such great taste in cars and a passion for racing? I don't know. But he loved all things mechanical. Recall the scene in *The Sand Pebbles* when he's in the ship's engine room, talking to the motor? That wasn't acting. That was just him.

Even though he never finished high school, he was motivated to learn about engines, electronics, suspension set-ups... and anything else that made a car or a bike run or go faster. Dad was way more concerned about having the right castor and camber settings than whether his brake calipers were painted to match the car.

Cars and bikes were woven not only into our family but into dad's movies. Who could forget *Le Mans*? The first day we arrived at La Sarthe, I couldn't believe my eyes. There were four Ferrari 512s on one side of the circuit, a row of 917s on the other; Lola T70s, Porsche 911s and a strange blue race car called a Matra. I thought, 'This is going to be one bitchin' summer.'

My dad wasn't afraid of the risks involved in racing, but he was well aware of them and took it all very seriously. One day, I heard there was a crash near the White House complex, and I so hoped and prayed it wasn't my dad. About 15 minutes later, he pulled up on his Triumph and said, 'Come here. I want you to see what can happen in racing.' I remember seeing a wheel, with its wishbones still attached, sitting out in the cow pasture next to the track. For a 10-year-old kid, it was pretty mind-blowing.

Some two dozen books have been written about my dad's life, but none has put the whole picture together, until writer Matt Stone came to me with this idea. I knew it was a major part of his story that still needed to be told, and I hope you enjoy it.

'Cars and bikes were woven not only into our family, but into dad's movies'

Steve in tank

After a tough childhood that included a spell at Reform School, Steve McQueen joined the US Marine Corps when he was 17. Assigned to the tank unit, he had a go at souping up the engine in an old tank with some army buddies. 'We took it out for a timed run... and the laugh was on us; it didn't go any faster,' he recalled later.

MG TC

Following three years in the Marine Corps, Steve moved to New York to become a jobbing actor. His first transport was an Indian motorcycle combination, but in 1952 he bought his first car, an MG TC, for $750. 'I sold it after three axles broke, and the spokes kept shredding out of those wire wheels.

Porsche Speedster

Chad McQueen still owns the Porsche 1600 Speedster that his dad bought new in 1958. It was Steve's first new car, the first one he went racing in (officially), and one of only three models he felt so attached to that he bought it back in later life, from enthusiast Bruce Meyer (on right), seen here delivering it back to Steve in December 1974. In the background are Steve's Mercedes-Benz 300SEL 6.3 and his then-wife Ali MacGraw's 280SE 3.5 convertible.

Siata 208S

As Steve's career took off, he started buying more expensive sports cars. Reputedly, he owned this Siata 208S for less than a year because his TV studio thought it 'inappropriate'. In this 1958 pic, taken very soon after Steve sold it to its next owner, the newly qualified Dr Bruce Sand, it still wears its original silver paint.

→

Jaguar XKSS

Originally off-white with a red interior, this XKSS was repainted BRG with black interior after Steve bought it in 1958 – and fitted with a glovebox door by Von Dutch, to keep McQueen's shades in place during fast driving. Steve nicknamed it The Green Rat and sold it in 1967 to the Harrah Collection – then bought it back in the late '70s.

CHUCK QUEENER

Ferrari 275GTS/4

A Ferrari 275GTS/4 NART Spyder was driven by Faye Dunaway's character in *The Thomas Crown Affair*, and Steve subsequently ordered chassis 10453, the sixth of just ten cars built. Typically, the first thing he did was have it repainted and mildly customised; just a few days later it was badly damaged by a truck, and during the rebuild a small rear spoiler was added. Steve sold it in 1971.

EVAN KLEIN

Mini-Cooper

About the time that he sold the Ferrari Lusso (above right), Steve bought this Mini-Cooper S from Hollywood Sports Cars. It was originally green with a white roof but Steve had it painted a brown metallic, like the Lusso, with a beige top – 'Steve liked browns and greys and other subtle colours,' says painter Lee Brown, who took this pic – and had it fitted with wooden dash and pleated seats.

Ferrari 250GT

Famously auctioned by Christie's for $2.3 million in recent years, Steve's 250GT Lusso was his first Ferrari, bought for him by wife Neile in March 1964 (see the feature in *Octane* issue 50). Steve drove the chestnut-metallic Ferrari extensively until worn valve guides and consequent oil burning made him disillusioned, and he sold it in 1967.

Hudson Wasp

This haunting study, taken by Steve's widow Barbara Minty McQueen in 1979, captures Steve in contemplative mood as he hoses down the hardstanding outside his airport hangar. In the background is his Wasp, which had a twin-carb version of Hudson's straight-six coupled, unusually, to automatic transmission. Barbara refers to this model as Steve's 'Sunday go-to-church car', and by this time in his life he seemed to have adopted a more relaxed approach to driving.

Ford F100 pick-up

In later life Steve liked to spend time with Barbara on his ranches in California and Idaho, where he kept several ratty old pick-up trucks, including this 1957 Ford. The pick-ups may have been part of his movie-star disguise but there's no doubt he genuinely loved driving them – he kept a 1958 GMC truck in the parking garage of the Beverly Wilshire Hotel for undercover jaunts around Los Angeles.

BARBARA McQUEEN

BARBARA McQUEEN

Pitcairn PA-8

Aircraft were a late-developing passion for Steve, who obtained his private pilot's licence in July 1979, just 16 months before his death from cancer in November 1980. Among the six planes he owned was this Pitcairn PA-8 Mailwing, built in the early 1930s for the US Mail Service. His 1945 Boeing Stearman's registration no. was 3188, supposedly Steve's ID as a teenager in reform school…

Porsche 911S

The 1970 slate-grey 911 that features in the opening scenes of *Le Mans* is the identical twin to Steve's own 1969 911S, which stayed with him the rest of his life and has now passed to Chad. Steve's old car still has its original paint and just 48,000 miles on the clock; it drives superbly even though, as Chad recalls, 'My dad drove the crap out of that thing.'

Triumph

Although we've had to restrict this feature mainly to Steve's cars for reasons of space, motorbikes were also a huge part of his life. He was an enthusiastic dirt racer and this 1960s photo shows him at the peak of physical condition aboard his beloved Triumph scrambler.

McQUEEN'S OTHER CARS

STEVE IS BELIEVED to have owned about 40 cars and literally hundreds of motorbikes. In addition, he raced machines that he didn't own and, of course, he drove lots of other vehicles as part of his movie career.

To further muddy the waters, some models were purchased by Steve's production company, Solar Productions – notably the Porsche 908 Spyder that he raced in the 1970 Sebring 12 Hours in preparation for the filming of *Le Mans*.

Then there are cars that he was lent for a while – a 1963 Shelby Cobra is one, for example – and ones that he definitely drove, but about which very little is known. Several biographies mention a VW Beetle of indeterminate age, and Steve had a whole assortment of old pick-ups at his properties in Santa Paula, California, and Ketchum, Idaho. The following are vehicles that he's known to have personally owned:

1930 Cadillac V8 coupe
1931 Lincoln club sedan
1935 Chrysler Airflow
1939 Packard Super 8
c1939 Packard Super 8 convertible
1940 Packard 120 convertible
1940s WW2 Willys Jeep
c1946 MG TC
1949 Cadillac Series 62
1951 Chevrolet convertible
(ex-*The Hunter*)
1951 Hudson Hornet
1952 Hudson Wasp
1953 Allard (Chrysler hemi)
1953 Siata 208S
c1955 Chevrolet Nomad estate
1956 Austin-Healey
1957 Chevrolet Bel Air convertible
c1957 Chevrolet Corvette
1957 Ford pick-up

1957 Jaguar XK-SS
1958 Ford Fairlane convertible
1958 GMC pick-up
1958 Porsche Speedster 1600 Super
1959 Lotus XI
1962 Cooper T52 Formula Junior
c1962 Land Rover SWB
1963 Ferrari 250GT Lusso
c1964 Chevrolet Corvette Sting Ray
c1965 Jeep CJ (Chevy V8)
c1967 Ferrari 275GTS
1967 Ferrari 275GTS/4 NART Spyder
1967 Meyers Manx dune buggy
(ex-*The Thomas Crown Affair*)
1967 Mini-Cooper S
1968 Ford pick-up
1969 Porsche 911S
1972 Mercedes-Benz 300SEL 6.3
1976 Porsche 911 Turbo
1978 Rolls-Royce Corniche conv

PORSCHE 914/6

Pedigree
MONGREL

The stock 914 was underwhelming. But, as this original
914/6 GT shows, there was a great car waiting to get out

Words: Delwyn Mallett   Photography: Andy Morgan

The nine-fourteen (or nine-one-four, should you prefer) was the lovechild of two of Germany's most high-profile parents. Think hugely successful (but increasingly boring) Volkswagen inseminated with the genes of glamorous, race-winning sports car manufacturer Porsche.

The car world eagerly awaited the new arrival but between conception and birth the parents bickered and couldn't even agree on what to call their offspring. The baby was unveiled in September 1969 at the Frankfurt show, where the 'coochy-coos' from the world's press were distinctly muted.

The faint praise and sense of disappointment was best summarised by *Auto Motor und Sport* magazine, which could muster no more than the observation that 'the 914 is not exceedingly pretty, but it is functional, low and sporty'. But the 914 did come good – just look at the 914/6 GT here.

It is all too easy to forget that Porsche was once a one-horse stable. From 1948 to 1965 Porsche built the exquisite but quirky and expensive 356, which was replaced by the still-unconventional and almost →

twice-as-expensive 911. The ever-cautious Ferry Porsche was worried that they may have been pricing themselves out of business.

VW and Porsche were, of course, more than kissing cousins. Ferry Porsche's father, Professor Ferdinand Porsche, had designed the Beetle, and Ferry's creation, the 356, had evolved from it after WW2. Porsche's survival in the difficult post-war period was certainly aided by the royalties it received for every Beetle sold.

Once again an opportunity presented itself from which both companies could benefit. Porsche needed a cheaper entry-level model to boost volume, while VW was wondering not only how to replace the ageing Beetle but how to add some spice to the company image. VW was well advanced with the deeply dull 411 when boss Heinz Nordhoff and Ferry Porsche met to discuss a joint venture.

By the mid-1960s the mid-engined sports car, already well-established on the racetrack, was becoming the 'hot' choice for the road. Porsche had always been a proponent of the mid-engine layout: the very first Porsche had been a mid-engined roadster and every purpose-built racer it had made since placed the engine ahead of the rear wheels. The gorgeous 904 of 1964 could have, and probably should have, provided the styling cue for a new road car but the marketing requirements of the two partners dictated that the car should look unlike anything that had preceded it from either company. In this objective there is no doubt that they succeeded.

The 914 project progressed with high hopes but then the unexpected happened, with dire consequences for Porsche. In April 1968 Heinz Nordhoff died from a heart attack. Nordhoff and Ferry Porsche, old-school car men both, had done business on a verbal agreement and a handshake. Nordhoff's replacement, Karl Lotz, recruited from outside the auto-world, was neither committed to nor convinced of the value of the 914 and applied a completely different costing to the project, scuppering Porsche's calculations. The 914

bodyshells, and in VW's case the complete car, were produced in Osnabrück by Karmann and Lotz's pricing policy meant that Porsche was forced to pay more for a 914 body than it was paying for its much more complicated 911 bodies – supplied by the same company! The 'cheap' Porsche was no longer looking so cheap.

The raison d'être for the 914 was further confused by a VW decision to name all US-bound cars, whether four- or six-cylinder, as Porsches, and sell them through a new Porsche-Audi network, while in Europe they would be called VW-Porsche – but none of the cars would have a Porsche badge on the nose! US cars would have Porsche script on the engine grille but European cars would not – confusing, huh?

Many US customers were disappointed by their underpowered, four-cylinder 'Porsches', though what the 914 lacked in go it made up for with handling, which met with almost universal praise.

Mechanically the new 914 was a mixture of Porsche 911 and VW 411. The front suspension and rack-and-pinion steering were pure 911 but the mid-mounted engine required not only a lengthened wheelbase but a new rear suspension utilising, for the first time in a road-going Porsche, box-section trailing arms and coil-over-shocks.

Engines were the fuel-injected 80bhp, 1.7-litre 411 unit in the 914 and, in keeping with its 'entry level' positioning, the 914/6 used the least expensive 110bhp Porsche 911T 2.0-litre engine running on Webers. The gearbox in both cars was the five-speed Porsche 911 transaxle turned through 180 degrees, with the crownwheel swapped side-to-side to give the correct number of forward speeds.

It was obvious that the 914/6 chassis could handle a lot more power and

Below
Extended arches were for function, not form, but lend an air of aggression to the 914's slimline shape.

'The 914/6 changes direction with kart-like alacrity, and barely a hint of roll'

FBY 541H

1970 PORSCHE 914/6 GT

ENGINE
Mid-mounted 1991cc flat-six, magnesium crankcase, SOHC per bank, twin-plug cylinder heads, dry sump, two triple-throat Weber carburettors

POWER
210-220bhp @ 8000rpm

TORQUE
145lb ft @ 6000rpm

TRANSMISSION
Five-speed transaxle, limited-slip differential, external oil pump, rear-wheel-drive

SUSPENSION
Front: torsion bar and struts. Rear: box-section trailing arms and coil-over-shock absorbers. Anti-roll bars front and rear

BRAKES
Discs all-round

PERFORMANCE
0-60mph 6sec (est). Top speed c150mph (depending on gearing)

the first two uprated cars were real hot rods. Built for Ferry Porsche's 60th birthday and chief engineer Ferdinand Piech's personal use, the two cars were fitted with the 3.0-litre flat-eight racing engine from the 908. Ferry's car had a detuned 'street' version with 260bhp, while Piech's was a 300bhp road-rocket. The 914/8 demonstrated that a hot 914/6 would be a potent machine.

For racing in the Group 3 GT category the FIA permitted wheelarches to be extended by 5cm and Porsche took full advantage of this, welding boxy steel arches into the bodywork, front and rear, covering 6 or 7in Fuchs wheels. Aesthetic considerations were almost certainly not a priority with this modification but it immediately turned the rather wimpish whippet of a 914 into an aggressive-looking pitbull of a motor. At last there was a seriously sexy 914/6 – the GT.

A weak point of the 914 chassis was around the rear swing-arm pick-up points, which flexed under hard cornering. The Zuffenhausen race-shop fixed this by welding in reinforcement plates from the jacking-points to the rear wheelarches. Anti-roll bars, deemed unnecessary for the road cars, were grafted on, the rear bar actually located inside the luggage compartment! The front compartment was almost filled by a long-range fuel tank and the shrouding for the nose-mounted oil-cooler.

The extra weight of all this added steel was offset by Porsche's meticulous attention to weight-saving in other areas. Glassfibre was used for the front and rear bumpers as well as the bonnet and boot covers, flexing in the latter being minimised by bonding in balsa-wood strips!

The pop-up headlamp motors and mechanisms were deleted (not, however, on rally cars) and interior trim much simplified. Overall the weight-saving resulted in a car hitting the scales at 897kg, 90kg less than the street

Below
Original brochures herald the 914's racing heritage, both in its own right and as stablemate to the 917.

version. One curious option was a roll-up rear window blind for night racing: wonder how many of those still exist?

For 1970 the 911 series moved up in capacity with the introduction of the 2.2-litre engine, and the 914/6 was homologated as Porsche's weapon in the up-to-2.0-litre category.

Power was supplied by the 901/20 engine, the well-tried racing version of the 911 engine, as fitted to the Carrera 6 sports racer. A higher compression ratio, twin-plug heads, bigger valves, counterweighted crank and lightened valvegear resulted in a guaranteed 210bhp, and often more.

The racing record of the 914/6 GT got off to a promising start, with the four cars entered in the Nürburgring 1000km race finishing second to fifth in class – behind a 911. But better was to come. A solitary 914/6 GT entered in the 1970 Le Mans 24 Hours, running under the banner of long-time French importer Sonauto, finished a stunning sixth overall – ahead of all of the 911s and overall winner of the GT category. This, incidentally, was the race that saw Porsche's first overall Le Mans victory, with the 917, and formed the background to Steve McQueen's famous film.

Later in the year a factory team of three cars headed the field at the Marathon de la Route, a gruelling 86-hour blast around the full Nürburgring circuit. The 914/6 GT had become the 2.0-litre GT of choice, being virtually unbeatable on the track.

The Porsche racing department eventually built 12 cars for the factory's own use and a further 47 cars under the M471 option, which gave customers the possibility of ordering a GT to their own specification – and road legal if required.

One of the first was for wealthy Swiss businessman and enthusiastic privateer →

Above and right
Lightweight rear deck
lid is authentically
rippled. Note quick
filler instead of usual
filler inside front boot.

'When Simon found the car it had covered a mere 12,000km – all of them on the track'

Ernst Seiler, who ordered chassis 914 043 0181, our featured car. Seiler, often using his soubriquet 'Hunter', campaigned a 911T/R through the '68 and '69 seasons before transferring to his freshly delivered 914/6 GT in 1970, racing under the banner of Ski Hart Racing and then switching to Squadra Tartaruga ('Team Turtle') for 1972.

Octane caught up with this gorgeous 914/6 GT, now owned by Simon Bowery, at a Silverstone test day, a shakedown in anticipation of campaigning the car the following year. Beautifully repainted by Porsche specialist Bruce Cooper's Southend-based Sportwagen, the car gleamed on one of the few mercifully dry days of early November. Simon was quick to point out that the car is not a restoration in the conventional sense but rather a refurbishment and reassembly.

When in 2006 Simon found the car in Switzerland, where it had languished with a damaged engine since 1974, it had covered a mere 12,000km – all of them on the track – and was complete, bodily sound but shabby. Sportwagen stripped the body back to bare metal before repainting it in the original shade of *Zitronengelb*. Meanwhile the engine and gearbox were sent to German specialist Karl Hloch for a careful rebuild. The freshly painted body was reassembled by Steve Winter at his North London independent Porsche specialist Jaz Porsche before being trailered to Karl Hloch's premises in Schorndorf to have the whirly bits refitted.

The first impression of the car is how tiny it is. The 914 series was four inches lower than a contemporary 911 and the smaller frontal area resulted, despite its boxy look, in a lower drag coefficient than the 911's. The spartan cabin, however, is extremely roomy, with space in every direction except directly behind, as the reassuringly snug bucket seat is right up against the rear bulkhead and vertical screen. The pedals, in familiar 911 fashion, are offset slightly towards the centre of the car.

From cold the engine needs a bit of pumping and churning before it catches but once warm all that's required is a turn of the key and the motor roars into life – and what a roar! The bark of a barely silenced Porsche flat-six is sensational. A staccato, crackling, ripping rasp that sets the nerves tingling. Despite the exotic machinery testing that day, heads turned in our direction every time the Porsche fired up.

Porsche UK kindly allowed us to use its Experience Centre track for photography before letting me loose unencumbered by a camera car. By chance, former ace Porsche pilot Richard Attwood was attending a Porsche drivers' day and I asked him for any recollections he might have of the 914/6 in period. He recalled driving a factory GT down to the Targa Florio in 1970 to use in practice but after discussions with fellow factory drivers they concluded that it didn't offer them any great advantage over the tried and tested 911. He did, however, feel that the 914/6 was easier to drive near the limit for a driver of average talent, whereas the 911 required a special level of skill to extract the maximum from it. That was good news, then.

Porsche's tight little sprint track is designed to test agility rather than all-out speed and comprises a twisting, uphill section leading into a blind right-hander at the crest, followed by a similar series of looping downhill curves, some slightly off-camber, ending in a sharp right-hander. A wiggle-woggle of abrupt transitions that in an early 911 can easily catch out the unwary.

The flat-six spins effortlessly through the revs and really takes off at 6000rpm and beyond to the 8000rpm redline, effortlessly thrusting the car uphill. The only parts of a 914/6 visible beyond the scuttle are the tips of the vertical sidelights in their razor-thin wings, and they provide perfect sights with which to aim the car, which simply changes direction with kart-like alacrity, barely a hint of roll, and none of that 911 feeling of sitting at the pivot-point of a pendulum.

Exiting bends under power, early 911s squatted, lifting the inside front wheel – sometimes well clear of the tarmac – but the 914/6 displayed none of those antics. A hefty boot of power in an attempt to break traction resulted in nothing more than an increase in lateral *g* and a slight sideways drift – helped no doubt by the wider, but original to the car, eight-inch wide magnesium (crack-tested) Minilites at the rear. Admittedly I was not in a 150mph bend but both Simon and Steve confirmed that on the much faster Silverstone track the handling remains quite neutral and predictable at the limit.

In common with all mid-engined cars the level of grip flatters to deceive – when ultimately it goes, it goes so rapidly that a spin is almost inevitable. They did, however, tend to spin in their own length, unlike a 911 or 356, which, when the laws of physics were exceeded, either left the scene backwards at a tangent or got into a sphincter-dilating tank-slapper.

The weak spot in the 914/6's mechanical chain is the gearchange. Gone is the butter-smooth gear-swapping of the 911, to be replaced by

Below
Engine is in the back, spare wheel is in the front, and the interior is a curious mix of standard and rally.

'Richard Attwood felt that the 914/6 was easier to drive near the limit than the 911'

a worryingly imprecise, notchy adventure into the unknown. The linkage is long and convoluted and Steve is working on ways to make it more precise but I must confess that on my brief acquaintance with the car I was never entirely confident that I was about to let the clutch out in the right gear.

A few times I let the revs drop and provoked considerable coughing and spitting from the Webers, requiring a bit of desperate rev-raising downchanging before urge was restored. Keep the revs where they should be and the 914/6 is a fabulously rewarding ride, going exactly where you aim it and hanging on like a leech having lunch.

The 914/6 might have been successful on the track but it wasn't a success in the showroom. Despite the 914 being Germany's biggest-selling sports car in 1970 and '71, Porsche sold only 3332 sixes before ceasing production in 1971. The 914, much improved, was finally dropped in 1975. It would take almost 20 years before the public could once again enjoy the thrills of a mid-engined Porsche, with the introduction of the Boxster.

Thanks to the Porsche Experience Centre, www.porsche.com/silverstone.

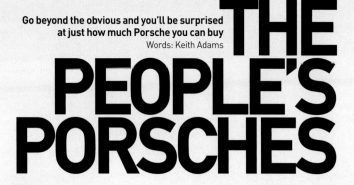

Go beyond the obvious and you'll be surprised
at just how much Porsche you can buy
Words: Keith Adams

THE PEOPLE'S PORSCHES

The 911 Turbo might be fantastic value for money, packing 260-300bhp for a very reasonable outlay, but if you cast your net somewhat wider, the sinful pleasures of Stuttgart's fastest can be had for even less than you'd imagine. The world of balanced handling and V8 grunt is closer than you think – and you don't even have to exclusively alter your Porsche mindset from trad 911 to a front-mounted water-cooled engine to bag a bargain. Happy hunting starts here.

PRICE
£800-£5500

Porsche 924 Turbo

FOR THOSE with long enough memories to remember the aftermath of the 1973-'74 energy crisis, the spine-chilling notion of the death of the supercar was an all-too-believable reality. The 924 was supposed to be an insurance against the ensuing world recession – it was designed to be inexpensive to buy and run, but great fun to drive.

Being front-engined, water-cooled and sporting a rear-mounted transaxle, it was something of a culture shock for Porsche fans – especially as it relied so heavily on the Volkswagen Group parts bin. But it was exactly right for the time, even if that time didn't actually last very long.

Dynamically, the 924 was spot-on. Chassis balance was excellent, and it was quick enough to worry owners of 911Ts. But as sweet as the 924 was, Porsche knew it needed to go faster.

The obvious answer was to turbocharge it – the 911 had already been transformed into a supercar thanks to the addition of a KKK blower, and Porsche decided to repeat the process on its entry-level car, under the codename Type 931/932.

> **'It gives you the bragging rights to say you own a Porsche Turbo'**

The turbocharger was set-up to deliver 12psi boost, and the end result was a power output of 170bhp along with 175lb ft of torque. That might sound unimpressive today, but 87.5bhp per litre was from the top drawer in 1978.

The 924 Turbo also looked special thanks to the addition of a rubber rear spoiler framing the curved glass hatchback, and cross-spoke alloys. You could even order yours with two-tone paint for a more striking look.

It had its fair share of problems, though – under-bonnet heat build-up and turbo oil-cooling issues were a bugbear on the earliest cars. In 1981 a raft of changes was introduced to cool the 924 Turbo, but by that time the 944 was about to hit the market –

a sure sign that the popular model's evolution was about to take another turn.

Like all early turbos, the 924 Turbo is a flawed diamond. Throttle response isn't especially lively, and there's a distinct off-boost lethargy that takes time to acclimatise to. However, when that KKK 'charger has spooled up, it's an exciting car to drive that's easily able to keep pace with a 911SC. 0-60mph comes up in 6.8 seconds, and top speed is north of 140mph – quite an improvement over the original car's 9.1sec and 125mph.

But given that prices range from £800 for a condition three car to over £5000 for the best of the best, these flaws are entirely forgivable, especially when it gives you the bragging rights to say you own a Porsche Turbo. It's fragile compared with a 911, so check for signs of cooked electrics, body corrosion and smoke from a worn-out turbo. It's also rare, now that the process of natural selection has sent inappropriately maintained examples to the crusher, so be prepared for a long search for the right car.

Porsche 928

PRICE
£3000–£18,000

DURING THE EARLY 1970S, Porsche management was becoming increasingly animated about life after the 911, as well as establishing a new direction for the marque. The assumption was that the rear-engined car had no future in a safety- and emissions-conscious world.

Managing director Ernst Fuhrmann cooked up the two-model strategy that led to the introduction of the 924 – and a new range-topping grand tourer, codenamed Type 928. Although the smaller car came first, product planners originally favoured an early launch for the larger car. But then the energy crisis intervened, forcing a reversal.

For the 928, the air-cooled flat-six was smartly dropped; upcoming noise regulations favoured water-cooled engines, and, befitting its grand touring ambitions, Porsche plumped for an all-aluminium V8. Originally the engine was designed as a 5.0-litre, but was scaled down to 4.5 litres during development. It was understressed, light and efficient, and the power reined in to 240bhp.

The lightweight 246kg engine and the rear transaxle resulted in near 50:50 weight distribution. Another clever innovation was the Weissach axle at the rear, which was a highly developed semi-trailing arm set-up that passively changed its alignment depending on chassis loading. Sweet and well-balanced handling was the end result.

The impact made by the 928's organic styling when it emerged in 1977 may have been lessened by the arrival of the 924, but that didn't stop it receiving a rapturous welcome from motoring journalists. Many saw it as the ethical face of the supercar of the future – fine handling and efficient performance combined. It became the second V8-powered car in succession (after the Rover SD1) to win the title of European Car of The Year.

However, the Euro gong represented the zenith of the 928's career. Sales never quite took off as Porsche had expected, failing to top 5000 units per year throughout its life. Buyers remained faithful to the immortal 911, which had been effectively updated throughout the 1970s.

The 928 also confused many potential buyers – it wasn't quick or agile enough to be considered a true sports car, and it was too harsh and cramped for the GT brigade.

It also found itself coming on stream as the second energy crisis of 1979 took hold. Who wanted to buy a 14mpg V8 Porsche (it wasn't *that* efficient, after all) with the cost of fuel spiralling uncontrollably? The company refused to give up on the concept, deciding that it needed to be turned into a sports car. A 300bhp S version arrived in 1979 and was followed by increasingly powerful derivatives, culminating in the 330bhp GT.

Fast-forward 30-odd years and the original 928 makes a great deal of sense. Values remain depressed compared with the immortal 911 and, despite one or two issues concerning engine and cooling, a usable 928 (in any of its incarnations) could be yours for well under £5000. If you want the absolute best, you'll still have enough change from £20,000 to go on a very nice holiday.

On the road, you get punchy performance, and the newer the model you go for, the more top-end bite you can enjoy. It's a much larger car than the 911, and that means it's a lot less wieldy – but its handling is more predictable, less of an adventure. So for those of you who don't enjoy sweaty-palmed moments, the 928 could be just your thing. →

'If you don't enjoy sweaty-palmed moments, the 928 could be just your thing'

Porsche 968

PRICE
£6000-£15,000

DESPITE the continued evolution of the four-cylinder 924/944 throughout the 1980s, it was the 911 that continued to be the buyers' favourite. Sales of the 944, in particular, remained slow – and, following the demise of the 924S in 1988, Porsche's principal income was generated by its oldest car. That's an interesting situation when you consider that the car wasn't expected to see out the 1970s.

Although the 924 dated back to 1975 and the 944 was launched in 1981, continuous development had allowed the four-cylinder car to keep ahead of upstart newcomers such as the Mazda RX7 and Toyota Supra. Progressive increases in engine capacity, the addition of a turbocharger, and then the fitment of a 16-valve cylinder head kept performance keen. And the roadholding improved as tyre sizes grew. All that really stood between the 944 and enduring success was a lack of cylinders.

When the recession of the early 1990s hit, 911 sales fell off a cliff and Porsche found itself with a real problem. The 944 looked old hat, and plans for its replacement had long since been dropped – sales were disappointing even during the boom-time '80s, but the 911 had been a major money-

spinner and Porsche was happy just to reel in the cash. But there was a lack of Deutschmarks in the kitty to start afresh exactly when Porsche needed an exciting entrée to encourage financially straitened customers into the fold.

And it was that lack of cash, and a desperate need to keep the bottom of the range fresh, that led to the appearance of the 968 in 1992. Despite its 928-esque front end, smoothed-out flanks and featureless derrière, few people were fooled into believing it was anything other than a major revision of the existing 944. But Porsche concluded that any car with 82% new body panels deserved a new moniker, rather than the expected 944 S3 tag.

The 'big banger' in-line four from the 944 S2 was retained (after abandoning the idea of buying in a six-cylinder engine from Volvo), but the addition of variable valve timing and a host of other upgrades upped the power output to 240bhp from three litres. A new six-speed manual gearbox was also introduced, as well as the Tiptronic automatic, and that effectively gave the 968 a reasonable armoury with which to fight upstart rivals such as BMW's E36 M3.

The driving experience was as expected – balanced, sweet, torquey and responsive. And just like the 944 before it, the 968 became the dynamic benchmark by which all rivals were judged. However, success remained elusive, most likely because it still looked and sounded like a 944, and that prompted Porsche into introducing a stripped-out and lightened Clubsport version. In doing so, a trackday legend was born.

Today, the 968 sits in that uneasy no-man's land somewhere between secondhand and classic; and that makes it a conspicuous bargain for those content to take the thinking man's option. You can pick up a standard coupé from around £6000, and for those looking for more thrills the Clubsport still commands a premium (you pay more for less, naturally), with nice ones regularly fetching more than £15,000 on specialists' forecourts. For that money, you're buying a car with genuine pace – 0-60mph in 5.9 seconds and 157mph.

By way of comparison, that's very nearly as quick as a 930 Turbo in a straight line – and a whole lot more capable in the bends. Not bad for a Porsche that potentially costs less than half as much.

'The 968 sits in that uneasy no-man's land somewhere between secondhand and classic; and that makes it a conspicuous bargain'

Porsche 911 Carrera 1974

RALPH NADER has a lot to answer for – his book *Unsafe at Any Speed* was the catalyst that helped coerce the US Government into introducing a whole raft of passive safety regulations. Good for driver and passenger life expectancy; bad for taste and style. By the mid-1970s, impact bumpers had become a reality for all producers selling cars in the USA, and it saw all manner of sports cars being defaced.

Porsche's solution was more elegant than what was done to contemporary cars such as the Fiat X1/9 and Jaguar XJ-S, but the 911's clean styling still suffered. However, 1974's changes extended further – additional equipment and safety features added weight.

The early 1970s were a time of major upheaval for the 911. In the background, product planners may have dreamt of a water-cooled future, but customers still couldn't get enough of the rear-engined car, and continued buying it in significant numbers. Development of the original car continued as Porsche worked to satisfy the demands of equipment-hungry customers.

The original 2.7RS – unless in Touring spec – was the antithesis of this industry-wide move towards more equipment. It was exceptionally light (900kg), and an absolute joy to drive as a result. Today it remains the ultimate focused 911, and its sky-high values reflect this. Without trying very hard at all, you can end up paying £150,000 for a well-sorted roadgoing RS Carrera.

When the '74 revisions were ushered in, the 2.7 Carrera gained its impact bumpers, put on about 100lb in weight, and the commonly held belief is that it lost some of its hard-edged driving appeal as a result.

Does its apparent middle-aged spread justify a market value of around 30% of that of the original *RennSport* car? With the same 210bhp at its disposal, your £45,000 1974 car is still a very quick thing indeed – and, just like the original, it's light, and features bold side graphics and Fuchs alloy wheels. It was also availiable with the iconic ducktail as an optional extra – unless sold in Germany. Unlike the 1973 Carrera RS, the '74 German-market cars weren't allowed to run the ducktail because the authorities considered it dangerous to pedestrians.

On the road, the differences between the two cars are only apparent if you're a 911 expert. The newer Carrera is still an abundantly joyful car to drive, featuring the same wailing flat-six, pin-sharp steering response – and hair-trigger oversteer in the hands of clumsy drivers.

It might be a tad softer, and a smidgeon slower, but the question it places squarely on your lips is – does that make the later car so much less capable, as the relative values would have you believe? Of course not.

And for us, that makes the '74 car the thinking man's Carrera, and something of a bargain (unless you're tempted to compare it with a 930 Turbo, of course).

Grab one before the price gap between 1973 and '74 Carreras closes up.

'The commonly held belief is that the Carrera lost some of its driving appeal'

PRICE
£40,000-£50,000

Porsche 911SC

PRICE
£6000-£12,000

FOR LATE 1977 the Porsche 911's evolution took a logical turn. Previously the domain of the Carrera 3, the expanded 3.0-litre flat-six was standardised, and a single model designation, SC, was used for all normally aspirated 911s.

The 911SC produced 180bhp, leaving those after more performance a simple choice – buy the Turbo. The revised engine was a development of the Carrera's and incorporated a new crankshaft, and larger main- and big-end bearings.

The toughened bottom end was under-stressed in the SC, promising excellent long-term reliability. The SC's arrival also marked the standardisation of a five-speed gearbox, as well as a more comfort-oriented interior (formerly optional items such as electric windows and air conditioning were made standard). Externally, the impact bumpers, deletion of exterior chrome and body-coloured

'Despite being an excellent all-round package, the SC is a 911 wallflower'

mirrors gave the 911SC a much less classical look that was in tune with the times.

For 1981 the power output was upped to 204bhp, and in doing so became the optimal sleeper 911. It might have sold through the depths of a recession, but the uprated SC hit the sweet spot – and it survived the downturn unscathed. It also proved popular enough to encourage a management turnaround on the 911.

Ernst Fuhrmann – a supporter of the 924/928 – was replaced at the head of the company by German-American Peter Schutz, and the new man immediately ploughed development funds into the 911. The plan bore fruit: first with the arrival of the convertible and then, ultimately, the 3.2-litre Carrera. Despite being an excellent all-round package, the SC remains a 911 wallflower – and values are a fraction of those of similarly performing, or slower, slim-bumper cars. In fact, with prices starting at well under £10,000 (and £14,000 being the absolute top-line), there's an awful lot to recommend it, especially if you go for one of the later 210bhp cars (146mph, 0-60mph in 6.5 seconds) that will stimulate your synapses just like any other 911.

Again, just like the '74 Carrera, our advice is to buy before the rest of the world catches on. △

HANS MEZGER

As the father of the 911 engine, creator of the all-conquering 917
and, later, the Formula 1 TAG turbo, Hans Mezger was
responsible for some of the fastest cars ever made

Words: Peter Morgan   Photographs: Porsche

There was a unique event at a very snowy Weissach back in January. The private reception in Porsche's motor sport department was marked by the appearance of nearly all the Porsche management board and a *Who's Who* of Porsche *Rennsport* over the past 60 years. In the complex and sometimes impersonal world of Porsche today, they had come together with fond affection to toast Hans Mezger, who celebrated his 80th birthday last November. CEO Michael Macht described the value of Mezger's 37-year contribution to Porsche as incalculable. Few would disagree.

Born and bred in the Stuttgart area, this unassuming engineer devoted his career to Porsche, combining a relentless work ethic with a gift for mathematics and mechanical engineering and a passion for car design.

He joined Porsche after university in 1956, immediately making a contribution to the increasing competitiveness of the four-cam 'Fuhrmann' engine by producing a mathematical model for the engine's complex camshaft timing. In 1960 he was drafted into the Formula 1 project and, learning the essentials of high-speed combustion chamber design, was instrumental in improving the competitiveness of the Type 753 flat-eight.

Mezger fitted straight into the 'can do' environment so carefully developed by Ferry Porsche. He recalls it as a way of working that he enjoyed very much.

'I don't remember when I first met Ferry and it took me some time to get an idea of what sort of man he was. I found him a quiet, very modest person, but it was always very good if you could talk with him. He always left a very good impression with you. He was quite different to what you would expect from a manager today and he became a perfect model for me.'

By the spring of 1963, Mezger had also found a kindred spirit with another new engineering graduate who had joined Porsche.

'Ferdinand Piëch came to us in the spring of 1963. We began working together right away and I must say I liked working with him. After all, he was also the nephew of Ferry Porsche! We were both very ambitious and wanted to prove ourselves on the new six-cylinder. I was about 33, but he was about six or seven years younger.

'It was my responsibility to redesign the core 901 engine. I did the general layout for the engine including the seven-bearing crankshaft, the first layout for the camshaft chain drive using hydraulic tensioners, the big change to the [dry sump] oil system and, most importantly, the new combustion chamber using larger intake and exhaust valves.'

Today, designing, developing and testing a new production engine would involve hundreds of engineers. But in the 1960s, it wasn't like that at Porsche.

Above
Colourful Porsche
race team at
Daytona, 1968,
with 907. Mezger is
fourth from right.

→

'Critics said "OK, Porsche was good in long-distance racing but F1 is different". But we developed the lightest, most efficient F1 engine'

Above from top

Hans Mezger with Porsche ambassador 'Huschke' von Hanstein, the racing baron; Porsche's 1970 Le Mans-winning 917; 1984 German Grand Prix; working at the drawing board in 1968.

'There were five or six engineers working on design, development and testing of the engine and there was another who was responsible for all the electrical parts. We were a small group and there were a hundred thousand things that needed to be done for a production engine!'

When Piëch became Porsche's technical head in 1965, Mezger was put in charge of the newly formed race design department, with responsibility for the complete race cars. The years from 1965 to 1973 were a blur of successive new engine and chassis designs and in all of them Mezger played a direct role as his fledgling department expanded their ideas and experience almost exponentially.

Porsche's engineers became the masters of tubular spaceframe chassis design, extending their knowledge with the 906, 910, 907, 908, 909 and finally the definitive racing Porsche – the 917. The incentive – the big prize that seemed always to be just out of their reach in the late 1960s – was to win Le Mans. And, fuelled by Piëch's relentless determination, they eventually found the winning formula.

'The 917 was an evolution of what we had been doing before. The engine evolved from the four-cam six- and eight-cylinder engines with a new, central output drive crankshaft design and low-pressure lubrication system. The chassis evolved from the 907 and 908 coupés. It was just the next step for the chassis, with more strength and wider wheels and so on.

'After the experience with the Ford GT40 in 1968, we believed that the 908 might not be capable of winning Le Mans. In 1969 it proved to be an even closer finish, but it showed that the 908 still wasn't enough.

'The 917 was the full-time project for the design team through late 1968. We had a schedule that the 12-cylinder engine would be on the dyno by December. We had to meet this time – and we did – because we knew that we had to achieve homologation by April. It took us nine months to complete the layout, finish the detail design, procurement and the first engine build. It was very tough!

'In 1969, the 917 long-tail wasn't easy to drive, but Vic Elford would have won at Le Mans if the gearbox housing hadn't cracked. He had a very big lead when that happened. It was because we hadn't had any time to do our usual endurance testing beforehand. We had to present the 25 cars to the FIA at the end of April and we finally received the homologation papers on 1 May. Six weeks later we had to go to the most severe race of all. It was a great pity because Elford would have won, even with the not-ideal downforce.'

That 'not ideal' downforce problem was overcome by the end of 1969, with aerodynamic changes developed in conjunction with JW Automotive. In 1970, the prize that Porsche had coveted for so long was claimed when Hans Herrmann and Richard Attwood won Le Mans. Another victory followed in 1971 before the 5-litre sports cars were banned from endurance racing. But by then Mezger had already turned his attentions to CanAm and the possibilities of turbocharging the 917's flat-12.

'It was a big decision to develop the turbocharger, because even though we had

Left and right
Jo Siffert debriefs the team, Le Mans 1971 – Mezger in black jacket, race engineer Peter Falk in light-coloured coat; Mezger with 'his' engines at the Porsche museum.

seen big power figures on the dyno, there were many problems to be solved concerning throttle response and so on. We knew that if we were going to turbocharge the engine we were going to have to do it very differently.'

Mezger's studies showed that for a road racing engine they didn't need all the exhaust gases to go through the turbo. Working with Valentin Schaeffer, a Porsche race technician, they went through a long list of experiments and testing that eventually delivered two back-to-back CanAm Championships in 1972 and 1973. In developing turbocharging for a road racer, Mezger and his team gave Porsche a technology leadership that they hold to this day.

Turbocharging opened new doors for Porsche with its production models and in endurance racing. And in the early 1980s, the Formula 1 regulations also tilted in favour of forced-induction engines. McLaren's Ron Dennis was not slow to appreciate what Porsche – and Mezger – might be able to contribute. Dennis agreed to finance a detailed design study into a new 1.5-litre twin-turbo V6, while he sought further backing for the full development. At Porsche, Mezger was put in charge; there was an obvious chemistry between the two men.

'From the beginning I had a very good impression of Ron Dennis. I had heard that many people didn't get on with him, but I found him 100% reliable. Even if we didn't write something down, if we agreed to do something, you could rely on him to do it. I would compare him to Ferdinand Piëch in the way he always wanted everything perfect. They were very similar.

'Ron knew everything about Formula 1 and John [Barnard – then McLaren's lead engineer] completely understood the requirements for the car. I remember that when we said we were becoming involved in F1 with McLaren, the critics said, "OK, Porsche was good in long-distance racing but F1 is completely different". But after that we developed the lightest, most compact, most efficient engine. In 1984 it was the most powerful and it increased every year to 1987.'

Meanwhile, Dennis had convinced Mansour Ojjeh of the benefits of becoming involved with McLaren and the new engine. The TAG turbo (named after Ojjeh's Techniques d'Avant Garde business) helped McLaren to three consecutive Drivers' World Championships (Niki Lauda and Alain Prost) and two Constructors' titles.

'F1 was a very different experience for me after working with sports cars. When I meet some of the older guys who were with McLaren in those days, they also say it is very different today. I used to meet Jo Ramirez at Hockenheim every year when he was still with McLaren. He retired a few years ago. But he would always say how much more fun it was in those days. There was much more time to talk together and to celebrate when we won.

'I have to say that while the parties after the Formula 1 races were good, we had some *very* good parties at Porsche after some of the long-distance wins, particularly after a Le Mans win. There, we always went back to the same place in Teloché – and that was after usually 48 hours away from a bed or any proper rest – and if we had won everybody was very happy and some

wine flowed. The mechanics would be very tired and often they would fall asleep!'

The TAG turbo engine took 25 grand prix victories and remains one of the most successful engines in F1 history. The 917 has been hailed by many as the greatest racing car of all time and the flat-six engine of the 911 is arguably the most enduring sports car engine of all time. Without Hans Mezger, none would have existed. △

Time with...
IN ASSOCIATION WITH
Chopard

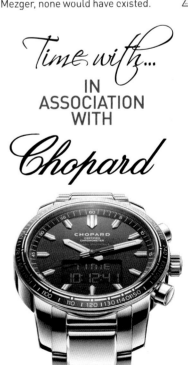

Although it's been said many times before, I have to say it again: Derek Bell is a really nice bloke. I first met him at the Nürburgring 1000km in the mid-1970s when I was a pit lane groupie, blagging my way in by festooning myself with a necklace of Nikons and Leicas and waving a piece of bogus paperwork (a sort of *Great Escape* in reverse).

Derek was one of my heroes back then – still is, in fact – and I was quite flattered when he struck up a conversation with someone whom he spotted as a fellow Brit. The race was underway but Bell, waiting for his turn in the car and with his race suit peeled back, was sunbathing. He might actually not have been as relaxed as he looked, but he certainly gave the impression that thundering around the tortuous and dangerous 14-mile 'old' Nürburgring circuit was not going to be much more taxing than any other Sunday drive.

Flash forward 30-odd years and I have arranged another meeting with Derek Bell MBE – still in the sun and in the company of fast cars, but this time in the calmer surroundings of the luxury auto dealership that Derek co-owns in Naples, Florida. Impressively for a

man now nearing 70, Bell looks as lean and fit as he did at the peak of his racing. Yes, the famous laughter lines have etched a little deeper into his face, but the Florida sun and orange juice have obviously been kind to him.

Much of Derek's racing was done in America (one source – not Bell, as he hasn't kept count – claims that 157 of his 350-plus events were in the States). This was not only when he was at his peak but also when, in his own words, he was 'struggling to stay in the game'. It was also later when, having decisively 'stayed in', he raced in IMSA, IROC and, for three years, a 4WD Audi S4 in the televised Speedvision GT Series.

'When I was a teenager my parents used to say, "C'mon, you ought to take a few years out and go overland to Australia and see your aunt Edith, or something,"' he recalls. 'I remember saying, "I'm going there one day, but as a racing driver," and them responding with, "What makes you think that? You're not even a driver!" But I just knew I would. My passion was motor racing and I wanted to compete around the world.'

Derek's first race in America was in 1968 at the beautifully situated Watkins Glen in upstate New York. →

Above
Derek reflects on glories past and present from his luxury car dealership in Naples, Florida.

Time with...
DEREK BELL

The straight-talking driver – one of Britain's
truly great racers – reminisces about the
ups and downs of his career, as well
as his long-standing friendships with
Steve McQueen and Stirling Moss

Words: Delwyn Mallett
Photographs: Delwyn Mallett and Getty Images

To this day he still has vivid memories of – of all things – the smell of his motel! He says that the tang of cedar wood simply left an indelible and powerful impression on him.

Here he was, a few weeks short of his 27th birthday, on the grid in his second outing in a Formula 1 Ferrari. He was replacing Jacky Ickx, who had broken his leg in the Canadian GP, and it was a big step from the Lotus Seven with which he had started racing only four years earlier.

'The atmosphere at Watkins Glen was fantastic,' recalls Derek, who was made a Grand Marshal at the circuit a few years ago. 'It was a hell of an experience for my first race in America – a lovely track. I remember walking it one morning with Jacky Oliver as we were, I think, the only drivers on the grid who hadn't raced there before. Little did I know that I would end up holding the lap record on that original track. Not in an F1 car, of course, but in a Porsche 917.

'We all stayed at the Glen Motor Court, which is still there today, overlooking the lake. It was run by an Italian family, with two gorgeous dark-haired daughters whom everyone wanted to go to bed with! Everyone stayed there and the atmosphere was just fantastic.

'Then, on race morning, we were all picked up in a shaky old ex-military helicopter with rattling doors, and flown into the track. From up there, you could see why we flew. There was only one road in, and the whole of New York state was there. It was just a massive party. The big races of that era – the GP, the Sebring 12 Hours, Daytona – were just like going to Le Mans. Fans camping out, cutting down trees and setting the

toilets alight. They had a famous bog there, a pit of muddy water, and one year the fans drove a city bus in and let it sink! On the way home in the evening all these ponds were just full of people absolutely covered in mud and the police trying to fish 'em out with hooks. Amazing!'

Derek's Ferrari retired in the 1968 race, but he was to score his only F1 Championship point there two years later in the Team Surtees TS7. He finished sixth – yet as part of the driving deal he had to supply his own engine!

Bell returned to the Glen in 1971 but now at the wheel of the fabled Porsche 917, finishing third. The '71 season saw the emphasis in his career begin to shift from single-seaters to sports cars. Most of his drives in an F2 March 712M frustratingly ended in retirement. However, his ten outings in the John Wyer/Gulf 917 resulted in seven podium finishes, including a season top-and-tailing of victories in the Buenos Aires 1000km, on his first pairing with Jo Siffert, and the Paris 1000km at Montlhéry, with Gijs van Lennep.

Despite his success in sports cars Derek's sights were still set on F1, but his ambition was increasingly frustrated by underdeveloped and unreliable machinery. His final F1 drive was in the Surtees TS16 at his beloved Nürburgring in 1974. He finished 11th on that occasion, yet failed to even qualify in four of the car's five other appearances and retired once. It was sports and touring cars all the way now (well, nearly – an ex-works Penske PC3 turned up for a few non-Championship F1 outings in 1977), high-pointing in 1975 with a victory at Le Mans with Jacky Ickx

in the Mirage GR8, and wins at the Glen and in Austria in the beautiful Alfa T33TT12, partnered by Henri Pescarolo.

Derek's sports car career was looking on the up, but then British Leyland beckoned with the ill-fated Jaguar XJC. The Jags were super-fast when they were going – but rarely kept running, quite often retiring immediately after being overtaken by one of their own freewheeling rims! Of nine outings in the Jag in 1977, Bell's car made it to the finishing line only once... It was a magnificent second place, with Andy Rouse, at the Nürburgring.

By the end of the decade Derek was disillusioned, fed up, hard up and thinking of packing in the whole game. He remembers: 'Sports car racing was really in the mire. The problem for guys like us was that the big teams such as Renault and Porsche wanted top drivers only for the big races, like Le Mans. Yet if you had a deal with one of the lesser teams for the whole season they'd want you for Le Mans, too, so it was a bit like shooting yourself in the foot. But you couldn't live for a whole year on the fee for just one race.'

Derek struggled on, picking up drives in a varied assortment of cars. 'I was chasing drives like a cheap whore, taking money wherever I could get it. Eventually I decided to quit and go back to farming. In the early 1970s my sports car racing kept my morale up when whatever shit-box F1 car I was driving failed to qualify. By the late '70s, though, the really top drives seemed to be drying up.'

He continues: 'There was a financial reward

'Despite his sports car success Derek's sights were set on F1, but he

From top right
In the Porsche 956, 1983 Brands Hatch 1000km; at his Naples, Florida, dealership; early days; the Jägermeister Porsche, 1975 Nürburgring.

was increasingly frustrated by underdeveloped and unreliable cars'

for getting points in the World Championship, and I didn't have any. There was this lovely, lovely guy in Canada called Chet Vincentz who used to run a 934 Porsche. Chet always used to finish in the top ten in that bloody car, he'd get in the way but he'd always finish – and there was money down to tenth place.

'So I rang him up and said, "Chet, look, I'm in the shit. My career's over, but for one last fling can I drive your car at Mosport?" He said, "I can't afford to pay you but I'll help with travel and accommodation." So I bought my ticket, said cheerio to the wife and flew off to Toronto. That bloody thing! It had finished every race, but in this one it misfired and farted around and finished about 17th!

'While I was at Mosport I got chatting to Giampiero Moretti. He said, "Why don't you drive my car next week at Elkhart Lake? Can't pay you, but I'll pay for your hotel." So I got down there – can't remember how, probably in the back of a truck – and on the grid I was next to Alvin Springer's really trick Andial 935 Porsche, and Alvin said, "Hey, why don't you drive for me next week at Mid-Ohio; there's $60,000 prize money?" I went, "God, not arf!" Alvin followed up with, "You'll drive for a percentage, yes?" So I said, "No, I'll have been here three weeks and I'm broke. I'll need a few thousand up front."

'Anyway, in the Elkhart race the bloody engine blew up in the warm-up and we had to run the spare, which had fuel pick-up problems. We

ended up tenth or something, and I thought, "Bloody hell, not much money in this!"

'Well, we got to the Lumberman's 500 at Mid-Ohio and we were on about the fourth row of the grid, behind all the fast stuff – Can-Am cars and really quick little 2-litre sports cars. The track was like Brands and we were in this lumbering 935 with stacks of power but nowhere to let it go. We were on the grid, literally on the grid about to start, and Alvin was still saying, "Derek, you go for the percentage?" and I was arguing, "No. Cash."

'Of course, we won the bloody race! I would have been on 10% of $60,000! So I came back with no money, but everyone remembers your last race and I'd had a good one.'

Curiously, despite his early achievements in Porsches, the first time that Derek drove an official works entry was in the 1980 Le Mans 24 Hours in one of a trio of 2-litre 924 Carrera GTRs. Bell and co-driver Al Holbert got the car up to fifth place by Sunday morning before a burnt valve dropped it to 13th at the finish. Derek still has a road version of this car, one of 50, given to him by the factory after the race.

He was asked back for 1981, this time partnering Jacky Ickx in something a little more substantial. Their Jules-sponsored 936 won and Bell sees this moment as the turning point in his career, with the pair winning Le Mans again in '82 in the Rothmans 956.

Derek's career didn't look back from then on,

with an extraordinary run of success through the '80s as a Porsche factory driver in the fabulous 935, 956 and almost-unbeatable 962. He eventually notched up well over 30 wins for the factory, brought his Le Mans tally to five, had three Daytona 24 Hours victories and back-to-back World Sportscar Championships in 1985 and 1986. The Rothmans/Porsche programme ended in 1988, and Bell remembers Professor Helmuth Bott, who also retired from Porsche that year, saying to him: "You know Derek, you haf won more races for the Porsche factory than any uzzer driver."

Bell's racing continued through the 1990s, but largely in America and out of sight of his British fans. He says: 'I wasn't as desperate, and I'd drive anything because I wanted to stay in racing. There's nothing against a guy being older here. The sponsors actually like the old guys with a bit of character.'

In the latter half of the 1990s Derek's personality and famous gift of the gab' landed him Formula 1 commentating stints on US TV with the ESPN Sports Channel and later with Fox. This led to him becoming both driver and in-car commentator for a Speedvision-sponsored World Challenge GT Championship series.

He says: 'I raced a BMW the first year, and I used to have three or four cameras in the car and they talked to me during the race. They loved it, as they hadn't at the time seen that sort of thing in America.' He pauses for a chuckle: 'But →

From far left
Derek and McQueen in Brabham F2 at Le Mans, 1970; at Watkins Glen in 1994; with Porsche 962, Amelia Island concours.

'McQueen gave me an engraved watch and I've bloody lost it!'

I did have a ****ing big crash at Laguna Seca! Someone tail-ended me and I went into the dirt and kicked up a dust storm and went round and round, with Corvettes and Mustangs and all kinds of shit bouncing off me. Bam! There was nothing left of the car, just me sitting in a seat! Justin [Derek's son, also racing at the meeting] saw it all on the TV from the motorhome. He came rushing down and leapt over the spectator fencing, shouting: "You all right dad?"' Fortunately Bell was 'all right' and drove several more seasons for Speedvision in an ex-Richard Lloyd 4WD Audi S4.

Derek's anecdotes relating to his work as a driver in the 1970 Steve McQueen feature film *Le Mans* are well documented, but I do have to ask him one question. Bell was going flat-out in a 917 through Whitehouse when he was stunned to find a cameraman lying prone in the road! While he managed not to run over McQueen – for it was indeed the star doing the filming – it was a hairy moment.

I ask if he ever wakes up in the middle of the night thinking he might have been remembered only as the man who squashed Steve McQueen? Derek replies: 'Funny, I get reminded of him all the time. Yesterday I was in a watch shop getting a strap repaired, and I was looking at the TAG Heuers. Of course, Steve gave me one when we did *Le Mans*, engraved on the back 'To Derek, best wishes, Steve', and I've bloody lost it! But while I was in there I started to think about him. He used to write letters to me – I mean, I didn't

even know he could write! Way back I opened a motoring accessory shop in Bognor and I received this letter one day and it was from Steve, wishing me good luck. Which was nice, as we were really good mates and shared a house during the filming, But I threw it away! Stuff like that didn't seem to mean much back then.

'Yet I keep stuff these days. Stirling Moss wrote to me the other day and I keep all of his letters. He's my real hero. I even have the envelope that he sent me with photographs in back when I was in school aged 14. Now, of course, we're really good mates and see each other for dinner about twice a week when he's out here.

'Stirling is one of the reasons I have a house here. Back in 1985 I won the Miami Grand Prix [driving a Porsche 962], which was a tough race, fighting back from third in the last ten laps. I'd been to the prizegiving and I was walking back through the paddock. It was dusk on Sunday night, and most people had gone, when Stirling came up to me and said, "Well done, old boy, that was a fantastic drive."

'I said, "That's very kind of you, especially so coming from my idol." His response – "What do you mean? You're my idol" – knocked me out. I've got a photograph from him on the wall at home, and he's written on it: "From Stirling. If only..." He's always said to me if only I'd been born 15 years earlier we would have made the greatest pair of sports car drivers in the world. A wonderful compliment.'

It is obvious that Derek is genuinely touched

that he has become a close friend of his childhood hero and the man whom he entered motor sport to emulate. And that's what makes Bell such a nice bloke: he still retains his teenage passion and enthusiasm for the sport, and he genuinely likes people. He doesn't seem to have a bad word to say about anyone. Either that or, like the true gentleman he undoubtedly is, he keeps his less flattering opinions to himself. He even graciously ended our session together by signing some photographs that this fan took of him racing a quarter of a century ago. Thanks Derek. △

Time with...
IN
ASSOCIATION
WITH
Chopard

CLASH
OF THE
TITANS

They skittered and snaked their way round Le Mans at well over 200mph, scaring off some of the world's finest drivers in the process. But how do they compare now in a full-on test?

Words: Mark Hales   Photography: Paul Harmer

I had never driven a 917 but I know the Ferrari 512S, which is the other half of this test, pretty well. Owned by Nick Mason, it was a factory team car for 1970, driven by a good selection of the greats – Ronnie Peterson, Mario Andretti, Derek Bell, Arturo Merzario, Jacky Ickx... It won Sebring's 12-hour race in 1970, finished third at Daytona, then the following year starred in *Le Mans*, Lee Katzin's biopic with Steve McQueen. I raced it at Silverstone, leading all the Lola T70s until the engine tightened. I led the Le Mans Legends race in 2004 for a bit longer until I got a puncture. Fast but fragile, now as then. Yes and no...

More to the point, the drive wasn't as frightening as the prevailing wisdom had promised. Both the 512 and Porsche's 917 have a reputation as the last of the real scary monsters; the 200mph-plus brigade. The most power available from a five-litre engine in the lightest possible car and with no aerodynamics, or not the kind that you'd want anyway. Forty years on, it's perhaps easy to forget that at the time this was the fastest any sports racer had ever gone and the tyres, the brakes, the way the thing cut through the air, were all unknown

territory. And it's equally easy to judge these things in the context of more modern racers because, if the Ferrari's 500-plus horsepower made sure it was brutally fast in a straight line, it seems by comparison quite leisurely through the corners and it feels heavy, even though it isn't. A touch under 850kg is a sack of potatoes more than the 917's total, but still not a great deal for a 5.0-litre coupé; a Shelby Cobra looks as if it should weigh a great deal less but is actually heavier. The 512 was soft and sat high too, seemed to move about a great deal on its suspension, slid and drifted everywhere, just like it would have done 30 years earlier.

The front would dip sharply under braking for Tertre Rouge, then, having already squared the shoulders and made sure I was in whichever gear was needed by the end of the corner, I would ease a wheel that was far too small for the weight of steering, and wait... The nose would lean, edge left away from the apex, then bite. Another pause and the rear would waft to the left, lifting and rocking like a boat on a swell. That was the only point where you needed to be careful and, whatever instinct might tell you, it was time to get on the power and sit

'Both the Ferrari 512 and Porsche's 917 have a reputation as the last of the real scary monsters; the 200mph brigade'

the tail down again. Call up that raucous disembodied bark that bellowed on demand from the four white-painted megaphones buried under that sawn-off shelf of a tail. Plant the back and head like a missile for the first of the straight's chicanes.

It is still one of the loudest cockpits I've ever inhabited but that was all a part of something utterly intoxicating, as was the throng of wide-eyed watchers who gazed at the red shape crouching before them in the collecting area. Men sought eye contact, clenched their fists, stuck their thumbs up. Women tilted their heads and smiled... Hard to say whether it was, in René Arnoux's words, 'simply the power of the red cars', or whether they would have paid it less attention had there been a 917 alongside. I was about to find out.

Mention the number 917 to most motor sport enthusiasts and it will need no further explanation. The reaction will be part veneration of an icon, part awe for its fearsome reputation, part marvel at the engineering lengths – and expense – to which Porsche was apparently willing to go with the technology

Above
The tails of both Ferrari and Porsche are more than half the cars' lengths, emphasising how small the cockpits are and how far forward the drivers sit.

of the time; the magnesium chassis, drilled ignition key and balsa wood gearlever knob are already the stuff of lightweight legend. They will doubtless also know that several of the all-time greats, drivers of the calibre of Brian Redman and Jo Siffert, refused to drive the early 917 at long, fast tracks like the old Spa-Francorchamps and the Targa Florio, opting instead for the open-topped 908.

The green model which is the other half of our test is one of David Piper's stable, and is absolutely correct in period specification but a test mule rather than a racer with illustrious history like Mason's 512. I can say with a fair degree of confidence that neither a 917 nor a 512S has ever been to Cadwell Park but, seeing the two cars parked next to one another in the collecting area, I was struck by how similar they looked. Fashion, and aerodynamic expediency, has often made for consistency of line, and the bubble cockpit, low, sloping nose and humped front wings are even today still the best aerodynamic solution for the front of a closed top sports car. The pair's hindquarters are similar now too and for the →

same reasons, even if both have been through a few changes. Or in the Porsche's case, a very large number of them. If the cars look alike from the outside, though, they could not be more different under the skin.

The Porsche has a glassfibre body and tubular aluminium spaceframe chassis (later to be made of magnesium in a yet more expensive attempt to reduce weight); the Ferrari a steel frame with riveted aluminium sheets to form a monocoque tub. Each has a 12-cylinder engine developing about 550bhp at around 8000rpm but the Ferrari's is arranged in a relatively compact 60-degree vee and cooled by water, while the Porsche's is horizontally opposed (like the later Ferrari 512BB) and cooled by air from a large engine-driven fan, like the traditional 911's. This is driven from the centre of the engine by a train of gears that also feed the shaft that runs down the side of the crankcase, sending drive to the gearbox. There are just two valves per cylinder and, although Porsche insisted that the engine is not two six-cylinder 911s strapped together, it certainly looks that way.

The 512's engine features four valves per cylinder operated by twin overhead camshafts on each bank, these driven by a geartrain running up the front of the engine, but this and the other fundamental differences are surely a reflection of each company's engineering culture. Ferrari went for the best conventional technology of the time (monocoque, vee engine, four valves per cylinder), while Porsche decided the promise of lighter weight from a tubular chassis and the advantage of a flat, air-cooled engine's lower centre of gravity would outweigh the possible downsides of lesser torsional stiffness and

extra engine width just where you don't need it. Clearly, they also believed they could engineer their way round such details. Nobody had ever done it that way before, or on such a scale – and nobody has since since.

I take the Ferrari first because I know it better and that will help get me get accustomed to the combination of 500bhp and Cadwell's narrow strip of grey. The targa top makes it easy to get in but the cockpit feels more cramped than from memory; my knees are almost touching the dash and my helmeted head pokes out of the roof. The 512 measures 39 inches from ground to roof, already lower than the GT40's legendary 40 inches but taller than the 37 inches of the 917, which now sits quite a bit lower on its suspension.

The wheel is way down under the windscreen and the shift for the 512's five-speed ZF gearbox is where you'd expect – to the right of the seat and via a short lever poking out of a magnesium gate. Amazingly there's another gate in the gearbox. I have experienced what happens when the two move slightly out of synch – like when the chassis flexes – so the senses are already finely tuned to pick up anything that doesn't feel right, like the wrong kind of snick when you move the lever. There's also a lock-out on the shift – common on long-distance racers of the period – which forces you to go up or down the sequence in gear order, the idea being that in the heat of battle or the fatigue of night – or both – you can't go from third back to second instead of up to fourth. Or worse, such as fourth to first instead of third.

'It pitches and rolls about on its
suspension, and rough handling only
dumps it on the nose and gives
a big handful of loose tail'

The gears themselves are dog-engaged with no synchros and there's a gentle grating as I pull the lever across and back for first, then ride the clutch against the tall first gear and away. Fumble across the dog-leg for second, squeeze on the power and feel the back end squirm, then feel out the steering. It's as heavy as I remember and a touch lifeless on the treaded period Dunlops – like trying to turn your daily driver's wheel with the engine switched off. I soon remember that you can't rely on a pointy front end like a more modern car's. You have to flow the 512, make it turn almost before the corner so you can carry the speed, then settle it after the apex. Do it all smoothly as well, because it pitches and rolls about on its suspension even more over Cadwell's humps and bumps, and rough handling only dumps it on the nose and gives a big handful of loose tail. A couple more laps then...

The engine, meanwhile, is as wonderful as ever. It shrugs off and spits out the carbon from the plug tips, finding the last four cylinders one by one, the sound gathering in intensity as it climbs up the scale. A ragged growl sliding into a hoarse multi-layered bark, it doesn't sound as if it's revving at all. They used eight-five in period but I set a limit a thousand less for today. I've already studied Ferrari rev counters that are out by more than that.

Two or three more tours to settle in and already I'm seeing 7500 in fifth by the end of Cadwell's long straight. Not the 220 or 230mph-plus of Les Hunadières in '70, I know, but a good 165 and it certainly feels fast enough when it's time to get on the brakes for the second-gear right at Park. The pedal is as long and soft as last time, so a quick double-pump and then squeeze. I feel the nose dip and the back go light, teetering about behind while I pick my way carefully down the ratios, trying so hard to get a clean downshift without locking the rears. It's a long time spent treading on the middle pedal and all too easy to blip the engine slightly too much and get a rattle from the dogs, or not enough and get the same. There are big gears inside that box, wide enough to stand 500 horsepower for 24 hours, so there's a lot of inertia and it's better to get closer to the corner and

try and tickle the accelerator almost after I've slotted the lever rather than attempt to do any proper double de-clutching.

Gears tend to dominate the proceedings, not least because the consequences of missing one, or knocking the teeth off the dogs, is horrible to contemplate. The aforementioned brakes are the other issue. At Silverstone, the pedal lasted about two laps before I had to pump it every time, so how the good guys managed at Spa or the Nurburgring, I can't imagine.

Time for the Nine One Seven. It's more of an athletic exercise to thread myself in past the top of the windscreen and slide down the hammock of a seat but there's a surprising amount of room when I get there. The pedals are well offset to the left to clear the big front wheels so I sit, or rather lie, at an angle across the car, chin pressed firmly against chest. The wheel is huge and deeply dished to bring it close and allow a bend in the arms, but the chunky rim completely obscures my line of sight. I soon discover that I can't see any apex to the left of the nose and to drive at all I have to look through the rim. Piper says the wheel is smaller than the original, and is adjustable for height, but when the engineer moves it downwards it neatly rubs on the seatbelt clamp, which pings open at the hairpin. I hunch down, try to roll my body round and bring the knees up, and, once the door is closed, pull my head further down into my shoulders, otherwise my helmet is firmly pressed against the roof. The Ferrari would have been even worse in this respect, but for the targa roof.

To the right of the seat is a long gearlever – minus the balsa wood knob – and another difference in culture and operation is about to become apparent. The 917 has a synchromesh gearbox, as have most competition Porsches throughout the years. The rationale is that the synchronisers equalise the gear speeds as well as hold the ratio in and because there's no clash of dog's teeth then the gear selection is likely to survive a long race and an aggressive or tired driver. There's a lock-out, just like the Ferrari's, but the pattern is a conventional 'H' like a modern road car's, with fifth as a dog-leg to the right and forward. →

'Air under the car, lift, in the middle of the night, at 200mph. You'd know what was going to happen, but be unable to do much to stop it'

It's also true that the two-valve Porsche engine is historically less tolerant of an over-rev than the four-valve Ferrari, so the synchro might be an engineer's defence against that; the heroes used eight-five, but I'll stick to seven-five, short-shift from second to third and rely on the torque. The starter whirrs asthmatically, then the cylinders catch, smokily and in pairs. Push the clutch right to the floor as instructed, then hold the gearlever against first gear synchro until, like a knife cutting a piece of rubber, it gives and goes into the slot. Sticky throttle, instant response from the engine, but no real temperament. It pulls almost from tickover and, like Piper's engineer says, you could go shopping in it. Well, maybe he could. A bit more speed and the car feels more darty at the front than the 512. The big wheel fidgets in my grip as the car senses out the ridges in the road and feels like it's walking from one tyre's edge to the other.

Possibly it's the slick Avons over the treaded Dunlops, possibly it's the fact the suspension is set lower and with little or no droop. Air under the car is still the major source of instability at speed and the passing of years has shown running lower is a good defence. The engine, meanwhile, is much quieter than the Ferrari's; a smooth wail rolls from the two big pipes under the gearbox, accompanied by an odd harmonic thrum at certain rpm which you feel through the seat. It pulls from lower down against longer gears and I soon find you have to shift with a very long and

'Once you get beyond 150mph, every 10mph or so extra adds to an other-worldy dimension. It's like entering a forbidden zone'

deliberate movement, and hold the lever against the synchro until you're sure it's engaged, both up and down. I'm sure you get used to it, but it feels so very different to the snick, click and clatter of the Ferrari's ZF. Fifth turns out to be completely redundant – even on Cadwell's long straight – then, picking my way carefully down the gears in turn for Park, holding the lever against the slot and feeding up the clutch brings a fusillade of crackling and popping on the overrun. Pull lever back, across, count one, hold against the synchro, rev up... and bring up the clutch again. *Rat, tat, crack-tat, ping, brap.*

Up the speed a bit and that initial sharpness disappears. The Porsche is more stiffly sprung than the Ferrari, and there's more grip from the slicks, but while the back end feels rooted to the road there's still that occasional vague feeling as you commit to a corner, the more so the faster the turn. And it's different depending on how the road lies. At Charlie's, the long, fast climbing right at the end of the bottom straight, the 917 sweeps into the uphill bit with reassuring confidence, then, as the road falls away for the shallower second half, the front loses interest. The road is narrow so a lift is the best trick to tuck it in again. Tread the power hard and early as a possible defence and the grunt will just pick up the front and make the push worse earlier in the turn.

It's actually difficult to loosen the Porsche's tail with power and I get the sense that most of the time it's as Jean-Pierre Beltoise observed: →

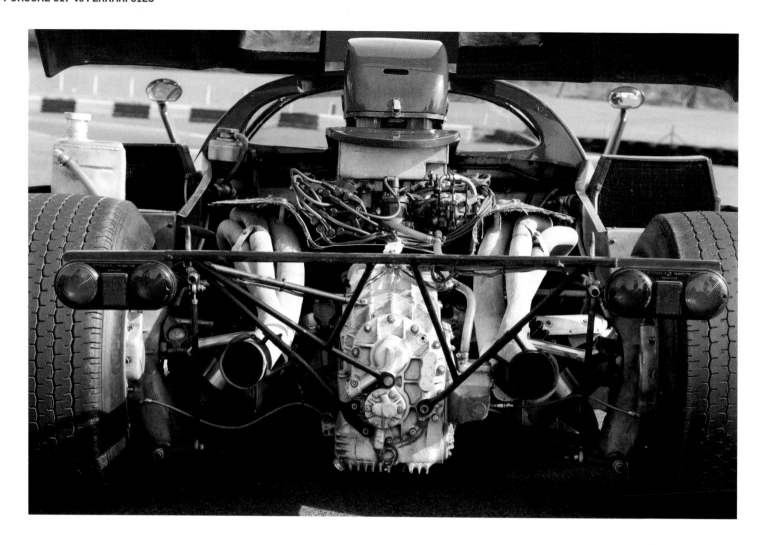

'Call up that raucous disembodied bark that bellows on demand from the four white-painted megaphones under the tail'

**1970
FERRARI 512S**

ENGINE
4993cc water-
cooled V12,
DOHC per bank,
four valves per
cylinder, Lucas
fuel injection

POWER
550bhp @
8000rpm

TORQUE
371lb ft @
5750rpm

TRANSMISSION
Five-speed manual,
rear-wheel drive

SUSPENSION
Double wishbones
and Koni coil-over-
damper units
all-round

BRAKES
Girling discs
all-round

WEIGHT
856kg

PERFORMANCE
Max speed
200mph+

that all cars understeer and have bad brakes. He was talking about things as they were then, but just occasionally I got a glimpse of what might lurk in store if I was careless

Peering beneath the wheelrim to find the turn-in for the Gooseneck, the downhill right/left which is one of Cadwell's signatures, I arrived a touch too quickly over the crest, without settling the nose properly. The car simply halved its obedience to the amount of lock and washed wide across the track. Then, as the road levelled and the front came back to attention, the tail flicked to the right. Air under the car, lift, the enemy of stability and a reaction that would get suddenly worse with any increase in speed. I can just imagine that in the night, at 200mph in the cambered kink through Masta. You'd know what was going to happen, but be unable to do much to stop it.

This 917 has all the updates that came so thick and fast in the two years of the car's professional career, and it's probably more stable than it was, or than the Ferrari is now, and yet over the crest of Cadwell's Mountain I have to lift off for at least a couple of tenths to stop the engine climbing into the danger zone beyond 8500 while the rear wheels part company with the road.

The 512 merely shimmies the revs and slithers the tail. I'm fairly sure though that the scary bit, if there still is one, would always depend on a set of circumstances and, like the Gooseneck experience, it would be different every time. It would be a gust of wind at the wrong moment, or a slipstream disturbing the air in front. The time when you just didn't pin the nose quite hard enough on the brakes and keep the air from getting beneath. You can cope with something awkward when you know what's likely to set it off, and if it's the same response every time. It's when you can't see it coming that it's difficult. That's what will have spooked the Sifferts and Redmans of the world.

I also know that once you get beyond 150mph in something like this, every 10mph or so extra adds to an other-worldly dimension.

It's like entering a forbidden zone. The car seems to float above the ground, and there are strange noises, jigglings and little but insistent swerves as the airspeed exerts a different influence.

Those strange sounds. A whistle, a roar, a hum. Is it just the air tearing at the surfaces or is it the prelude to take-off? Is it an engine cover coming loose? Is it a tyre shedding its tread?

These are things that drivers of modern cars simply won't know about. The science has been done on the computer and the faster they go, the more the car is pressed to the ground. Other than the fact that they will have to shed it with absolute accuracy before the next corner, these days more speed equals more security.

Before the day it was impossible not to be mindful of the 917's advance press. If it worried the best in the world, what chance might I have? But that would be to overlook the work they put in during the type's short yet illustrious career. The shorter channelled tail on each car had cost a vast amount of money, and too much blood and bone, but was one of the things that turned an unpredictable beast into a sorted racing car – consistent with the science of the times.

The more surprising thing perhaps was that such a hugely differing engineering approach felt much the same on the track. The 917's engine is torquier than the Ferrari's, makes less noise on the gas and more off it, but they get the car to much the same point at much the same time and in much the same style.

For me, the biggest ingredient was simple ergonomics. There was more headroom in the 512 and, like Dan Gurney and the hump in the GT40's roof, without it I simply wouldn't be able to race the car effectively. Seems such a small detail when the original quest was to stop the car taking flight. △

Thanks to David Piper, Nick Mason and Ten Tenths, and Cadwell Park, www.motorsportvision.co.uk/cadwell-park.

1969 PORSCHE 917

ENGINE
4494cc air-cooled flat-12, DOHC per bank, two valves and two spark plugs per cylinder. Mechanical fuel injection

POWER
580bhp @ 8000rpm

TORQUE
332lb ft @ 6850rpm

TRANSMISSION
Five-speed manual, rear-wheel drive

SUSPENSION
Unequal-length wishbones with titanium coils over gas dampers all-round

BRAKES
Ventilated cast-iron discs with aluminium hubs, Alfred Teves aluminium calipers

WEIGHT
800kg

PERFORMANCE
Max speed 200mph+

'Pull lever back, across, count one, hold against the synchro, rev up... and bring up the clutch again. *Rat, tat, crack-tat, ping, brap*'

40 years OF HEUER MONACO

With its square case and blue dial, the original Heuer Monaco is arguably the most recognisable watch ever made. And, thanks to the ever-present McQueen and the film *Le Mans*, it's also the coolest

Words: Simon de Burton

'In real life Siffert wore an AutAvia but McQueen preferred the Monaco'

The image of Steve McQueen looking skywards with the right cuff of his racing overalls conveniently pulled back to reveal a prominent Heuer Monaco is so well-known to so many watch and car enthusiasts that it has almost become a cliché. You probably won't need reminding that the shot comes from the 1971 motor racing film Le Mans, in which McQueen plays Michael Delaney, a driver who spends as much time wrestling with his mental demons as he does with the controls of his Porsche 917.

Even McQueen's greatest fans must agree that the film's dialogue is somewhat sparse, the plot rather feeble and the thrill factor on the low side – yet, although Le Mans met with a lukewarm response on initial release, it is now regarded as an all-time classic among petrolheads the world over.

From a marketing perspective, the placement of the Heuer Monaco on McQueen's wrist was nothing short of an act of genius because now, four decades after it was launched, the model is still regarded as one of the coolest timepieces on the market.

So what lies behind the making of such a horological legend? To find out, we must engage reverse gear and revisit the 1960s, when almost as much exciting stuff was happening with watches as it was with cars – not least the development of the first automatic chronograph movement. In 1964 Jack Heuer, the great-grandson of Heuer founder Edouard Heuer, had already made his mark on the car-watch world by creating the Carrera chronograph and, as the decade continued, he set about building up the US market and bringing a new breed of buyer to the brand.

'We knew back in 1965 that, four years down the line, we would have perfected the automatic chronograph in collaboration with Breitling and Hamilton,' Heuer told Octane. 'We had already made plans to use it in the Carrera and the AutAvia – but as the time came nearer we realised that what we really needed was a waterproof chronograph that would appeal to a more fashion-orientated

clientele. In those days, the case makers used to call at the factory with brass dummies of new designs, and one showed us his latest waterproofing system for square cases that used four notches cut into the back, which created water resistance through tension. It was entirely new and patented, so we negotiated world-wide exclusivity for chronograph use.'

That breakthrough provided an unmissable opportunity for Heuer. 'It meant we had a case and we had a movement – what we needed next was a dial that was really different. We came up with a blue finish with horizontal indexes, white subdials and a red chronograph hand that would give the watch a unique look, especially combined with the fact that technical reasons meant it would have a left-hand winding crown. We already had a watch called the Monte Carlo and, since 1969 seemed to be the year of Grace Kelly, we opted for the Monaco,' explained Heuer.

The Heuer Monaco chronograph was launched simultaneously in Switzerland and the US on 3 March 1969, but it was during the filming of Le Mans the following year that the watch enjoyed its finest hour. Since his was a small company with little marketing budget, Heuer had decided to promote it through the more cost-effective means of product placement – the first attempt at which involved getting Swiss racing driver Jo Siffert to wear a Heuer AutAvia.

'In those days racing drivers enjoyed little help from sponsors and carried very few badges on their overalls, so the "Chronograph Heuer" logo really stood out,' Heuer told us.

'I had learned that Hollywood product placements were done by specialist property masters, so I called up our Hollywood outlet and it put me in touch with a property master called Donald Nunley who worked on many major productions. We agreed that I would give him a box of chronographs every now and again and, when appropriate, he would use them in films – he got them onto all sorts of people.

→

Those film stars ranged from Jack Lemmon and Burt Reynolds to Charlton Heston and Bo Derek.

'Often, the stars grew used to wearing the watches and would ask to keep them – all I ever asked for in exchange was a signed photograph. Anyhow, in 1970 I got a call from Nunley to say that he was doing a film about motor racing and needed timing boards, stopwatches, chronographs and so on, so we sent a guy from the factory to Le Mans, where part of the film was being shot.'

And here begins the story of a legendary watch.

'McQueen was to play the lead and, although he was passionate about fast cars, he had never driven anything so powerful as a Porsche 917 so he was appointed two professional racing drivers as tutors – one was Derek Bell and the other was Jo Siffert. They later told me that they scared the hell out of McQueen on the track by putting him under just the sort of pressure you'd get in the real race.

'The day before they began the actual shooting the producer told McQueen that he had to decide once and for all how he wanted to look – and he chose to look like Siffert, so Siffert lent him his overalls with the Heuer logo and Nunley produced one of the boxes of chronographs I had provided and asked McQueen [who usually wore a Rolex] to choose one. In real life Siffert wore an AutAvia, but McQueen must have preferred the Monaco because that's the one he decided to wear.

'Afterwards Nunley asked me what to do with all the watches, so I told him to keep them and he gave them to various other people involved in the film. For some reason this angered McQueen, so to appease him Nunley told him a lie and said that everyone who had a watch had bought it. In order to back him up we had to send everyone a spoof invoice!'

Sales of the Monaco continued until around 1976, when the Buren chronograph movement that powered it became unavailable and the watch gradually disappeared from retailers' windows. In 1998, however, long after most Heuer enthusiasts thought the Monaco had been consigned to the history books, it was

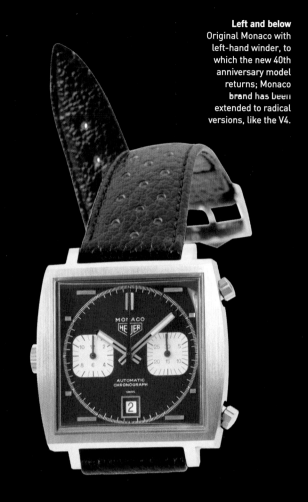

Left and below
Original Monaco with left-hand winder, to which the new 40th anniversary model returns; Monaco brand has been extended to radical versions, like the V4.

'What we needed next was a dial that was really different'

re-launched in a limited run of 5000 pieces which sold so well that the following year TAG Heuer, by then owned by LVMH, put the Monaco back in its catalogue and into series production – albeit with some significant changes, the most obvious being a right-hand winding crown.

The clever bit, though, was to negotiate permission from the McQueen estate to use those now-celebrated images of the actor wearing the Monaco and the 'Chronograph Heuer' race suit – because that's what converted the Monaco from just another wristwatch into one of the coolest timepieces on the planet.

June 2009 saw the launch of the TAG Heuer Monaco 40th Anniversary Re-edition, 1000 examples of which were made available at a cost of £6250 each. One of the two original Monacos used in the filming of *Le Mans* is now on display in the TAG Heuer 360 museum in La Chaux de Fonds, Switzerland. Visits are by appointment: call +41 (0) 32 919 800. See also www.tagheuer.com.

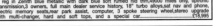

SHAKEN

Derek Bell tries the first 935 and recalls how, in
the 1970s, Porsche's brute-force racer opened
the door for his own return to the factory team

Words: Peter Morgan Photography: Ian Dawson

AND STIRRED

The 935 may have been the bastard son of all those gorgeous 906s, 908s and 917s, but there's no doubting it delivered the goods. This monster of a racing car helped Porsche to the World Manufacturers' Championship in 1976, and in the coming years would win all the major endurance classics.

The first season of what was hailed as a new era in endurance racing began in '76. In truth, it was a last stand in a fragile motorsport world that had been starved by the crippling OPEC oil embargo. Group 5 was the headline class – a politically correct, production-based formula that nonetheless gave considerable development freedom. So much freedom, in fact, that virtually only the car's silhouette had to conform to the mass-produced original's.

Even given this loose rein, just Porsche and BMW ran works cars. The latter's 3.5-litre CSL 'Batmobiles' were the prettiest – and often the fastest – machines. But Porsche wore them down with the 935. →

'My long-lasting impression is that it is an absolute animal! This is a car you talk to and drive the heck out of. You attack it and fight it!'

Above
Bodyshell is steel Type 930 with glassfibre doors, bonnet and engine cover, plus single-piece front air dam and front wings.

This car is the development prototype, 935001 – the first of many 935s and one that played a pivotal part in that 1976 campaign. There's no doubting the production model on which it was based: the then-new 911 Turbo. Nevertheless, although the bodyshell is recognisable, virtually everything else is different.

The engineer charged with this incredible transformation was Norbert Singer. Singer had joined Porsche in 1970, not long after he graduated from Munich University. His degree was in technical engineering but it was Singer's relentless thrust and parry with the rulemakers that turned the 935 into a winner.

Car 001 was built over the winter of 1975-'76. It was used for testing at Paul Ricard, and for the integration of the 590bhp, 2.85-litre, single-turbo flat-six. And as a result of this thorough pre-season testing, the competitiveness of the team's primary race car, 002, was not in doubt when it lined up for the first event.

Ickx and Mass won the first two Championship races at a canter. But perhaps it was such dominance so early into the new Championship that drew attention from the scrutineers. Whatever the reasons, they homed in on the 935's air-to-air intercooler installation.

To accommodate the highly effective but bulky unit, Singer had modified the underside of the standard 911 Turbo engine cover. And in so doing, the scrutineers said, the car was now in violation of its homologated silhouette. In the coming races 001 found itself at the centre of a running battle as Singer sought to extract the most

from the regulations yet keep the car competitive. A more compact but heavier water-to-air cooler was run on both 001 and 002 at the Nürburgring 1000km. This installation satisfied the scrutineers, but meanwhile Singer delivered a riposte that caught them completely off-guard.

Car 001 debuted an outrageous flat-sculpted nose – one that eliminated the classic 'frog-eye' headlamps of the standard 911 and significantly improved the car's aerodynamic penetration. Of course, it completely changed the car's silhouette, and the almost universal first reaction was that Porsche must be joking.

This time Singer had found a real unfair advantage. Hidden deep in the regulations was a clause that allowed manufacturers to fit wider wheels and tyres to their cars. Not expecting an interpretation as extreme as Singer's, the rule also allowed any modifications to the car's wings – defining them as 'free'. For a BMW or other front-engined saloons with a high bonnet line this didn't offer much scope. But for the rear-engined Porsche, with its sloping front bonnet, it was a gift. The slant-nose 935 may not have been in the spirit of the regulations, but nobody could argue it didn't comply with the letter.

Car 001's day of days came at Watkins Glen in July. Rolf Stommelen and Manfred Schurti led home a Porsche one-two-three ahead of the outpaced Bavarian cars. The win evened up the score with BMW and set up a grandstand finish to the season. When 002 won at Dijon in August (with 001 third), the Championship fell to Porsche. And with its development and race duties complete, 001 was retired.

Below
Cabin is surprisingly large, and extremely hot and noisy; cooling fan sits on top of the flat-six engine.

1976 PORSCHE 935 001

ENGINE
2857cc air-cooled flat-six. Chain-driven single overhead camshaft per bank, Bosch mechanical fuel injection

POWER
590bhp @ 7900rpm

TORQUE
434lb ft @ 5400rpm

TRANSMISSION
Four-speed all-synchro transaxle gearbox. Solid differential

SUSPENSION
Front: MacPherson principle titanium coil springs over gas dampers. Rear: semi-trailing arms with titanium coil springs over gas dampers. Anti-roll bars front and rear

BRAKES
Cross-drilled and ventilated discs with four-piston alloy calipers

WEIGHT
2138lb (970kg)

PERFORMANCE
0-125mph 7.1 sec
Top speed 200mph

Below
Before the 935, Porsche campaigned the RSR-Turbo – it finished second at Le Mans in 1974.

Today, this car is as it finished at Dijon. And it's to the great credit of current owner Kevin Jeannette that things remains that way. Part of this car's mystique is that it still has its race-etched stone chips, hand-painted Martini stripes and a host of details that underline the fact it was a development car. You can almost sense the team's intense struggle to keep the car winning during that long, hot summer of '76.

The pair of Martini cars that Jacky Ickx, Jochen Mass, Rolf Stommelen and Manfred Schurti drove to the Championship were the only full-specification 935s that season. But several of Porsche's closest customers were given the parts to update their less-modified Group 4 934s to full Group 5 specification.

It was one of these hybrid cars that gave Derek Bell his first taste of 935 power. After Le Mans that year he had received a call from Porsche asking him to drive the Kremer brothers' 934/5 at the Österreichring 1000km. The car was fitted with a factory-fresh 2.85-litre 935 engine. And, after a strong showing, Derek and Vern Schuppan finished fourth overall.

In the coming years Bell would 'guest' in other privately entered but works-blessed 935s. In 1980, having made all the right impressions during these drives, he was invited to join the factory team for its Le Mans campaign with the 924 Carrera GT. So began a run of nine straight years with the factory team. 'I think that 1976 represented my informal return to the Porsche fold [Derek had

driven for the Gulf-Porsche team during the 1971 season]. In the coming years [after 1976] the marque repeatedly asked me to drive its cars at Le Mans, but by that time I was involved with Renault. By 1980, though, I was happy to say yes.'

So after a Porsche career where his 935 experience was book-ended by the exotic 917 and the much-loved 936 and 956 prototypes, were Derek's 935 memories positive?

'My long-lasting impression is that it's an absolute animal! When you get into the car, you start it up, put it into gear and you sort of talk to it. You say: "It's either you or it's me, and one of us is going to have to give. And today it's you!" This is a machine you talk to and drive the heck out of it. You attack it and fight it!

'The whole thing was just a total compromise. It's the turbo lag and the sheer weight. The engineers had to make this big car with all that horsepower go round corners. It was a real animal – probably the biggest animal I've ever driven.'

With these ripe comments still fresh in our ears, Kevin Jeannette's mechanics wheel out 001 for Derek to drive. Just watching Derek climb in conjures up images from another time – and not from motor racing. Perhaps it's the extra brackets, the bare tubes of the roll cage and the many umbilical lines that thread through the cavernous cabin, but the impression is of an armoured fighting vehicle. And Derek is the commander sitting there in the turret, directing operations.

Above
Mid-1970s tyre technology was on the limit of coping with 590bhp and violent turbo lag.

Far right
Derek Bell returns
to the Porsche 935,
three decades on.

Bottom right
Chassis 001 won
the Watkins Glen Six
Hours in July 1976.

'Every time Derek backs off, a long finger of flame spurts from the car. Then the 935 twitches and bounds into the bend before catapulting along the straight'

Watching from the pits, the 935 appears to be anything but a tank. It is a big car, certainly, but it comes across as a gentle giant, the aggression of its exhaust note softened by the muting influence of the turbo.

All that is forgotten once you watch this car negotiate a corner. As I recalled from seeing 002 at Silverstone in 1976, the 935 doesn't sweep through bends, it hustles. And it does so with a full pyrotechnic display.

Every time Derek backs off, a long finger of yellow flame spurts from the rear of the car. Then the 935 twitches and bounds into the bend before catapulting along the next straight. Even from the outside, you get the impression there's nothing subtle at all about the way this car gets round corners.

In the cabin it is war. It is incredibly noisy and the sound is like an out-of-control food blender with gears. The flat-six's note is light years away from being a delicate Italian rasp or a stirring Detroit rumble. Nevertheless, wide open and near maximum revs, there's no mistaking that it's the sound of extreme horsepower.

But despite all this, and his earlier memories, Derek is indeed having a lot of fun. After several laps intimidating other track users, he peels off the racing line and heads for the pits.

As we open the familiar 911 door, a wave of heat floods out from the cabin. Derek doesn't lose any time unbuckling and climbing out into the relative cool of the pitlane. 'It's really hot in there – and very noisy,' he says, wiping the perspiration from his face. The extra effort of driving the car, compared to an open prototype, is all too apparent.

'This is a single turbo and I didn't race this particular one. But I felt immediately at home in there with that chunky old gearbox. Without all the power [of the later cars] it is a very neutral car. All the same, you knew that when the power came on, it was going to come on with a heck of a rush. And when it started to go I thought it was quite progressive, considering it is such an early model.

'The cornering technique is to come in as smooth as you can – it's no good trying to chuck it. If you chuck it, there's nobody at home when you attack the throttle. The answer is to go in as smooth as you can, get turned in, get the bite on the front and get your foot on the gas as early as you can. And then hopefully during the corner you don't have to back off. You just keep your foot on it and it'll understeer, understeer, understeer – then it'll really start to spool up and the tail will go out. And then you go Whoaa! – it's such an incredible rush! It comes across as a very agricultural racing car. But at the time it was the best there was. It's easy to forget that.'

And that sums up the 935. It may not look like the other Porsche racing cars of its era, but it shares one very important feature – it is a winner. △

Thanks to Kevin and Sharon Jeannette and the team at Gunnar Racing (www.gunnarracing.com; tel: +1 561 844 8482), to Ottocar Jakobs and to Moroso Motorsports Park (www.morosomotorsportspark.com).

FREISINGER
MOTORSPORT

Porsche 964 Turbo S Leichtbau

Porsche 993 RSR

Porsche 964 Carrera 3.8 RSR
ex. Larbre Competition

Porsche 996 GT3 RSR

Porsche 924 GTR (Rennwagen)

Porsche 934 (Rennwagen)

Porsche 906

Porsche 914/6 GT Replika

Porsche 911 Carrera 2.7 RS Leichtbau

Porsche Kremer CK 5

Porsche 911 2,3 ST Replika

Porsche 906

Porsche 934 (Rennwagen)

Porsche 908 Spyder (Rennwagen)

Porsche 917 K (Rennwagen)

Large variety of favorite Porsche Cars, Classic Porsche Racing cars, Largest facility of historic Porsche racing and serial parts, Restoration, Tuning & much more, a Porsche needs to be a passion

Fon: 0049 7 21 / 55 49-26 | Fax: 0049 7 21 / 55 49-25
www.m-freisinger.de | info@m-freisinger.de

WATTIE AND THE
962

The Porsche 962 represented Group C racing at its absolute pinnacle. Twenty years on, John Watson drives the most original surviving example and relives its spectacular performance

Words: Tony Dron   Photography: John Colley

'When I stopped racing F1,' says John Watson, 'I agreed to drive some sports cars for one reason alone: to get off the motor-racing drug in a progressive manner rather than going cold turkey.'

Mention John Watson and most of us will recall his fine victory in the 1981 British GP at Silverstone. Seeing him hillclimbing with a Porsche 962 in Sussex, however, was a reminder of his less well-known sports car racing days. At the 2008 Goodwood Festival of Speed, Watson was back in a Porsche, the 1987 Leyton House sponsored 962 which now belongs to Paul Michaels of leading London BMW dealer, Hexagon of Highgate.

Back in 1984, after his solid decade in Formula One, John agreed to drive for Jaguar at Le Mans. Over the next five years he drove Jaguar, Toyota and Porsche Group C cars in the world's top 24-hour sports car race, plus a few other endurance events, as well as doing some development driving. Such is the fickle nature of 24-hour racing that he finished at Le Mans only once, in 1990 with the late Richard Lloyd's Porsche 962C – sharing with Bruno Giacomelli and Allen Berg, he was 11th that year – but few can match his variety of experience.

'Wattie' remains one of a tiny handful of people to have driven many of the top cars in a golden era of Group C racing. We tracked him down to get his thoughts on the 962 and discover how it measured up against its rivals.

First of all, what was it like being back aboard a Group C car at Goodwood, nearly 20 years on? 'It gave me a good sense of the past, bringing it all back,' says John, 'and Paul's car ran perfectly, doing everything it should do up the hill. I have always thought of the Porsche 962 long-tail as a supremely good car to drive.'

Wattie did have one experience of racing at Le Mans before his F1 career really got going. Back in 1973, he shared a Cosworth-powered Gulf-Mirage M6 with Mike Hailwood and Vern Schuppan. This foray to France marked his return to racing after being injured in the F1 Race of Champions early in the season. But, as things turned out, that Le Mans drive was brief; just six hours in, Vern was unfortunately caught out by an accident that flipped the Mirage onto its roof and out of the 24 Hours.

That was all a very long way back when Wattie returned to sports cars in the mid-1980s, just as endurance racing was rapidly →

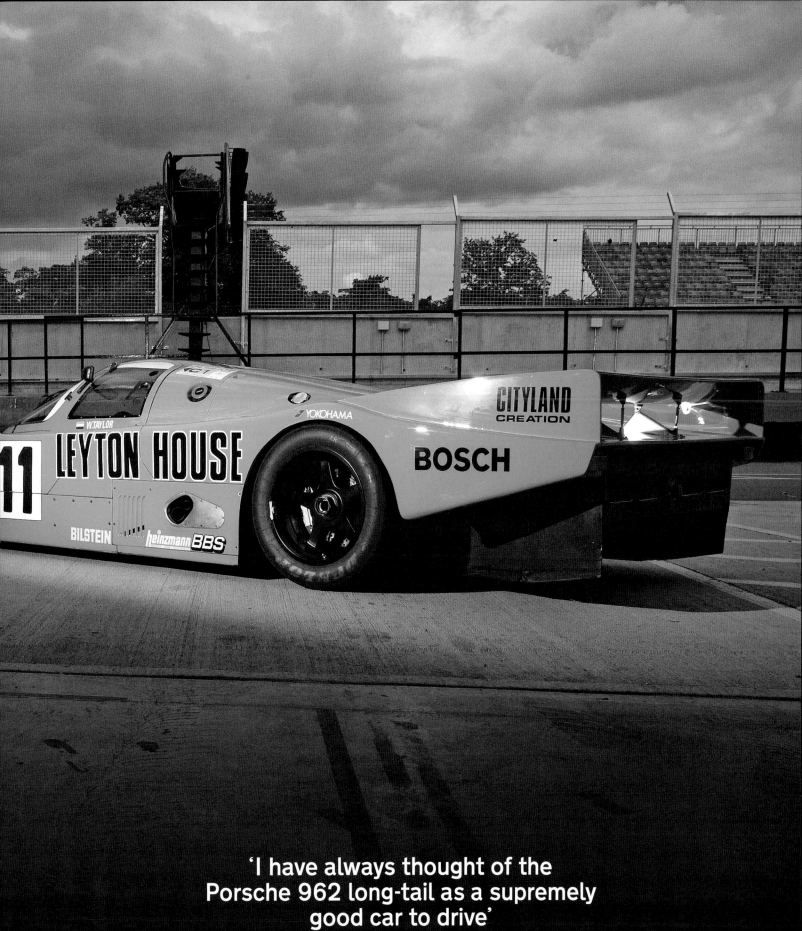

'I have always thought of the
Porsche 962 long-tail as a supremely
good car to drive'

The Leyton House Porsche 962C

Porsche's 956 and 962 sports-prototypes became the most successful series of endurance racing cars ever made. By racing car standards they were mass-produced, even coming with an ignition key. The 956 dominated the early days of Group C after its introduction in 1982. To meet American IMSA rules, the design was revised in 1984 as the 962, with a longer wheelbase and a pedal box placing the driver's feet behind the front axle line. All had versions of Porsche's classic flat-six engine of varying capacity, the 962 with a single turbo to the IMSA rules and the later 962C with twin turbos for World Endurance events.

Constant development kept 962s competitive for ten years. Over 100 of all types were made and, with pressure on production capacity, favoured teams were permitted to construct their own modified versions, using Porsche parts. The Leyton House-sponsored car, chassis 962CK6-87 with a 2826cc twin-turbo engine, was built in this way by Kremer Racing for the 1987 Le Mans 24 Hours, in which it finished fourth. That was its one and only race, the car being retained in the Kremer collection until 1998. As a completely unaltered one-race original, it must be unique.

Collector Paul Michaels acquired it in 2006. Preferring to preserve it, he will never drive it himself but he enjoyed watching John Watson in action at Goodwood. It is maintained by Roger Heavens Racing.

becoming much quicker. When I asked him how different were the Group C cars from the single-seaters he was used to, his unexpected answer caught my interest.

'Well, I don't suppose anyone would know this but I did actually drive a 956, just once, when I was still with McLaren in F1. It was at Weissach [the Porsche factory's own test track] and in the very early days of the Formula One TAG engine, the turbo 1.5-litre V6 that Porsche had built for us at McLaren. During the final stages of development I flew out to Weissach – it must have been August 1983 – ahead of Ron Dennis and John Barnard, and when I got there I saw a 956 development car sitting there. It looked quite rough and purposeful, like any development hack, and they had installed a TAG turbo engine in it for their test driver Roland Kussmaul to go pounding round.

'No McLaren chassis was available but they needed to get the mileage on the engine and that's why they used the 956. They had built the engine and they wanted to find out what it was like. They did find out but they didn't tell McLaren, who actually owned the TAG engine, how they'd done it. When Ron saw it in a 956, it caused one almighty row. It's amusing to remember it now but, I tell you, it was one of those "light the blue touch paper and stand back" moments.'

A 956 with a TAG turbo F1 engine in the back? The secret has long been out in the public domain but I had no idea that John Watson had actually driven it. This got my attention. What was it like?

'Well, the thing was, I had nothing to compare it with at the time. What did interest me was that the TAG-Porsche engine seemed very impressive in the 956 but, when I got to drive it in the McLaren F1 car, there was terrible throttle lag at first. The installations were apparently identical but there's so much more room in a sports car – I have always assumed it had something to do with that.'

Although Wattie was entered to drive the Group 44 Jaguar at Le Mans in 1984, that was no more than a toe-in-the-water first effort for Jaguar; his testing and occasional races with Porsche continued throughout the year.

'The first time I drove a 962 was in a test down at Paul Ricard in spring 1984. I hadn't driven a performance sports car on a circuit with a long straight for years and the thing that struck me was the amount of grunt, particularly the torque from that flat-six turbo engine, which I found very impressive.' Although the first racing 962s had the 2.8-litre engine, with its single KKK turbo meeting US IMSA GTP regulations, this test car had the far more powerful 2649cc twin-turbo from the 956 works racers.

'Of course,' Wattie adds, 'it was much heavier than an F1 car, correspondingly slow in its responses and it took much more physical effort to drive it. You needed to get up closer to the wheel, just to get the leverage, because the steering weights were much higher than in an F1 car. Then, when I got onto the long straight at Ricard that first time I can remember thinking, "****ing hell, this is quick!" But it was a very well-balanced car and once you got used to the effort of it and the feel of that Porsche speciality, the spool diff that locks up, it really was nice to drive.'

Later in 1984, on 30 September, there was a high point when he joined Stefan Bellof in a works Rothmans Porsche 956-83 for the Mount Fuji 1000km, a round of the World Endurance Championship. Our man was standing in for Derek Bell in Japan, as it clashed with an IMSA round in the USA, and Derek was in with a chance of winning the American championship.

'What I remember most clearly from that race in Fuji is that, being Porsche, they'd put the seat on a nicely engineered adjustable slider, just like a road car. When Stefan came in to hand the car over to me in the race, he slid the seat right back to get out fast and I jumped in, not realising what had happened. Being of nearly the same height, we shared the same seating position. The belts were done up and I rushed away to spend the whole of my stint with my arms just about straight. It was extremely difficult to drive like that as I could only just apply the leverage required to turn the wheel.'

Modestly, he did not mention that they took pole and won the race. Bellof became the World Sportscar Drivers Champion for 1984 but was killed at Spa only 11 months later. So how did the Porsche, Jaguar and Toyota Group C cars measure up?

'At Le Mans, the long-tail 962 was about as good as it gets, in my knowledge and experience,' says Wattie. 'Through all those years, the Porsche was just a nice, easy car to drive, with a lovely balance. →

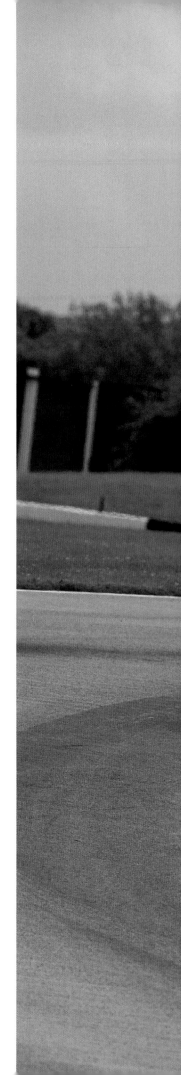

'I can remember thinking,
"*****ing hell, this is quick!"'

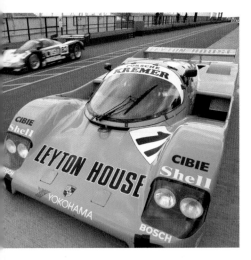

Above
John Watson reunited with the 1987 Leyton House-sponsored Porsche 962. His experience in the golden age of Group C is almost unrivalled.

At Le Mans, where we ran with relatively low downforce to get the speed on the straights, I well remember the high centre of gravity of the Jaguar in 1987; this made it less relaxed than the Porsche. With little aerodynamic help to hold it down, that particular Jaguar felt dominated on that circuit by its great boat anchor of a V12 engine.

'Porsche just seemed to have a better feeling of what was required at Le Mans and, even through to 1988, the 962 remained a more pleasant car to drive there. The cars were closer on lap times by then, but I think the Porsche still felt better and it was also certainly more highly developed as an effective low-downforce car.

'In 1989, the Toyota was another very good car but they had got themselves tied up with the wrong tyre contract. Had we been able to run on Michelins, then the best tyres in endurance racing, I think that Toyota would have been very good indeed. The Japanese are very methodical, setting themselves long-term goals and not expecting to win in the first five years. The British teams, being more adaptable, can get results quicker.'

'One thing I don't miss is how sports cars let water into the cockpit when it rains – it's unpleasant and they all do it'

Wattie's only Le Mans finish came with his drive in Richard Lloyd's 962C in 1990, by which time chicanes had been added to the Mulsanne Straight.

'With the chicanes, the character of the race had changed. There was a drop in top speed of around 20mph but, unlike before, it was held only briefly. Le Mans was well on the way to becoming a 24-hour sprint race and, naturally, the quickest cars were suddenly short-tailed sprint cars. The deal with Richard, who had been a good friend of mine since the early 1970s, came in April, I think.

'That particular car was not one of his specially-built 962s: it was a brand new, bog-standard, long-tail customer model which needed a bit of sorting when we got to Le Mans. It was all over the place on the straights at first so we changed the springs – all straightforward mechanical stuff – and we started the race with a very adequate, comfortable car. We were not there to win – we hadn't the pace for that – so we drove a traditional endurance race, simply aiming to last the distance, and we managed to do that.

'I was driving it in the night when some rain came down, making the car feel very nervous and squirrelly on its Goodyears. I think it was a bit cool for those tyres but, anyway, the handling came good again as the dawn came and the circuit warmed up a bit. It was not a "wring-its-neck" kind of race car, that one, but apart from that brief spell in the dark and wet it was very good to drive.'

What other reflections does he have, looking back on the Group C days?

'One thing I definitely don't miss is the way that sports cars let water into the cockpit when it rains – it's really unpleasant and they all do it. Not even the 962 was immune. But, to be more serious, if the 962 had any weaknesses, one was Porsche's desire to stick with an aluminium chassis when others were going over to stiffer carbonfibre structures.

'Also, Porsche's flat-six engine was magnificent but it took up a lot of width in a critical area and that was not ideal for ground-effect aerodynamics. Such considerations were never such a great issue at Le Mans, even with chicanes, but they certainly were elsewhere. When Porsche, ever focused on Le Mans above all else, had to compete against serious opposition from the likes of Jaguar and Mercedes-Benz, it gradually became clear that ultimately the traditional flat-six engine was a drawback to aerodynamic performance when set against a V6, V8 or V12. The 962 enjoyed a lengthy racing life but Porsche probably clung on to that flat-six concept for a couple of years too long.' △

Thanks to John Watson, Paul Michaels and Donington Park, www.donington-park.co.uk.

'At Le Mans, the long-tail 962
was about as good as it gets,
in my experience'

BRAINS v

Twenty years ago, the high-tech Porsche 959 made the aggressive Ferrari F40 look crude and outdated. But how do they fare now as modern classics, not just in terms of the driving experience but for value and practicality?

Words: Robert Coucher   Photography: Michael Bailie

If you read new car magazines you cannot have failed to notice the latest hyper sports car grudge match featured on every cover: Porsche 911 GT2 versus Ferrari 430 Scuderia. And long has this battle for ultimate road car performance been raging.

It all began in 1983, when Porsche topped Ferrari's beautiful 288GTO with its technological *meisterstück*, the *Gruppe B*, soon to become known as the 959. Enzo Ferrari was smarting from the trumping meted out by the men in white coats from Stuttgart. He had to ignominiously pull the GTO from any racing programme because he knew it could not beat the Group B contender. A change in the Group B rules helped – but his GTO was effectively bested in the engineering shop without even venturing onto a circuit.

In 1987 Enzo celebrated his 40th anniversary at the helm of his eponymous sports car operation by launching the F40, a racing car destined for... the road. Here was a limited-production flagship Ferrari to take the fight to Porsche and win. With a claimed top speed of 201mph and a 0-60mph time of 3.7 seconds, Ferrari grabbed the Fastest Car in the World crown. But, most importantly, it was faster than the 197mph 959. On paper...

Initially Ferrari planned to limit F40 production to just 400. This →

s BRAWN

'Why is it that the more numerous F40 commands a premium over the rarer, more sophisticated 959?'

This page
Porsche is the more civilised machine on the road, but doesn't turn nearly so many heads as the Ferrari.

was then increased to 1000 and final production ran to 1315 examples by 1992. When sales began in the UK the F40's list price was £193,000, but immediately cars changed hands for up to half a million and Nigel Mansell sold his for £800,000, making him as good a car dealer as he was a racing driver. Good F40s command £200,000 today.

First seen at the Frankfurt Motor Show in 1983, the Porsche 959 went on sale in 1987, with a limited run of 200 examples. Demand was high so a total of 268 was manufactured, including the racing and test cars. Far fewer than the F40, then. The 959 cost £145,000, speculators drove the price to more than double that and now a good example is worth £150,000.

By late-'80s standards the 959 was an incredibly advanced and complicated machine. It is reputed that Porsche sold them for half of their actual cost as showcases for its engineering prowess. And the ploy worked: the 959 was a well-proven competition machine, dominating the 1986 Paris-Dakar Rally by finishing in first and second places, with the heavily laden back-up car coming home fifth. In the same year a 959 finished seventh overall at Le Mans, headed only by Group C Porsches. An incredible result.

In the meantime Ferrari constructed its (relatively) mechanically simple F40 racing car for the road, but never went racing. A couple of privateers campaigned F40s in the IMSA Series at Laguna Seca and the BRP Global GT Series in Europe. In LM guise they were beaten by the McLaren F1 GTR at Le Mans.

Today, as modern classics, why is it that the more numerous Ferrari F40 road car commands a hefty premium over the rarer, more sophisticated, race-proven Porsche 959? As our American friends are wont to say, 'Go figure'.

But let's leave that aside for a mo', and go and drive these two examples, warmed and ready for action on the shoreline of Lake Geneva. Our man in Switzerland, Simon Kidston, procured this immaculate 1990 Ferrari F40 Berlinetta, a rare early example with pre-catalyst exhaust and non-adjustable suspension, and just 11,250 miles showing on the clock. I personally am not much taken with the F40's Pininfarina-styled looks, but there is no denying it has a pugnacious presence. With that sharply drooping snout and high rear wing it does look like a road-racer, and a quick one. The 2936cc V8 engine, an evolution of the previous 288GTO mill, with the help of two Japanese water-cooled IHI turbochargers, promises 478bhp at 7000rpm. And most of this forced-induction plumbing is visible through the rear plastic engine cover. Very boy racer.

Open the flimsy carbonfibre door and the F40's interior looks like that of a kit car: simple to the point of appearing homemade. The requisite Momo steering wheel is in place, there is a set of very red racing seats, the exposed Ferrari gearshift gate, a sprinkling of instruments and that's it. No carpet, no door trim, →

no weight. And that's where this Ferrari is a bit special – in the construction of its body and chassis. Using F1 composite technology of the day, the F40 features a tubular steel spaceframe chassis with bonded-on panels of Kevlar, imparting torsional stiffness without weight. The doors, bonnet, bootlid and other removal panels are all carbonfibre. The result is an all-up weight of just 1100kg, about the same as the notably light Porsche 911 2.7RS Touring of the early 1970s.

Once clambered over the wide sill and cupped into the figure-hugging seat, you clack the door behind you. The Momo is set high and at quite a flat angle. The bare, black composite floor is shiny underfoot and gaps are sealed with what looks like green mastic. The pedals are naked metal and the dash is covered in cheap-looking carpeting, but the instruments are right in your line of vision, with the tacho redline marked at 7750rpm, and the long gearshift perfectly placed.

Check for neutral, turn the key and punch the starter button. The V8 behind you fires without much drama. It initially runs a bit unevenly, but dab the throttle and it revs cleanly. Having a flat-plane crank arrangement, it sounds like two eager four-cylinders rather than whoofling lazily like an American V8.

Depress the clutch – ouch, it is heavy – and pull the stiff gearlever back and down towards you for first. You would think that this Ferrari might choose to stall in true race-car style but no, just engage the clutch, add some throttle and the ample quotient of 425lb ft of torque eases the light F40 away. Trundling through the centre of busy Geneva, the Ferrari is tractable and remains largely calm and docile. The clutch and gearshift are both heavy and you cannot see much behind you, yet the steering is alive and sharp, and the car seems to swivel from your hips. The untrimmed interior sounds just like a racing machine: engine and suspension noise crash through the cabin, while every piece of grit thrown up from the road can be heard hitting the composite tub. Tyre noise rises markedly as we head out onto the motorway leading to the mountains.

Kidston and snapper Bailie in the photo car ahead wave me past as the motorway clears, so I drop a gear and depress the throttle. The Ferrari's engine spools up and the rev-counter breaches 4000rpm. In a flash it is at 5000rpm and then in the next instant at the seven-and-three-quarters redline. Whilst not quite an on/off switch, the twin-turbo V8 gathers speed at a terrifying rate after about five thou'.

Lifting the throttle to go for the next gear, there is an explosive *phzzzooooo!* noise from behind my right ear, loud enough to make me almost jump clean out of the seat. Thank goodness for the racing harness. My first thought is that something must have blown in the engine bay but then it strikes me: must be the turbo pop-off valve. With my heart rate slowly coming down from about 170bpm, I give the F40 another squirt and change up through the 'box, enjoying the accompaniment of the pop-off with each cog swapped.

This Ferrari is frighteningly fast. Your need to recalibrate your brain to absorb information at the speed the Ferrari requires: the rise of revs, the concentration required for the recalcitrant gearshift, the way speed piles onto the speedo, the way the motorway narrows and other cars come back at you as you fly past... Then the need to process the fast-shrinking distances that are screaming towards you through the large windscreen. After driving 'normal' historic cars, this is like a computer game – a very hot and noisy one.

Settling in and becoming more comfortable with the Ferrari, you notice that the firm ride is acceptable on the smooth Swiss motorway and the car always feels securely planted. Peeling off and into the mountain roads, the Ferrari attacks a steep climb with gusto. Twirling it through the corners it shoots to the next bend, where you can throw it in, quickly. The well-sorted suspension keeps it flat at all times and on these dry roads grip is no problem, with massive 335-section Pirelli P7s at the rear. But the brakes begin to prove a bit of a challenge, needing a firm shove and not biting with much conviction. As you climb higher up the mountain, the road gets tighter and the Ferrari begins to feel a tad wide. Also, the corners come up more quickly so you have to be careful to judge when the turbos cut in, trying to get them on-boost on the way out and not boosting when going in. Damn hard work but enormous driving fun.

The F40 is basically a large go-kart. It has that typical Ferrari nervousness, feeling tightly wound and super responsive. As well as the less-than-co-operative gearbox, the throttle pedal is awkward, being sticky when you drive slowly. It much prefers to be down more than half its travel, at which point all hell breaks loose.

Clambering out of the now very hot Ferrari atop a mountain, I am perspiring and shaking a little. What a car! What an adrenalin pump! This is a supercar of the late '80s but it feels

Below
Ferrari F40 looks all race-built aggression – ironic, then, that it's the Porsche 959 that has the competition history. →

'Clambering out of the now very hot Ferrari atop a mountain, I'm perspiring and shaking a little. What a car!'

like a classic of the '60s. Much faster and more effective, of course, but providing that pure driver feel, unsullied by power assistance, servo assistance, rubber bushing, sound deadening, suspension compliance and all that boring stuff. Fortunately, Kidston has arranged a luncheon at his favourite restaurant stop, so I have a chance to calm down.

The other protagonist is the Porsche 959, brought along by historic racer and Lancia aficionado Anthony Maclean. He explains that his 959 is a high-mileage car, having covered 40,000km. That's apparently a lot in the 959 world. He says that the Porsche has proven totally reliable and is perfectly happy to potter about in urban traffic. When the 959 was launched it caused a sensation but today, apart from its large rear tail, it looks almost ordinary. That's because so much of it is so sensible and has been adopted by mainstream manufacturers: flush headlamps, integrated bumpers, aerodynamic side mirrors and swoopy, slippery shapes are now seen everywhere.

The Porsche boasts a proper race-proven engine, as fitted to the 956 and 962 Group C cars. The 2.85-litre flat-six has water-cooled heads, twin superchargers and was quoted as producing 450bhp. Maclean's car has had the desirable factory upgrade

which includes smaller, more efficient turbos with more vanes, and a re-mapped ECU. It now puts out 585bhp, with torque upped from the standard 369lb ft at 5500rpm.

As well as the sensational engine, the Porsche features four-wheel drive with variable torque split, with manual and electronic adjustable settings for different road conditions ranging from Traction, to Ice & Snow, to Dry. It has a six-speed 'box, double-wishbone suspension with height adjustment, hydraulic and mechanical damping, 51% of the bodywork is of composite material and the drag co-efficient is a slippery 0.32. Phew! Oh yes, it also features on-board tyre-pressure monitors as developed for the Le Mans car. And hollow magnesium rims. And run-flat tyres... The list is endless.

Open the aluminium door and you are met by what looks like a bog-standard 911 interior, apart from the very 1980s metallic-looking, *Star Wars*-inspired seats. Porsche has often gone off-piste with its seats. Remember the lurid Hounds Tooth cloth it used in the '70s?

The engine fires up like a 911 but the note is slightly deeper. A chatter from the gearbox is slightly odd, yet slot the lever into first and the noise stops as you release the light and easy clutch. The throttle response is a little soft but the racing car pootles

Below
Both F40 and 959 looked outrageous in the '80s. Now the Porsche seems more 'normal'. Is this echoed in the driving?

off down the road with no fuss at all. Through villages the Porsche is much easier to drive than the Ferrari. All is cool and quiet inside, with an occasional discreet hydraulic noise from deep in the bowels. The car is narrow and rides beautifully, and vision is 360 degrees with no blind spots; the gearshift is a little rubbery and the steering is power assisted. And yes, it has electric windows, unlike the Ferrari's quaint manual winders.

Once out on a clear and open road, it's time to see what happens when you give the 959 its head. Drop down a few gears and let it go. Initially the motor spools up gently. Then it starts to tingle – you can feel the engine through the bodywork as if it has very firm engine mounts. The unit wakens one of its turbos, then at about 4500rpm the second turbo cuts in. *BANG*! The feeling is like someone kicking the back of the driver's seat. Warp speed: the Porsche seems to physically leap down the road, and in an instant you are into the next corner. Hit the brakes hard and the thing just stops. Goodness!

This is a ferociously fast machine once the engine wakes up. It emits a lovely wail which is never intrusive, and through the mountains the Porsche feels fast and composed. It is softer than the Ferrari but more manageable. The brakes are sensational and show up the relative weakness of the F40's; →

'It is abundantly clear that the 959 is the more advanced car: it feels decades ahead of the F40'

'Maybe the F40 was a money-making exercise. But maybe Porsche was showing off with the 959'

the ride is fluid, the steering nicely weighted but not as sharp as the Ferrari's.

Coursing through the Swiss mountains it is abundantly clear that the Porsche 959 is the more advanced machine: it feels decades ahead of the F40, even if not quite as fast. That is probably because it is so refined. In my hands it is faster on the road because the chassis is so clever. It has that typical 911 rear-end weight and the front suspension bobs a bit, but it tracks around bends with precision. You guide the Porsche with your fingertips, where you have to hustle the less-obedient Ferrari with your shoulder and arm muscles.

So how do these classic supercars feel today? Both are blindingly fast. Maybe the F40 was a cynical money-making exercise but, then again, maybe Porsche was just showing off with the 959. These machines were built to challenge each other but they are entirely different. The Ferrari is a hot rod, a go-kart that snaps, crackles and pops. The Porsche is a cerebral tool that is immensely capable, if a little sterile. When you drive through towns and villages, small boys react to the F40 with glee. They don't notice the 959.

The Ferrari is a fantastic, hard-core road rocket. It is the perfect track day car and attention-grabbing device. It makes you feel like a racing driver every time you fire it up, and that's why it commands a higher price today than a 959. The Porsche is the better machine and is quicker in the real world. On motorways the 959 does feel more capable than the F40 and it's the sort of mile-eater that will get you across Europe in comfort – especially this example, which has the factory engine upgrade.

But the reality is that, in the 24 years since the Porsche was first seen at Frankfurt, technology has caught up. Now, a standard 911 will do almost everything the 959 does, and the latest £130,000 GT2 will do most things better. The 959 is an iconic car but modern engineering has it eclipsed.

The Ferrari F40 eschewed technology when it was launched in 1987. By today's standards, it is a crazy weapon that sticks two fingers up to automotive convention. That's why we love it.

Thanks to Anthony Maclean and Simon Kidston, www.kidston.com.

'We've had to fix a few that have been spun. They can spin like a top when the turbo cuts in'

FERRARI F40

ENGINE
2936cc dohc V8, four valves per cyl, fuel injection, twin IHI turbos

POWER
478bhp @ 7000rpm

TORQUE
425lb ft @ 4000rpm

TRANSMISSION
Five-speed manual, rear-wheel drive

SUSPENSION
Front: double wishbones, coil springs, telescopic dampers, anti-roll bar
Rear: double wishbones, coil springs, telescopic dampers, anti-roll bar

BRAKES
Vented discs all round

PERFORMANCE
0-60mph 3.7sec
Top speed 201mph

WEIGHT
c1100kg (2425lb)

VALUE
£200,000

F40: the sensible supercar

The F40 is simple, tough and robust. Ferrari specialist Bob Houghton (+44 (0)1451 860794, www.bobhoughtonferrari. co.uk) says, 'The F40 is one of my favourite Ferraris. It is a pussycat off the throttle and a tiger when you are on it. You have to treat it with respect, especially on roundabouts. We've had to fix a few that have been spun – they can spin like a top when the turbo cuts in.

'Servicing is no problem at all. The fuel bladders are "lifed" for ten years and companies like ATL manufacture FIA-approved replacements [bladders are even listed in the Demon Tweeks catalogue].

'The cars should have an annual service, where it's important to change the brake fluid. Oil changes depend on mileage, and the cambelts need to be done every two years but that's a simple engine-in job, as is the clutch change.

'Obviously rear tyres can be gone through quickly, and we do offer a couple of brake upgrades depending on what you want to do with the car. The standard brakes are not great.

'Quite a few German examples have been modified but the standard turbos are nothing tricky. We have only ever had to do a gearbox once: that was Nick Mason's car, which is high mileage and has seemingly been driven by everyone. Second gear was replaced.

'The F40 is wonderful to drive, if very physical. It teaches you all the time. Ultimately it is a Ferrari supercar that is easy to maintain.'

→

'The technician at the factory usually
has a few 959s in needing work because
they do not get driven enough'

959: costly if not used enough

Motor cars in general tend to command more money on the market if they have covered a low mileage. The problem is that vehicles which are not driven tend to throw up mechanical problems, and this is particularly true of the 959.

Anthony Maclean tries to use the example featured here as much as possible, driving it from Geneva to the factory at Stuttgart for its annual service. 'The technician at the factory usually has a few 959s in which need work because they do not get driven nearly enough,' he says.

This is borne out by John Manning, who is operations manager at Porsche Cars GB. Manning was one of only two British technicians who was trained by the factory to look after the 959. 'When the cars stand around, the seals in the drive pump for the four-wheel-drive system can stick inside the cylinder. This causes leakage, which in turn sets off the warning systems and cuts the drive. The parts alone for this job add up to more than £6000,' he explains.

He continues: 'There is a lot of magnesium in the engine, and if electrolysis occurs it can cause things like cam covers to be eaten away. Parts are expensive but Porsches are very well engineered, so if a 959 is used often it should need only an annual inspection service, which will cost around £2000.'

PORSCHE 959
ENGINE
2850cc flat-six, four valves per cyl, sequential twin turbo, fuel injection
POWER
585bhp @ 6500rpm
TORQUE
450lb ft @ 5500rpm
TRANSMISSION
Six-speed manual, four-wheel drive
SUSPENSION
Front and rear: double wishbones, adjustable damping, two dampers per wheel, electronic and hydraulic adjustable ride height, anti-roll bars
BRAKES
Vented discs all round
PERFORMANCE
0-60mph 3.7sec
Top speed 197mph
WEIGHT
c1600kg (3527lb)
VALUE
£150,000

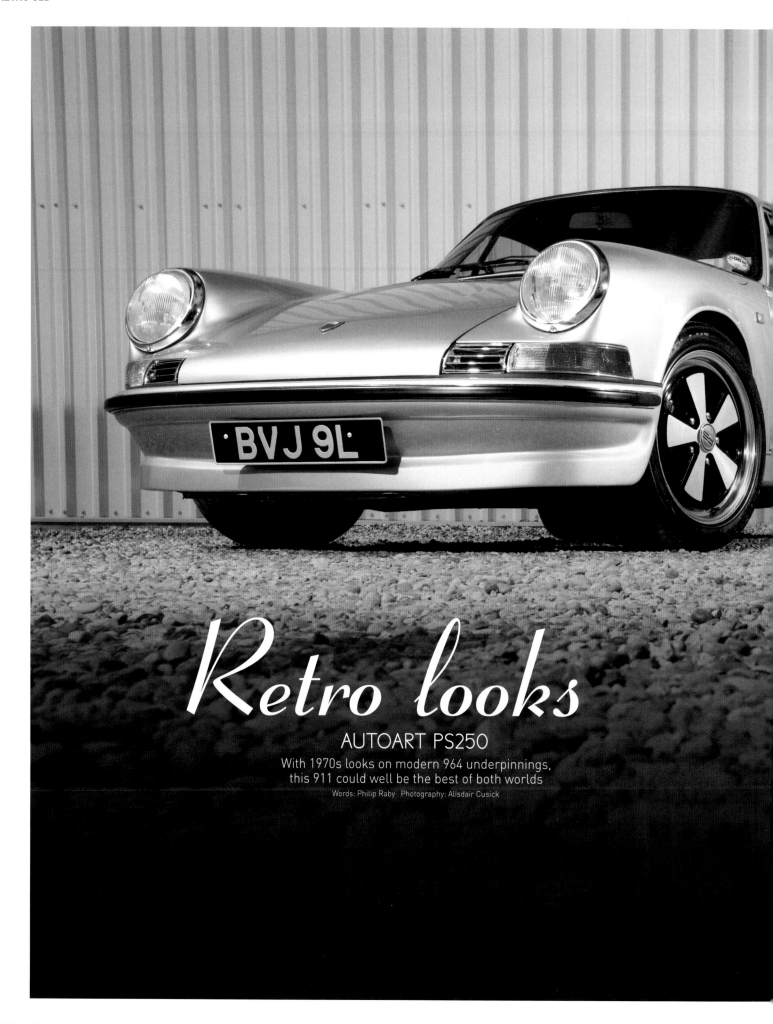

Retro looks

AUTOART PS250

With 1970s looks on modern 964 underpinnings,
this 911 could well be the best of both worlds

Words: Philip Raby   Photography: Alisdair Cusick

Pastiche is a dirty word these days,
used as a derogatory term for something that is
a tacky and muddled imitation of an older style. That's a
shame, because it would otherwise be a useful way
to describe this Porsche 911, for which I'm struggling to
find an appropriate word.

You see, Paul Stephens' PS 250R is a 964-model 911
Carrera 2 that's been fettled to look like a 1970s 911S. Yet
it's by no means a replica; anyone with a passing
knowledge of Porsches will see that this is not a genuine
911S, even before they get behind the wheel.

No, this is a car that draws inspiration from the classic
911s from the 1960s and 1970s, yet unashamedly clings
onto the best parts of its 1990s heritage while adding
some unique 21st century bits into the mix.

Suffolk-based Porsche specialist Paul Stephens came
up with what he calls his PS Autoart series as

a means of offering the best of both worlds – classic looks
with modern comfort and reliability. He's built several,
based on various donors and mechanical specifications.
This one is based on a 1992 911 with a standard 250bhp
flat-six engine (hence the name, 250R – the 'R' stands for
Retro), so it features coil spring suspension rather than
the torsion bars found on pre-1989 911s.

The 964 (as this era of 911 is known) was a radical
update in 911 terms, with smooth plastic bumpers and a
retractable rear spoiler giving the car a more modern
appearance. Yet the basic shape remained virtually
identical to that of earlier 911s.

The first things to go were those polyurethane bumpers
with their heavy steel mountings, to be replaced by
lightweight glassfibre items. These look like '73 bumpers
but are, in fact, slightly deeper front and rear, to cover the
different metalwork behind. On previous PS cars, →

Stephens fitted RS-style front bumpers, which have a boxy section behind the numberplate, to accommodate the 964's spare wheel well. However, the owner of this car insisted that he wanted a standard 911S bumper, so the wheel well had to be modified and a new panel welded in to give clearance – a job that's been done remarkably neatly when you look inside the luggage compartment. There's still room for the spare, but the jack has to reside elsewhere.

Changing the bumpers was challenging in itself, but the bonnet was more difficult. In 1974 Porsche had redesigned the 911 with US-friendly 'impact bumpers' and the bonnet was shortened accordingly. With earlier-style bumpers, Stephens had to lengthen the bonnet (an early bonnet won't fit the 964) by modifying the frame and then reskinning it aluminium.

Next, the front wings had to be modified to match the pre-'73 profile. Stephens had previously done this by adding glassfibre fillets to fill the two-inch gap left by removing the old bumpers, as genuine early wings won't fit the 964, but he'd never been happy with the results. Now the wings have been fabricated in steel to create the correct look while still fitting the 964 inner structure.

The finishing touches are period-style front and rear indicators with chrome horn grilles at the front. The light units were made specially because genuine items wouldn't fit, but the lenses and grilles are originals.

Below and left
Fuel-injected 964 engine produces an easy 250bhp; new wheels look like original Fuchs at a glance but are actually machined, not forged.

At the rear the 964's retractable spoiler, which rises at 55mph and then drops back down at 5mph, has been retained (it's essential for high speed stability and for engine cooling) but cleverly modified so that, when closed, it sits flush with the engine cover and so looks similar to the fixed grille on earlier 911s.

The 964 had matt black window frames and handles, which have been stripped back and given the correct anodised aluminium look, while the doorhandles have been chrome-plated, and the front and rear window surround are also now in chrome. The door mirrors are small round items, which contain the internals of the original Porsche electric mirrors.

So far so good, but Stephens admits that the sills stumped him. Pre-1989 911s had slim steel outer sills but Porsche equipped the 964 with chunky plastic sill covers to hide the comprehensively revised inner structure of the 964 beneath. Removing the covers was not possible without exposing the unattractive inner sills, so they were retained and visually slimmed down by painting the lower parts black. Stephens also removed the plastic 'shark's fins' which led up from the sills to protect the leading edges of the wings. Despite his efforts, it's the sills that let this car down: they're obviously from a later 911 and the black lower sections make the car appear to sit higher off the ground.

The other giveaway is the wheels, but here Stephens isn't pretending that they're the real thing. From 1966 to 1989, forged Fuchs alloy

'It draws inspiration from the classic 911s yet unashamedly clings onto the best parts of its 1990s heritage'

wheels were de rigueur for 911s but, today, good originals are hard to come by and, besides, they only go up to 16in diameter and don't fit the 964.

Stephens, therefore, decided to commission his own wheel design. These are machined alloys and, while obviously based on Fuchs, have a style all of their own and look much more modern with their sharp-edged spokes. You'll either love them or hate them; Stephens is also producing a more realistic Fuchs replica using the correct forging techniques.

But this isn't meant to be a replica, remember. And that becomes more apparent when you get inside. Anyone who tells you that the 911's interior didn't change over 30 years is wrong. The basic architecture remained essentially the same, with the trademark five dials in front of the driver, but the detail was refined with each new model. Which means that the PS250's cockpit is years ahead of the rather basic interior of an older 911S. It's also much nicer than you'd expect to find in a standard 964, and that's thanks to Stephens' retrimming.

He's created a mix of RS functionality, with lightweight door panels and no rear seats (these can be fitted if required), mixed with opulent smooth black leather that covers the dash, centre console, doors and steering wheel. The seats, meanwhile, are a modern take on period rally items, complete with corduroy centres.

It's a sumptuous place to be, with a smell of leather that you don't get in today's sanitised cars. Pull the door with the simple pull strap and it shuts with a rock-solid

AUTOART PS250

ENGINE
3600cc air-cooled flat-six, OHC per bank, fuel injection, Motronic engine management, Hayward & Scott exhaust system

POWER
250bhp @ 4800rpm

TORQUE
229lb ft @ 4800rpm

TRANSMISSION
Five-speed manual, rear-wheel drive

SUSPENSION
Front: independent via lower wishbones and MacPherson struts with Cargraphic coil springs and dampers, anti-roll bar. Rear: independent via semi-trailing arms with Cargraphic coil springs and dampers, anti-roll bar

BRAKES
Discs all round, servo assisted with ABS

WHEELS & TYRES
Front: 17x6J with 205/50ZR17 tyres
Rear: 17x8J with 225/40ZR17 tyres

PERFORMANCE
0-60mph c5.5sec.
Top speed c160mph

clunk that hints at the 911's legendary build quality. The engine starts on the first turn of the key. There's no messing with a hand-throttle between the seats thanks to the 964's fuel injection and Motronic engine management, and it settles to a deep burble, thanks to a Hayward & Scott exhaust system. That's all that's non-standard back there.

Yet on the road, I have to keep reminding myself that this is the case. I've driven countless 964s over the years and know the model intimately, but this feels quite different, as if it's pumping out nearer 300bhp. The exhaust system will account for maybe 10bhp, but the main reason for this illusion is the fact that the car is lighter than standard, thanks to the removal of the heavy bumpers, rear seats and much of the original sound-deadening material, plus the addition of the much lighter aluminium bonnet.

While it doesn't have the delicate fingertip control and lift-off oversteer of a classic 911, the PS250R does feel lighter and more controllable than a standard 964, which had some of the feedback dampened out of it. Yet nor is it as communicative as a 964 Carrera RS (one of my favourite 911s), which is lighter and more extreme, thanks to firm springs and dampers. The PS250 has been fitted with uprated Cargraphic springs, but mainly because lowered springs were needed to compensate for the reduced weight (the standard 964 has a high ride height anyway) rather than to improve the handling. They're compliant springs – rather too much so for my liking – which ensures a comfortable ride. →

Clockwise from above
Chrome horn grilles are essential to classic look; spoiler cleverly drops into engine lid; period-style sports seats in unashamedly modern cockpit.

'It's a 911 you could use every day, something you'd be hard-pressed to do with a genuine 911S'

And that sums up this car. It's a 911 that you could happily live with and use every day, something you'd be hard-pressed to do with a genuine 911S. It gives you the best of both worlds – classic looks with relatively modern technology. You have the benefits of the 964's more modern interior, complete with electronically controlled heating system (early 911 heating controls are quirky, to say the least), not to mention its 3.6-litre engine (don't believe the horror stories – it's a fundamentally good unit), excellent G50/03 gearbox, power steering, ABS braking and improved chassis. Oh, and a fully galvanised bodyshell that ensures 964s don't rot like older 911s.

Certainly it's never going to be mistaken for the genuine article by Porschephiles but, if it did, you'd have to compromise on the car's usability – in which case you might as well go the whole hog and buy a real 911S.

For me, Paul Stephens has got this car just right, to the extent that it's a 911 I'd be happy to own myself. It's been beautifully finished, with great attention to detail. From the solid silver 'PS Autoart' badge on the bonnet to the period-style corded carpets, everything smacks of quality. Stephens is also keen to protect his customers' investment, so each PS is individually numbered (this car is 005) and he will keep a record of their history.

Because each car is handbuilt to order, you can have whatever you want. The owner of 005 had, in fact, owned the Porsche since it was just six months old, and when he took it to Paul Stephens

he chose to have a full respray and to concentrate on the appearance. The plan is he'll return next year for brake and engine upgrades, when money allows. Stephens is now on build 015, with each car personalised to the customer's requirements.

You, too, can go down this route and have your own car treated to a PS Autoart conversion, or you can get Stephens to source a suitable donor. This could be a 964, like this car, or an older Carrera 3.2 or SC, if you prefer a more classic feel and appearance. If you go down the 964 route you can, if you wish, opt for Tiptronic transmission or four-wheel drive, while a Targa roof is available in all models.

In addition, you can choose colour, trim and specification, while Stephens offers a range of mechanical upgrades which, in the case of the 3.6-litre 964, will take power to over 310bhp.

Because each car is bespoke, it's hard to give a precise cost. But as a guide, a decent 964 donor will cost between £15,000 and £18,000, to which you have to add around £25,000 for a body conversion like the featured car's. Or you can budget £60,000 for a full build, including the cost of the donor car. There's also a 300R conversion available, based on 3.8RS running gear and lightweight panels, for serious performance.

A PS Autoart, then, is something very special and exclusive. Whether it's preferable to a '70s original is your decision. △

Thanks to PS Autoart, Suffolk. +44 (0)1440 714884, www.psautoart.com.

Looking to buy or sell an air cooled or exclusive Porsche?

At Paul Stephens we are proud of our reputation for sourcing the finest examples and making them available to our customers.

We also restore and enhance Porsche to specification, applying our same exacting standards.

- We always have a hand picked selection available to view in our showroom.

- Our cars are all fully prepared and serve as recommendations for the future.

For a current stock list or to enquire about our bespoke, hand built PS cars please contact us or visit our website

www.paul-stephens.com

SPECIALIST IN AIR COOLED AND EXCLUSIVE PORSCHE

01440 714 884   email@paul-stephens.com
Sudbury Road, Little Maplestead, Halstead, Essex, CO9 2SE

www.paul-stephens.com

SPECIALIST CARS
OF MALTON LTD

APPROVED MOTOR CARS

Official Distributor

WANTED

356 Speedster	993 Carrera 2	996 GT3
2.7 RS	993 Carrera 4	996 GT3 RS
2.8 RS	993 Carrera S	996 Cup Car
3.0 RS	993 Carrera 4S	996 RSR
3.2 Speedster	993 Turbo	996 GT3R
959	993 GT2	997 Cup Car
964 RS	993 GT2 Evo	997 GT3
964 Turbo	993 RS	997 GT3 RS
964 Cup Car	993 Cup Car	Carrera GT
964 Speedster	GT1	Le Mans cars

Any other interesting or rare Porsches
RHD OR LHD

Telephone: 0844 7000 997 • 0844 7000 993 • 07794 911 911 (after hours) Fax: 0844 7000 959
Visit our award winning site – www.specialistcarsltd.co.uk
22 York Road Business Park, Malton YO17 6AX
Part of Specialist Car Group of companies

END
OF THE
AFFAIR

Last of the air-cooled RennSport 911s, the 993 Carrera RS is one
of the most exciting Porsches ever made. Now is definitely the time to buy

Words: Peter Morgan Photography: Paul Harmer

'A 993RS cost £9500 more than a regular Carrera and, as is usual when it comes to faster Porsches, this meant you got less for more'

There is something reassuring as well as thrilling about the prospect of driving a Carrera RS. You can be sure of an uncomplicated, well-built car that's focused on one thing only – delivering an outstanding driving experience.

RS is not a title given to just any Porsche. Over the Stuttgart company's many years of sports car production, only a handful have been of sufficient calibre to be awarded the RennSport title. And each has made its mark in unique ways. So back in 1995, when news leaked that an RS version of the 993 was to be produced, Porsche found no shortage of customers.

The 993 had proven to be the 911 that put the stake in the sand for Porsche after a difficult trading period in the early 1990s. Planned only as an interim model until the new – and water-cooled – generation arrived, it emerged as the most accomplished, prettiest 911 of them all. And sales out-stripped all expectations.

The new RS wasn't the product of a few quick engineering meetings, either. It was the culmination of a development cycle that had begun with the Carrera Cup 911s back in 1990. The one-model racing series which supported European grands prix was a great success. The 964-bodied Carrera RS of 1992 – a 911 still regarded as the best trackday Porsche of them all – was one by-product of this work. And, by 1994, the Carrera Cup had become the Porsche Supercup and was using a race version of the new 993.

Over the coming year, it was but a small step for the motorsport department to pool its experiences of the 911-based race cars to produce what is arguably the definitive road-going 911 Carrera RS.

In total, 1064 examples of the 993RS were built during 1995 and 1996, compared with a total of 2051 for the preceding 964RS and 1580 for the classic 1973 2.7-litre RS.

It's easy to see why today the 993RS has collectors and enthusiasts alike straining to track down the best examples. Besides giving you its pedigree, voluptuous curves and stunning performance to enjoy, this RS could well provide a top-up for your grandson's pension.

Few would argue against it being a modern classic. Walk up to one and you'll feel the electricity immediately. As the last air-cooled 911RS, its engineers set out to underline that it was the thoroughbred sports car of its generation – an unmatched climax of more than 35 years of 911 development – and the last hurrah before the nature of Porsches changed forever.

This is a machine that's doing 150mph before you even open the door. So good was the original 993 that the RS version didn't need to go much further in terms of its visual appeal. But look closer at this example, which has the optional Club Sport bodykit, and you'll enjoy its many elegant flourishes: flourishes that contribute a unique signature and, importantly, keep the car planted on the ground when other makes would fly.

A 993RS cost £9500 more than a regular Carrera in 1995 and, as is usual when it comes to faster Porsches, this meant you got less for more. Its real secret is not outright power – 300bhp is barely in the supercar league – but power-to-weight ratio, where it has more power and less weight.

It might not look that much different from the outside, but there's an aluminium bonnet, thinner outer-skin steel, lighter glass and an electrical system that's been pared down to the bare essentials – well, almost. There is no sunroof and no rear seating. Most of the weighty sound-deadening material has been removed, simple cards have replaced the door trims and there are manual window lifters. Out have gone the electric mirror adjustment, central locking and air-conditioning, and even the interior lighting is relegated to a small bulb in the driver's footwell.

The heart of the new RS was its 3.8-litre, air-cooled flat-six. Developed from the 964RS models, it was significantly more tractable thanks not only to more sophisticated engine management but also because of the new Varioram variable intake ducting system that vastly improved the mid-range torque. Below 5000rpm, the intake ducts are almost twice the length of those on the earlier 'fixed duct' engines. As the revs build beyond 5000rpm, intake vacuum shortens the telescopic ducts in two stages. The effect is to significantly increase the area under the torque curve at lower revs.

The suspension is rigidly mounted, with aluminium top mountings for the shocks and ball-jointed bushes elsewhere. Automatic Brake Differential provides traction control and there's ABS as well to help →

RS story

RS stands for RennSport, the German word for motorsport. The 110bhp 550 Spyder 1500RS was the Stuttgart car maker's first no-nonsense customer racing model in 1955. Since then, the RS designation has been used sparingly, and only on those normally aspirated street cars that have a strong racing spirit.

The 1973 911 Carrera RS is viewed by many as a Porsche icon. This 210bhp limited edition (eventually 1580 were made) was built to qualify an improved-specification 911 for racing. The competition version, called the RSR, would dominate international GT racing during the mid-1970s.

In 1983, the 911 SC-RS was developed for international rallying. Just 22 cars were built, largely for competition. The Rothmans-liveried 280bhp SC-RS gave Finland's Henri Toivenen a strong run in the 1984 European Rally Championship.

The 1991 911 Carrera RS was developed from the special model used in the Carrera Cup race series. This RS is based on the 964-bodied production car and is still notable for the vitality and sound of its blueprinted 260bhp flat-six engine. With 1250 examples made, customers could choose between Lightweight and Touring models.

With the huge sales success of the last air-cooled 911 model – the 993 – it was inevitable that there would be a Carrera RS model. The 300bhp engine featured Varioram variable intake ducting, transforming the torque delivery. Just 1064 examples were built.

In 2004, Porsche announced the first water-cooled 911 Carrera RS. The 996-bodied GT3 RS delivered an incredible 381bhp and maintained the RS pedigree. At the time of its introduction, Porsche said just 200 cars would be built.

Left from top
550 Spyder 1500RS was first Porsche customer racer; 911SC-RS competed in 1984 European Rally Championship.

'This 993 has the optional
RSR biplane rear spoiler
fitted, and the view behind
is like a bad TV picture'

Above
RS proves as
user-friendly as an
ordinary 993, thanks to
large glass area and
tractable engine.

contain the excesses of the most enthusiastic pilots. Despite its low-profile 18-inch Bridgestones, the ride is nonetheless far better than the earlier car's. All 993s benefit from multi-link rear suspension, which finally consigned the old swing arms to history. The result is firm, but far more composed over rough surfaces.

The 993RS also benefits from arguably the best conventional brakes Porsche has ever fitted to its street cars. The huge, red-painted Brembo four-piston calipers and cross-drilled cast iron discs complement elegant three-piece Speedline alloys.

This RS was supplied by Dick Lovett in August 1995. Its clock now registers just over 26,000 miles; Porsche specials tend to be bought for fun use rather than everyday mileage, so many have covered lower-than-average distances, but the downside is that they have often been used very hard. As well as checking their authenticity, you should also ensure that everything is documented in the service history.

As I strap in, I'm aware that the cabin isn't really much different from a regular 993 Carrera's. OK, there are no rear seats and the

door trims are lightweight, but I'm sitting in a comfortable sports seat and I even have power steering. The Weissach engineers finally realised with this RS that customers didn't need to wear a hair shirt to enjoy their products.

My view behind isn't great, though. This 993 has the optional RSR biplane rear wing fitted, and the view is like a bad TV picture. I also have to wind down the windows and prod the door mirrors with a finger to see what's happening either side of me. But who's complaining – this car is all about the driving experience.

The good feeling starts within the first hundred metres. Manoeuvring into the relentless congestion of the A41 from Hendon Way Motors in North London is not the usual moment of terror that you often get in a no-compromise supercar. I can see all around and I'm amazed how easy it is to drive.

There isn't a rattle or squeak anywhere. Everything is beautifully taut, and you get the impression that the whole car could have been laser cut from a billet of high-carbon steel. Nor does it behave like a stallion on a short rein, or splutter and cough like a recalcitrant

Air-cooled RS performance

Model	Year	Maximum Power (bhp)	Kerb Wt (kg)	Top Speed (mph)	0-62mph (seconds)
1955 550 Spyder 1500RS	1955	110	590	122	8.3 (est)
1973 911 Carrera RS Sport	1973	210	995	152	5.8
1983 911SC-RS	1983	280	960	152	5.0
1991 911 Carrera RS (964)	1991	265	1230	162	5.3
1993 911 Carrera RS 3.8 (964)	1993	300	1140	172	4.9
1995 911 Carrera RS (993)	1995	300	1270	172	5.0
2004 911 GT3 RS (996)	2004	381	1330	191	4.4

1995 993RS

ENGINE
3600cc, air-cooled flat-six, single overhead camshaft per cylinder bank, dry-sump lubrication. Twin-spark ignition, Bosch Motronic engine management

POWER
300bhp at 6500rpm

TORQUE
262bhp at 5400rpm

TRANSMISSION
Six-speed manual, rear-wheel drive via limited-slip differential and ABD traction control

SUSPENSION
Front: ind, coil springs over gas dampers. Rear: ind, multi-link, coil springs over gas dampers

BRAKES
Cross-drilled and ventilated discs with four-pot calipers, ABS

WEIGHT
1270kg (2780lb)
Performance
0-62mph 5sec
Top speed 172mph

VALUE
Cost new £68,495
Value now £50-70,000

---

bull when pulling away at low revs. This drivability at any speed reveals the real calibre of this Porsche.

Only the 1973 2.7RS gets close to the same level of sublime composure as the 993RS at both low and high speeds. And both machines reflect Porsche's years of making their race cars sail over the bumps at Spa and Sebring. It's a depth of all-round balance as a combined road and track car that the 964RS arguably didn't manage, since that car was far more focused on pool-table-smooth track performance.

The 3.8-litre flat-six is the biggest-capacity air-cooled engine ever to find its way into a 911, and this one sounds gorgeous. I could hit you with superlatives about how spectacular the car is when delivering its 0-60mph acceleration in under five seconds, or how it will run up to its maximum speed of 175mph. But what sets this motor apart – a real tribute to all those years of air-cooled flat-six development – is that sheer tractability at any speed.

It will pull in any of its six gears from as little as 1000rpm, yet the real power starts between 3000 and 4000rpm. Around 5000rpm, it takes on a hard edge and the tacho needle flies round the gauge to the red line at 6800rpm. By this time you're barrelling forward with relentless force.

And it's this which is the main selling point for me over the equally awe-inspiring 993GT2. That instant RS punch makes the car far more suited for street use, in addition to being ideal for the twists and turns of the Nürburgring. The 430bhp GT2 has the grunt, no question, but you'll get the best out of it only on the long straights of Le Mans.

That brings us to the crux of this car. From the moment you slip behind the steering wheel, you want to be heading for the Eifel mountains. I cannot think of any other vehicle that is so perfectly attuned to lapping the 'Ring as this Carrera RS. Best of all, it gives you complete confidence that it will get you there and home again. That's quality. △

Thanks to Hendon Way Motors, www.racecar.co.uk/hwmnet, +44 (0)20 8202 8011, for supplying the featured car.

Above
Clockwise from far left Varioram intake tubes improve torque at low revs; wheels are split-rim Speedlines; seats comfy despite looks.

GMÜND

The Austrian home of Porsche

The first Porsches were built in a remote alpine village in Austria. The company may have moved on, but visitors can still enjoy the rich legacy it left behind

Words: Delwyn Mallett
Photography: Delwyn Mallett
and Porsche Archives

Above and left
Ferdinand and Ferry Porsche with the first car to carry their name; very early model with slotted engine cover leads production version on test in 1948.

If you find yourself kicking your heels in Kitzbuhel or Klagenfurt, or perhaps feel like slipping away from Salzburg for an hour or two 'off-piste', a visit to the nearby village of Gmünd will provide a pleasant and illuminating diversion. Of course, if you already worship at the shrine of Porsche, no introduction to this picturesque alpine village is necessary. Secreted in a beautiful valley in the southern Austrian province of Corinthia, Gmünd is the spiritual home of all cars that bear the Porsche name. Today the badge on the bonnet may incorporate elements from the coat of arms of Stuttgart, but the first car created to display the family name, the 356, was built in Gmünd in 1948. With an anticipated run of perhaps a few hundred cars spread over a couple of years, the 356 would confound expectation and, with continuous development, stay in production until 1965. At that point it metamorphosed into the 911, which is still with us today. Not bad for a car that started life in a woodshed.

Ferdinand Porsche was born a subject of the Austro-Hungarian Empire in Maffersdorf, Bohemia, on September 3, 1875. At the end of the First World War, Bohemia was declared part of the independent state of Czechoslovakia and Ferdinand found himself a Czech citizen. Porsche retained his Czech nationality until 1944, when Adolf Hitler 'asked' him to become a German passport holder, an offer it would have been foolhardy to refuse. Despite these technical changes of nationality, the Professor always considered himself an Austrian, as were most close colleagues during his long and productive career.

Porsche had spent his life designing for most of the major motor manufacturers of middle-Europe when, at the age of 55, he decided that rather than continuing to move around the car industry as an employee, he would let the car industry come to him. In 1930 he opened a small consultancy in the centre of Stuttgart. Famously, his first commission was given the work number 007 so it would not look as if it was the →

Above (top to bottom)
Recreation of the 356 body buck; early Porsche engine built on VW crankcase; Gmünd 356 coupé in bare metal.

'One cheerful British official said that if Prof Porsche had been a cobbler he would have plenty of work, but as an automotive engineer he would never design another vehicle'

consultancy's first assignment. Some, if not most, of those projects have become legendary. How would you like the 16-cylinder Auto Union Grand Prix car or the Volkswagen Beetle on your CV?

Inevitably for such a talented design house, the outbreak of war meant it became deeply involved in developing military hardware. By the closing stages of World War Two, Stuttgart was taking a pounding from allied bombers and Albert Speer, minister of armaments, ordered Porsche and his valuable team to relocate. They rejected a location in Czechoslovakia and chose a spot not far from the family's country retreat at Zel am See, southern Austria.

So, in the autumn of 1944, 200 skilled designers and engineers found themselves operating from a disused sawmill in the tiny and remote alpine village of Gmünd. At the end of hostilities, this particular corner of Corinthia fell into the British sector of control. Clearly, there weren't a lot of

design commissions heading Porsche's way. One cheerful British official said that if Professor Porsche had been a cobbler he would have plenty of work, but as an automotive engineer he would never design another vehicle.

Finding themselves stranded in a woodshed in Austria, albeit quite a large one, the team of workers turned their skills to anything that would earn a living. Repairing abandoned Kubelwagens was an obvious choice, as few people could be better qualified for the job than the team that had originally designed them!

Back in Germany, under the direction of the British REME (Royal Electrical and Mechanical Engineers), the Volkswagen factory had commenced production and, in 1946, built an astonishing 10,000 vehicles. Encouraged by this guaranteed source of components, Ferdinand's son Ferry pursued a long-held ambition to build a small, lightweight, sports car based on VW

mechanicals. Work commenced on project number 356 in the summer of 1947, and in March of the following year car number 356/001, a lightweight, space-framed, mid-engined roadster, rolled into the sun. Work was also progressing on a coupé which, for reasons of practicality, was rear-engined as in the Volkswagen. The chassis of this car, 356/002, was ready for road testing in April 1948. It soon gained a streamlined, aluminium body and the 'jelly-mould' 356 was born.

Banging out aluminium bodies on an upturned log was not how Ferry Porsche saw the company's future and, in late '49, plans were made for a return to Stuttgart and the series production of a steel bodied car. So the Porsche works slowly seeped out of Gmünd, which reverted to a sleepy alpine village, doing what alpine villages do best – a bit of farming, some wood chopping, and looking beautiful. And that could have been the end of the story, but one man had not forgotten the Porsche connection. As a young boy, Helmut Pfeifhofer had watched the Porsche chassis tearing around the dirt roads of his village. His family had even helped the Porsche concern move in all its equipment back in 1944. In 1982 Helmut fulfilled a dream by opening his own private museum as a tribute to Porsche and its time in Gmünd.

These days Gmünd is far easier to reach, nestling, as it does, virtually under a spectacular flyover of the A10 highway. Mr Pfeifhofer certainly doesn't want you to miss his museum, and even the highway exit signs announce 'Gmünd – Porsche Museum'. Once off the slip-road, signs abound in metal, card, wood or stone, with arrows pointing in the direction of the beautifully converted barn that houses the collection.

A large metal canopy, a patchwork of small panels welded together in the form of a 356 front end, hovers above the museum entrance as a witty prelude to the treasures within. Inside, unrestored, unpainted and standing next to a beautifully sculptural ash body buck, a Gmünd-built aluminium coupé

is, fittingly, the first exhibit to greet visitors. Battered by time and the impressions of the original panel-beater's hammer, this fragile-looking shell sits next to a late 911, demonstrating, in one glance, Porsche's extraordinary 70-year commitment to the rear-engine concept.

An adjoining room has a TV presentation of Porsche history and a display of flat-four boxer motors. These start with the humble little Volkswagen engine and progress through various versions of the Porsche 356 engine to its ultimate development in the form of the glorious and desirable four-cam Carrera.

Upstairs, a large and tightly packed wooden-beamed gallery contains the bulk of the display, which kicks off with a Steyr, designed by Professor Ferdinand Porsche in 1928. A whole rainbow of 356s follows and early VWs are also well represented, with a very rare wartime four-wheel-drive Kommandeurwagen chassis sitting on oversize 'balloon' tyres being of particular interest. A lovely little 550 Spyder sits next to yet another wooden buck, with a large

poster of James Dean in the background to remind the viewer that this is the Porsche model which the actor was driving when he died.

A 'Safari' 911 rally car and even the gorgeous 906 sports racer remind you that there was a time, not too long ago, when road cars and race cars had not diverged to the extent where their functions had become mutually exclusive. By contrast, the Mario Andretti-piloted 962 looks like a Space Shuttle parked in a hanger full of bi-planes.

When you've done the cars, a pit-stop in the picturesque and immaculately kept village is well worthwhile. Here it is not too difficult to conjure up images of Porsche designers scribbling ideas on the backs of envelopes while they relaxed over a beer or two, or imagine little four-wheeled alloy boxes dashing off into the surrounding mountain passes. Further up the main street, and easily overlooked, is the Porsche Park – a quiet, leafy oasis where a bronze bust of Professor Ferdinand Porsche presides as a simple reminder that a great man once passed this way.

Clockwise from below
Body buck for the immortal 550 Spyder; split-window Beetle; rare wartime 4wd chassis; sparse interior of 1948 car.

'Here it is not too difficult to conjure up images of Porsche designers scribbling ideas on the backs of envelopes while they relaxed over a beer'

GMÜND

Not a destination, but a worthwhile diversion

Gmünd was once a remote alpine retreat. Today, the A10 super-highway sweeps through this part of Corinthia providing breathtaking views of the surrounding mountains. Salzburg lies 130km to the north of Gmünd and is an easy run along the A10. Kitzbuhel is to the east and requires a bit of road-hopping but, if you approach from this direction, you can stop off in Zel am See where the Porsche family estate is situated, and also storm the famous Grossglockner. More and more people are re-discovering the joys of Slovenia, which lies just to the south of Austria, and are either flying into Klagenfurt on the Austrian side of the border or Ljubljana 150km to the south of Gmünd, but still within easy striking distance. Approaching from the south gives the visitor the chance to stop at the beautiful resort of Bled on the lake of the same name.

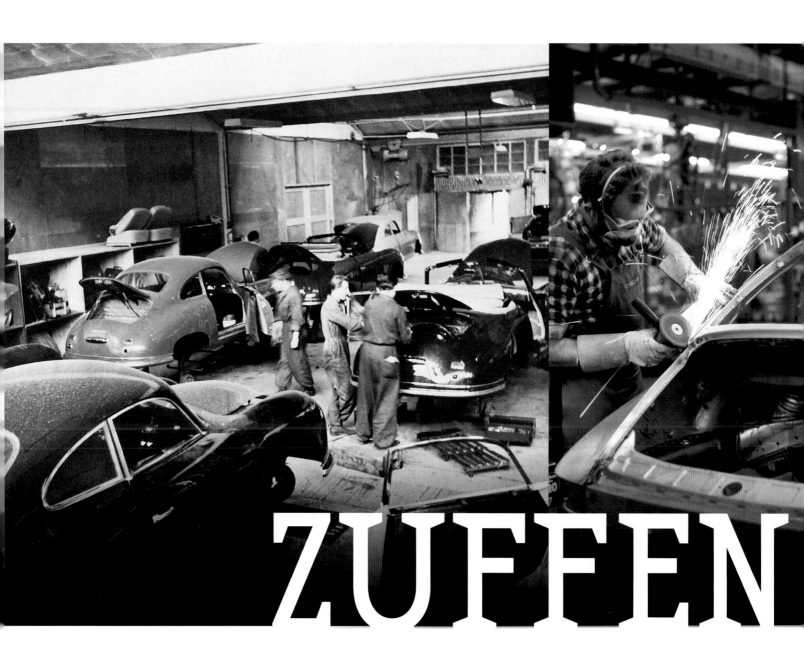

ZUFFEN

Sixty years ago, Porsche moved its production lines from Gmünd to Zuffenhausen.
These evocative pictures show how conditions and techniques have progressed since 1950
Words: David Lillywhite   Photography: Porsche AG

HAUSEN

The picture above left says it all, really. Cramped and dusty, with only basic facilities, this is how Porsche's car production started in Zuffenhausen, Germany, 60 years ago.

The company's Design and Construction offices had moved from central Stuttgart into the Zuffenhausen district of the city as early as 1938. However, by the time production was able to resume after the war, the Porsche factory was still occupied by the US military, and the marque instead built its first few cars in the Austrian Alpine town of Gmünd. The models made there have since achieved near-mythical status.

But it's in Zuffenhausen that Porsches have been built ever since. Coachbuilder Reutter & Co was already based there, and the auto manufacturer initially rented a production hall on its premises. Assembly started in early 1950, with the first Zuffenhausen-built 356 emerging on 6 April of that year. By the end of 1950, 369 cars had been produced there.

In 1952 Porsche Plant 2, designed by architect Rolf Gutbrod, was opened; just four years later the 10,000th 356 left the factory. Now there are five plants, with a new, state-of-the-art ecological paintshop about to be built. It's a far cry from those early, dusty days.

Above from left
Assembly of the 356 in the building rented from Reutter; finishing the welds on a 911 body; spot-welding a 356; Plant 2 in 1955.

→

Above
Zuffenhausen Plant 2, where 2.0-litre 911s are moved between assembly stations on cradles dangling from overhead tracks, and then on wheeled dollies.

'PORSCHE HAD BEEN PLANNING TO PHASE OUT THE 911, SO PRODUCTION TECHNIQUES HAD BARELY CHANGED'

Left
Crankshafts for the 356 were laboriously built up from separate parts in the early days, using roller big-end bearings; this is a later 356A crank, easier to make, with shell big-ends.

Right
At the Zuffenhausen test station, circa 1969, the engine, transmission and gearshift of a 911T 2.0 Targa are tested on the chassis dynamometer.

Above
An early 1950s 356 Cabriolet nears bodywork completion. Construction was complicated, with small panels welded and the joints lead-filled.

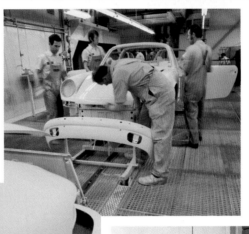

Above
Body prepping the 356. Primer and a guide coat have been applied, and power sanders are being used to prepare for top coats in the spray booth.

Left
Porsche paint inspectors descend on a freshly sprayed 911. This must be around 1970, as this style of front end was replaced with an S-style spoiler for the 1972 model year.

Above
The trim shop at Zuffenhausen. This photo looks to date from the early 1960s, but the techniques used today aren't so different.

Left
Assembling a 911SC 3.0-litre engine: Porsche had been planning to phase out the 911, so production techniques had barely changed even by the early 1980s.

Above
Production of the 356B in the early 1960s would typically see 32 models turned out each day. Cars are pushed around on three-wheeled dollies.

Left
Today's factory is state-of-the-art but traditional craftsmanship is just as important. This 911 has its characteristic instrument panel already in place.

PORSCHE 356
(1950-1964)
£15,000-100,000
A 356 can be a joy forever, but prices have risen
dramatically of late – so invest your money wisely
Words: Richard Dredge

You may not realise it, but you want a 356. Drive a decent one and you'll want it so badly it'll hurt. But buy a bad one and it'll be even more painful.

Ever since its launch in 1950, the 356 has been accused of being a poshed-up Volkswagen. While early 356s featured some Beetle parts and the same basic layout, the Porsche was an all-new model with very different construction – plus superior aerodynamics and a far better power-to-weight ratio. So 356s accelerate quicker and top out higher than you'd think.

It's not just about speed though: while the 356 has a reputation for being tricky to drive in a hurry, the reality is that the rear-mounted engine and torsion bar suspension allow you to hustle the car along much faster than most of its contemporaries. Such agility and frugality are why the 356 has always been so highly sought after – although it's always been an expensive car, too. In 1953 you paid a 50% premium for a 356 over the price of a Jaguar XK120.

If you're tempted to take the plunge, there are plenty of pitfalls. Fred Hampton, 356 registrar for the Porsche Club GB, offers several words of warning: 'Beware of cheap cars: they're heartbreakers rather than bargains. These cars are also extremely costly to restore properly and there are few genuine 356 experts – these cars demand expert restoration. Any decently priced right-hand-drive car is likely to increase in value, as there are probably fewer than 200 genuine UK examples left.'

ENGINE

All 356s have a relatively straightforward flat-four (apart from the hyper-rare quad-cam Carrera models). None of these engines are quiet, but they should idle smoothly and rev cleanly with no misfiring or spluttering. There shouldn't be any oil leaks evident, although the clip-on valve covers sometimes weep slightly, so interiors usually smell of oil; major puddles under the car mean an expensive rebuild is imminent.

If any major work is needed, you can get any parts you need for a complete overhaul, although a total rebuild including ancillaries will cost anywhere between £5000 and £8500. With genuine parts prices being very high, some pattern parts are now being used; not necessarily inferior, just more affordable.

The first sign of engine work being needed is blue smoke from the exhaust, indicating that oil is being burned through worn valve guides. Fumes leaking into the cabin are a sign of the exhaust leaking, and the best solution is a new factory system for around £650.

TRANSMISSION

A four-speed gearbox was fitted to all 356s, with synchromesh on all ratios from 1952. Until then, none of the gears featured synchromesh, but whichever unit is fitted it should soldier on for huge mileages.

First to go are normally the bearings, which will start rumbling while the car is cruising. The next stage in the gearbox's destruction will be first and second-gear synchromesh giving up; you'll pay £750 to fix it, while having a rebuilt gearbox fitted costs close to £3500. If you're struggling to get the gears it's merely because the linkages need a fresh set of bushes; an easy and cheap fix at £75.

SUSPENSION, STEERING AND BRAKES

The torsion bar suspension used at each end of the 356 is simple and reliable, although at the front you need to make sure there's no play in the bushes that support the four arms. There's a pair on each side and they link the arms to each kingpin and stub axle assembly.

To test the front suspension properly you'll need to put the car on

'While fixing the mechanicals can be costly, the value of any 356 is in its bodyshell'

PORSCHE

axle stands. Grab the top and bottom of each wheel and try rocking them; if you can feel or hear any movement the kingpins need replacing, and doing the whole job can easily cost the thick end of £1000.

Until 1957 there was worm-and-peg steering; after this it was a worm-and-gear system. Whichever set-up is fitted, the steering should be light and direct, with no tight spots. As long as the box is kept lubricated it'll keep going with no appreciable wear. However, if it runs low on oil and starts to develop play, some owners then tighten things up and that's a recipe for disaster because the whole unit will deteriorate quickly.

Drum brakes all-round were standard fare until the all-disc 356C of 1963. However, these weren't the usual cast-iron drums seen elsewhere: they were huge, finned aluminium alloy castings with a steel liner. In good condition they work well because the 356 weighs so little.

Unfortunately, any car left standing for ages will have suffered from electrolytic corrosion between castings and liners. The game will be given away by violent pedal judder under braking, due to the liners being pushed out of shape. New drums cost £730 each, and 356A items aren't even available.

BODYWORK, ELECTRICS AND TRIM

They all look much the same, but there were masses of panel changes throughout the 356's 15-year life. Crucially, there are two key factors you shouldn't under-estimate: the complexity of the bodyshell and its tendency to rot.

Major corrosion needs expert attention and many cars have been crashed at some point, so bodyshells can be twisted. That's why you must ensure the car sits square on the road, that the panel gaps are tight and even and that none of the metal

is rippled. While fixing the mechanicals can be costly, the value of any 356 is in its bodyshell, and rebuilding one costs anywhere between £18,000 and £30,000, which is why annual bodywork inspections are essential. Cheap rebuilds invariably entail the car losing its contours, which is why recognised specialists have to be used.

If you're happy the car is straight, you need to ensure it's not riddled with rot. Although the 356 can corrode anywhere, it's the front wings, wheelarch lips and headlamp bowls that are usually the first to go. These are usually quickly followed by the nose panel, leading edges of the rear wings, the door bottoms and the upper rear corners of the front wings where they meet the scuttle. These latter areas are a particular pain to fix and one of the most common bodge areas.

Basically you need to check every square inch of metal, but other key rot spots include the spare wheel well in the nose, all panel edges and →

PORSCHE 356B 1600 SUPER
BUILT
1960-62
ENGINE
1582cc flat four, OHV, two Zenith 32NDIX carburettors
POWER
60bhp @ 4500rpm
TORQUE
81lb ft @ 2800rpm
TRANSMISSION
Four-speed manual, rear-wheel drive
SUSPENSION
Front: trailing parallel links, transverse torsion bars, telescopic dampers, anti-roll bar. Rear: trailing arms, transverse torsion bars, telescopic dampers
BRAKES
Drums all-round
WEIGHT
870kg (1914lb)
PERFORMANCE
0-62mph 16.5sec. Top speed 96mph
VALUE
Cost new £1885 Value now £15,000-45,000

'While fixing the mechanicals can be costly, the value of any 356 is in its bodyshell'

the seams where the floorpans meet the sills. Lifting the carpet for these latter areas is essential; at least it's easy to check the sills as they're of very simple construction with a box section behind a cosmetic outer panel. While you're on your knees, take a look at the jacking points, the support panels for the front axle beam and the locating panels for the rear suspension torsion bar tube.

Most 356s featured six-volt electrics, although from 1958 some 1600GS models and all Carreras had 12-volt systems. Most owners have converted their cars to run on the higher voltage.

Apart from the earliest pre-A cars, it's possible to buy most interior and exterior trim. The repro stuff is generally well made, with original parts now very hard to track down – steering wheels are notoriously tricky to source. It can also be difficult establishing exactly what's right for any car; many 356s have been restored with little regard to originality. Any 356 expert will tell you which way to proceed.

CONCLUSION

While the coupé offers the purest drive, it's the glamorous drophead that most buyers want – which is why you'll typically pay at least twice as much for a convertible over its fixed-head equivalent. Chances are that you'll end up with a left-hand-drive car imported into the UK long after production ceased; genuine right-hand-drive UK cars are scarce.

The general rule says that the newer the car, the more usable it is; Bs and Cs have much nicer gearboxes, for example. They became progressively more powerful, better built and more thoroughly engineered, but any 356 can go wrong expensively. That's why, before you commit to any purchase, you must drive the car for at least 50 miles over a variety of terrains. Everything needs to be given a thorough workout, with engine, brakes and transmission allowed to get fully warm.

Genuine right-hand-drive 356s are especially expensive – and in open-topped form they're

astonishingly pricey. The most affordable 356 is a B coupé. Usable but rough examples cost £15,000 but buying one is just the start of the expense, because it needs to be looked after by specialists.

Values have risen noticeably, and at the top end things have gone crazy with mint Carreras and very early 356s selling for well over £100,000. That's dragged up the values of more ordinary examples, with a decent 356A, B or C coupé now fetching £27,000-30,000. Fancy the top down? Call your bank manager: cabriolets are double that .

The bottom line is that any 356 with the steering wheel on the right is very rare, so you're going to have to look hard to find a good one. However, mint left-hand-drive cars in the USA are much easier to track down – if still not exactly chicken-feed to buy.

Still, you can't take it with you. △

Thanks to Fred Hampton of Porsche Club GB, Bruce Cooper of Sportwagen, and Andy Prill of Maxted-Page and Prill.

TIMELINE

1950: 356 arrives with 1086cc, 40bhp
1951: 1300cc and 1488cc derivatives offered with 44bhp and 60bhp
1952: gearbox now has synchromesh
1955: 356A on sale with 1290cc, 1498cc or 1582cc powerplants. Curved instead of split 'screen. Carrera on sale
1959: 356B bodyshell has higher bumper and headlamps, opening quarterlights and larger rear window. 1582cc or 1966cc options
1960: 1600GS GTL Abarth-Carrera for this year only, with alloy body
1963: 356C arrives with disc brakes all-round.

SPECIALISTS

Maxted-Page & Prill, Essex
+44 (0)1787 476338,
www.maxted-pageandprill.com.
PR Services, Essex
+44 (0)7000 356911,
www.prs356.com
Retro Motor Company, Hants
+44 (0)1425 483841,
www.retromotorcompany.co.uk
Roger Bray Restorations, Devon
+44 (0)1404 822005,
www.rogerbrayrestoration.com
Sportwagen, Southend
+44 (0)1702 535350,
www.sportwagen.co.uk
Klasse 356, Pennsylvania
www.klasse356.com
NLA, Nevada
www.nlaparts.com
Restoration Design, Michigan
www.restoration-design.com
Stoddard, Ohio
www.stoddard.com

CLUBS

Porsche Club GB,
+44 (0)1608 652911,
www.porscheclubgb.com
Independent Porsche Enthusiasts Club, +44 (0)1246 279358, www.tipec.org.uk
For 356-only clubs:
www.356registry.org or
www.speedsters.com

PORSCHE 911
(1963-1989) £12,000-250,000
Air-cooled 911s are truly iconic. Here's how to buy well
Words and photography: Richard Dredge

Above
Impact-bumper cars
are the most practical
and plentiful of the
classic 911s.

PORSCHE 911 CARRERA (1983)

ENGINE
3164cc air-cooled flat six,
SOHC per bank, Bosch DME
electronic fuel injection

POWER
231bhp @ 5900rpm

TORQUE
210lb ft @ 4800rpm

TRANSMISSION
Five-speed manual,
rear-wheel drive

SUSPENSION
Front: independent,
MacPherson struts, torsion
bars, telescopic dampers,
anti-roll bar.
Rear: independent,
semi trailing arms,
torsion bars, telescopic
dampers, anti-roll bar.

BRAKES
Discs all-round

WEIGHT
1165kg (2569lb)

PERFORMANCE
0-60mph 5.4sec
Top speed 150mph

VALUE
Cost £21,464 new (1983)

VALUE NOW
£7,000-£20,000

The name hasn't changed

for almost half a century, but the Porsche 911 has evolved massively, from a peaky race car for the road that was likely to bite you, to a docile, usable supercar that's as easy to drive as a Toyota – only far more exciting. No car is more iconic than the mighty 911.

If you decide to take the plunge, it's essential that you inspect lots of examples first and buy from a reputable source. Asking prices are all over the place, while specification, history and condition make a huge difference to values. As a rule, the impact-bumper cars are worth the least, and of the earlier models, it's the T that's the least valuable. The most valuable is the S, which leaves the E in the middle. A Sportomatic gearbox chips 20% off values, while Targas are worth around 10% less than an equivalent coupé. Conversely, Cabriolets are worth 10-15% more than an equivalent coupé.

You'll need at least £7000 to buy a project 911SC or neglected early car, but you'll need a lot of time, patience and expertise to revive it. You're better off finding at least £13,000 for a reasonable T or SC, but if you want something tasty you'll be doing well to spend less than £30,000 on a good Carrera 2.7 – which is

the price of a really superb Turbo. If money really isn't an issue, you could try finding an RS 2.7, but depending on which model you want, a running car will cost upwards of £70,000 – and easily three times that for a good Lightweight.

ENGINE

All 911s have a flat-six engine, with an alloy cylinder block as well as alloy heads. The block was aluminium alloy until 1969, then changed to magnesium until the 3.0-litre cars came along in 1974 (Turbo) and 1975 (Carrera).

The early aluminium casings are weak and most have been replaced with an improved design. It's the same story for the magnesium units, especially where the 2.7-litre engines are concerned, as distortion is common, leading to oil leaks. Even when new there were reliability issues, usually from the cylinder head studs pulling out because of differential expansion of the aluminium cylinders. Porsche later moved to a steel alloy called Dilavar, but this has proved brittle over the years, with SCs and 3.2-litre cars affected by the studs breaking. If the studs have been replaced things should be fine, but if the originals are still fitted, expect problems when the engine comes to be rebuilt. To guard

against future problems, specialist Autofarm offers a dowelling service.

Within the period we're covering, in theory it's possible to fit any engine to any car because the mounting points didn't change across the various generations. It's also possible to tune the powerplants in various ways, so it's worth establishing exactly what's nestling in the car's rear end. Most US cars featured less powerful engines than equivalent UK models, so expect an import to serve up a little less fun.

The 911's flat six is generally durable if maintained. The first sign of impending expenditure is (blue) oil smoke when the car is started up and on the over run, signalling that the valve guides have worn out. By the time the guides have worn the timing chain will also have seen better days, so listen for rattling when the engine is revved. There's a better tensioning mechanism fitted to post-'81 cars, while the post-1984 design is even better – and often fitted to earlier 911s.

Low oil pressure isn't necessarily a concern; the dash-mounted level gauge is only accurate at tickover once the engine is up to temperature, which is why it's best to rely on the dipstick instead. Expect to see 45psi at 2500rpm and ask for evidence of the lubricant

having been changed regularly, using high-quality oil. Also, because the sump holds 10-11 litres of oil, engine life is much extended by getting the engine up to temperature before revving it hard.

Of more concern than apparently low oil pressure is any sign that the remote oil tank has rusted. When this steel tank corrodes, the debris finds its way into the engine and destroys the main bearings. Replace it with a stainless item at the first sign of rust.

TRANSMISSION

There were three types of manual transmission fitted across these various 911s, the first type being fitted to 2.0- and 2.2-litre cars. It's generally tough, but will wear out eventually, so listen for bearing rumbles. It's the intermediate gears that are affected, so listen for any whining, which will disappear in fourth. Between 1972 and 1985 the stronger 915 gearbox was but, like any, it has a finite lifespan, so listen out for bearing wear and feel for baulking as you swap ratios.

Whichever gearbox is fitted, rebuilding it will cost anywhere between £800 and £3500, depending on what needs replacing. A reputable specialist will overhaul your gearbox, replacing only what's necessary.

The G50 gearbox fitted to post-1986 911s is the strongest of the lot, but the linkages might be past their best, making gear selection difficult. A fresh set of bushes will usually work wonders.

Clutches were better engineered as time progressed, with a marked improvement since 1970. However, once again it's the G50 clutch that's the best of the lot – but whatever is fitted, make sure it isn't slipping because they all have a finite lifespan, which can be severely shortened with abuse.

SUSPENSION, STEERING AND BRAKES

There have been all sorts of detail changes to the suspension specification over the years, with poverty-spec cars not usually getting an anti-roll bar while poshers editions did. Fiting an anti-roll bar to any 911 is worthwhile, particularly as modern tyres don't give their best when the car is really leaning over.

As long as decent dampers are fitted, any 911 should handle pretty well; many owners take the Koni route but Bilsteins are favoured by most people who really know these cars. Obviously the dampers need to be in fine fettle, as do the bushes, so look for any evidence of perishing because the handling will be adversely →

'As long as decent dampers are fitted, any 911 should handle pretty well. Bilsteins are favoured by most people who really know these cars'

Top and above
1970s interiors are sparse but often feature period trim colours; all-important fan dominates engine bay.

'You'd be surprised how easy it is to work on the 911 yourself. Even an engine rebuild isn't difficult'

affected without a doubt. If the bushes have perished it's worth getting a fresh set fitted; costs vary depending on which generation of 911 you're looking at, but in general you should expect to pay around £1000 to have the work done – and on top of this you'll need to pay for a geometry check, which could add another £500 to the bill.

Any car that's been converted from left- to right-hand drive should be avoided, even if it's temptingly priced. There aren't many such cars about, but there are some – and because the conversion is rarely done well you're better off simply, ahem, steering clear.

Although brake specifications evolved, there aren't any weak spots as long as the car is used regularly and properly serviced. Cars that haven't had enough use will probably be suffering from calipers that have seized up, while the rubber pipes and seals can disintegrate with age too. At least everything is available, but if the whole system needs a complete overhaul it's going to be an expensive job.

There are all sorts of aftermarket wheels available for the 911, and if you're not into originality, as long as what's on there has the correct clearances there's probably not much to worry about. However, you must ensure the tyres have a decent speed rating (VR or ZR). If you want original wheels you'll need to look closely at what's on the car because there's a good chance some refurbishment will be needed. Fuchs alloys, seen as the most desirable 911 wheels, are strong but can crack around the spokes if the car has been driven hard. If an overhaul of each wheel is required, Fuchs charges £300 to put each one right.

BODYWORK, ELECTRICS AND TRIM

The 911 has always been a very costly car, but that didn't stop the early ones rusting badly; it wasn't until August 1975 that the bodyshells were galvanised. Even then, many early cars still corroded; the plating initially merely slowed the rate of rusting. However, Porsche's production methods got much better with the passing years, as the 1970s became the '80s, the cars are much better protected from the elements.

Many early-1970s cars suffered from undersealing lifting to allow the moisture in, with the metalwork then quietly dissolving, out of sight. Poorly repaired accident damage is also a very real possibility; panel damage is common after off-road excursions, and repairs aren't always what they should be. The result of these bodged repairs is often extensive corrosion – which isn't always obvious.

Whatever the age of car, start by looking at the bulkheads at each end of the car, as rust can spread from the base of the front and rear screens. If there's any corrosion in these areas, you're better off finding another car because the necessary repairs will be involved and very costly.

Early galvanised cars tend to corrode where stone chips haven't been attended to quickly enough; cracks also develop in the paint around areas such as the A-posts and anywhere that the car has been jacked up. If you're lucky the corrosion will be no more than cosmetic, but there's a good chance that some structural rust will be present – that's why you must inspect the front fuel tank support, inner wings, sills plus the A- and B-posts.

Early 911s could corrode pretty much anywhere, and even relatively new cars, such as many from the 1980s, will have rusted unless they've been well looked after. You need to make sure that you take a look at the inner and outer wings, sills, battery boxes, floorpans and door bottoms – be on your guard for any evidence of plating or filling. Also scrutinise the front crossmember,

Above
Pre-1973 cars have
the purest looks. Not
surprisingly, they also
command a premium.

battery boxes, heater tubes and the windscreen surround – as well as the sunroof surround, if one is fitted.

On this latter point, you're generally better off without a sunroof as they add weight and don't really work very well. They're often unreliable and tend to add wind noise when open – they also remove valuable headroom. If there is one fitted, open it and look for evidence of corrosion around the edges; the drain tubes also tend to block up, leading to the screen pillars rusting from the inside out.

If it's an impact-bumper 911 you're looking at, it's worth ascertaining whether there are hydraulic rams behind the bumper, or crushable steel structures. The former tend to shrug off any minor knock, while the latter squash, with the metal then corroding. Only some UK cars featured the rams, while US cars all had them; your best bet is to open the boot and see if the inner wings have started to rust, signalling that the steel has been crushed. While you've got the lid open, check the state of the boot floor; a hefty crunch will have led to rippled panelwork. Finish off in this spot by looking at the fuel tank, which tends to rot underneath, leading to fuel leaks – a strong smell of petrol will soon give the game away.

There have been huge numbers of trim changes over the years, with some bits now proving hard to find. However, in general there shouldn't be any issues with finding replacement parts as good used components are often available.

Also, the trim is generally hardwearing so often survives well, but check that the seat bolsters haven't frayed and worn through. Also make sure the door trims and carpets haven't rotted – if they have, it suggests there are wider problems that need sorting.

You should make sure that the heating works, as the heat exchangers can prove problematic. They're prone to corrosion, but it can smell oily inside even when everything is in good condition. The heater controls can also seize up, while the semi-automatic system fitted to the SC onwards (but not cabrios) can be temperamental.

When it comes to exterior trim there's not much to worry about. Early (steel) rear-quarter bumpers can corrode, as can the aluminium impact bumpers, although in the latter case it's only cosmetic. At least everything is available, with the exception of the horn grilles of the earliest cars – but just because it's available it doesn't mean it's affordable.

CONCLUSION

With such a wide array of models over the years, you've got a lot of choices to make if you want a classic 911. What you buy is usually dictated by your budget, but regardless of what you can afford there are certain gems worth seeking out. You'd be surprised how easy it is to work on the 911 yourself; even an engine rebuild isn't difficult although you'll need to trust certain items, such as the fuel injection system, to the experts. Buy well and costs, unlike the enjoyment, will be minimal.

PORSCHE 912
(1965-1969/1976)
£4500-15,000

More than just a cut-price 911, a decent 912 is an entertaining, nimble sports cars in its own right

Words: Robert Coucher Photography: Michael Bailie

INTRODUCTION

GOOD, EARLY PORSCHE 912s are at last appreciated for what they are – and no longer regarded as just cheap alternatives to the 911.

The 912 is a nimble, quick and very drivable sports car in its own right. Launched in 1965, it outsold 911s in 1966 as it was considerably cheaper, more economical and used the proven, air-cooled four-cylinder engine from the well-loved Porsche 356 that preceded it.

The engine produces a mere 90bhp (early 911s have 130bhp) but

the 912 weighs 250lb less, and all that weight is lost behind the rear wheels, significantly improving the handling. American racing driver Mark Donohue found the 912's handling 'most impressive'; he found the 911S 'disappointing'.

With disc brakes all-round, independent suspension and razor-sharp steering, a 912 can be very quick across difficult roads. Expect to pay between £8000 and £15,000 for a good one and enjoy it not being a thirsty, tail-happy early 911.

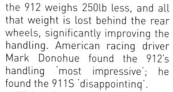

MODEL HISTORY

1965 Launched as a transition model between the 356 and 911, the 912 had the modern developments of the 911 but used the 356's trusted 1588cc air-cooled pushrod engine, producing 90bhp. The 912 was available as a coupé or Targa with removable roof panel. Four-speed standard, five-speed optional. Soft-window Targas now very collectable.

1968 911-style long-wheelbase bodyshell launched, with rear wheels moved back by 57mm to improve handling. Wheelarches were flared.

1976 912E was launched with impact bumpers and 2.0-litre VW engine. Heavy, underpowered and slow, this is an ignominious Porsche and is best forgotten – or stripped and tuned to the max!

MARKET VIEW

'A few years ago you could buy the best 912 in the world for about £10,000. Now the best one in the world costs about £15,000, so they have not gone mental like early 911s,' says specialist Andy Prill (pictured above).

'I think a properly set-up 912 is great fun to drive. They are unique Porsches and have a very strong following.'

The 912 is eligible for racing and rallying as it has competition form: Polish driver Sobieslaw Zasada won his class in a 912 in the 1967 European Rally Championship.

A good road car can be bought for around £8000, but best to look at better examples starting at the £10,000 mark as any work required is expensive.

912

ENGINE
1599cc flat four, OHV, alloy heads and block, twin Solex carbs

POWER
90bhp @ 5800rpm

TORQUE
90lb ft @ 3500rpm

TRANSMISSION
Four-speed manual (five-speed optional), rear-wheel drive

SUSPENSION
Independent, torsion bars, telescopic dampers

BRAKES
Discs all-round

WEIGHT
970kg

PERFORMANCE
0-60mph 11.9sec. Top speed 119mph

'A 912 weighs 250lb less than an early 911, and all that weight is lost behind the rear wheels, significantly improving the handling'

IN A NUTSHELL

Porsche parts prices are heinous. Buy a car that has had money spent on the engine and bodywork already. 912s rust like any other classic but most body panels are available. Importantly, check there is no rot around the tubes in which the torsion bars run. Rust here is rare but uneconomic to repair.

Although the air-cooled engines are tough, they don't last more than 100,000 miles and cost at least £8500 to rebuild properly with a big-bore kit, cam, full-flow oil system and other upgrades.

Early cars came with a four-speed gearbox; the five-speed a desirable option. Gearboxes are rugged but the nylon bushes under the gearlever wear out, making the shift loose and imprecise.

The engine is oil- *and* air-cooled so the oil must be changed every 3000 miles. Check the tappets at the same time – the alloy engine expands and contracts a lot.

The original Solex carburettors wear out and were not easily rebuilt so Webers are often fitted. The more efficient Solexes can now be rebuilt and benefit from Porsche set-up and original airboxes designed to keep noise down.

Early cars are desirable but less refined, long-wheelbase variants are heavier and make better tourers. Targas are becoming cool again – but be careful, as the expensive Targa tops get stolen!

CONCLUSION

The Porsche 912 is a well-balanced, quick and sophisticated sports car that is great fun to drive on challenging backroads, where it will romp away from many less sophisticated but more powerful classics. But it is not a 911.

If you want a fast racing or rallying 912, there is plenty that can be done but refinement will suffer. Excellent fun, though! The engine is noisy out of the box, so be careful with big carburettors, high-lift cams and open exhausts. Big-bore kits (1720cc) are an improvement but must be fitted by an expert. Keep the cams mild and go for torque over revs and horsepower.

It's best to go for a clean, straight, original example that has benefited from the attention of respected Porsche specialists. In that way you will have a proper Porsche that is most enjoyable to drive in the real world.

SPECIALISTS

Maxted-Page & Prill
+44 (0)1787 476338
www.maxted-pageandprill.com
Autofarm +44 (0)1865 331234
www.autofarm.co.uk
Chris Turner +44 (0)20 8451 6000
www.christurner.com
Gantspeed +44 (0)1507 568474
www.gantspeed.com
Historika +44 (0)1473 713989
www.historika.com
Karmann Konnection
+44(0)1702 601155
www.karmannkonnection.com
Paul Stephens +44 (0)1440
714884, www.paul-stephens.com
PR Services +44 (0)7000 356911
www.prs356.com
Revival-Cars +44(0)7768 791802
www.revival-cars.com
Roger Bray +44 (0)1404 822005
www.rogerbrayrestorations.com
Porsche Club GB +44 (0)1608
652911, www.porscheclubgb.com
912 Register
www.912register.co.uk

Below
Flared arches and jacking point position show this is a long-wheelbase model.

PORSCHE 914
(1969-1975) £3000-25,000
The mid-engined 914 is an acquired taste, but will certainly stand out on the road
Words and photography: Richard Dredge

If you've always hankered after a Porsche but don't want to follow the crowd, this could be the car for you. Thanks to the 914 being built with left-hand drive only (apart from just a dozen Crayford conversions), many potential buyers are put off the idea of tracking one down. There aren't many around either; this may have supposedly been a sports car for the masses, but it was still expensive. When new in 1969, it was £1000 more than an MGB.

However, this is one of Porsche's rare attempts at a production car with the engine in the middle, and as a result the 914 is endowed with fabulous handling. While the 1.7-litre cars aren't at all quick, at least the bigger-engined versions are. But what all 914s offer is reliability in spades, but perhaps the clincher is the fact that when you take one out, nobody will know what it is.

In the mid-1960s, Porsche and Volkswagen had opposing problems. While the former wanted to expand but was constrained by the exclusive nature of its products, the latter needed to inject a bit of glamour into its line-up – and hence its image. A marriage was the perfect solution, and at the September 1969 Frankfurt motor show two versions of the Karmann-built 914 appeared.

Compared with the contemporary 911, the 914 is a doddle to drive quickly. While the iconic rear-engined monster can easily be provoked into exiting corners backwards at high speed, the 914 has much more grip than the chassis needs – especially if there's just a 1.7-litre engine fitted. This air-cooled four-pot managed to take the 914 to 107mph with its modest 80bhp, so if you're a speed demon you won't get your kicks here.

However, the 1.8- and 2.0-litre cars feel much more lively and are even better to pilot; with beautifully fluid handling and excellent stopping power thanks to disc brakes all-round, you can really exploit their power. The 914 tips the scales at under a ton, so not only is it quicker than you'd think but it's fabulously agile too. The only fly in the ointment is the gearchange; while the 914 has the same 'box as the 911, the smaller car's tortuous linkage doesn't make swapping cogs an experience to savour. However, upgrades are possible and you can adapt to it, so all is not lost.

WHAT TO LOOK FOR

Rust is the major problem, with the battery tray usually the first place to go. Once corrosion takes a hold here, the whole engine bay can corrode quickly. If left, the rear suspension mountings will rot through and the car will collapse around its wheels. Also check the sill steps, door bottoms plus front and rear boot floors, as rot is common here. The same is true of the boot floor, as the rear light seals can leak; the floorpans behind the seats also need checking. The key thing is to remove the targa top and try to open and close the doors; if the bodyshell has been weakened you may not be able to do that, or to refit the roof panel either.

The engines are generally reliable, although valves can drop. Potentially more serious is perished rubber fuel pipes; if these split the car can quickly become toast. Check to see how flexible they are; there's a good chance they'll be hard and brittle, and there

'What all 914s offer is reliability in spades, but perhaps the clincher is

that, when you take one out, nobody will know what it is'

TIMELINE

1969 The 914 goes on sale in Europe; cheapest is the 914/4, powered by a fuel-injected 1.7-litre VW 411 engine; available alongside is the 914/6, with a 2.0-litre Porsche flat-six engine.

1970 The 914 becomes available in the UK, but at £2261 for the 914/4 and £3475 for the 914/6, there aren't many takers.

1971 A right-hand-drive conversion is now available from Crayford. At £550, it's too costly for most.

1972 The 914/6 is replaced by the 914S/SC 2.0, fitted with an enlarged and strengthened Volkswagen 411/412 2.0-litre engine.

1973 The 1.7-litre powerplant in the 914/4 is taken up to 1.8 litres; power remains unchanged at 80bhp while the B-pillar (or 'sail panel' in Porsche parlance) is now trimmed in vinyl.

1975 The final 914 is built in September, when the model is replaced by Porsche's new collaboration with VW/Audi: the 924.

SPECIALISTS
RSK
Cheshire. +44 (0)1829 752 597
Carrera Performance
West Sussex. +44 (0)1403 891 911
www.carreraperformance.com
914 Conversions
www.914conversions.com
Automobile Atlanta
Georgia, USA
www.autoatlanta.com
Mittel Motor
Germany.
www.mittelmotor.com

CLUBS
Porsche Club GB
+44 (0)1608 652 911
www.porscheclubgb.com
The Independent Porsche Enthusiasts Club
www.tipec.net

BOOKS
914 and 914/6 Porsche A Restorers Guide To Authenticity by B Johnson. ISBN 0-929758-21-8
How To Restore & Modify Your Porsche 914 & 914/6 by Patrick Paternie. ISBN 0-7603-0584-6
Porsche 914 & 914/6 by Brian Long. ISBN 0-1-84584-030-5

will probably be signs of the rubber cracking.

Considering its lowly status relative to its bigger brother the 911, the 914 was more technically advanced in some ways. The 914 featured Bosch fuel injection while some 911s still had carburettors and, although some owners aren't comfortable servicing this engine themselves, preventative maintenance is possible. When major engine work is required it's easy enough to drop the unit and work on it outside the car, but general work is easy, with no special tools required.

The fuel-injection system is reliable, but it can go wrong and when it does it's usually costly to fix. That's why some owners convert to carbs; various set-ups have been tried, but none of them work as well as a decently set-up fuel-injection system, which is why you're better off keeping things standard and getting an expert to sort it out properly.

Slotting a six-pot engine into a four-pot car spices things up, but it is rarely cost-effective. That's why you're better off looking for a 914/6 – although they're not easy to track down, which is the reason why most such conversions have taken place.

PORSCHE 914 2.0
ENGINE
1971cc flat-four, OHV, Bosch D-Jetronic fuel injection
POWER
100bhp @ 5000rpm
TORQUE
115lb ft @ 3500rpm
TRANSMISSION
Five-speed manual, rear-wheel drive
SUSPENSION
Front: independent, Macpherson struts, torsion bars
Rear: independent, semi-trailing arms, coil springs, telescopic dampers
BRAKES
Discs all-round.
WEIGHT
950kg (2090lb)
PERFORMANCE
0-60mph: 10.5sec.
Top speed: 118mph
VALUE
Cost new: £3689 (1973)
Value now: £8000-£16,000

Try to roll the car on the flat and see if it quickly grinds to a halt; seized rear brake calipers are common, with replacement costing £150 apiece. Pre-1973 cars were fitted with a tortuous gearshift linkage that rather spoils the driving experience – especially once it's worn. A common trick is to upgrade the linkage, at a cost of £300.

CONCLUSION

Just 100 examples of the 914 were officially imported into the UK. Some of those haven't survived, but lots more have been brought in from Europe and the US, and there are now reckoned to be 350 examples here. You can pick up a 914 for as little as £3000, but you're better off avoiding any 1.7-litre model priced much under £5500.

An equivalent 1.8-litre car is £7000 and it's another £1000 for a 2.0 example. Add £2000 for anything nice; the best examples can fetch over £15,000, while you won't buy a decent 914/6 for less than £17,000, with a really nice one more like £25,000. △

Thanks to Bruce Manning of Porsche Club GB.

PORSCHE 928
(1977-1995) £3000-15,000
Porsche's grand tourer is also grand value
Words and photography: Mark Dixon

INTRODUCTION

IF THERE CAN BE such a thing as a 'forgotten Porsche', the 928 is it. Although built for a remarkably long period – about 17 years – it's not a car you read much about in the classic press. And yet the 928 is quick, extremely comfortable and has a big V8 under the bonnet. What's not to like?

'Thirst and complexity' are the usual retorts. It's true that 20mpg is a best-case scenario for any 928 – but with most of the survivors now being kept as second cars, that's less of an issue. And while there seems to be an awful lot of engine shoehorned under the bonnet, it's really a straightforward design that can rack up enormous mileages.

Of course, the 928 was an expensive car when new, with commensurately high servicing bills. But today's non-franchised specialists charge more reasonable prices and there are plenty of secondhand parts around – sadly, good cars are still being stripped out for track day or race use.

Despite its recently discovered potential as a race car, the 928 was always marketed as a GT and about 80% were sold with automatic transmission. Manuals are now sought after for track days, but the 928's big V8 is ideally suited to an auto 'box and gives a relaxing drive.

MODEL HISTORY

1977-1982 928 launched with new water-cooled, 4.5-litre V8 engine giving 240bhp and 140+mph top speed, five-speed manual or three-speed auto transmissions.
1979-1984 928S gains bigger, 4.7-litre engine, plus small front and rear rubber spoilers and side-protection strips. Power now 300bhp and top speed 152mph.
1984-1985 S2 has 310bhp; auto option now a four-speed.

1985 US-only cars gain new 5.0-litre V8 with DOHC, four-valve heads and unofficial 'S3' title.
1986-1992 S4 restyled with smoother front end, wraparound tail-lights and big rear spoiler. 5.0-litre V8 320bhp. Digital dash and auto standard for '89-on S4.
1989-1992 Manual 326/330bhp GT; stiffer suspension, wider wheels
1992-1995 GTS has 5.4-litre V8, 340bhp and 'Cup' alloy wheels.

MARKET VIEW

YOU WON'T hear a bad word said among 928 owners about Paul Anderson (above). He has been specialising in the cars for the past ten years, and race-prepping them for six – as a 1970s model, the 928 is fast catching on among the historic race and rally crowd.

'928s are definitely on the up at the moment,' he says, before adding: '...but prices are lower than they were four years ago. Interest goes in peaks and troughs, and it's the current price of fuel that dictates values.

'Condition is more important than model or year. A superb car might be £15,000 but good ones start around £5000; an S2 slightly less. A GT will be at least £6000 and the GTS £8000 upwards. But you can pick up a 928 for much less if you're lucky. A customer bought a tidy 928S for a grand.'

IN A NUTSHELL

FIRST, THE GOOD NEWS: the 928 bodyshell was galvanised right from the start of production, so structural rust is rare. Early cars will typically show the odd bubble around rear windows or hatch (where trim clips have broken the galvanising), but usually corrosion is restricted to paint scabbing on the alloy bonnet, front wings and door skins.

Mechanical parts also last well. Cambelt failure is the biggest danger: on 4.7-litre and later engines the valves can then collide with pistons (4.5s aren't affected). The belt should be changed every four years/60,000 miles; it's wise to renew the water pump at the same time, which accounts for over half of the c£500 that a specialist will charge.

The 928's suspension hardly changed during production: 'You could, in theory, fit GTS suspension to a 1970s car,' claims Paul Anderson. OE-spec dampers are now hugely expensive but Paul offers a set of specially produced gas-filled units for £700.

The 928 has its gearbox mounted just ahead of the rear diff, and it's connected to the engine by a torque tube. Manual 'boxes don't have the sweetest changes but are tough, while the automatics are Mercedes-Benz units, so very reliable. However, failure to check the flex plate tension regularly can lead to a worn crank thrust bearing and, ultimately, a wrecked engine block.

928s can suffer from electrical gremlins if not driven for any length of time – 'but the wiring is actually quite easy to trace,' says Paul – while air-conditioning will rarely work on an older car and may cost £500-600 to repair. Interiors last pretty well but the 1970s pyschedelic-check trim known as Pascha eventually falls apart at the seams. It's hard to find too, even secondhand.

Below
Nose and tail were updated with the advent of the S4 in 1986 Engine power increased gradually throughout 928 production.

1991 PORSCHE 928 S4

ENGINE
4957cc all-alloy V8, DOHC, Bosch LH-Jetronic fuel injection

POWER
320bhp @ 6000rpm

TORQUE
317lb ft @ 3000rpm

TRANSMISSION
Four-speed auto, rear transaxle

SUSPENSION
Independent via coil-and-wishbone, anti-roll bars

BRAKES
Discs all round

WEIGHT
1600kg

PERFORMANCE
Top speed 165mph
0-60mph 5.5sec

CONCLUSION

CHANCES ARE that if you fancy a 928 you'll already know what you want: either the design statement of the original car (no spoilers, no side strips, Pascha interior, telephone-dial alloys) or the sheer speed and greater luxury of the S4-and-later models. Buyers tend to fall into one or other camp.

The late-'70s cars are by far the rarest now and are the only 928s likely to have any long-term investment potential. They are not particularly fast by modern standards but they're the simplest and cheapest to run.

Moving on a few years, a 1980s S or S2 still has a certain period appeal, retaining the egg-shaped rear of the original car. With decent examples available from £2500, they're amazing value. Among the restyled cars, the S4 is the sensible buy – 'its engine is bulletproof,' says Paul Anderson – while the GTS is the most hardcore and most expensive to fix, having unique brakes and engine.

Buying any older high-performance car is a gamble. But one thing's for sure: petrol is never going to get any cheaper.

Above
Adrian Langford's superb S4 shows the model's bigger rear lights and spoiler; this car also wears later mirrors and Cup alloys.

CLUBS
Porsche Club Great Britain
www.porscheclubgb.com
The Independent Porsche Enthusiasts Club
www.tipec.net
928 web forum
www.928.org.uk

SPECIALIST
928 Spares (Paul Anderson)
Stroud, Gloucestershire, UK
www.928spares.co.uk

PORSCHE 968
(1991-1995) £8000-15,000
The most desirable of the classic front-engined
Porsches is probably at its cheapest now.
But for how long?

Words: Roger Green

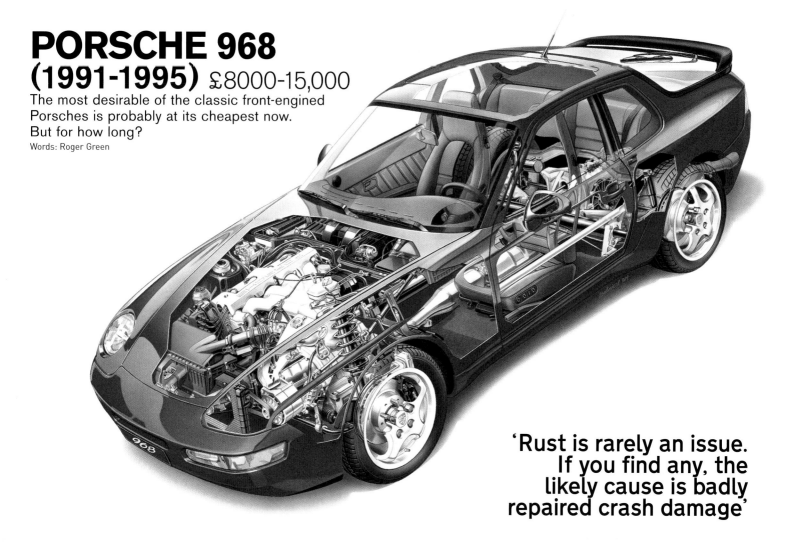

'Rust is rarely an issue.
If you find any, the
likely cause is badly
repaired crash damage'

When the 968 was launched
in 1991 Porsche was in trouble. The
world economy was imploding, the 911
of the period – the 964 – was barely
profitable, and the pensionable 928
had been propping up the range since
the mid-'70s. The 968 became pivotal
to Porsche's future and, despite being
little more than a revised 944 S2 and
selling only 12,776 examples in its
four-year lifespan, it helped to turn
everything around in Zuffenhausen.

Sales got off to a sluggish start for
the original coupé, but sparked with
the cheaper, stripped-out and lowered
Club Sport version, and peaked with
the more extensively specified Sport.

The 968 has resisted the ravages of
time, and its depreciation has hit rock
bottom. Increasing rarity and classic
status are edging prices back up; there
are still decent cars available for under
£10,000 at the moment, but the best
are heading for £15,000.

BODY
As with all Porsches of this era, rust is
very rarely an issue (slight bubbling
around the 'screen is the only area
where we've seen any) and, if you do

find some, the likely cause is badly
repaired accident damage.

The front and rear aprons will crack
if they've been bumped and really
should be replaced rather than patched
and painted. Check the inner wings for
signs of damage and have a good look
at the shutlines – they are generous,
but should be consistent everywhere.

The plastic mouldings that clad the
outer sills can warp, and if they do so
the only real solution is to fit new ones.
These plastic strips also act as a water
trap on each side and, although the
sills are zinc-coated, it is worth taking
the mouldings off to have a look at the
condition underneath.

At the back, lift out the carpet and
pay close attention to the area above
the lights – there should be a sticker
detailing the car's specification, so if
it's missing you need to ask questions.

The windscreen may have taken on a
milky appearance if delamination has
set in; watch out for this as replacement
is expensive (around £400 plus fitting)
because the glass is bonded and also
contains the radio aerial. Even the
cheaper Porsches can tend to be heavy
on parts parices.

The headlight pods cost around £175
each – thankfully, if they stick it's likely
to be a lubrication issue rather than a
problem with the motor – and finally
the bonnet and boot struts fail more
regularly than you might expect.
They're cheap, though, so the ensuing
headache won't be a financial one.

With a Cabriolet, examine the
condition of the rear screen and the
quality of the hood's electric operation.
All UK cars' hoods were powered, but
it was possible to buy cars with manual
hoods on the Continent.

ENGINE
Based on the 944 S2 block, the 3.0-litre
engine is reliable if it's properly
maintained. The only difference from
the S2 is the VarioCam on the top end
– its actuating solenoid can fail;
replacing it costs around £1000.

It's vital that cambelts are changed
at 48,000 miles or every four years (at
a cost of around £400-500). It's worth
replacing the water pump at the same
time. Also be aware of the condition of
the chain that links the two camshafts
– listen for a ticking noise at idle. The
chain and sprockets need checking

968
ENGINE
2990cc four-cylinder,
DOHC, 16-valve, Bosch
Motronic engine
management
POWER
240bhp @ 6200rpm
TORQUE
225lb ft @ 4100rpm
TRANSMISSION
Six-speed manual,
rear-wheel drive
SUSPENSION
Front: MacPherson struts,
lower wishbones,
coil springs,
telescopic dampers,
anti-roll bar.
Rear: semi-trailing arms,
torsion bars, telescopic
dampers, anti-roll bar
BRAKES
Vented discs all-round,
four-pot calipers, ABS
WEIGHT
1320kg
PERFORMANCE
Top speed 150mph.
0-60mph 6.0sec
COST NEW
£28,975
VALUE NOW
£12,000

and possibly replacing at around 70,000 miles, because if the chain slips you will be landed with a £2000-plus bill. If the chain needs renewing, the camshafts should also be replaced along with the tensioners: around £1500 for the lot.

Examine the engine mount near the exhaust manifold, as these collapse over time due to heat, creating a vibration, but replacement costs less than £100. Oil leaks are not uncommon, and oil is usually found oozing from the exhaust camshaft seals. This can be resolved easily and cheaply, though – just ensure the engine hasn't been running low on lubrication.

BRAKES & WHEELS

Vented brake discs can crack and warp, particularly if the car has been used on track. They cost £150 a pair to replace.

The only real issue is that the calipers need rebuilding every couple of years, as the spring plates holding the pads in place are lifted by corrosion. Remove the plates by heating the retaining screw to release the locking glue, file away the rust and fit a new plate.

The M030 Sport pack included larger cross-drilled 304mm front and 299mm rear discs, but these suffer from the same problems as the standard set-up. The ABS system is effective and should be trouble-free.

TRIM

Most faults inside are wear-related and easily visible when examining the car. Carpets, seats (particularly the

bolsters on the Club Sport's shapely Recaro buckets) and belts can look tatty, but all can be replaced or refurbished cost-effectively.

Glovebox lids can crack but repair kits are available from £25. Gearlever gaiters are easily replaced, as are all the black plastic console fittings.

Standard seats were cloth but leather was a popular option. Untreated hide is likely to be cracked.

TRANSMISSON

Clutches are strong and easily replaced, so expect an £800 bill. The 968 has a dual-mass flywheel to damp out engine vibrations from the driveline. It should therefore feel smooth, but a rattle and drivetrain slack indicate it's on the way out: £800 again. The gearbox is strong, with larger bearings than the 944's, but vibration is likely to be a worn pinion bearing: that's another £800. Biennial gearbox oil changes will help delay the onset of this problem.

STEERING & SUSPENSION

After the potential engine headaches, it's a relief to know that the MacPherson struts at the nose and semi-trailing arms in the tail cause little worry apart from the usual wear and tear. A knocking from the rear is usually a corroded mounting bolt in the trailing arm. If you're looking at either a Club Sport or a Sport (which are fitted with 20mm-lower springs) with the optional M030 Sport pack, take a peek at how

firm a ride the adjustable Konis have been set to. Stiff settings indicate a track-day car.

ELECTRICS

Porsche 968 electrics are very reliable, even on the Club Sport, which has a smaller alternator and battery plus a simplified loom. The sunroof is generally reliable, but ensure that the drain holes remain unblocked and seals are in good order to prevent overloading of the motor.

Central locking, electric windows and electric mirrors (where fitted) should all operate smoothly. Air conditioning is reliable, so it's worth seeking out a car fitted with it. Airbags were an optional fitment for the driver on pre-'93 model year cars; after that, they became standard for the driver and an option for the passenger.

CONCLUSION

The time to buy a 968 is now. Prices are right, maintenance levels are low and availability is good enough for there to be plenty of choice. It's likely that as the best-condition cars become scarce, so their values will increase to a corresponding degree.

The 968 is not a 'collect and protect' model, though – it's a car for enthusiasts, particularly in Sport and Club Sport form. It had the desired effect for Porsche, giving the firm a chance to draw breath, regroup and head towards a new period of prosperity with the arrival of the Boxster and 993. It's a car well worth seeking out. △

TIMELINE

August 1991
968 Coupé and Cabriolet launched in Germany
May 1992
First RHD cars go on sale in UK
October 1992
Club Sport launched
February 1993
968 Turbo S and RS announced
January 1994
968 Sport launched in the UK only
July 1995
968 production ends

SPECIALISTS

Autofarm
www.autofarm.co.uk
Gmund Cars
www.gmundcars.com
Hartech
www.hartech.org
Paragon
www.paragon.gb.com
Paul Stephens
www.paul-stephens.com
Pelican Parts
www.pelicanparts.com
Porsche Apart
www.porsch-apart.co.uk
Porscheshop
www.porscheshop.co.uk
Road Scholars
www.theaircooledguys.com
Specialist Cars of Malton
www.specialistcarsltd.co.uk

CLUBS/FORUMS

Porsche Club GB
www.porscheclubgb.com
Porsche 968 UK
www.porsche968.co.uk or www.968uk.com
The Independent Porsche Enthusiasts Club
www.tipec.net
Porsche Club of America
www.pca.org
Porsche Owners Club
www.porscheclub.com (USA)
Porsche Club NSW
www.porscheclub.org.au
Porsche Club of New Zealand
www.porsche.org.nz

BOOKS

Original 924/944/968
Peter Morgan
ISBN 190143205X
**Porsche 944 and 968:
Ultimate Buyers' Guide**
Peter Morgan
ISBN 0954557999
**Porsche 924, 944 and 968:
A Collector's Guide**
Michael Cotton
ISBN 1899870474
**Porsche 928, 924, 944 and 968:
The Front-Engined Sports Cars**
Marc Cranswick
ISBN 0786430400
Porsche 968
(Osprey Classic Marques)
David Sparrow
ISBN 1855324377

'The time to buy a 968 is now. Prices are right and maintenance levels low'

Left and below
Any 968 is still a great drive, the Club Sport especially so. Convertible has its own appeal; that big four-cylinder is tough and torquey.

ALL THE PORSCHES

1948–2010

From tiny beginnings in a converted Austrian sawmill to the products of a modern industrial giant, here are the cars that define the company

Words: Robert Scorah and David Lillywhite

356 Pre-A 1948-1956

Power 40bhp **Torque** 52lb ft **Weight** 770kg
Top speed 87mph **0-60mph** 23sec

Here's where the legend begins, and what keeps these cars relevant to today's enthusiasts is that you can still clearly see the company's embryonic design ideology. Beginning in 1948, the earliest cars were made at the Gmünd factory (a converted sawmill), featuring aluminium bodies built over a steel box-frame chassis. They incorporated swing-axle rear suspension and, most significantly, the air-cooled, boxer engine mounted in the rear. In this case it was a pushrod, overhead-valve 1086cc Volkswagen-derived unit fed by two Solex downdraught carburettors and producing 40bhp.

In 1949 Porsche contracted Reutter to build bodies, now in steel but still with a split windscreen. They gradually gained refinements – and weight, though their Bauhaus minimalism still appeals. Over five years, the split windscreen beloved of collectors disappeared and Porsche developed 1.5-litre engines up to 70bhp, and by 1955 engine parts were no longer VW sourced. The pattern had been set.

356 open-top 1948-1966

Power 75bhp **Torque** 86lb ft **Weight** 760kg
Top speed 109mph **0-60mph** 14.5sec (356A Speedster)

All variants of the 356, including the Gmünd cars, were built in open-topped form, and all carry a certain chic over their tin-topped sisters – at least to look at, if not always to drive. It's sometimes hard to know which one of the three you're looking at; cabriolet, convertible, speedster, but if you assume that as you go from the first to the last things get more stripped-out and lower, you get the idea.

Most enjoy the same options as the coupés, but you might also say that if the cabriolet is a car that should be driven with the top down, then the speedster is a car that *could* be driven with the roof up. But only in the rainiest of emergencies...

The speedster (1500cc only) didn't appear until 1954, developed in part due to the lobbying of Max Hoffman who was asking for a competition-oriented roadster for the US market. For many it's *the* one, but the privilege of ownership will cost you £30,000 to £50,000 more than the cabriolet.

550 Spyder 1954-1956

Power 110bhp **Torque** 95lb ft **Weight** 685kg
Top speed 136mph **0-60mph** 10sec

One of the ultimate icons of quintessential *Porscheness*, the 550 Spyder combined lightness with simplicity of design in a car that customers could take straight from the showroom to the nearest race track if they so wished – or dared.

Bodywork was of aluminium mounted on a steel ladder-frame chassis, and the whole rear structure raised for access to the mid-mounted 1498cc engine. Everything was done to save weight – the welded-in dashboard was a loadbearing member, and the leather-trimmed door panels were cardboard. Front suspension was by longitudinal crank arms, transverse leaf springs and anti-roll bar; the rear by a fairly lively swing-arm arrangement.

The little speedster had a darker side too – what was a multi-race winner in the hands of von Tripps or Polensky could be a death trap. Actor James Dean, himself a decent racer, was caught out by his 550 and killed on a California highway.

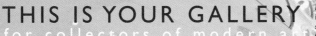
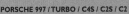

356 A/B/C 1956-1966

Power 60bhp **Torque** 81lb ft **Weight** 900kg
Top speed 95mph **0-60mph** 16.5sec (356B)

In the autumn of 1955, a more highly developed model replaced the original. There's something for most tastes here – the cars have a rawness and a delicacy that's hard to find elsewhere, with finely differing balances between comfort, performance and sophistication.

The car was offered with five different engine options, beginning with the 44bhp 1300 and moving up to 75bhp from a new 1600. The dashboard sported an ashtray and radio fascia. The 356B of 1959 brought a fairly subtle restyle including higher wings, Porsche crested hubcaps and a black three-spoke steering wheel. As well as the open cars (see previous panel), another coupé appeared; the hardtop coupé featured the convertible's hardtop welded in place.

In 1964, the 356C was introduced with a very tractable and torquey 1.6-litre engine. It's hard to find bargains among the 356s these days, but sometimes the B is neglected purely by virtue of being the middle sister. Happy hunting.

356 Carrera 1956-1966

Power 115bhp **Torque** 95lb ft **Weight** 845kg
Top speed 124mph **0-60mph** 10sec (356B Carrera)

That word entered the Porsche vocabulary in autumn 1955, when Porsche dropped its new 100bhp racebred engine into the body of the 356 1500 Carrera GS. The new motor boasted two overhead camshafts per bank, dry sump, separate oil tank, dual ignition and twin-choke carbs. Aluminium bonnet, doors and engine cover helped weight loss, as did Plexiglass quarterlights and throwing out the rear seats. It all made the car good for 124mph – and good for every road race from the Carrera Panamericana to the modern-day Mille Miglia. This is the 356 enthusiast's competition weapon of choice.

You need to be careful which you choose. From 1959 there was a fork in development with the 1600 GS Carrera De Luxe for pampered sybarites and the lighter 1600GT/GS Carrera with Weber twin-choke carburettors and 10bhp more for roadburners. The ultimate is the 1962 2000 GS Carrera 2: 2.0-litre engine and 140bhp in lightweight GT trim. Expect to pay £100k though.

904 Carrera GTS 1964-1965

Power 155bhp **Torque** 125lb ft **Weight** 740kg
Top speed 156mph **0-60mph** 5.5sec

The 904 Carrera GTS is one of those cars that enjoys the title road car purely because its maker needed to get 100 out the door to homologate it for racing. For DM29,000, what you really got was a detuned competition car.

But you got a lot of manufacturing innovation too: the Carrera was a composite construction using a steel ladder-section chassis joined to a (hand laid-up) glassfibre body. There wasn't much room inside, but the steering column featured two universal joints for driver safety and the pedals were adjustable for reach. Good job too, because the seats were bolted in place.

Fitted with the competition exhaust the 904 would kick out 180bhp and reach 163mph. Even in road trim it was no slouch; its light weight allowed it to dash to 60mph in under six seconds while, in early testing, a Carrera GTS with stock 155bhp engine broke the magic ten-minute barrier at the Nürburgring Nordschleife.

911 short-wheelbase 1964-1968

Power 130bhp **Torque** 128lb ft **Weight** 1075kg
Top speed 131mph **0-60mph** 10.6sec (2.0 L)

Original and best? Well, yes and no... For purity of styling and collector interest, the first of the 911s has unrivalled appeal. The houndstooth upholstery, skinny wheels, and the sweetness of the 2.0-litre engine make for a period experience – but handling is iffy on the limit, the brakes feel wooden, and performance isn't spectacular.

What you *do* get in an early 911 is the feeling that you could drive all day. They ride beautifully on the tall tyres and relatively soft suspension, while the engine bumbles away behind you. It's a world away from the typical British sports car of the period, and certainly an acquired taste.

Many of the best early cars have been snapped up by the historic rally boys, hence the high prices. The S is the best of the bunch, predictably, and is more exciting to drive than the lesser models, but don't let that make you feel you'd suffer with anything other than an S. They all have their appeal.

912/912E 1965-1969/1976

Power 90bhp **Torque** 90lb ft **Weight** 969kg
Top speed 121mph **0-60mph** 11.9sec

In 1965, Porsche faced a problem: the 911 was becoming too expensive for some of its customers. It's an issue faced by classic 911 enthusiasts too and in both cases the solution might be the 912.

Body and suspension are identical to the 911's, though inside you'll notice a few economies – only three round instruments as standard, and plastic in place of the 911's wood. Plastic steering wheel too. The big difference is the engine – no flat six here, but the 1.6-litre flat four of the 356SC. Fed by two twin-choke Solex carburettors, power was backed off to 90bhp. Body-wise it's pure 911, so in 1967 a Targa version appeared, and in 1969 the wings were slightly flared to make way for six-inch wheels. A bargain if you can find one for £10,000.

Although some might turn their nose up, that lighter engine makes for better weight distribution than the 911: it's chuckable and willing, especially with the optional five-speed 'box. Just avoid 1976's awful 912E, with its boat-anchor 2.0-litre flat-four in the tail.

911 open-tops 1966-on

Power 250bhp **Torque** 229lb ft **Weight** 1340kg
Top speed 152mph **0-60mph** 6.1sec (Speedster)

A true 911 has a tin top. But there are some strange types who prefer to spoil the looks, and to that end there are several choices.

First up, of course, is the Targa, a 911 staple since late 1966. The first Targas, with their collapsible rear sections, are now highly collectible. All proper Targas (ie, with lift-out roof panel) that follow are cheaper on the secondhand market than the coupés. The most recent Targas have a sliding glass roof panel, which actually doesn't look too bad.

Anyone else with an aversion to fresh air in a 911 will share a similar dislike of the Cabriolet that appeared in 1982. This full convertible has remained in the 911 range ever since.

In 1989 Porsche made an attempt to recreate the coolness of the 356, with the 911 Speedster. The cut-down windscreen and plastic hump to cover the folded-down hood nearly work, but not quite. In 911 land, tin-tops rule. OK?

911 (pre-1973) 1968-1973

Power 165bhp **Torque** 152lb ft **Weight** 1050kg
Top speed 139mph **0-60mph** 6.4sec (911E 2.4)

Here's where it gets *really* good. The wheelbase of these 'B-series' 911s was 57mm longer, achieved by lengthening the trailing arms. The engine stayed in the same position, which meant there was less weight hanging over the rear axle line, and therefore more predictable handling.

Engines initially remained at 2.0 litres but grew to 2.2 and then 2.4, which gave the 911 the performance it deserved. Interiors remained as starkly characterful as ever, and the exterior shape was, if anything, improved by the slightly longer panelwork between doors and rear arches.

There are four models: the basic but rather low-powered T, the fuel-injected E, the rather wonderful S and, of course, the Carrera RS 2.7 – so good that it's gone into silly money territory. The 2.4S in particular is a true great, but we'll always say that you're better off buying a good T or E or smaller-engined S than a ropey 2.4S.

914-914/6 1970-1976

Power 85bhp **Torque** 138lb ft **Weight** 950kg
Top speed 110mph **0-60mph** 12sec (914)

Yes, its time to mention the V-word again – the 914 was a joint venture between Volkswagen and Porsche, who in 1969 had both independently concluded that this mid-engined idea had possibilities. With its quirky angularity it does have a very 1970s 'designed' look about it; even an offbeat cool. Okay, some would say it's ugly. But it's great fun.

There were two engines available, the main one being the 80bhp 1.7-litre 'four' from the VW 411E. In 1973 this was upgraded to a 100bhp two-litre with D-Jetronic fuel injection and this one certainly makes for a very tractable usable classic – for around £4000 too.

But you'll be wanting to know about the other one; for little more than a year, Porsche made the 914/6 which used the 110bhp six-cylinder from the 911T. This one also had vented front disc brakes. Get a good one and it'll be good for near 130mph and will handle very nicely – but you'll be into same-era 911 money.

911 impact-bumper 1974-1983
Power 200bhp **Torque** 188lb ft **Weight** 1093kg
Top speed 141mph **0-60mph** 7.3sec (3.0 Carrera)

It didn't seem so long ago that the impact bumpers of post-'73 911s were as unacceptably ugly as a wart on Kylie's pert bottom. Somehow, though, the bumpers don't seem so bad any more and full galvanising of the body (from '76) tends to take the sting away from the less attractive styling.

Anyway, the plus side is that, thanks to those bumpers, these otherwise similar 911s are much, much cheaper than their predecessors, starting at £10,000. The first 1974-77 cars used 2.7-litre engines to compensate for the extra weight of the bumpers and more luxurious interior, with the Carrera the top model – a current performance bargain. A 3.0-litre quickly joined the range; it was quicker but not as enjoyably revvy. Then came the Turbos, and they're so good we've given them a section of their own.

Finally, the SCs, pretty much the same as the outgoing Carrera 3.0 but with less power. Doh! Not a bad car, all the same.

911 Turbo 1975-on
Power 300bhp **Torque** 319lb ft **Weight** 1335kg
Top speed 156mph **0-60mph** 4.9sec (1989 3.3)

The 911 Turbo. An icon within an iconic range. An accident waiting to happen within a licence-threatening line-up. A 911 Turbo takes the nimble, precise ethos of the 911 and – after a short pause – throws it away in a surge of outrageous power. We like 911 Turbos a lot, especially the early ones.

Whatever the year you get the enlarged arches, the Carlos Fandango wheels and the silly spoiler. What you don't get is the fierce exhaust note of a normally aspirated 911, because the turbo mutes that, and you do get lag. Choose a 3.0 for collector appeal, or a 3.3 for increased power and decent brakes. For ease of ownership, a 1984-on 3.3 is better, and the 1989 G50 gearbox model the toughest. The Turbo SE of 1986-'89 is the infamous slant-nose; controversial but collectible. Of more recent cars, the 964 3.6 is best – the last of the two-wheel-drive, all-or-nothing single-turbo models. Later 4WD twin-turbos are seriously fast and competent, but less involving.

924 1976-1988
Power 150bhp **Torque** 140lb ft **Weight** 1255kg
Top speed 133mph **0-60mph** 8sec (924S)

The car that all 'true' Porsche cognoscenti love to hate is actually a tight little performer. Intended as a successor to the VW-Porsche 914 but shelved as a joint venture, it was appropriated solely by Porsche and became its first front-engined four-cylinder model using an Audi 100-derived 1984cc motor. As well as hatchback practicality, the 924 offered beautifully balanced handling with its gearbox sitting at the rear, and a very usable if not astounding spread of power.

In 1979 a turbo gave the model 170bhp and more credibility, and in 924S form it became the car people said it should have been with engine, brakes and suspension components from the 944.

The biggest surprise is that you can pick up a decent 924 for about a grand – so it's easily the cheapest Porsche you can buy. But before you get too many ideas, we're not talking about the 1981 924 Carrera GT built for Group 4 homologation. For that rare flared-out 149mph missile, you'll be looking to pay nearer £20,000.

928 1978-1995
Power 320bhp **Torque** 317lb ft **Weight** 1600kg
Top speed 168mph **0-60mph** 5.9sec

The Great Heresy: Porsche's contemporary vision of a replacement for the 911 combined technological innovation with real-world savvy to become the only sports car to win the Car of the Year award.

It had everything a GT driver should want: near-perfect weight distribution from a water-cooled 4.5-litre V8 in the front, driving the rear wheels through Porsche's new Weissach transaxle. It was designed to eliminate the oversteer so beloved of its air-cooled, rear-engined 'predecesor'. Yes we know the rest of the story, but it doesn't alter the fact that, in all its incarnations, this is one hell of a car.

For design house purity go for the early cars (£4000), or for a tough do-the-maintenance-yourself bruiser, try the 155mph, 300bhp 928S of 1980 onwards (£6000). Sophistication and engine size increased in the 5.0-litre S4 of 1984 and culminated in the 170mph 5.4-litre GTS of 1992. A true intercontinental missile.

944 1981-1991
Power 190bhp **Torque** 170lb ft **Weight** 1280kg
Top speed 142mph **0-60mph** 7.9sec (944S)

The real entry-level Porsche, in the eyes of many fans, sported suitably more butch styling than the 924; wider wings, deep, body-coloured front spoiler, and black spoiler around the rear hatch.

And this time the engine was a proper in-house Porsche design, derived from the 928's V8 and using that car's cylinder head. One of the largest four-cylinders on the market at 2.5 litres, it knocked out a respectable 163bhp.

In 1985, the Turbo made it even more respectable with 220bhp. That model was also treated to a new nose, firmer chassis tuning and a higher-quality new 911-esque interior that worked its way into the rest of the range. 1987 saw the introduction of the 16-valve S.

These are all solid and exciting cars that make no excuses for their heritage but can still be found very cheaply on the market. The 211bhp 3.0-litre S2 and the very stylish cabriolet (both from 1989) are the best to go for, but they're extremely usable so expect high mileages.

Carrera 3.2 1984-1989
Power 231bhp **Torque** 209lb ft **Weight** 1210kg
Top speed 151mph **0-60mph** 5.3sec

Why separate the 3.2 from its impact bumper predecessors? Because it's so much better, regardless of whether the majority of casual admirers of the 911 have sussed that. If you're after reliability, then this is the classic to go for.

The engine is a peach, taken to 3.2 litres with wider bores but a slightly shorter stroke, to return to the revviness of earlier engines. The 911's first full engine management system helps with a boost in power and a roughly 10% improvement in fuel economy. Importantly, this is the engine with the hydraulic camchain tensioners, though most earlier 911s have been retro-fitted with these for much-improved engine life. Then there's the gearbox, from 1987 the stronger, slicker-shifting G50 unit, with reverse to the left instead of to the right. Well worth having.

The downsides? Heavier, not as nimble as the pre-'73s, and unpleasant interior colours are (as with all impact-bumper 911s) rather too common. Still great, though.

959 1988
Power 450bhp **Torque** 369lb ft **Weight** 1590kg
Top speed 196mph **0-60mph** 3.9sec

This technological tour de force became a legend in its own lifetime; a car that could do over 190mph in the days when 190 was *very* fast. Like the Ferrari 250GT SWB, it was designed to be driven on public roads and also entered in racing events.

The body boasted a low drag coefficient of 0.31, while the adjustable, speed-dependent damper valving allowed three-stage ground clearance. Its turbocharged engine came from the racing Type 962C, which dominated Group C at the time, and drove though a six-speed manual 'box and four wheel-drive.

The 959's main adversary was Ferrari's 288GTO, with much talk of Porsche's 'scientific' approach to 'the ultimate supercar'. A drive in it now is anything but clinical. Values are sitting at £200k-plus and don't expect them to go anywhere but up.

964 1989-1993
Power 250bhp **Torque** 229lb ft **Weight** 1350kg
Top speed 158mph **0-60mph** 5.1sec (Carrera 2)

The 964 was reckoned to be 87% new compared with the previous Carrera 3.2 – out went torsion bars, in came coil springs; in came a 3.6-litre version of the old 3.2, but with twin plugs, dual distributors and new engine management. And, for the first time, there was four-wheel drive (the Carrera 4).

So the 964 upset traditionalists, then nailed its own coffin with oil leaks and dual-mass flywheel problems. Porsche fixed the faults so now the 964 is a good buy.

There's little to choose between the Carrera 2 and Carrera 4. The Turbos (initially 3.3-litre) are less subtle, as befits the supercar performance – the Turbo S is the stripped-out lightweight, but the 3.6 Turbo is the best. The stars are the Carrera 2 RS 3.6 – lighter, lower, stronger and faster – and the even more extreme (and super-rare) RS 3.8.

968 1991-1995
Power 240bhp **Torque** 225lb ft **Weight** 1320kg
Top speed 157mph **0-60mph** 6.5sec (Club Sport)

Looking like the offspring of a 944 and a 928, the 968 was Porsche's final development of the front-engined, four-cylinder transaxle model. Some viewed it as a 944 rehash and, despite its performance nearly matching the 911's, the car didn't quite seem to distance itself far enough from the pumped-up hatchbacks of the 1990s that were hot on its heels.

Yet it's still a tidy performer, and a practical Porsche too. What's more, in trying to create an accessible entry-level model, Porsche created a cult classic: the 1993 Club Sport. With body-coloured cup alloys, Carrera RS bucket seats, and manual windows, this car has a focused track day feel. 157mph and 0-60mph in 6.5sec help too – it's a gem and could be yours for as little as £9k. If that's not enough, there's always the 305bhp turbo.

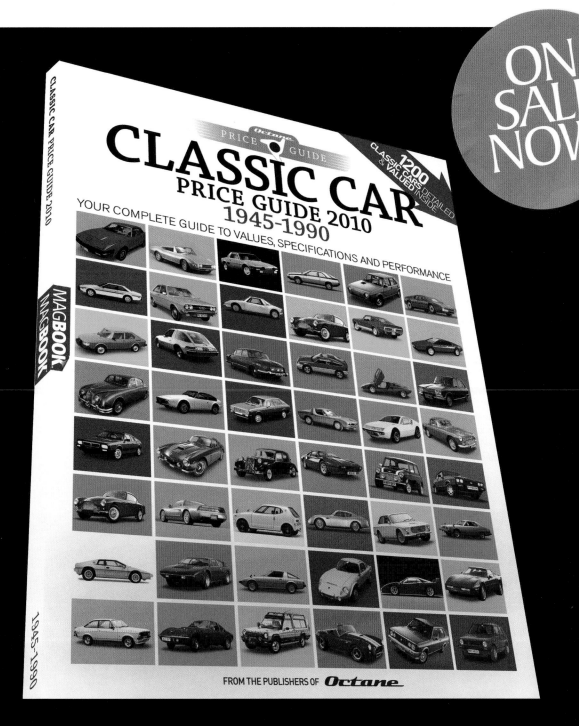

993 1993-1998

Power 272bhp **Torque** 243lb ft **Weight** 1370kg
Top speed 160mph **0-60mph** 5.2sec (Carrera 2)

The last of the air-cooleds! That in itself makes the 993 a bit special, but it's also widely said to be the last of the 911s that were built while engineering overruled accounting at Porsche. Certainly any 993 feels reassuringly solid, more so even than the current model.

The basic design was the same as the 964's but virtually every part was different – and improved. The biggest difference was to the rear suspension, with a new mult-link design with built-in passive rear-steer that reduced the lift-off oversteer and the road noise that had blighted the 964.

As with the 964, there's little difference between the Carrera 2 and the four-wheel-drive Carrera 4, and prices are as low as £15,000. Later Varioram cars have more torque but don't attract a big premium. Stars in the 993 range are the Turbo and the RS, but the Carrera 4S (a Carrera 4 that looks like a Turbo) is surprisingly popular. And don't forget the GT2 – the scariest 993 you'll find.

911 GT1 1997-1998

Power 544bhp **Torque** 443lb ft **Weight** 1120kg
Top speed 193mph **0-60mph** 3.7sec

Yet another race car for the road, Porsche produced 21 road-legal examples of the 911 GT1, a direct off-shoot of the Le Mans winner. The body was a composite of sheet steel and carbonfibre reinforced plastics, with a roof-mounted scoop to feed air to the engine.

The 3162cc motor itself was a four-valve unit producing 544bhp and based on the crankcase of the 964, driving through a six-speed manual gearbox. Maximum torque was 443ft lb at a fairly reasonable 4250rpm – so maybe not too bad behind a bus in the rush hour.

The suspension came straight from the track – double wishbones front and rear and single-tube gas-pressure dampers mounted with cylindrical springs. 380mm vented disc brakes with four-piston calipers could bring the GT1 down safely from its 193 top speed.

Despite the high rear wing and the Roman helmet crest to the roof, you can still see a certain 911-ishness in its looks. If you narrow your eyes. And squint.

Boxster 1997-2005

Power 204bhp **Torque** 210lb ft **Weight** 1250kg
Top speed 149mph **0-60mph** 6.9sec

Even though the 911's tail-end waywardness had long been cured, Porsche was still criticised for its rear-engined stubbornness – until it launched the Boxster.

Designed with a 'shared parts' policy along with a new 911 model that would follow, the new two-seater roadster would share lights, front wings, and many other parts. It was given a new water-cooled 2480cc flat six, driving the rear wheels through a five-speed manual 'box.

In 1999 the engine was enlarged to 2687cc (228bhp), but the big news was the Boxster S boasting a 249bhp 3.2-litre six and sports tuned suspension. In 2003, the model underwent a thorough cosmetic facelift, though performance changed little.

Early Boxsters look seriously tempting now at £6000. Check that service history though.

996 1998-2004

Power 300bhp **Torque** 258lb ft **Weight** 1320kg
Top speed 177mph **0-60mph** 4.6sec (Carrera 3.6)

Will time be kind to the 996? It's a great car, and actually it doesn't *really* matter that it's water-cooled (to keep noise levels down), however wrong it seems. But those headlights... they're a mess.

You can blame it on cost-saving. The all-new bodyshell of the 996 is near-identical to the cheaper Boxster's from the bulkhead forward, and unfortunately the headlights were left similarly near-identical. Foolish.

Once again there are Carrera 2, Carrera 4, Carrera 4S and Turbo versions, plus a still-more powerful Turbo S and a GT2 and GT3. Prices are at similar levels to the 993's, with the later 3.6s always likely to fetch more than the 3.4-litre version. The superb Turbo models are unlikely ever to dip far below their current £30,000 value, and the cult-status GT3s can only go up in the long term.

Cayenne 2002-on

Power 450bhp **Torque** 457lb ft **Weight** 2355kg
Top speed 165mph **0-60mph** 5.6sec (Turbo)

Did you ever wonder what the Ford Sierra might have looked like if it had been made into a bread van? Well look no further. The Cayenne is what happens when marketing departments try to squeeze one more niche out of a successful sports car 'brand'.

To be fair, the Cayenne is a formidable performer. The 450bhp Cayenne Turbo offered monumental performance in a 16ft long, 6ft wide bus with pretty gritty off-road ability and space for four adults with stuff for the boot. Fuel consumption was dreadful but the new 2010 edition offers diesels and a hybrid to cure that.

You'd think the marketing guys should take a 550 Spyder for a spin to get the gist of what the 'brand' is really about. But they got something right: this car has been a serious money-spinner for Porsche.

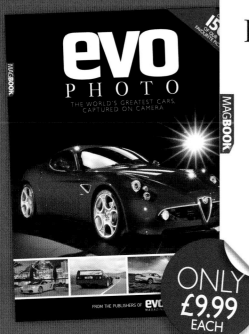

997 2004-on

Power 325bhp **Torque** 273lb ft **Weight** 1395kg
Top speed 177mph **0-60mph** 4.8sec (Carrera)

Funny, but the 997 is far easier to accept as a 911 in its own right than the 996 will ever be. It looks right, it sounds great and the driving experience is absolutely spot-on.

Aside from the headlights, there doesn't seem to be much difference between the 996 and 997 at first glance, but in fact over 80% of parts have been changed. The body is curvier, the front bumper different (more like the 993's), the rear track wider, the 3.6-litre engine a little more powerful and sharper to respond.

For the first time since 1977 there was a choice of normally aspirated engine sizes: the standard 3.6, and the 3.8 of the Carrera S and Carrera 4S. Turbos are as good as you'd expect; GT2s and GT3s icons in the making. At the moment there's still plenty of money to lose in depreciation for all except the first 997s but, as that great 911 cliché goes, they're great cars to be used every day. Not as engaging as an early car or even a 993 but damned good.

Carrera GT 2004

Power 612bhp **Torque** 435lb ft **Weight** 1445kg
Top speed 205mph **0-60mph** 3.9sec

Although the top Porsches have undeniable supercar ability, their personality often lacks the sparkle of their Italian counterparts. Not so the Carrera GT. Even so, Porsche hasn't wavered from its philosophy to craft the car; this flawlessly proportioned and sculpted ground missile is based on the purest racing car technology.

The GT's longitudinally mounted V10 is a 5.7-litre version of the 5.5 conceived for Le Mans. It drives the rear wheels through a gearbox transversely mounted so it's as close to the rear axle as possible, and was the first home for Porsche's two-disc ceramic clutch.

At one time it was an all-alloy body that made enthusiasts drool, but the Carrera offers us a carbonfibre sandwich monocoque tub bolted to a carbonfibre-reinforced chassis. The interior sports Kevlar composite seats covered in leather and a dashboard of titanium-painted carbonfibre. Magnesium decorates the centre console trim. And it does 205mph. Art in motion.

Boxster 2005-on

Power 306bhp **Torque** 265lb ft **Weight** 1355kg
Top speed 170mph **0-60mph** 5.3sec (S)

Time was when a loaf of bread cost 30p and only the Porsche 911 Turbo did 170mph and 0-60mph in 5.3sec. Well, now the mid-range Boxter S does it (and a loaf costs £1.30).

The latest incarnation took over in 2005 and, according to Porsche, shares only 20% of its components with the old one. The intake vents are larger and the wheelarches accomodate 19in wheels, but the main visual difference is Carrera GT-style headlights.

Power is up, with even the base 2.9 kicking out 252bhp and the S climbing into 1970s supercar territory.

A Boxster Spyder has also now been added with performance somewhere between the other two. The Spyder, of course, is an open version of the Boxster... which is an open car reminiscent of the 550 Spyder of 1955.

Hang on – run that by me again...

Cayman 2006-on

Power 316bhp **Torque** 273lb ft **Weight** 1350kg
Top speed 172mph **0-60mph** 5.2sec (S)

Just when you thought the company might be going soft at the edges, it came back with something so quintessentially Porsche it almost made you want to sell your 356.

The Cayman shares the same mid-engined platform as the second-generation Boxster, but there's enough here both architecturally (you can see a bit of 904 in it too) and dynamically to think of it as a model in its own right. It's powered by a 3.4-litre flat six, related to the Boxster's but with 10bhp more model for model, and it drives through a six-speed manual transaxle.

Here is a small, light, beautifully designed and executed car with just the right amount of power to make it enjoyable on *real* roads. It's a dynamic gem and they do it in some funky colours too – enough to make you think back to those early 911s, funnily enough.

Panamera 2009-on

Power 493bhp **Torque** 516lb ft **Weight** 1970kg
Top speed 188mph **0-60mph** 4.2sec (Turbo)

When you look at Porsche's new saloon, you get that familiar uneasy feeling you got when you look at the four-door 911 they did back whenever. That was ugly too.

But let's look at the positives. Porsche has packed all its dynamic, sporting know-how into a boardroom level autobahn-stormer. And it's taken the text-book corporate path by launching a model for every pay grade from 3.6 V6 to sledgehammer 493bhp Turbo.

With its engine set well back in the chassis, and its electronically micro-managed suspension, you can't argue with its dynamic abilities – in fact, if anything, the smaller-engined car is even better balanced.

So don't get carried away thinking this is just a soft limo with a Porsche badge. It's really a sports car with four seats. Shame it doesn't look sexy to match.

BADMINTON SCHOOL

THE FIRST 150 YEARS

BADMINTON SCHOOL

THE FIRST 150 YEARS

Nigel Watson

BADMINTON SCHOOL: THE FIRST 150 YEARS

Copyright © Badminton School

First published in 2008
by James & James (Publishers) Limited, a member of
the Third Millennium Information Limited Group

2–5 Benjamin Street
London
United Kingdom
EC1M 5QL
www.tmiltd.com

ISBN: 978 1 903942 88 8

British Library Cataloguing in Publication Data
A CIP catalogue record for this book is available
from the British Library.

Project Editor: Susan Millership
Designer: Susan Pugsley
Production Manager: Bonnie Murray

Reprographics by Studio Fasoli, Italy
Printed by Gorenjski Tisk, Slovenia

Photo Acknowledgements

All images provided by Badminton School unless
otherwise noted. Every effort has been made to
contact the copyright holders of all works
reproduced in this book. However, if
acknowledgements have been omitted, the
publishers ask those concerned to contact
James & James (Publishers) Ltd, a member of
the TMI Group.

Alamy Images: Clara Butt, p 27; Lynmouth
Harbour, p 68.
Bridgeman Art Library: The Lesson (how to sew),
p 12; Cat and Mouse Act poster, p 39; Wartime
recruitment poster, p 72.
Getty Images: Lord Robert Cecil, p 51.
Jack Rice: Clare Harvey, p 97.
Mary Evans: Girton College Lecture, p 13;
Lady Graduate 1885, p 13.
National Portrait Gallery: Peter Pears and
Benjamin Britten, p 71.
Reece Winstone Archive: VE Day, p 76.
TopFoto: Success in Life (Punch Cartoon), p 18.

CONTENTS

FOREWORD

To mark the 150th anniversary of Badminton this year, we have commissioned the first major history of the school.

Nigel Watson's fascinating and accessible account illuminates Badminton's origins and traditions, places its development into a historical and social context and captures the individuality of the school. Photographs and illustrations from our own archives are interspersed with more recent images. Candid observations and anecdotes from 'Old' Badmintonians give an intriguing glimpse into life at Badminton during its changing phases.

The strands of the past continue to underpin the school's values. Badminton retains the internationalist outlook which made it unique among girls' schools, and the self confidence to continue to be progressive and true to itself.

This book is dedicated to our predecessors whose conviction and leadership shaped and influenced the distinctive character of Badminton, and is a tribute to everyone who has been here.

Jan Scarrow
June 2008

ACKNOWLEDGEMENTS

Badminton is a special place. Many of the qualities established for the school by the great Miss Baker still flourish today, perpetuated from generation to generation. It is always fascinating to be reminded how innovative and even experimental schools once were and, despite the pressures of modern education, this ethos has not been lost at Badminton. I have been greatly helped and encouraged by many people during the course of writing this short history. The text benefits hugely from the books already published on the headships of Miss Baker and Miss Sanderson and from the typescript of a previous history by Patricia Morris. I was also able to speak with previous heads Clare Harvey (now Clare Feaver) and Clifford Gould as well as with the current head, Jan Scarrow, who was always available for help and advice. I was pointed in the right direction as far as school records were concerned by the Old Badmintonian archivist, Christobel Thomas, while Rebecca Robertson suggested former staff and pupils for me to talk to. I have appreciated the many contributions, verbal and written, provided by many former pupils and past and present members of staff and would like to thank the following: Rebecca Robertson, Christobel Thomas, Clare Archibald, Caroline Bateson, Malcolm Belfield, Gillian Benjamin, Stella Berkeley, Alison Bernays, Judith Catty, Deborah Couzens, Lyn Deas, Val Drew, Carol Dooley, Felicity Hazell, Janet Hazleton, Joyce Hitchcock, Richard Hodder-Williams, Venetia Hooper, Jane Jones, Ann Lloyd, Imogen McNulty, Elizabeth Palmer, Jean Pratten, Sue Reid, Sue Spanner, Jean Suckling, Richard Thorn, Katrina Tiley, Tabitha Tuckett, Andrew Urquhart, Liz Welsh and Julia Woodger. I apologise if I have inadvertently omitted anyone. I would also like to thank Portia Thompson who smoothed my path while I was working at the school and to Hamish MacGibbon to whom I owe the privilege of this project and many others.

Nigel Watson
Spring 2008

AFFECTION AND CONFIDENCE
1858–1893

When Mrs Miriam Badock opened her home in Burlington Road, Redland, a suburb of Bristol, for the education of a handful of young ladies on 1 August 1858, it was seen as a brave if not foolish thing to do. Educating the daughters of the middle classes was still largely regarded as a waste of time and money. All they required to prepare them for their future married lives were certain accomplishments, such as singing, dancing and needlework. Even if women were beginning to be perceived as equals within marriage, many of them still agreed with most men that their moral superiority was matched by an intellectual inferiority. What therefore was the point of educating them?

Men had invented a superior feminine morality so they could elevate women to a pedestal from which they were permitted to rule supreme within the home to justify the fact that the world outside the home remained a male preserve. While some women began the fight to break out of this sexual apartheid, there were still those who agreed with their male colleagues that the female brain was too tender to withstand the stress and strain of an intellectual education. It was only when the Victorian middle classes realised the cost of supporting their unmarried daughters that they admitted there might be occasions when young women would have to support themselves. This led to the foundation of Queen's College and Bedford College in 1848 for the improvement of

the education of young governesses, one of the few occupations open to young, middle-class women. The pioneer of education for middle-class girls was Miss Buss, the founder of the North London Collegiate School in 1850; but even the liberal curriculum she introduced included traditional accomplishments, mainly to appease fathers who were paying the fees. And the school she founded was aimed initially at the education of girls to be mothers, wives or governesses. Miss Beale, the great headmistress of the Cheltenham Ladies' College, was only taking up her post in the same year that Miriam Badock took in her first pupils. Seven years later, in 1865, the Schools Inquiry Commission found that in the few schools educating middle-class girls there was 'want of thoroughness and foundation;

The early curriculum was a mix of 'womanly' subjects such as 'plain and fancy' needlework, singing and deportment alongside more progressive ones such as modern history, botany and astronomy.

want of system; slovenliness and showy superficiality; inattention to rudiments; undue time given to accomplishments and these not taught intelligently or in any scientific manner; want of organisation'. Yet the Commission, which revealed the appalling condition nationwide of middle-class education for both boys and girls, was all in favour of small-scale schools which replicated the home environment and educated girls as decorative, modest and marriageable beings.

Badminton was just such a small school. It took its name from Badminton House, the larger property eventually bought by Mrs Badock in Clifton, another suburb of Bristol. There were only 55 girls when Mrs Badock retired in 1893. She clearly strove as far as possible to maintain the school on a domestic scale. But while the education she offered in 1858 for 50 guineas a year for full boarders (day boarders paid 20 and day pupils 12) included deportment and plain and fancy needlework, with extra being paid for music and drawing, it also covered writing, arithmetic, grammar and composition, biblical knowledge, French, geography, ancient and modern history,

natural philosophy, botany and astronomy. Girls could also learn German and Italian for an extra fee. Latin was added three years later. It was substantially similar to the curriculum which the new girls' high schools would offer from the 1870s onwards. The inclusion of science was unusual. The subject was often ignored in girls' schools although it scarcely fared any better in many boys' schools of the period. When Badminton began, it was the responsibility of William, Miriam's husband, who gave lectures and conducted elementary experiments in an amateur laboratory.

Nevertheless, like other forward-looking girls' schools, these progressive elements were matched by more traditional concerns designed to reassure parents still cautious about educating their daughters away from home. So gentility, morality and a concern not to induce mental exhaustion were all features of the first circular published by the school. The fear of mental exhaustion was another myth peddled by men who had seen how much more quickly the minds of girls developed and how much more eager they were to learn than boys; so encouraging the belief that the female mind was a much more sensitive and fragile thing, unsuited to competition, needing to be protected from ambition, was a way of holding women back lest they eventually outstrip men in their achievements. This view gained such a hold even among women that in the 1930s Badminton, according to an article in a women's magazine, was still ensuring that 'the work is very carefully arranged to avoid over-strain'. To persuade parents that their daughters would be well looked after, Mrs Badock wished, according to the circular, 'to secure their affection and confidence' and 'then by a careful study of the character and mental capacities of each to develop moral and religious principles and impart instruction in the manner best adapted to their individual tastes and dispositions'. The circular also emphasised the healthy, comfortable accommodation and the invigorating and beautiful surroundings. Each young lady was expected to bring with her 'a silver fork and spoon and chamber towels'.

Badminton began when the reform of girls' education, led by Miss Buss and Miss Beale, was still in its infancy. The girls' high school movement did not begin until the 1870s, under the Girls' Public Day Schools Company. Women first became eligible for degrees in 1877, at St Andrew's in Scotland, and in England at London in the following year. At Oxbridge, Girton, Newnham, Somerville and Lady Margaret's were all founded between 1869 and 1879, but women would only be admitted to full membership of Oxford in 1920 and Cambridge in 1948. There were only 21 women doctors in 1881 while the law remained closed to women until 1919 (solicitors) and 1922 (barristers). The only professions which welcomed, rather than tolerated, women were teaching and nursing. Marriage often brought a woman's career to a premature end. For instance, local education authorities could legally insist on the resignation of women teachers when they married and such practices were only outlawed in the 1944 Education Act.

This brings us to another singular fact about Miriam Badock. It is difficult to think of another major independent girls' school whose founder was a married woman. Most of the great Victorian pioneers of middle-class education for girls who dedicated their lives to their profession were spinsters. Miriam Badock was not. Nor did she come from a family with artistic or intellectual inclinations. Her father, Henry Trapnell, was a hard-working middle-class businessman. Miriam, born in 1831, was the eldest surviving daughter of his 13 children. With his partner, Henry ran Trapnell & Gane, a Bristol-based firm of furniture makers and timber importers. Henry himself came from humble origins. His father, William, had been apprenticed as a cabinet maker. Of Henry's two brothers, the eldest, James, sailed to Newfoundland where he made his living as a shipbuilder; while the youngest, John, joined a circus and married the proprietor's daughter. According to Miriam's daughter, Edith, Henry was not one of those self-made men who despised education. On the contrary, he was an enlightened parent who was determined that his daughter should be well educated. He sent Miriam to Miss Thompson's private academy at Camden House on St Michael's Hill. Miss Thompson was a Plymouth Sister, part of the Plymouth Brethren, the exclusive religious sect established in 1831.

Miriam, a bright, bubbly child, managed to submit to the strict discipline exercised by Miss Thompson without losing her sense of humour. She raced through the course of instruction at the academy but her father was eager that she should extend her education. This was partly because he feared that his pretty daughter would fall prey to the countless suitors already calling on her far too frequently at

Top: A tutorial at Girton College, Cambridge University, set up in 1869 as the first residential college for women in the country. Bottom: Women became eligible for degrees in 1877 but only a small number of universities allowed women to graduate. Shown here is a student at University College London in 1885.

Mrs Miriam Badock, Badminton's founding headmistress, 1858–93.

home. So Miss Thompson agreed to teach Miriam Greek which she turned to with relish.

Miriam met William Badock, a business acquaintance of her brother Caleb, when she was not yet 20. For both of them, it was apparently love at first sight. Spending the night at the Trapnell home in Victoria Lodge, Whiteladies Road, Clifton, William was introduced to Miriam by her mother, who announced, 'My daughter, Mr Badock'. The confident young man is alleged to have answered, 'And my wife, if I can get her, Mrs Trapnell'. Six months later the couple were engaged and in 1850 they were married. The ceremony took place in the parish church at Clifton where Miriam's father worshipped. Miriam, however, was a Baptist, like her mother; so from the very beginning the school would be shaped by a nonconformist liberalism.

The newly weds went to live in Clapham in south London where William had his business. Yet before they had a chance to start a family, bad fortune struck. William was thrown from his horse and while recovering from a broken leg contracted kidney trouble. He would never regain his full health. His business faltered and his income fell. Miriam asked her father for his advice. A generous-hearted man, he immediately called them back to Bristol where he housed them in one of the several properties he had acquired from the profits of his own successful business and found William a place in the timber-importing side of the firm. This new-found stability gave William and Miriam the confidence to begin their family and in quick succession they had three children, Walter, Will and Gertie. Although the family history suggests that Henry Trapnell was instrumental in advising his daughter to open her school, the family tree shows that he died at the age of 55 in the spring of 1854 and never saw any of his grandchildren. The first of them, Walter, was born shortly afterwards.

It was probably Henry's untimely death that brought about the next crisis in the family. Since Trapnell & Gane was a partnership, Henry's death brought it to an end. Any capital he had invested in the business would have been thinly spread among his wife and his nine surviving children. At the same time William's health was creating further anxiety. Miriam, with three young children and a fourth on the way, found that the family budget was no longer adequate. The couple's first inclination was to take in a paying lodger. An advertisement was placed for 'a Christian lady' to come and share their home. It was answered by a Miss Holborrow who soon took up residence.

Miss Holborrow was an older woman in whom Miriam clearly felt able to confide during the mornings they spent sewing together. This closeness allowed Miss Holborrow to take the liberty one morning of suggesting, ever so politely, that perhaps Miriam could do more to support her ailing husband, who had once again taken to his bed. Miriam, taken aback, wondered where on earth she would find the time to do anything else with such a young family to look after, especially since she was expecting her fourth child. Perhaps Miss Holborrow had already been in contact with her own younger sister. In any event, within a short space of time she brought a letter from her sister which she asked Miriam to consider seriously. Miss Holborrow's sister, Mrs Hillier,

The school had 18 boarders while it was at 31 Berkeley Square in Clifton.

31
BERKELEY
SQUARE

had three young girls, slightly older than any of the Badock children, and she was anxious about their education. This was unsurprising given the generally poor state of girls' education. She wondered whether Miriam, whom she understood from her sister to be a well-educated woman, would take them in. Many middle-class families would have been outraged by the suggestion. The idea that a married woman should consider earning her own living was often regarded as a slight on her husband. William did object but only because he believed his wife was already overstretched. This too was the reason why Miriam's mother, according to Miriam's daughter, Edith, also objected. She did not have any objections to the idea in principle because she herself had once helped out in her husband's business. The craftsmen in the firm's furniture workshop had held her in awe. She inspected every item being despatched to customers and they knew that she would swiftly return any piece that was not perfect. The firm's growth stemmed partly from the fine reputation it gained for the quality of its merchandise, attributable in large part to the quality control exercised by Miriam's mother. But whatever the attitude of Miriam's husband and mother, it is unlikely that the school would have been opened at all had it not been for William's ill-health and the financial worries which followed.

Once Miriam agreed to accept her first three pupils, word got around. She took in several nieces and the daughters of friends. Three months after the birth of her fourth child, Herbert, Miriam Badock started her school. The house in Burlington Road soon proved unsuitable and the family moved first to no. 1, Berkeley Square, and then a few years later to no. 31, Berkeley Square, Clifton. The school took in boarders, limited at first to 18 but increased in response to growing demand from parents. One girl, Pidgie Parnall, was left with Mrs Badock when her father was posted to the West Indies and spent nine years at the school, never once seeing her parents. But this infant establishment nearly came to an untimely end. Halfway through one term Miriam was asked to take two little girls from London who had been expected to arrive at the

start of the following term. After the girls had arrived and been shown to their rooms, the governess who helped them to unpack told Miriam how strange it was that they did not possess a single item of clothing which was not new. Within a couple of days both girls became very ill. The doctor announced they had contracted scarlet fever. In those days this disease regularly killed many children. Mrs Badock sent all the other children home. Soon afterwards the two little girls died. The family decided the house would have to be disinfected and they took a furnished property at Portishead, just outside Bristol. There William fell ill with the disease as did their second child, Will, who survived but was never strong again. The school did not close. Mrs Badock, like her successors, was a strong and

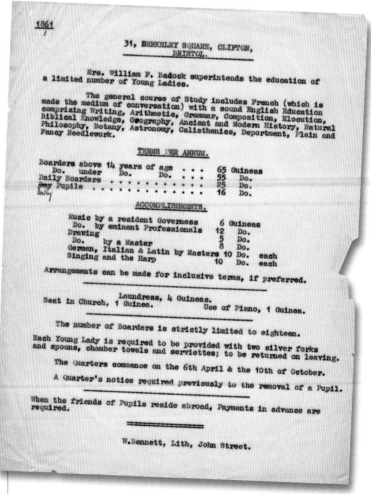

Details of subjects available and fees, 1861.

Badminton House.

Badminton House in Clifton Park, at the end of Worcester Terrace.

resilient character. The school re-opened with almost all Mrs Badock's previous pupils. The mother of the two girls who had died was distraught at what she had done. She told Miriam that one child had already died from the disease and she had thought that sending her daughters away would save them. She had bought them new clothes in the misguided belief that this would prevent this contagious disease from spreading.

According to Edith Trapnell, the Badocks moved from Berkeley Square to Clifton Park at the end of Worcester Terrace in 1868 because the character of the neighbourhood had changed. Edith blamed this partly on her father who had let the bottom of the large garden in Berkeley Square, which ran down to Park Street, for the development of shops, earning an income from the ground rents. Their new address, Edith recalled, 'was considered a most out of the world place, no gas, no light and no roads made … People thought they were crazy going into such an out of the way place'. The property was called Badminton House in Clifton Park, at the end of Worcester Terrace, and until the school moved again after the First World War it was known as Badminton House School. The house took its name from the estate of the Duke of Beaufort. Edith Trapnell relates how one of the first tenants had taken in the sons of the aristocracy as boarders and one of them had been the Marquess of

Fifth form classroom.

Assembly Hall.

Teachers from the School; from left to right: Miss EM Rees, Miss AS Boome and Miss M Blonvil.

Worcester, the Duke's eldest son. This seems incorrect since the eldest son of the Duke holds the title of Earl of Glamorgan, the Duke himself also being the Marquess of Worcester. More likely, both the name of the terrace and the house simply reflected the prominence of the Duke in the life of

the city. At first there was some local hostility to the school. Since William Badock was an Anglican, the family had previously been attending the parish church but on the move to Clifton Miriam began attending Highbury Congregational Church. The minister, David Thomas, then sent his three daughters to the school. A number of staunch Anglican residents were appalled that they not only had another nonconformist family in their midst (one was already living on the Terrace) but also a nonconformist school.

The school was among the earliest to enter girls for the Junior and Senior Cambridge Local Examinations. When the local committee asked Mrs Badock to send in pupils for the exams, she had no hesitation, calling for volunteers from among the girls. Her daughter remembered that 'it was considered a most advanced and dangerous thing to do and there was great excitement about it'. Competitive examinations, remember, were regarded as injurious to female health. All those first entrants passed. They were taught largely by unqualified staff because women could not graduate from an English university until 1878. One girl at the school in the late 1880s recollected that there was only one mistress on the staff with a degree. In 1889 there appear to have been around

Gymnasium and Display programme.

Badminton has a strong tradition of pupils entering the medical profession, dating back to 1892 when Maud Everett was accepted by the London School for Medicine.

nine members of staff, including William and Miriam Badock. Mrs Badock was by all accounts an outstanding maths teacher. Mr Morton Luce was lucid in his teaching of English and Latin while Professor Leipner from Bristol's University College taught botany and the girls dissected rabbits in Miss Knowles's anatomy classes. Swedish drill was taught by Miss Johnson and Mr Dahl in the newly built gymnasium. There was great celebration in 1892 when Maud Everett became the first girl from the school to study medicine, at the London School of Medicine for Women. But the school did not cater for girls who wished to progress to the Higher Local Examinations. One girl from the school, who went on to Newnham College, Cambridge, took her Higher Locals at University College, Bristol. Even when this option was eventually offered, it remained the preserve of the few until after 1945.

SUCCESS IN LIFE.

DR. ELIZABETH SQUILLS HAS BARELY TIME TO SNATCH A HURRIED MEAL AND HASTY PEEP AT THE PERIODICALS OF THE DAY IN HER HUSBAND'S BOUDOIR.

A *Punch* cartoon of 1867 pokes gentle fun at the novel idea of the role reversal faced when a woman goes out to work as a doctor. The previous year, Elizabeth Garrett Anderson, the renowed campaigner for women's rights, qualified as a doctor.

> 'Mrs Badock ... **was** the school for me, and I am thankful for her charm, her fortitude, her fun and her dignity – in fact for her whole influence'.

School photographs show a steadily increasing number of girls, from around 40 in 1880 to 60 or so by the end of that decade. There were few rules and no uniform except the school hat which the girls 'resented with fury'. Uniforms had yet to be widely adopted and tended only to be seen in endowed or charity schools, such as the local Red Maid's School. The school would always claim that rules were minimal throughout its history but as we shall see this was not quite the case.

Mrs Badock, wrote one former pupil, '*was* the school for me, and I am thankful for her charm, her fortitude, her fun and her dignity – in fact for her whole influence'. Such a tribute demonstrates the strength of Miriam Badock's personality and the impact a strong headmistress can have upon her pupils. It was a phenomenon which would be repeated regularly at Badminton. She retired from the school in 1893, aged 62, and lived until 1915. She sold the school to Miss Bartlett, who had been a pupil at the school and then returned to join the staff, and her two sisters. By now the outlook for girls' education was much changed. The new high schools were well established, offering a broad curriculum, encouraging academic achievement and fostering social and religious tolerance. Their drawback, shared by the new public schools for girls, was often an excessive regimentation, the absence of which was one of the strengths of the many good private schools, such as Badminton, which also flourished. But many of the pioneering schools, private or otherwise, were still torn between a need to observe ladylike conventions and a desire to provide girls with an education similar to that enjoyed by their brothers. It was this conundrum which now faced Miss Bartlett.

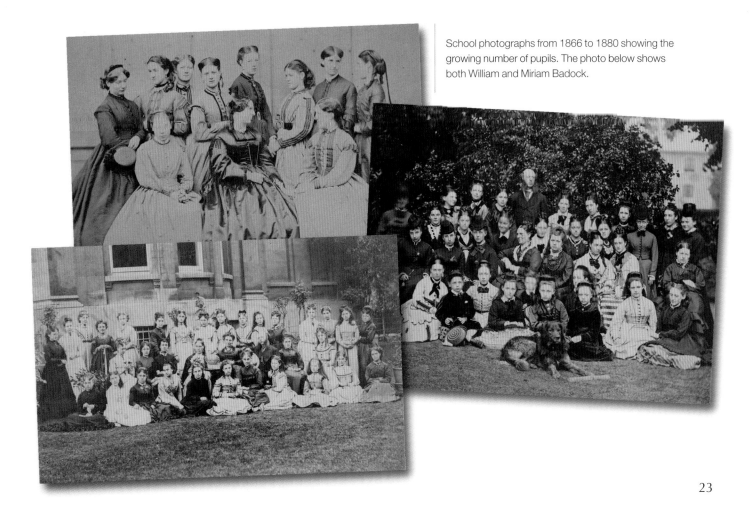

School photographs from 1866 to 1880 showing the growing number of pupils. The photo below shows both William and Miriam Badock.

A WIDE VIEW OF THINGS
1893–1914

Miss Bartlett was no radical but neither was she backward-looking. In her own gentle way she led a school which succeeded in offering an education to broaden the minds and widen the interests of the girls in her charge without offending their fathers. She ran the school with her two sisters, Florence, who taught art, and Gertrude, who taught music. The headmistress was a tiny woman but perfectly poised, dignified and immaculately dressed, 'a very erect little figure in rustling silk dresses'. According to her former pupils, she was strict but also 'human, sympathetic and gentle'. Another girl wrote how the school 'centred round Miss Bartlett and though we loved her, we all – girls, staff and parents – held her in a very wholesome awe'.

For Miss Bartlett, the ideal school was one 'where every single person does and is her very best'. She wanted the school, she wrote, 'to have an ever-rising standard of attainment, and to send out from its regulated and disciplined life an ever-increasing number of girls who take their places worthily in the great world'. Every girl should strive for the best since letting herself down was to let the school down. She wanted her girls to develop that *esprit de corps*, that public spirit, which had for so long been a preserve of boys' schools. An article in the school magazine defined this as 'being content to sink all personal interests, being content to be as he that doth serve, being glad and proud to fill in the smallest post, if, by filling that post in the most perfect way, you can help in the perfection of the

school to which you belong'. The writer continued that 'some say that women are incapable of such a masculine virtue; that women cannot put their private feelings in their pocket and act in subordination for the good of the whole; that they cannot sink their self-importance and their petty jealousies; that they cannot suppress themselves for the cause. Schools like ours have done a great deal for the mental education of women. They will do still more as they show that women can learn true public spirit, that school teaches *esprit de corps*'. This was treading on dangerous male-dominated territory and some critics might argue that by attempting to emulate the opposite sex progressive women were denying themselves and playing into the hands of their detractors. But this was an era when many women recognised that

Miss Bartlett, headmistress, 1893–1911.

advances would come only if they persuaded sufficient men to support them. What Miss Bartlett was doing, as in many other girls' schools, was trying to give her girls the chance to escape from claustrophobic domesticity and infuse them with the confidence to challenge existing orthodoxies in a way which would not antagonise those they needed as allies. In the school magazine for Christmas 1908 Miss Bartlett wrote that

> *in a girls' school we have woman in the making, and never was there a time in the history of the world when there was more urgent need for the right sort of women than there is now. Infinitely varied service is required of them in every department of public, philanthropic and religious work, and life was never more interesting for women and girls than it is now. For those who are to be of use in the world of the 20th century, a wide view of things, a sane well-balanced judgement, and the charity which is kind, are essential, and school is a training ground for the development of these qualities.*

Her rider, of course, was that while women may have had many more opportunities than ever before, one must not forget that 'home is the woman's kingdom, and to reign beautifully there her noblest work'. This was a theme to which her successors still subscribed well into the 1960s. And while a special debate was organised on women's suffrage in 1908 because the topic was exciting so much interest among the girls, this was balanced by the formation in 1909 of a school branch of the British Women's Patriotic League. This was a strange organisation which aimed to stir up among British women and girls the same degree of nationalist fervour perceived to exist among women in Germany and Japan. In 1910 the school was happy to have as a guest a male speaker from the League who told the girls that because women had always been hugely influential in the home, they must be to blame for the lack of patriotic feeling in the country.

According to the school magazine, public spirit demanded that for every girl 'her whole behaviour is marked by courtesy and self-control'. So manners and appearance remained important. The girls presented their nails for inspection every morning after prayers or marched past the

Miss Bartlett, left, with sisters Miss Florence (right) and Miss Gertrude (front), who taught at the school.

THE EXTRA FEES ARE:

PIANO	...	...	... 2, 3, or 4 guineas per term
VIOLIN	...	...	... 3 „ „
SOLO SINGING	...		... 3 „ „
DRAWING & PAINTING	...		... 1 „ „
GERMAN	...	...	... 1 „ „
DANCING	...	...	... 1 „ „
SWEDISH DRILL	..		... 1 „ „
LAUNDRY	...	...	... 1 „ „
SEAT IN CHURCH		...	10/6 „ „

Courses of Lessons and Lectures are frequently given in Home Nursing and Ambulance, Cookery, Wood Carving, Leather Work, etc., and Swimming, Riding, and Fencing are taught by competent Masters. The Fees vary according to the number of Lessons or Lectures in the Course.

The usual School Games are Tennis, Cricket, Hockey, and Basket Ball, and a Subscription of 5/- per term for Games is paid by every Pupil.

Daily Pupils remaining to Dinner pay Three Guineas per term.

A term's notice is required before the removal of a Pupil or the Fees for the term will be charged.

No reduction is made for absence during the term.

Miss Bartlett (centre right) with her pupils, 1906.

Miss Bartlett's list of school fees and charges.

headmistress in pairs from opposite directions so that she could ensure that Badminton girls would never push people off the pavement. Slang was strictly forbidden on pain of a halfpenny fine and Miss Bartlett cautioned against practical jokes. Discipline was effected initially by 'impositions' and 'hours' but these were replaced in 1908 by a system of order and conduct marks. Three of these marks in one week brought an hour's detention on Saturday mornings which cut into the shopping time allowed for pairs of girls in Clifton's Mall. A

head girl and prefects were also introduced by 1909. Decorum also meant that team games were played in uniform, complete with the dreaded school hats, and that gym and dancing were performed in the most ungainly costumes. Phyllis Higgs recalled that 'we wore heavy blue serge dresses … and underneath we wore a "singlet" (to fill up the space) … we had thick serge knickers and the whole kit weighed several pounds and was appallingly hot in summer'.

Charitable works were an integral part of Miss Bartlett's philosophy. Since 1895 the girls had been supporting a cot in the Bristol Children's Hospital. In the days before the National Health Service, all hospital care was provided privately and usually relied on charitable donations. On Saturday evenings in spring the girls made garments for Dr Barnardo's. They visited the local orphanage. They heard missionary addresses from women working in India and organised collections for the British & Foreign Bible Society. This, of course, was set against a belief at the height of Empire that the West was the fount of beneficence worldwide. A casual remark in one lecture given to the girls referred to poor food hygiene in China which caused so much illness in so many Europeans; but this 'will soon be overcome, as Europeans spread the scientific ideas of the West wherever they go, and the Chinese are ready to learn'. The internationalism for which the school is today

Hockey has played a role in the sporting life of the school since its early days.

renowned was barely in its infancy. A drama presented by the school under Miss Bartlett, *A Dialogue Between Two Negroes And How It Ended*, revealed the patronising attitude taken by whites towards blacks, who were depicted as stupid servants. This would never have reached the stage under her successor.

Sport was another way of encouraging *esprit de corps*. So hockey in particular and basketball were played. Hockey took place on Wednesday and Saturday afternoons and until transport was provided for the first time in 1911 the girls walked two and a half miles across the Downs to the hockey field at Stoke Abbey Farm. But fresh air and exercise were also an essential way of keeping the girls healthy. There were plenty of long country walks, although veils were worn to keep unfeminine ruddy complexions at bay. Beryl Latham wrote that 'we walked every day, wet or fine; it had to be pouring with rain to keep us in. If it was raining after lunch and we had just settled down to enjoy ourselves the moment there was a break in the clouds the bell would ring and out we should have to go with mackintoshes and

An early tennis game in Terrace Gardens.

umbrellas.' In the summer the girls were taught to swim at the local baths or played tennis. There was an annual sports day, the girls performed gym displays for their parents and there were dancing classes. In an age when child mortality was still high and antibiotics unheard of, all this healthy activity kept epidemics and fatal illness at bay. There was no repeat of the tragic scarlet fever case which had troubled Miriam Badock.

Miss Bartlett also made sure that her girls never suffered from examination strain. One pupil later recalled that 'public examinations did not loom large on our horizon; those who wanted to could take them but not very many did'. This reflected the expectations of many parents as much as those of Miss Bartlett. She also ensured that, as the school magazine noted, only 'suitable' girls were entered. So, for instance, there were three candidates for the Cambridge Locals in the autumn of 1906 and just two in the following year. Another girl looking back thought the school was already old-fashioned in its relaxed approach to intellectual achievement, 'not coveting academic honours but giving a very fair grounding in at least English language and literature'. But Badminton has always managed to avoid the atmosphere of the academic hothouse. The fact that few girls were entered for exams did not mean they were idle. Most of the teaching, one girl recalled, was 'adequate and some of it very good'. The girls had five periods of teaching every morning, worked at least two afternoons every week, and spent at least two and a half hours every evening doing their 'prep'.

What was best remembered from the classroom were the lectures Miss Bartlett delivered to her sixth-form girls on art and literature. While the school may not have stretched the minds of its girls by public examination, Miss Bartlett did her best to stimulate their interest in culture. There was drama ranging from Euripides' *Alcestis* and Sophocles' *Antigone* to the dramatisation of three scenes from a popular book of the time, *Mrs Wiggs of the Cabbage Patch*. There were junior and senior literary societies, visits to the local theatre and a party of 40 girls travelled to the Bath Pageant in 1909. Music was encouraged. A choral society performed plantation songs, a ladies' concert party performed for the girls, and there was a small orchestra under Miss Rootham, with a handful of strings, including three mandolins, plus a harp and a piano. The girls attended concerts given in Bristol by the popular contralto Dame Clara Butt (on Empire Day) and by great musicians such as Fritz Kreisler, the

Not all school outings had to be educational; the girls often took walks in spring and summer.

violinist, Pablo Casals, the cellist, and the pianist Wilhelm Backhaus. A series of lectures was given over successive Friday afternoons on the history of architecture. Visits were arranged to the city's art gallery. Girls were also encouraged in practical pursuits. An arts and crafts exhibition held in the summer of 1906 displayed the fruits of this encouragement with exhibits including plain needlework, hemstitch, Irish crochet, woodcarving, leather-work, book-binding and basket-weaving, as well as paintings, drawings and sketches. Cookery, dressmaking, first aid and hygiene were taught in classes for domestic arts and crafts. As well as a club for sketching, there was also one for photography. In many of these activities Miss Bartlett was ahead of many other girls' schools; indeed, clubs, societies and organised outings were rare in many boys' schools. Outings were not all educational. In 1906 the school magazine reported that 'many pleasant expeditions and excursions have enlivened this spring and summer', with the fifth form taken to Bath, and walks organised by the Field Club to pick flowers, primroses in April and foxgloves in June, in Portbury and down Carter's Lane. In the summer holidays of 1908 a number of girls attended the University Women's Camps for Schoolgirls. Royal visits to Bristol caused great excitement in an age before mass communications when the empire was at its zenith and the monarch was revered. Girls watched Queen Victoria's visit

WILL'S CIGARETTES

PHOTO ELLIOT & FRY

MAD^ME CLARA BUTT.

Girls were encouraged to study music and attended concerts in Bristol given by a range of musicians, including popular contralto Dame Clara Butt.

A bedroom shared by several girls at 7 Worcester Terrace.

to Bristol in 1899 from an overlooking room secured by Miss Bartlett. Huge crowds gathered for the massive procession, the streets and buildings were brightly decorated, and there were fireworks and illuminations in the evening, the suspension bridge and the surrounding roads lit up by glittering coloured lamps. The visit of King Edward VII and Queen Alexandra nine years later, which was also watched by the girls, appears to have been a rather more low-key affair.

There was a wide age range among the girls. In 1907 the youngest boarder was aged just seven. The wish for parents to send their daughters to the school at a younger age led to the creation of the 'Little Ones' Classes' around 1904 which in 1909 became the Badminton House Preparatory School, based at 7 Worcester Terrace, the forerunner of today's Junior School. The school had already added nos. 1, 2 and 4 Worcester Terrace to Badminton House, providing extra classrooms and bedrooms as numbers grew.

Most girls looked upon their days at Badminton House with affection. Many of them kept in regular touch with the school and the magazine regularly recorded their marriages (and sometimes their husbands' occupations), unlike the magazines of boys' schools which were filled with the exploits and achievements of former pupils. The only instance of this in Badminton's magazine occurred in 1912 when Gladys Matthews wrote from the London School of Medicine for Women about her work with the Red Cross in Belgrade during the Serbo-Bulgarian war. Garden parties were held occasionally for old girls and eventually it was agreed to form an Old Badmintonian Association. This was founded in 1911 and an annual weekend first took place in 1913.

Miss Bartlett and her sisters retired at the end of 1911 and the school changed hands for a second time. This time Badminton House was taken over by Miss Beatrice Baker, known as 'BMB' from her initials throughout her time at the school, and Miss Lucy Rendall – they were later joined by a third partner, Miss Mabel Webb-Johnson. They arrived one term before they took over from the Misses Bartlett. Even their appearance suggested imminent change. In contrast to Miss Bartlett's

Beatrice May Baker, headmistress, 1912–46.

spotless white silk blouses, dark skirts and high-heeled shoes, Miss Baker, recalled one girl, was wearing 'an olive green pinafore frock with a blouse underneath of a lighter green with very full sleeves'. She was a small woman, her hair often under an Alice band, who often seemed coiled like a spring, full of untapped energy, with piercing and beady eyes that never missed a thing. One girl described her as 'a mighty wind from the mountains of Wales'. She could be stern and intense, intolerant of fools, with a puritanical streak which tended to mask her natural sympathy and compassion. There were few who would regard her as loveable, as Miss Bartlett had been loved – she was, reflected one pupil, 'no mother figure' – but many would hold her in affection. Lucy Rendall, on the other hand, was a jolly woman with an obvious sense of humour, unlike Beatrice Baker who often kept hers well hidden. She could, however, be equally strict and could

have quite a short fuse. The Rendalls came from Bridport where Lucy's father would be mayor during the First World War. He and his brother ran the family's rope-works. Lucy was the eldest of the seven Rendall children, including six girls. Two of her sisters, Bertha and Janet, would later come to work at Badminton. In January 1912 Miss Baker became headmistress and Miss Rendall senior mistress in charge of physical exercise.

Beatrice May Baker was born in Hereford in 1876, the third daughter and youngest child of Edward and Catherine Baker. Her father was a successful tailor who sent all his children to high school. In 1896 Beatrice won a bursary worth £30 for three years to allow her to study for an arts degree at the Royal Holloway College. Although she remained only a year at the College, she gained her BA from London University. Career options were limited for well-educated single young women at the end of the 19th century. But Beatrice Baker always wanted to teach. She may have been influenced by the decision of her elder sister to enter the profession (she too became a headmistress although, one of Miss Baker's acquaintances later wrote, of 'the conventional kind and quite unlike BMB'). Whether or not she trained at one of the handful of teacher-training colleges which had been recently founded is unknown. Her first teaching post was at the Central Foundation School in Islington, where, the same acquaintance recorded, Miss Baker 'was shocked to see some anti-Semitic feelings among the children go apparently unchecked and her youthful experiences made her determined to educate women to fight for their social rights and racial understanding'.

After a short spell at Abergavenny High School, she was appointed in 1902 as head of maths in the upper school at the Cardiff Intermediate School for Girls under its headmistress, Miss Mary Collin. It was here that she met Lucy Rendall. She was at ease under the leadership of Miss Collin, who was liberally

'Miss Baker … wished to point out how the traditions of the school are built up by each succeeding generation of girls'

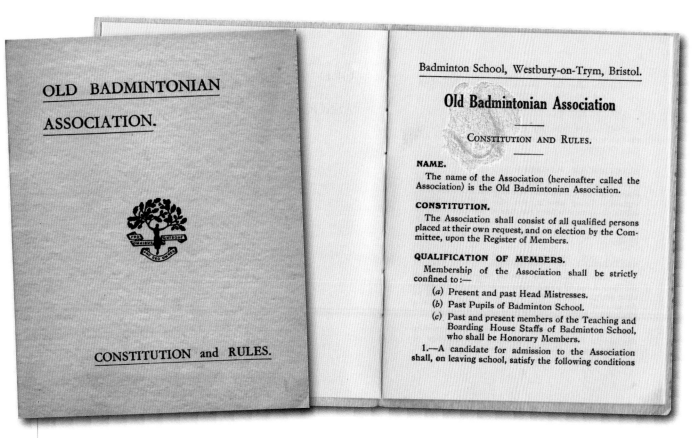

Badminton School, Westbury-on-Trym, Bristol.

Old Badmintonian Association

CONSTITUTION AND RULES.

NAME.

The name of the Association (hereinafter called the Association) is the Old Badmintonian Association.

CONSTITUTION.

The Association shall consist of all qualified persons placed at their own request, and on election by the Committee, upon the Register of Members.

QUALIFICATION OF MEMBERS.

Membership of the Association shall be strictly confined to :—

(*a*) Present and past Head Mistresses.

(*b*) Past Pupils of Badminton School.

(*c*) Past and present members of the Teaching and Boarding House Staffs of Badminton School, who shall be Honorary Members.

1.—A candidate for admission to the Association shall, on leaving school, satisfy the following conditions

Old Badmintonian Association handbook.

inclined, a supporter of women's suffrage, and whose reforms were carried out from a position of carefully cultivated respectability. Although Miss Baker and Miss Rendall were utterly different personalities, which accounted for the strength of their lifelong relationship, they shared the same philosophical view of the world. Here they shared their leisure time with their pupils, organising long walks in the Welsh countryside. Winfred Hurford, who later came to Badminton, was a pupil at Cardiff Intermediate.

> *Looking through the window in the passage leading from the Hall to the lower school … I saw Miss Beatrice M Baker for the first time. She was playing tennis, wearing a long green dress. From that moment she became a great influence in my life.*

In Cardiff many pupils lived in great poverty. The young teachers decided they should experience this for themselves and help their young charges at the same time. They took a filthy, bug-ridden house in the slums but the strain was too much for Beatrice. She suffered a nervous breakdown and

was sent at a friend's expense to recuperate in France. It was during this period of ill-health that Beatrice and Lucy first discussed running their own school. After considering schools in the north of England, they settled instead on Badminton House which was much closer to Cardiff. Winifred Hurford arrived at Badminton in advance of Miss Baker and unwittingly received prior warning of the ambitions of her new headmistress. At a garden party at Cardiff Intermediate School, Miss Baker asked her how she was getting on. Winifred told her that she had found herself well ahead of her peers at Badminton and consequently with very little work to do. Miss Baker assured her that 'You will work harder next term!'

The new headmistress did not wait long before shaking up her new school. Change was not universally welcomed. As one girl, 15 at the time, who had had spent her formative years under Miss Bartlett, put it, 'the school changed completely when Miss Bartlett left and Miss Baker became head. That is the most charitable way in which I can describe what took place!' Miss Baker announced at the first Old Badmintonian weekend in November 1913 that she 'wished to

Miss Baker had strong ideas on how to make her mark. Girls were allowed to go out in pairs unchaperoned and relax in Clifton Gardens.

The open air baths were popular with the girls in the summer time.

point out how the traditions of the School are built up by each succeeding generation of girls; that what we now are is the result of what we have been in the past, and what we do now is making our school for the future'. She was not going to re-write history but clearly she intended to put her own stamp on the school's future identity. Daily life took on a different pattern which remained the routine for more than 20 years. The girls rose early at 6.30 am and took an icy bath before breakfast. At the weekends, perhaps as a tribute to their endurance, they were treated to coffee and sausages. The weekends were much freer under Miss Baker. Gym dresses worn during the week gave way to blouses and skirts. In winter the girls still went shopping to Clifton Mall although sweet, fruit and cigarette shops were out of bounds, while the open air baths were popular in summer. The older girls were allowed to go for walks, four or five at a time, under a group leader responsible for their behaviour. On Sundays they were permitted to attend evening service at Highbury without a mistress. Such behaviour was considered very advanced for the day although Miss Bartlett had permitted girls to go out in pairs.

Indeed, so much changed that some girls convinced themselves that everything had altered, attributing to Miss Baker some of those things, such as excursions, lectures, theatre visits and social service, which had already existed under her predecessor. But her changes were radical and could be summed up in the words of Miss Baker's first head girl as 'an opening up of the world'. This revelation was not fixed on the pursuit of material benefits. Termly mottoes encouraged girls to keep in mind the spiritual dimension. Summer 1913 opened with 'By two wings a man is lifted up from things earthly – namely, by Simplicity and Purity'; a year later, prophetically, given the outbreak of war within months, the motto taken from Proverbs was 'Where there is no vision, the people perish'. Girls were expected to read newspapers and good

books, know about the political issues of the day and take an interest in social problems. When the local MP came to the school in 1913 to encourage a mock debate on the King's Speech, the girls' chief priorities were disarmament negotiations between Britain and Germany; the nationalisation of the railways; equal pay; and the abolition of corporal punishment (which was never used at

Miss Baker liberated the girls from many physical restrictions by ending the rule on the wearing of veils, hats and corsets for walks, games and gym.

Miss Baker with a guide on a school trip to Switzerland, 1912.

Badminton). Miss Baker's radical political views were already making an impact on her pupils. The girls raised funds for a Badminton Country Holiday Home for disadvantaged children. They formed a Settlement Guild, giving up their time at weekends to look after young children at the University Settlement. Exams became more important and qualified specialist teaching staff were appointed for the first time, a rarity in many girls' schools until the 1920s. Miss Baker knew from experience how travel broadened the mind and in 1912 a 'School Journey' was organised to Switzerland. Since foreign travel was uncommon before the war, this was probably one of the first overseas excursions ever undertaken by a girls' school. As if Miss Baker was signalling a fresh start, the drawing room was cleared of Victorian clutter, indicating to the girls that they too must clear their minds. Veils were abandoned for walks, hats given up for games and corsets discarded for gym. Cycling, still derided by some as a most unladylike pursuit, was taken up. Parents complained, residents protested, pupils were withdrawn, fees fell and a financial crisis was avoided only through the support of more enlightened parents.

IDEALISTS, VISIONARIES AND DREAMERS
1914–1931

On 29 July 1914, as Austria declared war on Serbia, two members of Badminton's staff, Miss Woollard and Miss Colebrook, accompanied by Miss Colebrook's mother, set off with impeccably bad timing for a holiday in Switzerland. Within a few days news of the spreading conflagration reached them and they had to make the best they could of difficult conditions in attempting to return home. Communications were already disorganised – their carriage driver turned up alone because his horses had been commandeered and their train journey through France on an overcrowded train was constantly disrupted. They went without food from leaving Berne on Saturday night until Monday afternoon when they reached Rouen, which they found crowded with soldiers. They squeezed onto a special boat sent over from Newhaven to Dieppe to collect stranded Britons, sailing away as the harbour master, supported by a French crowd, sang the Marseillaise, *followed by* God Save The King.

This incident is almost the only reference to the direct involvement in the war of anyone connected with Badminton. But girls' schools never suffered the trauma of many boys' schools, with ever-lengthening lists of the dead and the wounded and the regular recitation of the names of the fallen, including those who had so recently featured as school captains, prefects and sporting heroes. There are only passing references at Badminton to the engagement of former pupils on war work, usually in munitions factories or hospitals. At the school the main contribution of the girls was sewing and knitting a mountain of garments for the troops. No sooner had war broken out than Miss Baker issued the girls with patterns for cutting shirts, nightshirts and bed jackets as well as instructions for making pillow cases and bandages. The shirts were sent to the 6th Battalion of the Gloucestershire Regiment and other garments, including scarves, socks, gloves and mittens, to the Southmead Base Hospital in Bristol. A school concert raised money for the Queen's Work for Women Fund and the girls started a war relief fund. In all this Badminton differed little from the activities pursued by girls at other schools around the country. In fact, the scope of work done at Badminton appears rather more limited than at many other schools. Badminton did not, for instance, sponsor a motor ambulance, as at Queenswood, although they did take in Belgian refugees, as had North London Collegiate School.

Where Badminton girls did appear to differ was in the degree to which they were kept informed of the progress of the war. Miss Baker spoke regularly to them 'about our attitude [to the war] as individuals and as a school' and introduced the innovation of a 'Current Events' session every Tuesday morning when she delivered lectures on the causes of the war. Cultivating in this way an awareness among the girls of what was going on in the world around them would become one of the hallmarks of Badminton under Miss Baker. Another development which does not seem to have been repeated anywhere else was the formation in 1916 of the Badminton House Antelope Corps. Formed as an alternative for girls who did not take part in sport, this was run on the same lines as the scouts while mimicking the cadet corps common in most boys' schools. The Antelope Corps aimed to encourage smartness and efficiency, help girls to become morally and physically stronger, teach them handicrafts and develop their powers of observation. Officers were enrolled, 'Field Days' and 'marches' were organised and there was instruction in semaphore signalling and map-reading.

While the war scarcely touched Badminton, it had a profound impact on Miss Baker. It proved to be the catalyst for the distinctive philosophy she applied to running Badminton in peacetime and which created such a reputation for the school. She rarely hid her left-wing inclinations so for some the school became notorious while others looked upon it as a bastion of progressive learning. Her view of the world was essentially based upon a belief in Christian social responsibility. The open window on the world she had been encouraging at Badminton became the promotion of international co-operation. Beatrice Baker, like many others during the war, had become a convinced internationalist well before Woodrow Wilson conceived of his Fourteen Points. She was

Teamwork on a Duke of Edinburgh Expedition, 2008.

probably involved in the League of Nations Society from its inception in 1915. She saw the tragedy of the war as a failure of internationalism which must not be repeated. In an address to Old Badmintonians in the summer of 1917 she asserted that 'it is only in so far as the nations are prepared to sacrifice national advantage for the sake of international advantage that the brotherhood of man can become possible'. It was a message to which she returned again and again because she believed that Badminton girls could be the torch-bearers for this belief in whatever sphere of life they became involved. She was an admitted idealist but saw no reason why ideals could not be translated into reality. She took the inspiration for her address from Jan Smuts, the South African general and war leader, who had exalted idealists and visionaries in one of his speeches as 'the salt of the earth'. 'Hope sprang up in my heart,' she said, 'with a vision of the world in which our men of affairs would be idealists, visionaries and dreamers, and I felt that it would be a very different world from the world of today'. Girls coming to Badminton should find a place where 'the sordid and the mean were kept from them, and where they learned to admire their heroes, all idealists, all optimists – and then go forth again to renew the battle in the plain'. She warned them against 'the temptation to think that what we do does not much matter'. For her the war in all its darkness had nevertheless illuminated the indispensability of women in a time of national

THE CAT AND MOUSE ACT

PASSED BY THE LIBERAL GOVERNMENT

BUY AND READ 'THE SUFFRAGETTE' PRICE 1D

Miss Baker supported women's suffrage and made sure the girls were informed about national politics, including the Cat and Mouse Act of 1913, which attempted to control hunger strikes by suffragettes.

emergency. This revelation paved the way for women to make their mark after the war in a wider range of professions. Women's suffrage became inevitable and legitimised their active involvement in national politics. Beatrice Baker saw a great opportunity for women to influence the post-war settlement and wanted Badminton girls to become politically involved nationally and internationally. For her, she told Old Badmintonians in 1928, 'the ideals of the school may be summarised as the development of personality, so that you may be able to contribute to the progress of the world'. All this was underpinned by her Christian faith, embodied within the school in the motto adopted in 1918, Pro Omnibus Quisque Pro Deo Omnes, or Each For All And All For God. But her faith was not dogmatic. She saw no divide between the religious world and the secular and believed that the spiritual life, whether or not it was based upon belief in God, was the glue which bound the two together. It was this which led her

to become a Quaker, a member of the Religious Society of Friends, founded in the 17th century by those who felt their belief in God found no expression in existing forms of Christian religion. Assemblies at Badminton became heavily influenced by Quaker forms of worship, with periods of silent contemplation. Many Badmintonians, both during and after Miss Baker's time, would themselves turn to the Quakers. But her belief in the power of the spiritual, regardless of God, also meant that Badminton became a school which welcomed girls of all faiths and none.

After the war the practical manifestation of Miss Baker's views became increasingly obvious at the school. She encouraged the admission of girls from different backgrounds and cultures. This also applied to young boys admitted for some years to the kindergarten attached to the Junior School. In 1922, for instance, two young Hungarian boys, Lorand and Gaspar, spent a year at Badminton. The school became involved with Save The Children, founded in 1919 to raise funds for emergency aid to children suffering from the deprivation caused by the war. No doubt this was

Although the school observed Christian rituals, including this harvest festival in 1924, Miss Baker believed equally in religious, secular and spiritual life.

made even more attractive since both its founders were women, Eglantyne Jebb and her sister Dorothy Buxton, exactly the sort of role models Beatrice Baker was looking for. In 1929 Badminton was sponsoring three children, two in Germany and one in Greece. The League of Nations, also formed in 1919, became an important focus. One girl remembered a Christmas party where all the girls dressed up in different national costumes with Miss Baker herself as the League. Her tolerance shone through in the many talks she gave on international relations, reminding girls shortly after the war ended that they 'must not expect jam for tea while German children were starving'. After a lecture by a visitor in 1923, the school formed its own junior branch of the League of Nations Union. Six years later, Miss Baker was offering the prize of a visit to Geneva to attend the League's Junior Summer School for the producers of the best essays on languages. The school was divided into three so that more girls might study international affairs more closely. One section of the library was devoted exclusively to the League. Every week one period was set aside in English to study current events and read newspapers. At a meeting once a term the girls were kept informed about the international situation. Miss Rendall wrote in 1929 that it looked as if 'this "Peace Question" is inevitably becoming the most serious question for all generations'. It would certainly loom even larger at Badminton during the 1930s. The chapel-cum-hall opened in 1928 after the school moved to larger premises in Westbury-on-Trym would be named the Peace Memorial Hall, with Miss Baker observing how it symbolised the integration of the religious with the secular. In 1926, reviewing a period of domestic strife (this was the year of the general strike) and international tension (the British occupation of the Rhineland came to an end), she told former pupils gathering that summer that 'as individuals, each can do her share by reading, studying, thinking, in order to hold and promote an international point of view; by being a ready speaker, by reason of her sound knowledge; by freedom from prejudice, by sympathetic understanding of people in other nations'. She also believed that knowledge through travel helped peoples to understand each

other and it was this mutual understanding that prevented war. So school journeys abroad were quickly resumed when peace returned, often and appropriately to the rarefied atmosphere of the mountains, whether in the French Pyrenees or the Swiss Alps. This was also partly because of her view that in an era when she felt that 'the perpetual rush is working out badly for the nation from a physical standpoint', there was a need for greater leisure, quietness, relaxation and contemplation.

While internationalism set Badminton apart from other schools, both boys' and girls', the social work encouraged within the school was not unique. There was a desire in many girls' schools to foster links with the less privileged. This came not just from a sincere wish to improve society and eliminate poverty. Charity was also traditionally regarded as one of the characteristics which separated women from men; while men in the past had used this argument to confine women to activities within their own sphere, now women were confident enough to use this as a defining difference within the same world as the opposite sex. At Badminton a junior branch of the National Council of Women was formed in 1920. This aimed to foster the mixing of women of all classes so that 'by its means we should get to know girls of different social positions; and by possible discussions, lectures, or debates, obtain knowledge of social work and problems'. Soon afterwards the Country Holiday Home, a pre-war dream of Beatrice Baker's, became a reality. A cottage on Thornbury Road, beyond Almondsbury, close to the countryside, was lent rent-free to the school, repaired, redecorated, furnished and provided with a caretaker, largely

thanks to Phyllis Higgs, a former pupil, and a friend. A year later the cottage had already hosted more than 50 children from the east of Bristol, from the decaying, overcrowded, jerry-built houses by the cotton factory, north of the tramlines, where families often shared rooms and beds, where rickets and malnutrition were common, where recovery from common illnesses was slow, and for whose children three or four weeks in the country made all the difference. Miss Baker, remembering her own less than successful efforts to make common cause with Cardiff's working-class poor, formed a social services club which in 1925 made contact with individual children from the poorer parts of Bristol. Several of them came to tea at the school in December, an understandable shyness apparently fading away only during snowball fights and tobogganing. There would always be the danger of condescension in such relationships, no matter how sincere they might be, for they were always fleeting, one side withdrawing behind privileged walls, the other returning to poverty. Perhaps the name given to these get-togethers was symptomatic of such an attitude; they were called the Little Sisters' Tea Parties. Yet Miss Baker believed passionately that it was dangerous for the prosperous, materially and spiritually, to isolate themselves from the less well-off. Occasionally the request for involvement came from the other side. In 1928 the director of education for the Rhondda Valley, the heart of Welsh coal mining, asked Badminton to adopt one of the district's poorer schools, the Ynyshir Council School for Girls. Badminton girls raised money to pay for a school outing and they turned out underclothes which they sent to the Welsh girls with boots, socks, stockings and jumpers. This relationship would actually begin to have more meaning when it was most needed, during the terrible depression of the early 1930s.

Miss Baker was quite clear that cultivating the spiritual at Badminton depended on more than the talks she gave the girls. She exalted the life of the spirit as 'the basis of all our school activities'. Displaying a puritanical streak, she was fiercely critical of many aspects of the material world. Press coverage of fashion and celebrity, whether at Court or Ascot, squeezed out coverage of social

Like many girls' schools, Badminton has always encouraged its pupils to take an active role in charity work.

problems and fostered class hatred. The middle classes would do well to aspire to a more austere lifestyle, she thought, since she believed that the lower classes would always emulate them in dress and lifestyle. Photographs of Miss Baker herself show the apparent disregard she had for fashion, something she clearly passed on to many of her pupils; one only has to look at photographs of perhaps her most famous pupil, Iris Murdoch, to see the similarity in dress sense. She attacked the trend for more places of amusement to open on Sundays, penalising the poor who would have to work longer hours. 'None of us truly admires a business man who puts his profits before his sense of service or his duty to his employees', she wrote in 1927. The school, she had already written in 1923, had to inspire a love of knowledge and truth to prevent 'loose and superficial thinking' and the repetition of false generalisations on critical issues. A few years later she added that accurate knowledge, through reading and study, must be 'the basis of right thought, and right thought of right action'.

Music and drama were an important part of this spiritual cultivation although the small size of the school (there were only 64 pupils in 1916, 109 pupils in 1919 and 164 in 1928) limited the scope of both these activities. A major play was performed once a term and there was house drama and music, while the girls and the staff gave weekly musical recitals, there were talks on musical appreciation and visits to recitals by international pianists such as Cortot and Pachmann. Lectures by visiting speakers were used to widen the horizons of the girls' knowledge. During the war, for instance, lectures were given by Professor Skemp from Bristol University on Victorian literature; in 1922 they featured Walter de la Mare, the popular children's author and poet, alongside others who talked about China, Russia, Rome and art appreciation; while in 1930 their theme was the modern development of the English system of government. An annual essay competition set topics such as the Italian Renaissance (for the upper school) and the Great Explorers (for the lower school) in 1929. Miss Baker expected every girl to read and was always asking them what they were reading. She favoured a scheme of reading

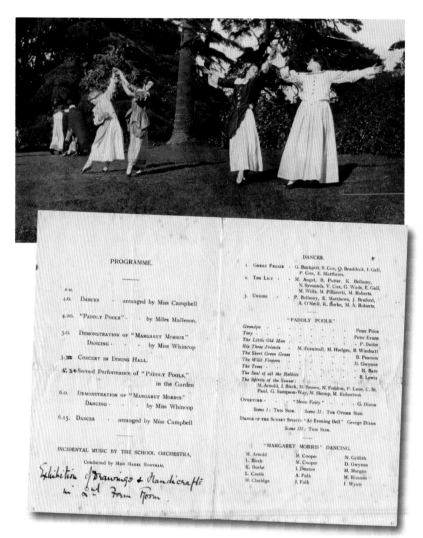

for every girl but good literature as defined by Miss Baker exposed weaknesses. The school inspectors in 1919, for instance, deplored the unrefined emphasis on contemporary literature for senior girls when they knew little of the great literary figures. The Golden Treasuries, they reported dismissively, were no substitute for a sound taste in English verse. Too focused on the present and the future, Miss Baker sometimes had a blind spot for the past.

All this helped to encourage an independence of thought and action among the girls. Many of these activities, plus others such as the wide range of clubs and societies introduced during the 1920s, a common feature of many schools at the time, were organised and run by the girls themselves. This was already an established characteristic of the school. The report of the inspection conducted

Pageant staged in 1920s.

Programme from 1921.

Although the school's small size in its early days limited the scope of productions, music and drama were seen as a vital way to cultivate spirituality. They continue to be an integral part of school life today.

in 1916 by the Oxford and Cambridge Examination Board had noted that in a school with few rules and no statutory punishments, the 'system of trusting the girls and the avoidance of undue "policing" works admirably'. The visiting inspectors in 1929 noted that 'the discipline and tone of the school are also largely in the hands of the girls, and they elect their own Form leaders and prefects'. Perhaps this was most vividly demonstrated by the adventures of one former pupil, Margaret Belcher, and her companion who drove from Cape Town to Cairo and then through Europe to Oxford during 1930. They left Cape Town on 1 April in their six-year-old Morris Oxford four-seater tourer with 25,000 miles on the clock, reaching Cairo on 15 September and Oxford on 1 October.

The school also wanted to foster an ethos of service and develop the potential of each girl. In 1919 the first inspection after the official recognition of the school as efficient concluded that Badminton encouraged girls 'to enter the many vocations that are now open to educated women'. This progress can be seen from the list of occupations of former pupils that began to appear in the school magazine. In the middle of the First World War, these included bank clerks, nurses, market gardeners and office clerks as well as girls studying music and medicine. In the early 1920s the range was broader, from secretaries and factory welfare workers to teachers and lecturers. Many of these positions required degrees and Badminton already had a reputation for preparing girls for university entrance where this was merited. Miss Baker's policy of appointing as far as possible only graduates to the staff helped to improve teaching standards at the school. So too did the introduction of setting in 1925, which the head believed would effectively create 'an individual timetable' for most girls. It also helped that, as the inspection report noted in 1929, 'the intention is that the school shall grow no larger, and that with small classes and a liberal staff, a good deal of individual attention shall be made possible'. By the late 1920s, when the roll was around 170, the school was sending an average of six girls every year to university. The school life of most girls, that is, the number of years they spent

at school, was also high. This contrasted with the struggle of many boys' schools, particularly grammar schools, to retain pupils for more than three or four years. Below the sixth form the girls enjoyed a single five-year course, ending for most of them in taking the School Certificate, the equivalent of GCSE. But the timetable had little space for maths and science and the latter was dropped by all but a few hand-picked girls before School Certificate. This remained a weakness of the school for some years. On the other hand, subjects more in tune with the school's aims received generous treatment – these included music and art (cultivating an appreciation of beauty), modern languages (French was taught from the age of seven upwards, all part of enabling girls to develop a closer understanding of other cultures), and PE (ensuring all girls remained healthy in body as well as in mind). Not all girls were entered for the School Certificate since another of the school's defining characteristics was the determination never to become obsessed with examinations. Similarly the Higher School Certificate, the equivalent of 'A' levels, was not usually taken. Partly this was because there was no tradition of doing so at the school so the sixth form was very small. In 1929 there were only 11 sixth formers. Many of these girls were persuaded to remain in the sixth form so they could follow a

Classroom, 1924.

The Studio at 7 Worcester Terrace.

A painting by old girl Mary Fedden, one of Britain's leading 20th-century artists.

13 girls who left Badminton in the summer of 1928 – three were at university, six were either at art schools or music academies, one was at the domestic science college in Swansea, another was studying French in France and two more were overseas girls who had returned to their home countries. Two further observations may be made. Firstly, two of the girls at university had won places at Oxford and Cambridge but such achievements were never feted at Badminton. The girls would all have applauded the success of their peers but such success was rarely singled out by the school. Secondly, a high proportion of leavers were furthering their study of art or music. One of the most talented pupils at the school during the 1920s was Mary Fedden, who later attended the Slade School of Art and became one of the leading British artists of the 20th century.

Although Miss Baker had very strong views and never hid her political persuasion, she would never admit that she wanted the character of every girl to be poured from the same mould. Yet there was a paradox here. While she wanted Badminton girls to cultivate independence, her approach relied a lot on personal contact which was obviously intended to influence the characters of her pupils; the inspectors said as much in 1929. In the early 1920s she would say goodnight every

more general course of education, a pattern followed in many other girls' schools of the time. It was only a few girls who either took the Higher Certificate or were prepared for open scholarship examinations. This fairly relaxed attitude was reflected in the diversity of destinations among the evening to all the younger girls before taking prayers for the older ones and shaking hands with each of them. This latter practice, known at Badminton as 'pump-handles', still continues, although now only at the end of term, with each girl shaking hands with every member of staff. It is partly symbolic of the trust and harmony which existed and still exists between girls and staff and partly an indication that whatever differences there might be between individuals, a new start is always possible. The head seemed to be a constant presence among the girls, appearing suddenly alongside them, hurrying them along. Again the small size of the school made this possible. Although she was critical of the pace of life in the outside world, she never allowed girls to dilly-dally at Badminton. One story has a girl, absent from the end-of-term assembly, asking a friend what the head had said. 'Oh, you know, the usual sort of thing – "Be kind to your fathers and mothers and *don't hang about*".'

Although the school was small, numbers almost trebled between 1916 and 1929. More property was added at Worcester Terrace during the war but it was becoming rather sprawling and unmanageable and lacked further capacity for growth. Miss Baker and Miss Rendall began searching for another property, helped by the third member of their partnership, Miss Mabel Webb-

The trio known as 'The Powers'; Miss Baker (right), Miss Lucy Rendall (left) and Miss Mabel Webb-Johnson (sitting), the school's chief decision-makers for almost three decades.

Johnson. This trio became known within the school simply as 'The Powers'. Miss Webb-Johnson, who laid the foundations of the school's musical tradition, was regarded as the most gracious and elegant of them. She was one of eight children born to Samuel Johnson and his wife, Julia. Her father was medical officer of health in Stoke on Trent. One of her brothers, Alfred, a renowned surgeon and medical administrator, was later raised to the peerage. All the children added their mother's maiden name to the name of their father.

'The Powers' found the Cote Bank estate, which belonged to Thomas Pease, the brother-in-law of the chocolate manufacturer, Lewis Fry. It

Northcote House, and its extensive grounds.

The 'sheep dip', which became an outdoor swimming pool in 1926; girls referred to it by its original name.

was situated to the north-west of Bristol and the north of Clifton, close to the small village of Westbury-on-Trym. The estate was being parcelled up for sale and advertised to developers. At the heart of the estate lay the 'big house', Northcote House, and its extensive grounds. It provided just what Miss Baker and her partners were looking for. A deal was done and in September 1919 the first phase of the re-location from Clifton took place when the Junior School moved to Northcote. The Junior School remained on its own at Westbury-on-Trym for the next four years. This was partly because building work was needed before the rest of the school could move and partly because all the necessary finance could not be found at once. As a private school, Badminton had no endowments and could only borrow at commercial rates. For many years the margin between profit and loss was very fine. The Junior School, which eventually moved into the wooden buildings known by later generations of Badmintonians as the OJS (Old Junior School), was run by Lyn Harris and his wife. Harris was a conscientious objector given employment by Miss Baker. He would leave Badminton to run his own school in Letchworth but was obviously much valued as an advisor to Miss Baker and later became chairman of governors. Among the 50 pupils he and his wife brought with them to Westbury-on-Trym from Clifton were a handful of small boys who stayed with the kindergarten until

they were eight years old. As well as the two Hungarian boys already mentioned, they included the young Joseph Cooper, who became a talented concert pianist, and later Brian Urquhart, a distinguished under-secretary-general of the United Nations, whose mother had been born Bertha Rendall. The dozen boarders among the junior pupils were housed in Northcote. The first new buildings erected on the site between 1920 and 1923 included the new Junior School and School House, with its dormitories and classrooms. At the same time a property in Westbury Road was acquired as a Junior School boarding house. Northcote, recalled one girl who came with the Junior School, was 'the only building in a huge garden that had already started to go wild. From the drive before the front door there was an uninterrupted view of fields stretching to Kingweston Downs. The Bee-Garden, the old clipped yew trees and the Rose Garden were relics of a magnificently laid out estate. It was a thrilling playground for children'. After the Lyn Harrises departed in 1923, Miss Hensley took charge.

The school changed its name to Badminton School when the senior girls arrived in Westbury-on-Trym in September 1923. After the Junior School, School House, containing more class-rooms and dormitories, was added in 1926. An open-air swimming pool was converted in the same year from a former sheep dip, fondly known

Lacrosse team, 1925

as such by generations of schoolgirls to come. The extensive grounds on the school's doorstep offered more than enough space for sport and physical exercise. Lacrosse was introduced and played alongside hockey, cricket, tennis and racquets. In November 1927 the library was added to School House. Miss Baker also had her heart set on a chapel, an idea first suggested as a peace memorial in 1919, but it was a struggle to raise the funds. It was opened as the Chapel Hall during the summer gathering of the Old Badmintonians in 1928.

In the following year, when the school was inspected, the report noted Badminton's ambition to become a 'Public School'. There was never any intention to emulate Roedean, St Leonard's or

The Hall.

Wycombe Abbey; it referred rather to a change in the way the school was run. Miss Baker, Miss Rendall and Miss Webb-Johnson wanted the school in which they would invest their lives and their savings to survive and prosper after they had gone. The proprietary school, handed on from one owner to another, was not the way to do it. Just as Miss Baker had proved such a radical departure from Miss Bartlett, so her successor too could prove equally different if the school was seen simply as a chattel without any real meaning, valued only for its bricks and mortar rather than for the type of education it represented. This was rather more far-sighted than the owners of most other private schools. Many disappeared during the next decade, unable to survive the savage depression, and the next world war saw off many of those which were left. In the late 1920s Badminton was feeling its way towards a change in status after the formation of an advisory council, consisting of Miss Baker, Miss Rendall, Miss Webb-Johnson and eight others. This was in effect a shadow board of governors, providing the ballast of experience needed when the ownership of the school was finally transferred. This took place at the height of the depression. On 10 June 1931 Badminton passed out of the hands of 'The

Powers' and became a limited company in which they were shareholders. The governing body, known as the School Council, was 17-strong, chaired by Dr J Odery Symes. A respected consultant physician at Bristol General Hospital who specialised in the diet found in boarding schools, he remained chairman until 1943. Miss Baker, Miss Rendall and Miss Webb-Johnson sat alongside him, while other members included Miss Bennett as a representative from the Old Badmintonian Association, Professor J F Dobson, the pro-vice chancellor and professor of Greek at Bristol University, and Miss H M Wodehouse, professor of education at Bristol and Mistress-Elect of Girton College, Cambridge. It was a distinguished board and illustrated the strength and influence of Miss Baker's social connections and the respect in which she was held.

The school's appointment of a visitor and president also revealed the high regard in which Beatrice Baker and her school were held in certain circles. These posts were intended to bring a degree of gravitas to the school in its new form as a self-proclaimed public school. Although the title of visitor was drawn from the system employed in universities where the visitor was a distinguished personage to whom students could appeal in the last resort for arbitration in any dispute, at Badminton it appears to have been entirely honorific. So too was the post of president. But having both posts rather than one allowed Miss Baker to welcome to the school two widely known and respected personalities. Both, incidentally, were male. The school's first Visitor was Viscount Cecil of Chelwood, better known as Lord Robert Cecil. The third son of the former prime minister, Lord Salisbury, he had served in the war cabinet under both Asquith and Lloyd George. The war had persuaded him, as it had Beatrice Baker, that the prevention of any recurrence was the only worthwhile thing in politics. He had been an influential proponent of the League of Nations and in 1919 was sent as an adviser to the Paris peace conference where he was instrumental in its creation. He then devoted most of his ability and energy to the League of Nations Union which became one of the largest and most active voluntary bodies in the country, with membership peaking at 400,000 in 1931. He was awarded the Nobel Prize for Peace in 1937. This appointment shows just how much Miss Baker was in tune with the times. Robert Cecil was a contrast to Miss

The Library in 1927.

English statesman Lord Robert Cecil, one of the school's earliest board members, addressing the Women's International League before the Geneva Disarmament Conference, 1932.

Baker in that he was a high Anglican Tory, although very much on the progressive wing of the party; in appointing him, Miss Baker was practising the political and religious tolerance she preached as well as showing how a common commitment to the cause of international peace and disarmament overrode any differences of opinion they might have. Gilbert Murray also had aristocratic connections, having married the daughter of the Earl of Carlisle, although he himself was the son of an Australian stock farmer. But Murray, unlike Cecil, was both agnostic (his wife, Lady Mary, later became a Quaker) and liberal. A distinguished academic, he was professor of Greek at Oxford from 1905 until 1936. The war too made him a convinced inter-

nationalist and he forged his friendship with Cecil through the League of Nations Society and later the Union, in which he was heavily involved. His politics were defined by one observer as aristocratic liberalism, which he had difficulty in adjusting to the growing demands of the working class to control their own destiny. Perhaps Miss Baker's middle-class socialism was more understanding of this trend although it came with a degree of condescension, as epitomised by the way in which social service was fostered at Badminton. Murray seems to have struck up a much closer relationship than Cecil with Miss Baker and the school, and he became a much more regular visitor to Badminton, although both men remained in post until their deaths.

THE WORLD WE WANT TO MAKE
1931–1945

The thread of internationalism ran through Badminton School's first speech day, held at the school in a large marquee on the lawn on 11 July 1931. House trophies were presented and a strictly limited number of prizes were handed out. Dr Odery Syme remarked in his speech that the School Council aimed to provide a sound education, both intellectual and physical, for girls of all abilities and to create 'a wide general outlook, without which permanent peace amongst the nations is impossible'. His was one of four speeches during what must have been a very long afternoon. Two other speakers proclaimed a patriotism and pride in the Empire which might strike one as in opposition to the school's philosophy. But they connected with the patriotism that had existed in the school during the war and which never seemed at odds with the school's international perspective.

This perspective was also enjoined in extolling the influence of the 'Public Schools' in creating a leading role for the country worldwide 'amongst the backward and weaker nations of the world'. This was a revealing phrase, demonstrating the limits of the progressive nature of the school's internationalist vision. The last speech came from Miss Baker. She listed the qualities Badminton intended to inculcate within every pupil – thoroughness; breadth and depth of interest (so that upon leaving they might 'employ themselves in a manner worthy of dignified gentlewomen'); service; and a spiritual ideal. She also stressed the importance of

that 'self-restraint and discipline which will stand them in good stead amid the temptations which await them in this era of social freedom'.

The day revealed in every speech the conservative parameters of Badminton's progressive ethos both socially and politically. This was not unique. In successive speech days in 1933 and 1934 Miss Baker stressed how girls faced 'a world of changing values, where the older standards of morality and religion are questioned' and then appeared to side with these 'older standards' by arguing that one of the advantages of girls following a general, non-examination course in the sixth form was so 'they could better be trained

to become good mothers and good citizens'. At speech day in 1935 the guest speaker, Professor Baker, displayed a very limited view of the role of women in a changing society. On the basis that many middle-class professional women were either teachers or doctors, he concluded that girls' schools should concentrate on training their pupils just for those professions. He could not conceive of the idea that a woman could have a long-term career, promoting the old concept that 'it was a woman's responsibility to make beauty in the home – music, song and "all the lovely interests and ploys".' And this was all at the invitation of Miss Baker! Yet this strange and contradictory mix rarely created much tension within the girls either while they were at the

First Board of Governors, 1931.

school or afterwards. On the contrary, it seems to have sustained many of them very well throughout their lives.

That very first speech day took place just 20 days before the publication of Sir George May's report into public spending. The shocking recommendations of the May report for swingeing cuts as a remedy for the public finances effectively brought down the Labour government as well as worsening the existing trade depression. The Labour party had been in and out of power, as a minority and majority government, since 1924. In the 1931 election, following Ramsay MacDonald's agreement to form a National government, the party was reduced to a rump. Unemployment, already acute, reached a peak in 1932, with almost half of all insured workers in the iron and steel industries and well over 60 per cent of those in shipbuilding out of work. With unemployment benefit slashed, it was a terrible time for many working families. All this must have seemed an enormous setback for Miss Baker and those like her.

State spending on education was slashed following the May report. Teachers, like many other public employees, were forced to accept a reduction of ten per cent in their salaries. Even though Badminton was outside the public sector, the school would also adopt these cuts. There appeared to be little need for this. In the autumn of 1931, as the school purchased another property, Cote Grange, the governors reported that the finances of the school, with its 89 boarders and 77 day girls, were sound. But there was some anxiety that the boarding side would decline and

arrangements were made in January 1932 to recruit more day girls. It was considered prudent to cut staff salaries for the following summer term. A member of the music department was also made redundant. The letter sent to staff by the School Council's secretary, Miss Colebrook, was not kind. They were told bluntly that, since salaries had to be reduced, they would be given a month's notice and should respond as to whether or not they wished to remain on the staff at a salary which was ten per cent lower. Despite the depression, the governors' anxieties proved unfounded, boarding numbers grew and the proposed salary cut was deferred. There were 97 boarders and 66 day girls in early 1933, 95 boarders and 72 day girls in mid-1934 and then a rise to 102 boarders and 74 day girls in the following autumn. As numbers rose, the school rented more property outside the school grounds at the end of 1932 for more boarders and planned an extension to the dining room. Perhaps it was these financial commitments which led the governors to revive the idea of cutting pay. At least this time the letter was sent out with a paragraph expressing the governors' regret and the hope that the cuts would quickly be reinstated. What it did not reveal was that a dividend, although small, had been paid on the ordinary shares. As the economy recovered so more parents began to send their girls to the school. The staff had their pay restored at the end of 1934. In November 1939, before the school was evacuated from Bristol, there were 125 boarders and 102 day girls. Most of the day girls were in the Junior School, most of the boarders in the senior

School, 1932.

Hazel Calvert-Fisher presents the key to the Bishop of Bristol during the opening of the Junior School, 1934.

school. Demand was high enough for applicants to be turned away.

With more girls, there was a compelling need to increase accommodation and improve facilities. Although revenue usually did little more than cover expenditure, the governors managed to finance more buildings during the 1930s through a judicious combination of acquisition, renting and developing. After the extension of the dining hall, a small wing was added to School House, with a geography room, more bedrooms and extra bathrooms. The new Junior School was opened in June 1934 by the Bishop of Bristol, the old one being turned into a department for domestic science and handicrafts as an inducement to girls to stay on into the sixth form. With the adjacent Cote Grange estate being broken up for development, three acres of land and a collection of buildings were bought from the estate in January 1935, partly to prevent development up to the school boundaries. In the same year a house, Little Grange, was built at Cote Grange for Miss Baker, Miss Rendall and Miss Webb-Johnson, allowing another dormitory to be added to Northcote House. Sixth formers were housed separately from the rest of the school in Cote Bank, rented from an anonymous benefactor in 1936. Odery Symes was eager to find more benefactors, conscious that school funds could do only so much without either endowments or state aid. Plans to establish a school sanatorium were eventually

Little Grange, built for the Misses Baker, Rendall and Webb-Johnson in 1935.

accomplished with the acquisition of The Beeches in the late 1930s. The financial constraints on the school's ambitions were evident to the inspectors who visited the school again in November 1938. They found many of the buildings were overcrowded and there was a need for more classrooms and much better science facilities. On the other hand, they noted that 'the prevalence of well-chosen pictures [usually copies of the great masters], furnishings, pottery and flowers provides an environment of culture which no mere perfection of bricks and mortar could effect'.

Lacrosse team, including Iris Murdoch, the novelist.

Following the inspection, plans were drawn up for new laboratories, cloakrooms and a gym but the war prevented their implementation.

The inspectors also drew attention to the fact that by now Badminton was well-known not just in Bristol but throughout the country and even overseas. In spite of the depression and the setbacks for world peace, Miss Baker strode through the 1930s with supreme confidence. She could talk about things others dare not, like sex, for instance. In an interview she gave to *The Queen* magazine in October 1931, she insisted that 'the girl of today wants to know more of the facts of life than her mother and grandmother did, and we speak frankly of many things that were not spoken of by an earlier generation of teacher'. One girl later remembered that at her final interview with Miss Baker before leaving school for university, she was given the distinct impression that it was quite all right to take a lover, although the consequences were never spelled out. Miss Baker was in her prime and took the school with her.

No one girl epitomised this better than Iris Murdoch. Although her Irish ancestry was a proud one, she came from a modest family background. Attending the progressive Froebel Demonstration School at Colet Gardens in west London where her family lived, she won a scholarship to Badminton in 1932 at the age of 13.

She would later write about how she

went to this eccentric and, I think, very good school. It was rather left-wing … with enlightened liberal views and an internationally-minded idealistic ethos. We were to serve the world and help our society, and also to seek academic excellence. We were interested in politics and world affairs, world peace and the League of Nations … It was a "progressive" school in the best sense, combining orderly discipline with government by consent. We worked hard and expressed our thoughts freely.

The essay Iris wrote on the 1936 Christmas lectures she attended organised by the League of Nations Union gained for her joint first prize in a national schools competition. In the summer of 1938, when she was head girl, she organised the publication of a collection of poems, *Poet Venturers*, by Bristol school boys and girls. This was to raise money for the Fund for Chinese Medical Aid in response to the plight of the Chinese in Manchuria under their Japanese invaders. The foreword was written by W H Auden and it was published at cost by Victor Gollancz, the eminent radical publisher, whose daughters were at the school. When Iris won an open exhibition to Somerville College, Oxford, in the autumn of 1938, the school enjoyed an extra half day's holiday at Christmas.

For Miss Baker, Iris became a paragon. One girl, herself later head girl and the winner of a Cambridge scholarship, recalled how Miss Baker would constantly remind pupils that 'You girls will never hold a candle to Iris Murdoch!' Miss Baker, for all her moral rectitude, or perhaps because of it, could sometimes appear an intellectual snob and something of this rubbed off onto the girls. Sometimes, it seemed, Miss Baker, despite everything she professed, fell prey herself to judging others by their appearance. One girl remembered how in particular the headmistress in plain pinafores was disdainful of some of the girls' glamorous mothers. Anne Valery, one of the girls with a glamorous mother, wrote entertainingly about her school days in her memoirs, *The Edge of a Smile*. She too recalled the distaste Miss Baker clearly exhibited not just for her mother but for her as well with her frivolous taste in clothes and her golden curls. Anne suffered from this mis-

judgement throughout her schooldays. Miss Baker equated her appearance with her intellectual ability and refused to believe that Anne might sail through her School Certificate and end up in the sixth form. When this happened, there was no apology from the headmistress. Yet it is equally clear from this memoir that Anne Valery still had considerable respect for this indomitable woman.

Iris Murdoch was not alone among Badminton girls in her enthusiastic commitment to the League of Nations and all that it stood for. Anne Valery, looking back, believed that many girls poured their passion into political causes because the headmistress frowned upon friendships between girls that were too close. While her progressiveness allowed her to contemplate girls taking male lovers, her conservatism led her to imagine too vividly where passionate friendships between girls might lead. So, Anne felt, many friendships were lukewarm, something another girl would pick up decades later.

In the early 1930s the League of Nations Union was at the peak of its influence. For many people, disarmament still mattered. Mussolini would not invade Abyssinia (now Ethiopia) until the autumn of 1935 and Hitler was not yet taken seriously as a threat to international peace. In late 1934 one Old Badmintonian, Margaret Rake, wrote from Cambridge describing the university anti-war movement with its dozen or so peace societies. She railed against the grants made to the University Officer Training Corps and Air Squadron and the research carried out on poison gas in the university's laboratories, which proved for her that the university was part of a national war machine. The National government of Ramsay MacDonald was shifting its stance and in the spring of 1935 published a White Paper committing the government to re-arm. Although this made surprisingly little impact, it was against this trend that the Union organised in the same year a house to house canvass as an unofficial referendum on disarmament. Opponents deridingly named the exercise the Peace Ballot but the mainly liberally inclined members of the middle classes who organised it were not pacifists. The aim of the Ballot was to test the national mood

Cover of school magazine.

League of Nations
Summer School,
August, 1931.

on international disarmament and collective security. It was a remarkable episode, handled almost entirely by volunteers all over the country. In Bristol staff at Badminton helped in the organisation while girls went out delivering ballot papers from door to door. There was an enormous response, with more than 11 million replies. While there was resounding support for disarmament, it was the answers to the final question which attracted most interest. Thrown in almost as an afterthought, it asked whether an aggressor should ultimately be stopped by war. Here too the vast majority of replies agreed that this was acceptable. The Ballot had considerable impact at the time but almost inadvertently had shown that as international relations deteriorated most people would still go to war as a last resort. The League, weakened from the outset by the refusal of the USA to join, was already debilitated by its inability to prevent the Japanese invasion of Manchuria and would suffer further humiliation when all its protestations and threats failed to stop Italy attacking Abyssinia. In the face of all this, the supporters of the League doggedly persisted in pressing the case for international peace. In 1937

Badminton was instrumental in arranging the British Youth Peace Assembly in Bristol which, Miss Baker told governors, would help 'to counteract to some extent the depression naturally felt by young people as a result of the international situation'. Even she seemed to be resigned to the way things were going. She was right. The vision of international peace and disarmament she shared with so many others was shattered by rising international tension and the failure of the League. By 1939 socialism and internationalism would appear to be on the back foot with Badminton just one tiny last bastion of hopes which had once seemed so attainable.

The central importance of an international outlook to the school between the wars brought with it an involvement of the girls in politics probably unmatched by any other school and which it is difficult to imagine any school taking up today. Miss Baker was aware that some criticised the school for being left-wing but in a paper written early in the Second World War she noted that 'my experience tells me that the question of bias is very rarely raised if the teaching leans towards the "right"'. On the other hand, as

Anne Valery wrote, Miss Baker was well known for being 'advanced', which Anne defined as meaning she was 'a champion of Ancient Greek thought, the Fabian Society, dreary Walt Whitman, and anyone else who combined socialism and the search for higher things'. Internationalism ran like a thread throughout so much of the school's activities. There was a dedicated International Room filled with posters and charts, weekly and monthly newspapers and journals. Miss Baker insisted that the theme of world interdependence and co-operation should be stressed wherever possible throughout the curriculum. Religious education, for instance, encompassed a study of world religions to foster, she said, 'a spirit of world fellowship based on spiritual ideas'; although she was emphatic that its primary purpose should be to the development of 'the progressive idea of God through the life of Christ'. The post-School Certificate sixth form course featured European history since 1918 while the history of civilisation formed part of the senior school course for all girls. The teaching of history at Badminton in the 1930s was also extraordinary for the time, focusing not on kings, queens and empires, but on the industrial revolution, the plight of the working class and the struggles of the suffragettes. One girl was apparently so enthused by this radical perspective that when she returned home she insisted on eating with the servants; she never came back to Badminton.

Internationalism for Badminton also meant embracing girls from overseas. In 1937 the school hosted three Canadians, part of a larger party in the country to watch the coronation of King George VI, who stayed for three weeks. One of two Indian girls was Indira Gandhi, daughter of Jawaharlal Nehru, later the first prime minister of an independent India, and herself a future prime minister. She had a mixed experience at Badminton. Her stay was brief she prepared at the school for Oxford during 1936–7 on the recommendation of a family friend – but she did become close to Miss Baker. With her father in prison and her mother having recently died, she wrote later that 'Miss Baker's sympathetic understanding helped me at a period which was an emotionally trying one'. But, recalling the

tearful reaction of her peers to the announcement of the abdication of Edward VIII in December 1936, Indira was convinced, as one of her biographers wrote, that 'imperialism lurked underneath the liberal socialist exterior of the students'. She was right. This was, as we have seen, part of the peculiar recipe which made up the Badminton ethos of the time.

There were also three German Jewish girls. The international tension of the 1930s, particularly stemming from Hitler's rise to power in 1933 and the discrimination suffered by minorities, especially the Jews, provided an opportunity for Badminton not only to show solidarity with these

Three young Canadian women who stayed at the school in 1937 as part of an international group in the UK to observe the coronation of King George VI.

A Christmas card sent to the school by Indira Gandhi, the first prime minister of India after independence. Gandhi studied at Badminton from 1936–37 to prepare for her Oxford entrance exams.

> *'Miss Baker invariably emphasised in assemblies the bonds which united girls of all races rather than those things which separated them'*

afflicted groups but also allow the school to become a refuge for some of them. One of the first was Liselotte Leschke. She was studying in England when Hitler took office and, half-Jewish, was no longer able to return to her home country to continue her studies. Miss Baker offered her a post at the school, where she taught German and helped in both the kindergarten and the Junior School. This allowed her to gain her degree at Bristol University in 1938 and a few years later she returned to join the staff at the school. A redoubtable figure in her own right, who devoted her life to the school and to Bristol University, she delighted in the freedom Badminton provided. She recalled how Miss Baker invariably emphasised in assemblies the bonds which united girls of all races rather than those things which separated them. More German refugees came to the school at the end of the decade, preceded by a series of Basques (escaping from Franco's Spain), Czechs and Austrians. For many of them, the offer of a place at Badminton also allowed their parents to come to Britain and the girls appreciated in retrospect how this often made the difference between life and death. One 17-year-old Czech girl, Sonja Morawetz, later recorded that Badminton meant 'everything' to her – 'it represents that most important turning point in my life; without it I truly do not know what would have become of me'. Margot Friedlein came to Badminton from Nazi Germany in 1939. Warmly welcomed by Miss Webb-Johnson who met her at Paddington station, she looked back on her time at the school as one when she was taught to appreciate 'the exciting concepts of freedom, of internationalism, of love of peace, of the dignity and worth of each human being'. Many of these refugees from the Nazis came, like Miss Leschke, from families of mixed marriages. Miss Baker believed that while children from Jewish or Christian families could rely on their co-religionists to help them, those from mixed marriages lacked similar advocates. The

commitment of the school to accommodate and educate these girls was undoubtedly a financial sacrifice but one which too few other schools were prepared to accept. Badminton eventually had about 20 such girls who came either through the Anglo-Czech Committee or the German Emergency Committee via the Quakers. Like others from overseas, they were called 'foreign friends'. Some girls found this rather patronising and would have preferred to have been known simply as refugees. One of them, Inge Frank, who had waved what turned out to be her final goodbyes to her parents at Hamburg station, recalled the condescending streak that Beatrice Baker occasionally allowed to come to the surface. Whenever Inge or another refugee had 'failed to volunteer for any particularly obnoxious task, like gardening in the depths of winter, we would be called to the study and told that, as we were "in receipt of charity" (her own words) the least we could do was to volunteer for unpopular chores'. Inge, from a family where demonstrating affection was second nature, found Miss Baker emotionally cold, even when Inge learned of the deaths of her parents and her brother after their deportation to Poland during the Second World War. Yet she recognised within Miss Baker the latter's desire to inspire affection. On Inge's last night at school, when she joined the queue of leavers saying farewell to their headmistress, Miss Baker leaned forward to kiss her and Inge instinctively recoiled. This prompted Miss Baker to ask whether Inge loved her; she was visibly hurt when Inge replied that while she respected and admired her, she could never love her.

But internationalism was just one part of the Badminton philosophy which sought in many different ways to open the minds of the girls to life beyond the school walls. All girls received a weekly lesson in current events while Civics Week, another innovation of Miss Baker's, gave sixth-form girls the chance to go out into Bristol, visiting factories, such as the Wills' tobacco

The Chorus, left to right; Miss White, Miss Parkin, Miss Jones, Miss Eagleson and Miss Wallace. Staff Revue, 1931.

Miss Rendall (left) and Miss Baker in a Staff Revue, 1931.

factory, schools and the courts. Although the tea parties at Badminton continued for less fortunate girls from the city, a more practical way of reaching out to the community involved inviting local children to use the school playing fields, an entirely spontaneous initiative. The tradition of visiting lecturers brought to the school not just Gilbert Murray but Laurence Housman, who on Armistice Day in 1932 read part of his introduction to *War Letters of Fallen Englishmen*, and W H Auden, who came to Badminton on 23 September 1937 to read from the play he was writing with Christopher Isherwood, probably *On The Frontier*, which eventually appeared in 1939. A school cinema was established which instead of some light relief from the worthy causes supported by the girls presented rather dreary educational films, such as *Great Cargoes*, *The Farm Factory* or *Heavy Industries*. More time was made available for clubs and societies, from the *French Circle* and the science society to the architecture club and the revived debating society. Miss Baker believed that extra-curricular activities should as far as possible aim for knowledge and training in service. Perhaps this was why the arts were not particularly prominent at Badminton. But there was a small orchestra, a choir and for a while a pipe band, and the girls attended concerts given by Schnabel and Menuhin, Furtwangler and

Beecham. Many girls also later attested to the influence of the reproductions of the great masters hung along the school corridors. The chance for staff and girls to let their hair down came through traditions like the staff pantomime and the sixth-form review. While girls in the Junior School seemed to have had the most enjoyable time, with their nature rambles and countryside treks, they too were made aware of what was going on around the world. Junior School girls were members of the Nansen Pioneers, a movement named after the great explorer who was also a prominent humanitarian and the first High Commissioner for Refugees at the League of Nations. They had talks on current affairs every week and prepared scrapbooks of happenings around the world. They even travelled overseas, visiting Holland in April 1936 with other boys and girls from the League of Nations Junior Branch. For Miss Baker the fundamental teaching at Badminton was always 'the realisation of the Unseen, the brotherhood of man and a sense of service, national and international, based on an increasing responsibility towards their present environment which should lead to a realisation of the duties of citizenship in a democratic state'. It was underpinned by her Christian faith, reflected in the choice of the school hymn, 'Come, Lord, and rule the earth', in 1931. It was only Christianity, she told the Old Badmintonians in 1937, which could save the world.

If civic duty and international awareness represented the radical side of the school, then Badminton's approach to discipline and academic study was part of the more conservative aspect of the school's character. Although the school was regarded as progressive, Miss Baker's 'Book of Regulations' for the summer term of 1933 suggests that boarding school life was just as regulated at Badminton as anywhere else. Presumably this is the only survivor of a whole sheaf of similar books. It contains a multitude of rules governing dress, behaviour and routine. For instance, the girls were not to perform 'stunts' on the play apparatus in the gardens or in the swimming pool. Any gramophone records the girls wished to play had to be approved by Miss Webb-Johnson. The rules for clothing were very specific – hats or 'tams' (tam o'shanters) had to be worn on the Downs or the High Road; fur-backed or gauntlet woollen gloves could not be worn for church; all girls under 16 had to wear overalls for letter writing (in case they stained their clothes with ink) and also for meals ('if girls spot their tunics or sacks'). Talcum powder was forbidden. It was also stipulated that 'no sweets, eatables or cakes or food of any description [are] ever to be taken to bedrooms even for one minute'. Girls late for meals were punished by losing their entitlement to butter or marmalade (breakfast), pudding (lunch and supper) or jam and cake (tea). The rationale for all these rules was that if girls learned to resist small temptations, they would not fall prey to larger ones.

Miss Baker also clung to the outmoded view that girls might be intelligent but they were also innately fragile and had to be handled with care. Younger girls, for instance, were still expected to take a regular rest each afternoon. This was in spite of the energy with which the girls threw themselves into the many and various extra-curricular activities at the school, and the success which they made of most of them. And although

the width of the curriculum was commended by visiting inspectors, Miss Baker never seemed to place much value on science, despite the fact that girls were regarded as ideal candidates for medical school and nursing. The school eventually made attempts to catch up, appointing a second science mistress in 1937 for the greater number of sixth-form girls interested in pursuing medicine.

The care taken to prevent overwork meant that, as many girls recognised later if not then, the pressure upon them to perform academically was never acute. It was a relatively relaxed environment in which to study. So examination results for those girls who took them were good. There were scarcely any failures. The school was sending a regular if small number of girls to university. Forms were small, each with no fewer than 12 and no more than 17 pupils. The teaching from the 19 full-time and 5 part-time staff, of whom the majority were professionally qualified, was applauded as confident and competent by the school inspectors in 1938. Music, history and

The official school hymn, chosen by Miss Baker in 1931 to reinforce Christian values.

English were particularly praised. Staff also had the opportunity of what would now be called in-service training on topics selected by the headmistress. This was the age of the dedicated spinster who gave her life to teaching, often to the same school, sacrificing many of the home comforts others took for granted by taking up inadequate accommodation within boarding schools. At Badminton staff turnover was low and those who left did so either for marriage or promotion. These committed women included Miss Skemp, known as 'Skempie', small, gorgeous and much loved, who came to the school in 1916 and remained in charge of the kindergarten until she retired in 1945. One mother introduced her young daughter to 'Skempie' as 'This is Elizabeth, who shouts'. 'Oh, no!', replied Miss Skemp, 'I'm sure Elizabeth doesn't shout. She just uses her outdoor voice inside.' And, politely corrected, Elizabeth never shouted again. Another was Leila Eveleigh, who had been at Badminton as a girl, returned to teach maths in 1931 and stayed until she retired in 1968. Her constant companion was Isobel Raab who initially taught Greek dancing to

the girls in their tussore silk tunics as well as drama and elocution. Later she would retrain to teach cookery and needlework. Some girls remember with less than fondness Rockie, the Shetland pony she kept at Lynmouth during the war, who had a tendency to bite the girls' bottoms. At the start of the autumn term in 1939, just as war was breaking out, Margaret Miles came to teach history. She became a house mistress (there were four houses, Badock, Brown, Burke and Blackwell) and later senior mistress. She remained only until 1945 and later achieved renown as an outstanding headmistress of one of the largest of London's first comprehensive schools, for which she became a dame. Throughout her career she acknowledged the influence of Badminton and Miss Baker. Mary Jeffery joined Badminton to teach classics in 1937 and stayed until 1971. Known as 'Jeff' by the staff and 'Japonica' by the girls, she was an elegant woman with an air of mystery supposed to relate to rejected lovers at Oxford. Equable, oblique, eccentric, with a warmth and sense of fun which quickly bubbled over into uncontrollable laughter, she was

Rockie, a Shetland pony notorious for his bad manners.

Teachers: (left to right) Nora Ford, violin; Jean Storry, music; Mary 'Jeff' Jeffrey, classics.

passionate about her subject and represented everything that was best about staff at Badminton. Her eccentricity and vagueness is illustrated in a wonderful tale told by Jean Storry, who joined to teach music in 1941. She recorded how, while the school was evacuated to Lynmouth, Miss Jeffery 'appeared in deshabillé at my bedside just after 8.00 one Sunday morning, wild-eyed, her beautiful long hair flying loose, and told me to get up at once as the Japanese had landed at Porlock Bay (just along the coast), having turned her radio on too late to hear that the Porlock Bay mentioned was somewhere in the Philippine Islands'. The school also depended upon its domestic staff, such as Edwin March, the house man, who retired in 1934 after 20 years. Another of the Rendall sisters, Janet, joined the school in the same year as matron.

The coming of war for the second time in a generation was bitterly resented by Miss Baker, no matter how clearly she had seen it coming. Yet her ideals never wavered. With the dissolution of the League of Nations and the transformation of the League of Nations Education Committee into the Council for Education in World Citizenship (CEWC), the Junior Branch at Badminton was reorganised into an International Club. Over three days in April 1940 the school hosted a conference on 'The World We Want To Make', attended by 180 boys and girls from 52 schools from all over England. Distinguished speakers were invited, groups discussed topics such as the conditions for an armistice and the settlement of territorial issues in Europe, and everyone joined in community singing each evening. One Badminton girl, Chitra Rudingerova, wrote that 'we knew that we were all going the same way in the search for truth, and that we, the young generation, are bound together

Conference at Badminton, 'The World We Want To Make', 1940.

Girls taking refuge in the school air raid shelter.

indissolubly by a common future and common responsibilities'. Another girl recalled that throughout the war the girls understood that they were never to hate the Germans, only the actions they took.

Every preparation was made to protect the school buildings from air raids although Bristol was classed as a neutral area at the start of the war. It became a retreat from London for bodies such as King's College, the Air Ministry, the BBC Symphony Orchestra and Imperial Airways. Another one, the Tank Corps, had threatened to requisition the school but found an alternative home. Under the circumstances, it was agreed there was no reason to evacuate the school. Miss Baker, like other heads, wanted to avoid the disruption and disintegration which evacuation brought to many schools. But on 19 June 1940 German bombs fell on the city for the first time. The last raid took place almost four years later on 16 May 1944. The bombers targeted Bristol's docks and aircraft factories but their bombs also killed nearly 1,400 civilians and damaged or destroyed nearly 89,000 properties. The school magazine recorded the events which followed that first

bombing raid – 'buses were commandeered, outings became both difficult and inadvisable and interest centred around air raid shelters [where the girls] sang, munched biscuits, knitted squares, played games'. Every night the boarders slept in the shelters, 'wrapped in eiderdowns and blankets, lying "top to tail", listening to Pinocchio's strange adventures in a world hardly more unreal than that in which we ourselves were living'. Before the end of that summer term many boarders had gone home, several day girls had left Bristol and others had sailed for the USA or India. With falling bombs and falling numbers, Miss Baker took the decision to move the school's boarding section out of Bristol. As the school moved out of Northcote in August 1940, the army moved in.

The chosen destination for the boarders was the holiday resort of Lynmouth on Devon's north coast. Removal vans brought books, furniture and other goods to the properties rented by the school, the Tors Hotel for the senior boarders and the Manor House, a Holiday Fellowship guest house,

The Tors Hotel in Lynmourh, Devon.

Manor House, temporary wartime site of Badminton Junior School, Lynmouth, Devon.

Miss Baker and Miss Rendall at The Tors Hotel, Lynmouth.

View from The Tors Hotel of the Devon resort of Lynmouth, to which school boarders were evacuated in wartime from the dangers of widespread bombing in Bristol.

for the juniors. Potential guests were turned away as cocktail bars became classrooms. Staff had gone on ahead to make preparations; and then 'at last the coaches from Bristol arrive and the sound of hammer, paint-pot and furniture removing gives place to high-pitched and excited exclamations'. By November 1940, there were 120 girls boarding in Lynmouth and 60 day girls still at school in Bristol. The Junior School was burnt out in December 1941 and to this day one girl can still recall the smell of phosphorus and water from her damaged school books. With numbers falling to fewer than 30, compounded by the heavy bombing raids, the school became uneconomic and it was feared that it would have to close. Instead it moved into Cote Grange where it was run by Mrs Bertha Urquhart with Miss Skemp and numbers climbed back to 60 by 1943. One fascination for the girls was the arrival in Northcote of American soldiers, including the first black faces some of them had seen. Links with Westbury were maintained during the war through intermittent visits of staff from Lynmouth, including Miss Baker.

Lynmouth was less than a hundred miles from Bristol but for Beatrice Baker it seemed like the end of the earth. When one local inhabitant asked her soon after the school had arrived whether she was glad to have come to such a beautiful place, she replied curtly that she would return to Bristol the following day if she could. At a later speech day she said that no boarding school should ever be forced to move to such an isolated place where contact with the outside world was so difficult. This was a feeling certainly felt initially by some girls. One remembered how those who were evacuated got off the train from Bristol at Dunster and onto a coach that took them to Lynmouth across the moors, a forlorn experience – it seemed to be the point of no return, the end of the world. One girl later wrote sniffily that Lynmouth was a place which 'offers little outside encouragement in the study of international affairs'. The Tors Hotel too turned out to be less than satisfactory. Some of the floors were so fragile that jumping too hard on them brought down ceilings below. The closed stoves smoked in each classroom, the corridors were draughty and the hotel was icy cold in winter. Some senior girls took board and lodging at houses in the village and in the blacked-out winter nights of wartime, one girl remembered, 'a nightly procession would set out, lit by one feeble torch which was all that the black-out regulations allowed, clinging to each other in the darkness to be set down, group by group, at our abode'. The food was dull although usually there was plenty of it. But hunger among growing girls was always a problem. One girl recalled that 'when hunger passed into schoolgirl greed, it could be assuaged only by mammoth quantities of brown bread; there were unofficial bread slice consumption competitions'. The record was apparently 13 at one sitting. Any sweets sent by parents were pooled for distribution among the houses, passed round the girls on a plate at the weekends. This practice was abandoned only once. A consignment of oranges, a rare fruit in wartime, arrived and Miss Baker agreed those to whom the oranges had been sent could keep them. She immediately regretted her decision, changed her mind and insisted they should be shared out. In an example of the feistiness which Miss Baker was surely encouraging, one group of girls refused to accept the oranges on the grounds that Miss Baker's decision amounted to tyranny. Feelings apparently ran high for days but there was a limit to the courage of the girls – no one was prepared to tell the headmistress that the tension was really all her own fault. There were occasional opportunities for other treats. On those rare days when parents came to take their daughters out,

they often flocked to the Lyndale Hotel, later badly affected by the disastrous floods of 1953, which still managed to provide good English home cooking. And on long walks into the countryside girls could still come across farmhouses serving up thick clotted cream on bread. Domestic staff were almost impossible to obtain, so in school the girls – and the teaching staff – carried out cleaning duties, made up beds, laid tables, prepared vegetables, waited on table and washed up. It was later said of Miss Janet Rendall at Lynmouth that she acted as 'a carpenter, cook, housekeeper, laundry-hand and plumber'. While Miss Baker regarded Lynmouth as far from ideal, she appreciated the warm welcome the locals gave the school. In return, the girls went round collecting paper for salvage every week while others helped out on local farms. 'We have collected hips, foxglove leaves and nettle leaves,' wrote Miss Baker in 1942, 'and sent them to the local centres to be used for medicinal purposes.'

Miss Baker was determined to make the best of things. She insisted that the school should function as near normal as possible. Academic standards did not appear to falter. Although the size of the school meant that examination groups were small, the pass rate continued to exceed 90

Members of staff with Miss Baker on the terrace at The Tors. Miss Webb-Johnson and Miss Valentine seated.

Peter Pears and Benjamin Britten gave concerts in the town hall at Lynmouth during the war.

per cent for the School Certificate. She insisted, unlike some girls' schools, that every girl should take at least five academic subjects. Badminton also sent a steady stream of girls up to university, with ten winning Oxbridge places in 1940 and 1941. Miss Baker persuaded distinguished parents visiting their daughters to step in as guest speakers. The author Naomi Mitchison decided to declaim Gaelic poetry in full Highland dress, much to the embarrassment of her daughter. Stanley Spencer, the artist, whose daughter Unity was at the school, visited several times and drew among the girls. Later, in the 1970s, with funds given in memory of Miss Baker, the school was able to purchase several of his drawings. The Ministry of Information delivered talks on the USA, Sudan and China. Russia became a popular topic for lectures and film shows and in 1943 there was a one-day conference, jointly organised with another evacuated school, Milton Mount College, when a speaker sympathetically described the work of Lenin and Stalin. Another came from the Free French to talk about de Gaulle. A group of girls were taken to hear a lecture in Lynton by the leader of the wartime Common Wealth party, Sir Richard Acland. It was apparently a terrifying experience for the speaker, floored by a flurry of questions from these intense schoolgirls on matters such as birth control in India and post-war reparations. A weekly newsletter on current affairs was still circulated and Miss Baker checked regularly to make sure it was being read. Margaret Miles ran the International Club and in 1942 the school hosted an International Teachers' Conference. The sixth form organised a mock election in 1941 as part of their civics course which returned a People's Party candidate although not with an outright majority over the Labour and Conservative candidates. The inspiration for the party tag of the winning candidate may have been drawn from the so-called People's Convention summoned by the Communist Party earlier in the year to agitate against the war. The better pianos had been moved from Westbury, plus the library of books, music and records, so the girls carried on giving recitals and the choir continued to thrive. There was house drama in the town hall as well as staff productions and nativity plays at Christmas. A number of distinguished visiting musicians, including Leon Goossens, Benjamin Britten and Peter Pears, gave concerts in the town hall. The girls made the most of the beauty of the surrounding countryside. On warm summer days Miss Baker would close the school and the girls would go off collecting wortleberries which were turned into jam by Miss Standring, the cook. The architecture club visited places like Paracombe and Dunster. Sketching and painting outdoors were popular although this was banned by the sea since it could rouse suspicion in wartime. Radclyffe Hall, the controversial novelist, best known for The Well of Loneliness, daring for the time in its treatment of lesbianism, was living locally for a while and the literary club visited her at Countisbury. Games continued as well, with hockey played against local teams in the park in Lynton, reached by the cliff railway. When the railway closed during winter, netball was adopted instead. There was very little cricket, a staple of the pre-war days, but a couple of hard courts allowed some tennis.

The girls too took the war in their stride. Each morning began the same way, as ever with a cold bath, followed by physical exercises on the terrace and a run round the hotel. Miss Baker would test the temperature of the water to make sure it was cold enough but some wily girls managed to escape by splashing around in the water with their

Junior School camp
at Lynmouth.

hands to give the impression they were in the bath. Arrangements were made for girls to remain in Lynmouth during the holidays and senior girls enjoyed summer camps on local farms. The war was brought home to them from time to time. One girl received news of the death of her brother on a training exercise. The refugees amongst them would talk about the parents they would never see again. The girls could feel in Lynmouth the thump of the bombs dropped on Swansea. The news of former pupils listed their contributions to the war effort, with many of them serving in the Air Transport Service, the Women's Auxiliary Air Force, the First Aid Nursing Yeomanry, the Women's Royal Naval Service and the Red Cross, or working on the land, acting as secretaries for the Home Guard and driving ambulances. At first the Old Badmintonians continued to hold their summer gathering at the school in Lynmouth. The description of the weekend held in 1941 by Iris Murdoch reveals a group of earnest, politically engaged and idealistic young women, struggling to form a view of how the country should be run after the war. She wrote that 'the argument, which began on questions of production, inevitably ended by turning on the problems which divide the left wing – the possibility of "gradual socialism", ends and means, the communist state'. One former pupil went so far as to describe the school itself as 'the perfect Communist state' – 'democratic underneath, with a strong leader at the top'. But these gatherings came to an enforced end, as did speech day, defeated by the increasing difficulties of travel in wartime. It was

no doubt with considerable relief that Miss Baker decided in March 1945 that it was now safe to return to Bristol.

Wartime recruitment poster; the school's ethos of public service spurred many Old Badmintonians to sign up and play their part in the war effort.

A Tremendous Richness
1945–1966

The school left Lynmouth on 26 March 1945 and re-opened in Westbury-on-Trym on 12 May 1945, four days after VE Day. The removal of the school's belongings took a month to complete. As the vans arrived in Bristol, 'there was all bustle, eagerness, enthusiasm', recorded Lucy Rendall in the school magazine, 'work, noise, dirt and cobwebs to be dislodged, windows to be scraped, walls and ceilings to be distempered, floors to be scrubbed, and finally vanload upon vanload of furniture – 43 in all – to be unloaded and distributed'. The military had left neither the house nor the playing fields in a fit condition and the fields were also littered with temporary army huts. There were more pupils than ever – 281 in July 1945, consisting of 175 boarders and 106 day girls.

Demand for places was so great that parents were putting down the names of their daughters several years in advance, but the governors were conscious that they did not wish Badminton to become so large that the special nature of the school was affected. Nevertheless, there was a need for more space. But although Britain had emerged victorious from the war, the country also found itself on the verge of bankruptcy. The controls and rationing of wartime were extended in peace, skilled labour and materials were in short supply, and the economy would not finally be freed from emergency regulations until the mid-1950s. So while the school drew up building plans and launched an

appeal for funds, the only addition before the 1950s was the acquisition of an existing army hut on the fields, which were not finally derequisitioned until the end of 1946, for conversion into 'temporary' laboratories and kitchens for domestic science.

Gradually things returned to normal. Miss Steede had taken over the Junior School from Mrs Urquhart, supervising the post-war merger of two different schools, the day girls in Bristol and the boarders from Lynmouth. With more girls, the Junior School also added two more houses, Skemp and Urquhart, to Marsh and Harris. In many areas throughout the school the pattern of past years remained unchanged. So the social services fund continued to support the country holiday home, re opened after the war, as well as the cot at the hospital. Both of these would soon disappear in the changing post-war world, one as a result of slum clearance and housing improvement, the other through the creation of the National Health Service. One of the great excitements of the first few months back in Bristol was the general election which returned Labour to power with an overwhelming majority. Badminton, of course, treated the election with all due seriousness, and representatives from every party were invited to the school. One girl whose father was a Labour candidate was allowed to go home to help his campaign. Badminton also carried on helping girls from distressed parts of Europe, where the scars of war had not yet healed, funding the education of girls from France, Holland, Germany and Czechoslovakia. The school also took part in a social experiment at home. In the wake of the publication of the Fleming report in 1944, which examined the relationship between the public schools and the state system, several education authorities experimented with sending pupils to public boarding schools. Badminton was among those which took part. London County Council sent the first girl under this scheme at the end of 1946. Somerset County Council also began sending a handful of girls. The scheme nationally proved unsuccessful and short-lived, partly because local authorities felt that the benefits did not outweigh the expense, and partly because there was little consideration of the suitability of some girls for a boarding-school education. At the peak of this relationship, in 1950, 11 girls from both authorities were attending the school but it had fizzled out before the end of the decade. Also in 1946, the Ministry of Education under Labour had finally caught up with Miss Baker and was urging teachers to relate education to the outside world. At Badminton the Citizenship Course continued, as did the International Club, where one debate covered what was known as 'the Colour Question', with a talk about 'colour-prejudice' from the secretary from the League of Coloured Peoples. The League, founded in London in 1931 to campaign for worldwide racial equality, but particularly for equal rights for black people in the

United Kingdom, was also another victim of changing times, dissolving in 1951.

Miss Baker and her colleagues had succeeded in sustaining the school and its ethos during the war. Seeing Badminton resettled after the war was one of the last important acts of Miss Baker's headship. She had apparently considered retirement on the verge of the outbreak of war. When the school returned to Bristol, she was nearing 70. Yet her energy and influence seemed infinite. Her impact upon the girls remained just as strong. One girl who left shortly before the school returned from Lynmouth recollected how Badminton had shaped her life. It had given her a wide interest in everything intellectual and visual. It encouraged her to be public spirited – 'if

VE Day, St Michael's Hill, Bristol, 8th May, 1945, after which the school moved back to the city from rural Devon, much to the delight of most staff and pupils.

something is wrong, I will do something about it'. Politically, she became 'an apologetic capitalist', while religiously she later became a Quaker, a combination which somehow seems apt for those upper middle-class girls from prosperous families infused with Miss Baker's spirit of Christian socialism. The school taught her about fairness and sharing and to regard everyone as an equal. She made very good lifelong friends. At university her new friends quickly grew tired of hearing how things were done at Badminton. Another girl, who left soon after the school came back to Bristol, remembered how Miss Baker wanted the girls to be pioneers, feminists, individualists, people in their own right, looking outwards and seizing opportunities. There was, she felt, 'a tremendous richness' at Badminton, even in those immediate post-war years when facilities and resources were so limited. In her final year as head, Miss Baker, writing to Old Badmintonians, summed up the school in expressing the hope that Badminton 'will go on from strength to strength and continue to send out girls with a tolerant and sympathetic approach to the social and international problems of the day, welcoming progress and change in a spirit of adventure and eager to carry on that tradition of service for which the school has always stood'.

In 1946, as she approached her 70th birthday, Miss Baker announced her retirement. At the same time the other members of 'The Powers', Lucy Rendall and Mabel Webb-Johnson, also stood down, as did Lucy Rendall's two sisters, Bertha Urquhart and Janet Rendall. Work also began on changing the unsatisfactory legal structure of the school through the creation of an educational trust, which was finally completed in November 1949. The school, despite its popularity, was scarcely prosperous and could not afford to pay pensions to Misses Baker, Lucy Rendall and Webb-Johnson, instead making them a gift of £250 each. Retirement did not mean the disappearance of the triumvirate which had been so influential over so long a time. The three lifelong friends and spinsters retired together to Little Grange in the grounds of the school. Miss Webb-Johnson suffered ill-health and after a stroke left to live with friends in London where she died in 1953. Lucy Rendall proved to be as indispensable in Beatrice Baker's retirement as she had been during her career. Miss Baker was hopelessly undomesticated and would become more and more arthritic, which in turn made her increasingly difficult. Lucy Rendall endured all this with great good humour and her death in 1966 was an enormous blow for Miss Baker. She ran out

Displaying characteristic goodwill and application, girls clean the school after their return from Devon; the Army used the buildings during the war while the school was in Lynmouth.

Brenda Sanderson, headmistress, 1947– 66.

Baker's eagerness 'to graft me onto the parent stock' and her frankness about the development of the school under her successor, it was clearly not an easy situation. The irony was that Miss Sanderson had turned down the chance of the headship at her previous school, Downe House, precisely because the retiring head, Miss Olive Willis, every bit as formidable as Miss Baker, had insisted on living within the grounds. When she announced this at her interview with the Badminton governors, whose chairman since 1943 had been Mr Burris, their jaws must have dropped. It must have been an equal shock to Miss Sanderson to discover the truth. In fact, the governors were understandably concerned that Miss Baker would interfere and Andrew Urquhart, son of Bertha and a recently appointed governor, was delegated to instruct her not to do so. Miss Baker and Miss Sanderson also took a turn round the gardens just to make sure that their personalities would not conflict too much. It was probably due largely to Miss Sanderson's tact and diplomacy that the differences between them, which did flare up from time to time, remained skirmishes rather than battles. One of Miss Sanderson's gestures was to send over to Little Grange newly appointed members of staff for an informal vetting by Miss Baker under the guise of taking tea with her.

Known as 'Ben' or 'BMS', Brenda Sanderson was a completely different personality. One telling remark of hers on Miss Baker, that 'today young people are less willing to accept such strong personal guidance', said as much about her as about her predecessor. The daughter of a doctor and the granddaughter of the second headmaster of Bradfield College, she was born in 1904 and brought up in Hove. After attending Brighton and Hove High School, she went up to Oxford to study classics at Somerville in 1924, changing to PPE (politics, philosophy and economics) as she became more interested in politics and history. Unlike Beatrice Baker, Ben Sanderson was not born with a burning commitment to education. Perhaps this was one reason why she was a much gentler yet no less persuasive headmistress. Teaching was certainly not a vocation she considered on graduation. She spent several years

of housekeepers willing to put up with her temper and, increasingly frail, moved out of Little Grange into a nursing home in Nailsea in 1971. Her last two years were sad ones for a woman who had been such a proud, energetic and engaging personality. The Old Badmintonian magazine noted at the time of her move that 'she naturally hated leaving Little Grange and we all sympathise with her in this but there seems to be no other solution. She *implores* all Old Girls to think of one'. She died on 28 September 1973 at the age of 97.

The histories of several girls' schools are marked by the stories of new headmistresses working in the shadow of predecessors who continued to live close by the school. At Badminton it was worse than that. Miss Baker's successor, Brenda Sanderson, would find that she had inherited their presence on the governing body as well. Miss Baker and Miss Rendall remained governors until the spring of 1966, almost as long as Miss Sanderson was headmistress. For several years, Miss Baker also continued to teach maths when an emergency arose. Miss Sanderson later wrote generously about her predecessor but, in mentioning Miss

Open Day, 1959.

in a variety of secretarial appointments, the last one as secretary to Somerville's principal. When this came to an end in 1932, she agreed to cover for a friend who taught maths at Downe House. It was not her subject but she found she enjoyed the experience so much that she accepted with little hesitation the offer of a permanent post teaching history and Latin. After a spell working for the civil service during the war, she returned to Downe House as senior mistress and was marked out as Olive Willis's successor. It was not to be. Instead, she was the unanimous choice of the Badminton governors and she took over as headmistress in January 1947.

Her own view of the role of headmistress was influenced by her time at Downe House. Miss Willis impressed her, particularly by her sense of proportion and the way she could be both informal yet dignified. Although as a more private and less expansive personality than Miss Willis, Ben Sanderson recoiled from what some regarded as the excessive intimacy that existed between Miss Willis and many of the girls, she learned the importance of pastoral care and a focus on the whole child. She hated the slapdash way Downe House was organised and the absence of professional training and development but she

saw the benefits in allowing staff considerable freedom, provided this was done with a guiding hand. As an agnostic (her application form for Badminton described her as a non-communicating member of the Church of England), she also grew to appreciate the role spirituality played within a school community. While she was warmly welcomed at Badminton by staff and girls, she felt that there was a certain spiritual deficiency. She wrote to a friend that this was probably because Miss Baker's generation 'is fundamentally nervous of religion as opposed to ours and I was not really happy with [Badminton's] morning prayers. It makes the place a shade too rationalistic to be really fruitful'. Here again was another clue that the regime was going to change.

As a result, there was some hostility to Miss Baker's successor, despite the optimistic clarion call issued in the school magazine that her appointment created 'a great opportunity for the school to show its readiness to receive new ideas and to respond to fresh leadership'. A number of older, longer-serving staff would grumble over the smallest change in attitude on the part of the new headmistress. This was a hazard faced by many new heads taking over from long-established predecessors. Ben Sanderson disarmed staff through a combination of rational clarity and direct firmness. The issue which quickly tested her mettle with Miss Baker and others was the future of speech day. Miss Sanderson, who firmly believed that every individual had the right to be treated equally, disliked the idea of singling out individuals in public through prizes. Towards the end of her first year in office she suggested that the time had come to look at an alternative. This came to nothing because of opposition on the governing body. She pressed the idea once more a year later and the minutes record that it was only 'after considerable discussion' that it was agreed the headmistress should present a suitable proposal. Another year further on and her plans were

'a great opportunity for the school to show its readiness to receive new ideas and to respond to fresh leadership'

81

View of the lawns with rose garden, 1958.

agreed but only 'as an experiment'. Then there appeared to be an impasse. Miss Sanderson showed herself to be a shrewd operator. She had overcome similar resistance to her plans to form a parents' association, already common in many schools. When the parents discussed the idea of an open day in preference to a speech day, their overwhelming support finally persuaded the governors to permit one to go ahead in 1952. No more speech days were held while Miss Sanderson was headmistress of Badminton.

The second occasion when she had to fight for what she wanted took place much later. The school had finally embarked upon a much-needed building programme in the mid-1950s as the last government controls on building were removed. When building was difficult in the late 1940s and early 1950s, the school had instead bought a series of properties close by the school, particularly in Downs Road, which were used as extra boarding and staff accommodation. Ben Sanderson saw new development as essential if the school was going to expand. She believed that one of the reasons the school struggled financially was because numbers were too low to be economic. She also felt that numbers could rise without compromising the nature of the school. She was proved right. In the early 1960s the school exceeded 360 pupils. Such growth was important,

she believed, to raise academic standards throughout the school, expand the sixth form and allow more girls to be admitted directly into the senior school rather than from the Junior School.

Miss Sanderson's views were shared by the other mastermind behind the building programme, the school's bursar, David Sherwood. Polite, courteous and professional, he was appointed to replace Lucy Rendall in 1945, retiring in 1974. He oversaw the extension of the dining room and domestic quarters at Northcote in 1955 and the addition of a classroom wing to School House in 1956. As numbers grew, the school became more profitable and Sherwood was able to transfer surpluses to reserves. The lean years had taught him never to be profligate with the school's money and in later years he did earn the reputation ascribed to so many school bursars of being unnecessarily tight-fisted. He was also the driving force behind the centenary appeal which raised the money to build the new science block. The absence of proper science facilities had been a failing of the school for a long time and the new block heralded a much-improved position for science in the Badminton curriculum. The foundation stone was laid in May 1957 by Professor Tyndall, professor of physics at Bristol University, who had been chairman of governors from 1949 until 1956, and the block was opened

Professor Arthur Tyndall, laying the foundation stone for the new science block, 1957, with the architect, Eustace Button, chairman of governors, Lyn Harris, the headmistress, Miss Sanderson, and the builder, Mr Brag.

by Countess Mountbatten, Lord Chelwood's successor as Visitor, during centenary year in June 1958. It was a momentous celebration for the school, marked in particular by the premiere of a cantata, *Crown of the Year*, composed by Michael Tippett with words by Christopher Fry, which had been commissioned by a parent, Eric White, on behalf of the school. The composer attended the performance given at the school on 26 July. But it came at the end of a wet and dreary summer's day when most girls were just eager for events to end so they could go out for supper with their visiting parents.

The struggle for Miss Sanderson came over the proposal for a new library in 1963–4. The governors, now chaired by Lyn Harris, who had headed the Junior School all those years ago, supported the plan submitted by the school architect for another extension to School House. Miss Sanderson very much wanted a separate building to give the library the status it had never really had before. Her most formidable opponent was Miss Baker, still a governor, who refused to countenance any building which might take up part of the rose garden. The governors procrastinated once more, deferring any decision until the new gym had been built. This was opened by Dame Sybil Thorndike, the eminent actress and Gilbert Murray's successor as President, in November 1965. Plans for the library were revived and it was agreed to ask the distinguished architect, Sir Hugh Casson, to design a building to be sited on the shrubbery which ran alongside the rose garden. Miss Baker was appeased, Miss Sanderson was happy and Casson accepted the commission. The library, however, a striking but elegantly simple modern design, was not finished until 1968, two years after Miss Sanderson retired, when she was invited to return to perform the official opening.

Like Miss Willis, Ben Sanderson had the knack of cultivating an informal and relaxed atmosphere while remaining very firmly in command. For girls

The Governors, Headmistress and Staff of

BADMINTON SCHOOL

request the pleasure of your company at the

Celebration of the School's Centenary

on Saturday, 26th July, 1958

and also at a performance of

"Crown of the Year" a Cantata by Michael Tippett with words by Christopher Fry, followed by a play "The Hour Strikes" by Jean Rowntree with music by Robin Milford

on Friday, 25th July, Saturday, 26th July or Sunday, 27th July

R.S.V.P.

on the enclosed slip to the Centenary Secretary not later than 10th July.

Countess Mountbatten visited as part of the Centenary Year celebrations, 1958.

who remembered Miss Baker, the contrast was marked. Although the very nature of her position created a degree of remoteness, and she never had the same rapport with smaller girls as she had with older ones, she was much more approachable than her predecessor and girls generally felt at ease in her company. Yet there was always a certain enigmatic air about her. She might come to know much about you but you rarely got to know much about her. She expected girls to learn what they could and could not do. They understood the trust she placed in them. Where girls misbehaved, it was the breach of that trust, rather than the nature of the offence, which mattered most. 'Where behaviour and attitudes are concerned,' she said, 'mere obedience is no help. You cannot impose high standards of honesty, kindness, courtesy, careful work and the rest by punishing children who do not reach them. You can show your own respect for these qualities, point out the consequences (which are real, natural punishment) of low standards.' As she told two girls who had truanted one weekend to the Old Vic in the city, 'we trusted you and you let us down'. When a group of girls was sent to her after chanting at a younger member of staff, they were neither told off nor punished, but left to see for themselves how rude, silly and unkind they had been. She believed that care and patience were the best approach to take towards members of the awkward squad. She hoped that girls with problems would either come to her or to other members of staff. The rebellious were never squashed; rather they were encouraged to ask themselves why they were rebelling. She encouraged intellectual curiosity for she always wanted girls to think things out for themselves, to make up their own minds. This, recalled one former pupil, created a liberal and free-thinking atmosphere which from time to time could perplex the headmistress when girls, having been asked to consider whether they would abide by certain rules, still refused to conform. One governor later remarked that this environment led at first 'to some rather hairy moments, girls reported missing and that sort of thing, before people came to realise that greater freedom involves greater responsibility'. While it was said

of her that 'she slowly built up a form of self-discipline to replace the more formal authority of her predecessor', this never entirely solved the problem of what to do with those who failed to recognise their transgressions since expulsions and suspensions were almost unheard of. When there was a need to tackle such situations a little later, the revival of the ultimate sanction, so long disused, would cause consternation.

Tolerance and understanding were two of the hallmarks of Miss Sanderson's term in office. It seemed appropriate as society itself became more liberal during the 1960s. Ben Sanderson very probably approved of this change. She was always considered to have socialist inclinations (Miss Baker would never have approved of her otherwise) although these were always well hidden. The difficulties faced by the Attlee government had removed some of the gloss from the socialist ideal and many older girls were sceptical about socialism in practice. The 1950s were a much more conservative period politically and socially. When the school organised a mock election in 1950, returning a Conservative candidate, many girls were convinced that their headmistress had expected a socialist victor. But the girls also returned Conservatives at further mock elections in 1955 and 1964. In the latter election, in a year when the country was almost evenly split between Tory and Labour, the Conservative candidate attracted almost four times as many votes as the Labour candidate. Perhaps the girls were in reality much more conservative than they perceived themselves to be for the consensus among them in the late 1960s was they were still egalitarian, socialist and left-wing, and very much in tune with the times. Perhaps their headmistress was also rather more conservative than they understood. As she was leaving the school, she told the girls that 'her main aim had been to make us good citizens and good mothers', which was almost exactly what Miss Baker had said more than 30 years before.

Yet many girls were conscious of how the times were changing, as young people created their own distinct culture rather than apeing their parents. It was expressed through their dress, their music and their politics. One girl remembers vividly discussing at a midnight feast the anxieties caused by the Cuban missile crisis and the fear that they might not wake up the next morning. Where Miss Baker would have taken up the cause of nuclear disarmament with enthusiasm, support for the Campaign for Nuclear Disarmament (CND) was tolerated rather than encouraged at Badminton. In 1963, when CND activity was at its height following the Cuban missile crisis, one girl, Polly Toynbee, the daughter of Philip Toynbee, the writer and journalist, and great-granddaughter of Gilbert Murray, sent out to schools around Bristol an invitation to attend a meeting at Badminton to be addressed by a speaker from CND. She had already started a CND group at the school. Some heads reacted adversely, unused to pupils taking the initiative, and Miss Sanderson had to soothe some ruffled feathers. One head wrote to Miss Sanderson that 'while I sympathise with the progressive ideas of our modern pupils, I do feel it is desirable that we should participate as little as possible in controversial political matters, and would like you to know that, after a certain amount of hesitation, I consigned the letter concerned to my wastepaper basket'. The situation was aggravated because of the publicity given to the meeting in the local press. It turned out that Miss Sanderson, unknown to Polly, was opposed to any such publicity, which Polly, once she found out, tried her best to halt without success. The meeting, however, still went ahead, leading to the formation of a Bristol schools CND branch with 23 schools as members.

If Miss Sanderson lacked the overt political sympathy of her predecessor, she displayed sympathy in other areas, particularly in relation to individual girls. Never completely won over to the idea that girls were best educated away from their parents, she always had great warmth for those girls who came from broken homes, who came from overseas, who saw their parents once a year. When one set of parents complained about the poorly written and badly spelled letters they were receiving from their daughter, she told them it was surely better that she was writing at all and with affection. Repaying the faith she placed in you was a heavy burden for some girls. One told of her dismay many years later on hearing of Ben

Study bedroom overlooking Northcote House.

Sanderson's death in 1980. 'I wanted to have done something really good. I wanted to go to her and say, look, I have done this, and does that now justify your expectations of me? There was no one whose good opinion I care so much to have.'

For staff, wrote Joanna Piercy, who joined the school in 1949, 'the atmosphere of freedom, happiness and endeavour in which we seemed to work was created by Miss Sanderson'. Her staff meetings were informal affairs but ones where she clearly set out her educational philosophy, her belief in the importance of the individual, the need to encourage latent talent and foster confidence. Just as with the girls, she believed that relationships with her staff should also be based on trust so she was willing to allow them considerable freedom, still possible in an era without a prescribed national curriculum, key stage tests or league tables. She never believed in collecting trophies just for the sake of it. Learning, she felt, was about more than examinations. She also made sure that staff could always come to her at any time. She pressed at an early stage for better staff accommodation and persuaded the governors to adopt a scheme in 1948 permitting

'Make and mend' in one of the school houses after supper.

of which she was entirely unaware. Gilda Thorak, the senior languages mistress until 1962, had been brought up in Germany and France, studying at Heidelberg and the Sorbonne. She had been unhappily married to the Austrian sculptor, Josef Thorak, who later became one of the Nazi regime's two official sculptors. But it was only this that enabled her, as the daughter of a Russian Jew, to escape from Germany before the war. At Badminton she taught alongside Liselotte Leschke, another Jewish refugee, whose personal circumstances had been rather more difficult. Gilda Thorak was a warm, enthusiastic and impulsive woman, often unorthodox in her teaching methods yet producing a stream of fluent French speakers. She was also an elegant woman who, wrote one girl, was 'a swirl of floating scarves and baroque jewellery with her neat ankles encased in little boots'. Among other members of staff appointed by Miss Sanderson were Penelope Ellis and Sue Spanner. Penelope Ellis, who had studied sculpting at the Slade, joined the art staff in 1958 and remained at the school for 39 years, working not just in stone but also in wood, card, paper and many other materials. She also introduced the girls to photography, establishing a school darkroom. Sue

staff to take regular sabbaticals, with grants available to encourage overseas travel. In 1954, for instance, three staff took their sabbatical terms abroad, in Italy, Austria and Switzerland.

It was an environment which allowed every member of staff, as well as every girl, to be themselves. There were still many larger than life characters on the staff and Miss Sanderson added to their ranks. Muriel de Ville and Gilda Thorak, for instance, joined together in 1948. Muriel de Ville, astride her motorcycle and with her dyed red hair, could appear terrifying to a young girl. A particularly skilled choral instructor, she was a demanding teacher. One gifted piano pupil recalled how Miss de Ville had a detestation of music exams, instead taking her gradually through more and more difficult pieces, the grade

Girls today enjoy photography.

Spanner came to Badminton in 1962 and stayed until her retirement in 2000. She ran PE at the school and also became an outstanding hockey coach. Later she would also introduce the Duke of Edinburgh Award Scheme to the school.

The social trends creating a teenage culture were also affecting the staffing of the school. Firstly, men became an accepted part of the Badminton teaching staff. When Miss Sanderson spent the term before taking up her post in visiting other schools, she had been impressed by the teaching skills of the male staff she had seen. It was some time before this belief made itself felt at the school. Only in March 1964 did the governors agree that men could be appointed to full-time teaching posts. The two who made most impact were Richard Thorn and Harry Hesketh, both joining the school in the early 1960s. Harry Hesketh came from Kenya to teach geography, later became deputy head and eventually left to become a deputy head elsewhere. Richard Thorn came from teaching music in Bulawayo in Rhodesia. He formed part of a strong music team at Badminton, including not only Muriel de Ville but also Jean Storry, who had joined the staff at Lynmouth in 1942 and remained with the school until her retirement in 1969. The arrival of more sympathetic younger staff, both male and female, was welcomed enthusiastically by the girls during the 1960s as their own sympathy waned for the spinster lifestyle of so many older staff. The tradition of unmarried women devoting their lives to teaching in a single school was reaching its end. At Badminton it was becoming difficult to attract single women for even a short period of time to take up residential posts. One reason was the appalling state of staff accommodation. Married staff sometimes had the chance to take up residence in one or other of the individual properties outside the school on condition that they also took in a handful of boarders. But there was no married accommodation on the school site and the accommodation for single staff left much to be desired. Little had been done about this before Miss Sanderson left.

The encouragement of staff to take time off to travel abroad and the international backgrounds of some new staff showed that the school's

Orchestra practice, c.1957.

international outlook remained strong. Miss Sanderson was involved in the foundation of the Council for Internationally-Minded Schools (CIS) under the auspices of UNESCO in Geneva in 1949. This later became the International Schools Association. The purpose of CIS, which had just 20 member schools in eight countries in the early 1950s, was exactly the same as the League of Nations Junior Branch a generation earlier although the CIS came without all the crusading zeal and political ardour that had characterised the League of Nations Union. Nevertheless, Miss Sanderson was carrying on Miss Baker's work. A CIS international arts festival at Badminton in 1954 echoed similar gatherings at Badminton before the war. Miss Sanderson was CIS president in 1957 and perhaps her most important work was her involvement in the development of the

International Baccalaureate (IB). There was even talk about Badminton adopting the IB for a while in the 1950s. The school also continued to welcome girls from overseas, either as pupils (in 1954 there were girls from Norway, Colombia, Hong Kong and Malaya), on exchange or other specially arranged visits. At one session in the gym, when an exasperated teacher demanded to know where one girl was from, she received as an answer not the girl's form or house but the chirpy 'I'm from Peru!' One girl at the school during the 1950s recalled how Ben Sanderson relished the international aspect of the school. From her final interview with the headmistress she remembers not any words of wisdom for the future but Miss Sanderson telling her how much she would miss meeting her parents, her mother a Russian pianist, her father a Romanian doctor.

Miss Sanderson also wanted girls to widen their cultural interests. Perhaps it was music which developed most. Under a strong music staff there were, in addition to the usual musical events, the first joint concerts, in partnership with the girls of Clifton High School and the boys of Clifton College. The first one was probably a performance of Verdi's *Requiem* in the cathedral in 1955. Miss

School magazine cover.

The International Arts Festival, hosted by Badminton in 1954 to promote friendships with overseas students. A Madagascan student gives a tune to four Norwegian girls.

Tennis coaching, 1958.

Since the 1950s the school has developed music as a popular and impressive part of the curriculum.

Sanderson, with her dislike of too much public competition, had the house music competition replaced by a music festival in 1961, which was intended to foster higher standards among participants of equal talent.

Yet, despite the changing world outside the school, much in school life remained untouched. Sex education remained elementary. One girl remembered that the only discussion on the subject during her time came after one girl reported to her mother that she did not understand what the other girls had been laughing about after lights out in the dormitory. The whole dormitory was invited along to Miss Sanderson's house where they were told that sex was such a wonderful and beautiful thing, it could not possibly be anything to laugh about. School film shows, theatre visits, concert visits, lectures on international and other issues, the same clubs and societies, school dances, Christmas parties, social service and sport all continued to be a routine part of the school lives of many girls throughout the 1950s and 1960s. Sport perhaps

tended to suffer from some neglect, judging by reports in the school magazine which usually failed to mention opponents and, in the case of a report on one cricket season, simply read, 'As can be seen from the results, the cricket season was not very good'. One change was Miss Sanderson's creation of a school council to encourage responsibility and self-discipline, with representatives elected from among the girls. No doubt she approved of the resolution passed by the council in 1962 to abolish the annual sports day, 'partly because we disliked the compulsory and competitive atmosphere and partly because the PE staff felt we were neither fit enough nor careful enough unless we took up athletics seriously'. So athletic sports that year were 'purely voluntary and purely amusing'. It was not a decision many other schools would have countenanced.

The organisation of the school also remained much the same. Every girl belonged to one of six houses, each of 35 boarders and day girls, representing a cross-section of ages, but these houses were for administrative as well as competitive purposes. They bore no relation to sleeping arrangements which changed every term. By 1959, when the school was inspected once more, there were 346 pupils – 90 in the junior school and 44 in the sixth form, with 202 boarders. Most girls stayed on until they were at least 17, spending one or two years in the sixth form. Of the 104 leavers during the previous three years, 32 had won university places, 45 had one or more 'A' level passes and only seven left with fewer than four 'O' levels. Academically, girls between the ages of 11 and 16 were organised into five 'Groups', each group divided into A and B. Otherwise, setting took place only for English, maths and modern languages, with mixed-ability classes for all other subjects. There were no class marks, no prizes, the focus of the teaching was on the individual child. The inspectors were, as ever, impressed with the spirit of the place. They found that 'zest is indeed the keynote of all that goes on here' and commented on 'the vigour and liveliness of the girls … their sincerity and independence of thought … their fluency in speech'. They found that Badminton girls 'combine bounding vitality and energy with a most charming courtesy and friendliness to visitors and they seem to enjoy their school life very much'.

Miss Sanderson never had much time for inspections, once being seen dropping the final report of one inspection into her wastepaper bin. She could never be accused of arrogance but did

From a wing of the science block: tennis coaching in progress, and in the foreground, a group of juniors.

that action reveal just a touch of complacency? While the inspectors gave the school overall a glowing assessment, in terms of academic attainment they were rather more circumspect. Standards of work they described as 'creditable'. They concluded that 'the school has never set out to be intellectually exclusive [but] the level of ability of present entrants is good' and 'there is no general need at present to temper the rigours of the curriculum for the less able pupils'. Badminton has never in its history been a school which set out to be intellectually exclusive but in more recent times it has developed an outstanding reputation, in the jargon of modern education, for 'adding value', by

Swimming, 1957.

taking girls of modest ability and producing excellent academic results. If one reads the governing body minutes in particular for Miss Sanderson's era, one gets the clear impression, often from the comments of Miss Sanderson herself, that academic results during the 1950s and 1960s were inconsistent and sometimes disappointing. In 1951, for instance, results, according to the headmistress, were 'reasonably satisfactory'; in 1956, they were 'very satisfactory'; in 1959, they were 'disappointing'; in 1961, 'O' level results were indifferent but 'A' level results were good; in 1964 the position was reversed. By then, too, the one-year general course in the sixth form was proving less popular for the obvious reason that it yielded no qualification. It was no longer appropriate in an era when more and more young people were being encouraged to go to university.

In November 1964 Miss Sanderson gave notice to the governors that she intended to retire at the end of the summer term in 1966. The governors already had their eye on her successor, Joanna Piercy, and the chairman, who, it transpired, had directly invited her to apply, even asked if it was worthwhile advertising the post. A majority of the board insisted it was but even then the selection committee, having conducted preliminary interviews, decided that only Miss Piercy should be interviewed by the full board. In September 1966 she became the fifth headmistress of Badminton School.

School photo, 1965.

TESTING TIMES
1966–1981

When Joanna Piercy took over in 1966, everyone was expecting the school to follow much the same pattern as it had under Ben Sanderson. Miss Piercy was not just the governors' favourite to take over as headmistress. After 17 years at Badminton, the greater part of her teaching career, she was also the favourite of both her predecessor, to whom she had become close, and the staff. She would not have stayed so long at the school if she had not felt instinctively sympathetic to its ethos. Joining Badminton while she was still in her 20s, she had taught briefly at Downe House under Olive Willis and at Gordonstoun under Kurt Hahn. She came to Badminton not just because she was inclined towards progressive education but because of Ben Sanderson whom she had first come to know at Downe House.

Born in 1923, Joanna Piercy was the daughter of the financier, Bill Piercy, later Lord Piercy. A supporter of Attlee's government, he was reputed to have been the front-runner to succeed Montagu Norman as governor of the Bank of England had his friend, Hugh Dalton, remained in office as chancellor of the exchequer. His first wife, Joanna's mother, was also a woman of socialist sympathies and both parents passed on their Christian socialism to their daughter. Although she lacked the charisma of both Miss Baker and Miss Sanderson, and could be scatterbrained, sometimes disappearing for periods without letting anyone know where she was, she knew everyone in the school and was always willing to give up her time to listen to any girl who came to her. The governors could scarcely have chosen anyone more attuned to the character of the school developed with such constancy over several decades by her two predecessors.

Miss Piercy continued where Ben Sanderson had left off. This involved a greater liberalisation of the school routine. So house games were banished to end-of-term tournaments, replaced by Thursday afternoon projects, which were intended to allow girls to follow their own interest. Car maintenance proved the most popular choice. Several individual sports, such as fencing and judo, were introduced. Attempts were made to widen the contact of the girls with boys by

Several new sports were introduced to the school, including fencing.

Joanna Piercy, headmistress, 1966–69.

arranging dances with an international school, Atlantic College, in Llantwit Major. These staged events were not the best way of bringing the sexes together. As one girl recorded, the dance was 'rather gruelling' although the girls apparently impressed by their 'ability to converse with reasonable intelligence'. What were in effect tutor groups were created, with girls being allocated to specific members of staff who would entertain them in their homes during the year. The girls were also allowed to wear jeans at the weekends. The school magazine recorded that 'the mixture of mini-skirts, maxi-skirts and jeans at Saturday lunch certainly adds to our famous relaxed atmosphere'. More men joined the staff, while more married women were appointed, replacing long-serving staff, such as Leila Eveleigh and Isobel Raab, who both retired in 1968. Harry Hesketh took over the role of deputy head.

Then, in the summer of 1968, Miss Piercy suddenly announced that she was marrying a long-standing friend, Group Captain Turner, and wished to leave the school before Christmas 1969. In the event, she left in the spring of 1969 and Harry Hesketh took over as acting head for the summer term. This must have come as a shock to the governing body. There were no obvious successors among the staff. The next headmistress would have to come from beyond the school, something which had not happened since 1947. The governors, now chaired by Andrew Urquhart, received 60 enquiries about the post and 34 applications. They interviewed nine applicants and drew up a shortlist of four. Their unanimous choice in November 1968 was Miss Clare Harvey.

As it turned out, the next decade proved difficult both for the school and its new headmistress. Although Miss Harvey came from a completely different background to her predecessors, she was aware of the liberal ethos of the school and was eager to widen her educational horizons. She was, however, assured by the governors at her interview that Badminton was essentially a Christian non-denominational school rather than an inter-religious school. But staff were protective of the ethos of the school which had been fostered under Miss Sanderson and from the beginning were wary of an outsider whom they feared would undermine this. The girls reacted adversely to a headmistress whose concept of discipline was rather less tolerant than they had been used to and who seemed much less approachable. Governors, torn between the headmistress whom they had appointed and the school's loyal and long-serving staff, found navigating a course between them fraught with hazards and ultimately were less than supportive of the headmistress. The situation was aggravated by the severe recession which affected many British boarding schools in the early 1970s. As numbers dropped, schools often looked overseas for pupils to fill places and keep the money coming in. Girls' schools were faced with the additional complication that many boys' schools in the same situation boosted their numbers by admitting girls to their sixth forms. At Badminton, as no doubt at other similar schools, questions began to be raised about the number and calibre of girls coming from overseas. Running an expensive institution like Badminton on a shoe-string budget added to the tensions. The cumulative effect was that by the late 1970s the school had a headmistress who regretted that she had not looked for another position earlier and a board of governors reluctant to press her to go for fear of the embarrassment it might cause the school.

Clare Harvey was the daughter of an Anglican clergyman. Taught at home until she was 15 she was the only pupil at her local school who studied for both the School Certificate and Higher School Certificate. Winning a place to read history at St Hugh's, Oxford, she agreed to take a four-year course, culminating in the Diploma of Education, since this was the only way she could receive the financial assistance to make it possible for her to afford university. The schools at which she taught were very different from and much more conventional than Badminton. After five years at St Albans High School, she spent six years as head of history at Portsmouth High School before becoming headmistress of the School of St Clare in Penzance for seven years. In common with Badminton, it was a small boarding school which prided itself then, as it does now as the co-educational Bolitho School, on a caring, family atmosphere. But in contrast with Badminton, St Clare's was a denominational school, a girls' Church of England high school founded in 1899. The chapel lay at the heart of St Clare's communal life. This aspect of the school became even more pronounced when in 1928 St Clare's became part of the Woodard Foundation, established by Nathaniel Woodard in 1848 to provide an Anglican education for the middle classes.

Clare Harvey, headmistress, 1969–81.

Clare Harvey was conscious, as she admitted in the school magazine, that she was 'a complete outsider' although she believed that she had grasped 'all that Badminton stands for and the changes that I envisage will be those of adjustment and adaptation to the demands and pressures of the 1970s while preserving the essential values of the school'. The first of those changes she pursued was the reform of the sixth form which proved to be probably the most important achievement of Miss Harvey's headship.

Making the sixth form attractive enough to persuade girls to stay on was crucial in any girls' school and particularly so in a boarding school. Miss Baker had recognised this during the inter-war years, developing the general sixth-form course to keep up numbers, regularly exhorting parents to allow their daughters to remain in school after the age of 16. Miss Sanderson too had appreciated the value of a strong sixth form and numbers had grown steadily. In the late 1960s and early 1970s this was even more important. Not only were girls drifting away to the sixth forms of boys' schools, they also had the choice of carrying on their studies at further education colleges.

School magazine cover.

Junior School, 1976.

Shortly after she arrived, the new headmistress spotted that Marlborough College, the first boys' school to admit girls in the sixth form, was already attracting fifth formers from Badminton. So it was important, as she noted in the school magazine, that sixth formers at Badminton should be seen as students, not pupils, and be given many of the concessions they would enjoy as students elsewhere, such as wearing their own clothes, having more time out of school, especially in the evenings, and taking up driving lessons. To foster more serious relationships between the sexes than was possible in the false atmosphere of an organised dance, she began experimental joint general study lessons in association with Clifton College. In particular she was very keen to improve the standard of sixth form accommodation. Initially she pressed for the conversion of Little Grange into a sixth-form house with study bedrooms for the lower sixth. But she wanted more than this. Her ambition was to build a dedicated sixth-form centre, creating a part of the school that sixth formers could call their own, which would enhance their independence.

Miss Baker had pioneered this concept in the 1930s when Cote Bank had been rented specifically as separate accommodation for the sixth form yet she was unhappy about Miss Harvey's proposal. So too was Miss Sanderson. Both of them wrote letters of protest to the governors. They disliked the idea, as did some governors, on the grounds that the separation of the sixth form from the rest of the school would create a school within a school. Miss Harvey pointed out that sixth formers would still carry out duties in school and take their meals with the rest of the girls while the new building would be more centrally situated than the existing boarding houses. The governors agreed to form a working party to assess what Badminton needed to do to retain more girls for the sixth form. When the working party reported in June 1971, it had discovered that although a third of Badminton's fifth formers were leaving the school every year to pursue their education elsewhere, this was apparently the average for similar schools within the Girls' Schools Association. Nevertheless, this was clearly undesirable and it was agreed that

The Duchess of Kent opening the new Sixth Form Centre, 1976.

The Governors, Headmistress and Staff of

BADMINTON SCHOOL

have much pleasure in inviting you to the

OPENING OF THE SIXTH FORM CENTRE

on Thursday, 14th October 1976 at 2.15 p.m.

by

HER ROYAL HIGHNESS THE DUCHESS OF KENT

R.S.V.P. on enclosed slip by 4th October.

more should be done to make the atmosphere, accommodation and curriculum in the school's sixth form more attractive. Two years later the governing body finally agreed to press ahead with a separate sixth-form centre although delays in construction meant it was not handed over until early 1976. The gestation of the project had been lengthy but this was also a time when the school was short of money. Jane Jones, for instance, who joined the staff in the early 1970s to teach domestic science, recalled how the bursar at one point told her that things were so bad that the staff were lucky to have jobs. In fact, David Sherwood, the bursar at the time, delayed his retirement to oversee the special appeal which financed the project. It was designed, like the library, by Casson, Conder & Partners, furnished by former pupils in memory of Miss Baker and officially opened on 14 October 1976 by the Duchess of Kent. The opening should have taken place in March but the Duchess had been ill; some of the sixth-form girls could not wait for the rearranged ceremony so in true Badminton style organised their own mock official opening, one girl even impersonating the Duchess. 'A bouquet of dock leaves,' wrote one girl, 'was presented to the straw-hatted substitute, who gallantly opened the heavy teak and glass door.' Inside were single or double bedrooms, with bathrooms, a common room, kitchens and a laundry room. It was a critical step forward.

Science also benefited from physical improvements, with an extension added to the science block soon after Miss Harvey took office. There were also benefits from improved timetabling of the subject, which at last allowed girls to take all three sciences at 'O' level, rather than one science subject plus combined science as in the past.

Resolving the situation surrounding resident house-mistresses proved much more difficult. The main obstacle was the lack of decent residential staff accommodation, including accommodation for married staff. Jane Jones recalled how eccentric the living arrangements were for residential staff in the early 1970s. Without any central heating, the building could be very cold so she sensibly had electric fires on in her room. Leaving her door open, the heat escaped into the entrance hall, creating such an unusual sensation that other staff seriously believed there must be a fire and spent ages searching for its source. She remembered too how all staff were paid not monthly but termly and the bursar expected her to have private means to see her through to pay day. She had to resort to help from her father. But a growing number of younger staff pressed for change with some but not complete success – the bursar agreed to pay them a monthly sum with the balance paid at the end of term.

Miss Harvey felt that without improved accommodation it would be more difficult to recruit good staff. She had seen the advantages at her previous school where, although the school was small and badly off, it had still managed to make improvements to attract better calibre resident staff. At Badminton some resident staff had to share bathrooms with the girls. It was hardly surprising that all except one housemistress in the early 1970s were non-residential. Those house-mistresses who did live out were all capable individuals but their absence after school hours left the houses in the hands of inexperienced junior matrons. This was an unsatisfactory situation which resulted in lax control in the houses and contributed towards a lack of discipline among the boarders. It was this combination to which the new headmistress was referring when, shortly after she arrived at the school, she asked the chairman of governors whether he realised that school was in chaos. He conceded that he did and promised her the governors' full support in tackling the problem.

Dining.

Miss Harvey was firmly of the view that progressiveness did not mean the complete absence of discipline. On the other hand, some within the school felt that the head herself failed to exert sufficient control. One member of staff also believed that Miss Harvey's very arrival, someone so different after the unexpected departure of her predecessor, caused some girls to behave 'as if they had lost their favourite teddy', while others believed this reaction came because Miss Harvey had misread the character of the school. In the past some misdemeanours had gone unpunished. The head had to act to prevent girls from going on to the Downs during their free periods, unaware of the potential danger to their safety. Then she felt compelled to expel two popular girls who had been out of school overnight. The incident brought unwelcome newspaper headlines and caused equal consternation within the school. Many girls in the fifth year believed the girls in question had been harshly treated and about half the year did not come back to the school after 'O' levels. Some staff too felt that the case had been badly handled. Although the headmistress believed this illustrated her point about the need to appoint more resident house-mistresses, she made little headway with the governing body which was more intent on keeping a careful watch over the

In the 21st century, Science is a core subject in the curriculum.

school's finances. By 1981 her only success had been the creation of one flat. By then the headmistress, whose concerns about pastoral care had been echoed by the school inspectors in 1980, had improved the standard of matrons and was hoping to create a system of year tutors.

The financial pressure on the school was acute. Badminton would always welcome girls from overseas – this would apply just as much to the school in the 21st century as it would to the years under Miss Baker and Miss Sanderson for they brought a cherished diversity to the school and Miss Harvey was keen to continue this tradition. But during the 1970s, during the severe economic recession, British boarding schools, suffering from a drop in domestic applicants, turned to pupils from overseas to sustain their finances. Badminton was no exception. As the chairman of governors since 1975, Sir Maurice Dorman, a former diplomat, whose wife had been to the school, had pointed out, it was critical for Badminton's financial future 'to fill all places in the school'. The headmistress believed that the school was taking in no greater proportion of overseas pupils than any other girls' school although some governors by the late 1970s were concerned that the number was too high. There was also anxiety that this

policy was not proving a financial panacea. From 335 in 1975, with record numbers in the sixth form, the roll had fallen steadily to 279 in the summer of 1981, dented partly by yet another recession. Matters were not helped when on one particular occasion, in September 1980, 26 girls expected to start at the school failed to turn up.

Until the roll began to drop, the school's overall academic performance had probably been better than during the 1960s. In the mid-1970s the 'O' level pass rate was around 80 per cent and the pass rate at 'A' level around 75 per cent. But performance began to tail off at the end of the decade and in the summer of 1981 the 'O' level pass rate had fallen to 65 per cent.

By then the relationship between head-mistress, staff and governors had almost broken down. Miss Harvey was very different in character from her predecessors, more formal, less consensual, much shyer, more distant, which masked her compassion and sense of humour. It did not help that many staff felt that it was much more difficult to see the head than it had been to see Miss Sanderson, partly because of an over-protective secretary. Miss Harvey, conversely, regretted more staff never felt able to approach her directly. This distance did not help the impression

that Miss Harvey differed from her predecessors and did not understand the school about which so many staff felt so protective. Nor did it help the head in the changes she wished to make. It also led some staff and parents to take their grievances, however small, to the governors rather than to the headmistress. This only magnified minor problems. For instance, although the head had been assured that the school ethos was underpinned by Christianity, objections were made to her reading the Lord's Prayer in assembly. The difficulty was probably that Miss Harvey's Christianity was much more overt than many in the school were prepared to accept. Among the staff and the girls there was a feeling that the headmistress, despite what she had said on her arrival, did not truly understand the school. The situation reached the stage in the late 1970s where a staff consultative committee and staff forum were created as a direct line of communication between staff and governors. One gains the unhappy impression of a gulf between the headmistress and staff and the headmistress and the governing body, with the latter ready to become involved in a mechanism which could only widen such a divide. The headmistress, particularly after the pledges of support she had received from the board on her appointment, was understandably dismayed by the attitude of the governors. It was a shock after the complete support she had enjoyed from the board of governors at her previous school. But the relationship between head and governors at Badminton was much more strained and among those who would normally have supported the head there were some who found it difficult to do so. What was really needed was firmer leadership from the governors but, as one of them later acknowledged, they were reluctant to part with the headmistress for fear of the impact on the reputation of the school. Nor was the head prepared to resign – with hindsight, she believed that she should have done so once she realised how little help she felt she received from the governors but she always felt she must get things right first. By 1979 things were getting out of hand. The headmistress's proposal to create year tutors was opposed by the house-mistresses who demanded that the issue should be discussed at an extraordinary meeting of the staff consultative committee. The two sides had reached an impasse and a resolution came only when Miss Harvey was appointed as headmistress of St Mary's Hall, Brighton, in 1981.

School, 1976.

PURPOSE AND VISION
1981–1997

Badminton had lost its confidence. There was a danger that the distinct reputation the school had developed over so many years would be lost. After the stand-off which had neutered leadership and almost paralysed progress during the previous decade, it also needed to be brought up to date. Restoring confidence, reviving the Badminton ethos and modernising the school – these were all tasks that faced the new head. The governors, under the chairmanship of E E Sabben-Clare, made a startling choice – they appointed as Badminton's seventh head the first man to hold the post.

Clifford Gould had been educated at Haileybury, Trinity College, Dublin, and King's College, London. Starting his teaching career at Glastonbury secondary modern school, he went on to teach in a wide variety of schools, from Bedales and Frensham Heights, schools perhaps even more progressive in their outlook than Badminton, to more traditional schools, such as the City of London and Latymer Upper. At Frensham, where he became deputy head and also took charge of a girls' boarding house, he and his wife, Patricia, helped to revive a failing school. They made a formidable partnership and their experience would prove invaluable at Badminton where they arrived with their young family in the autumn of 1981. Gould also became only the second married head of the school since Mrs Badock more than a century

before. This seemed particularly appropriate when the majority of staff at any school were also married and with families of their own.

Clifford Gould gave the school the confident leadership and sense of direction it was crying out for. When he told staff that he failed to understand why the school's academic results had been so poor, they applauded him. It was a point he repeated in the article he wrote for the school magazine. He knew that Badminton had always welcomed able girls willing to challenge what others said and to think for themselves and he wanted this to carry on. He stressed the importance of service and responsibility. He believed boarding, whatever difficulties it may have encountered, remained central to the future of the school. Like his predecessors, he believed in the value of culture and extra-curricular activities

Clifford Gould, headmaster, 1981–97.

transformed the outlook of everyone within the school. He shared with Miss Baker and Miss Sanderson the knack of allowing staff considerable freedom while remaining firmly in control. As a result he could take staff with him in the decisions he made. The staff consultative committee was sidelined and faded away. He was able to implement the changes in pastoral care previously advocated by Miss Harvey, with the appointment of year heads and form tutors. In his belief that teaching at the school was sacrosanct, he abolished the half-day off most staff had previously enjoyed. No longer was the teaching day interrupted for the sake of school trips and other activities. He also adopted the principle in appointing staff that every one of them should be a better teacher than he was himself.

His forthright leadership, shrewd decisions and strong support of teaching led to the reinvigoration and renewed commitment of staff. The governing body was clear that it wanted academic excellence while providing every girl with the support she needed to find her own niche in life and the girls too responded to the zeal of their new head. Changes included a greater concentration on fewer 'O' levels, creating more time per subject and smaller classes, and the restructuring of the school day so that the first half was devoted entirely to teaching. All girls were at last required to study science to 'O' level. The result was that academic results improved almost out of recognition in a very few years. Within two years the pass rate at both 'A' and 'O' level had risen from 65 per cent to 82 per cent. By the end of the 1980s, as GCSEs and the national curriculum appeared, heralding almost unceasing change in the world of education, 90 per cent of girls were passing 'A' levels, with 48 per cent achieving grades A or B, and 96 per cent were passing GCSEs, 56 per cent at grade A. This outstanding achievement proved a revelation to the rest of the independent sector when school league tables first began appearing in the early 1990s. In 1993 with a pass rate at 'A' level of 98 per cent (65 per cent at A or B) and of 99 per cent at GCSE (60 per cent at grade A), Badminton found itself one of the top 50 schools in the country. Those who still perceived the school as a 'dame school' were astounded.

in widening educational horizons. 'Have you ever heard,' he asked, 'of an artist or a musician who wants to build a nuclear arsenal?' His concluding remarks could also easily have been written by Miss Baker: 'I would like Badminton to be a happy school and I think mostly it is: it is, however, one of the ironies of life that no one ever finds happiness by pursuing it. Happiness follows from leading a busy life and being self-fulfilled, so that is where my priorities lie'.

He was, remembered one member of staff, 'an absolute dynamo'. Where his predecessor had rarely been seen around the school, he had the habit, as had Miss Baker, of suddenly appearing in places where he was least expected. He resurrected the practice of taking his morning break with the rest of the staff, he participated in the annual staff entertainments (once notably appearing as Snow White), and he was a constant spectator at school matches. His own lively personality infected those around him and

Collaboration is seen as a valuable skill for life.

commitment and hard work is rewarded with first class teaching and a wide range of extra curricular activities'. While this had probably always been the case at Badminton, the difference accentuated by Clifford Gould was that the school had the highest expectations of every girl; in the past, as already noted, even the sixth form had been divided between those considered capable of higher exams and those who were not. By the time Gould left the school in 1997 girls from Badminton were achieving a success rate of 100 per cent in both exams.

The school's performance by comparison with others also came as something of a surprise to staff. One teacher recalled that 'we were amazed that we were doing so well'. She attributed this to various reasons – the calibre of teaching, the generous staffing, the small class sizes – but also to the fact that the girls led such busy lives that they had to get the balance right between work and other activities. The head pointed out that the school emphasised 'the balanced day where the

And the school had done this while continuing to admit girls covering a wide ability range. Clifford Gould told parents that year that the results had been achieved 'without being narrowly selective in our intake and by creating a climate in which

107

Harp practice.

Sir Michael Tippett opens new music school, 1983.

academic curriculum is pursued in parallel with the creative arts and music and sport'. Under Richard Thorn and his staff, musical participation rose steadily so that by the late 1980s four out of every five girls were taking instrumental tuition, there were three orchestras, four choirs and 47 ensembles. Christopher Francis, who had succeeded Muriel de Ville and would take over the department from Thorn on his retirement in 1993, instituted tours overseas with the choir and chamber orchestra. A new music school was opened by Sir Michael Tippett in 1983. One of the highlights of this period was the visit to Badminton of a party from a Leningrad music school in October 1990. This proved to be a revelation for Badminton's girls. No sooner were the Russians off the bus from the airport than they began practising and their talent inspired the girls whom they played alongside to greater heights. Soviet communism had not yet collapsed and the party were loaded down for their return journey with electrical goods, tobacco and sweets. There were more school drama productions than ever

Production of
The Crucible, 2004.

The new indoor swimming pool is a far cry from its 'sheep-dip' predecessor.

A hockey game today.

before, from Shakespeare to *Oh! What A Lovely War*. Although sport was never the school's strong point, partly because of its size, Badminton did produce a county championship hockey team, a new swimming pool was built to replace the aged 'sheep dip', and more individual sports, including fencing, were introduced. Girls also had an increasing choice of other interests. These ranged from subjects introduced to expand the sixth-form general studies course, such as child development, self-defence and first aid, to debating, pottery and the Christian Forum. One innovation which came rather later to Badminton than other schools was the Duke of Edinburgh Award Scheme, introduced in 1993 under Miss Spanner.

Badminton's characteristic internationalism was reinvigorated. The school was a pioneering member of the European Youth Parliament (EYP), one of the few schools to compete to represent the United Kingdom when the EYP was formed in 1988. The headmaster noted that this seemed to him to be 'entirely in keeping with Badminton's international tradition and reputation, and a perfect example of how we expect to educate girls

Canoeing is a popular option for sixth formers preparing for their Gold Duke of Edinburgh Award.

to take their place in the world with some real sense of purpose and vision'. Badminton's participation, initiated through a sixth-form English teacher, Leslie Drew, stimulated interest in the EYP in other United Kingdom schools which Patricia Gould took the lead in co-ordinating. Girls began to take a lively interest in the United Nations through the United Nations Association, the successor to Miss Baker's beloved League of

National Youth
Parliament Video.

School magazine cover.

were the youngest there by a long way. In 1988, when Andrew Urquhart retired from the governing body after 40 years, he established with his brother Brian a fund which for several years financed a biennial lecture held in Bristol on international themes. The first speaker was Sir Sonny Ramphal, the Commonwealth Secretary-General, in 1989. The fund was later used to make travel bursaries available for girls at the school. Themed international food nights, with the girls taking over the kitchens, were introduced, reflecting the multi-cultural com-position of the school population, and were very popular, coming to an end under the burden of health and safety regulations.

With a return to prosperity in the United Kingdom during the 1980s and 1990s, barring a recession in the late 1980s and early 1990s, combined with the publicity given to academic results through league tables, there was a rising demand for places at the school. When he arrived, Clifford Gould had been particularly concerned that the composition of the international section of

Nations Union. They attended the International Model UN at The Hague and when a party of fourth years turned up to the UN Association Study Day on Conflict Resolution in 1994, they

'... to educate girls to take their place in the world with some real sense of purpose and vision'

the school was dominated by pupils from just one African country. A greater number of applications made it possible for the school to ensure that there was a better cosmopolitan mix among overseas girls. The head also made sure that Badminton developed closer relationships with feeder schools in the United Kingdom. The idea of taking part in the Conservative government's Assisted Places Scheme was discussed several times but always rejected. At one governors' meeting concern among some governors was recorded that as fees began to rise Badminton might 'come to be regarded as a school exclusively for the rich'. It was important to make sure that the school tried as far as it could to offer bursaries and scholarships in deserving cases. Rising numbers, bringing in increased revenue, made this possible. From 269 pupils in 1982, the school had grown to 320 in 1985 and 355 by 1990. The sixth form in particular was expanding as every year a higher proportion of fifth-form girls decided to stay on. In 1990 the

senior school contained 300 girls, 75 per cent being boarders, and the Junior School 55 girls, 40 per cent being boarders. In the senior school 20 per cent of boarders had families living or working overseas and five per cent of all girls came from overseas. Eighteen scholarships, for academic talent, music, art and all-round ability, had been awarded in the previous year. By the time Clifford Gould left in the spring of 1997, there were 370 girls at Badminton.

The Junior School became an important contributor towards the rising number of girls. The environment of the school had been transformed under the leadership of Marilyn Lane from 1977 who, with her staff, had created, recorded the school magazine, 'a much warmer and more stimulating atmosphere in which every girl could blossom'. It became much more attractive to parents and this development continued under Ann Lloyd, who took over as head in January 1989. She recalled the magical

Acorns' nativity play 2006.

Opening of new science laboratories, 1988.

redecoration and refurbishment, and then on the development of new improved facilities to meet changing parental expectations. With the support of the governing body under Mrs Pat Stone, who became chairman in 1985, and the bursars, Major Gerard Cox until his departure in 1992 and Rodney Goodwin thereafter, the head oversaw the construction of a series of new buildings. Early on these included the music school and the modern swimming pool. While the latter was being built, the bursar, Major Cox, recorded in all sincerity that the presence of so many men caused enough anxiety to consider whitewashing the windows in the science block and the gym which overlooked the site. New science and technology facilities were opened in 1988, two new tennis courts were added in 1989, a design workshop was completed in 1990 and a striking art and design centre established in 1994. The latter was opened by Dame Iris Murdoch, the school's Visitor, in May that year. By then the renovation programme had almost been completed, covering the classrooms, the boarding houses, theatre and gym. The final project, the overhaul of the kitchens in Northcote, was achieved in 1995. The results revealed just how different expectations had become. At Open

moments of having young girls boarding at the school, when, for instance, they would come down in their pyjamas in the evenings to watch chickens hatching. But boarding for children under 11 was becoming less popular for a variety of factors – the recessionary blip of the late 1980s made parents reconsider the cost of a boarding education, social trends made parents increasingly likely to keep their children at home while they were young and, in relation to overseas pupils, fewer families were posted abroad and, for those who did, overseas schools were being established. But as the number of boarders fell, the number of day girls steadily rose. At the same time, in response to demand from parents, the school began to admit younger girls. This group of four to seven-year-olds, known as the 'Acorns', began with just six youngsters in the early 1990s. By 1997, the 23 'Acorns' accounted for the growth in the Junior School to 75 pupils.

The school's expansion beyond the record numbers achieved in Miss Sanderson's day placed pressure on existing accommodation. But more girls also brought in more revenue. The school was able to spend money on a backlog of maintenance,

The Creative Arts Centre.

A sixth form study/bedroom today.

Day in 1992 the head remarked how one former pupil said the only privacy she ever had as a boarder was when she retreated to the lavatory with a book. He pointed out that most fifth years now enjoyed single or double bedrooms and all sixth years had single or double study bedrooms. When the Girls' School Association carried out a Quality Management Audit at the school in 1994, it was concluded that the school's facilities were either good or excellent and that every department was well equipped.

The audit summed up just how far the school had travelled since the early 1980s. There were bouquets for the curriculum, for extra-curricular activities, for pastoral care, for the staff and for the pupils. The inspectors concluded that the girls were 'articulate, friendly and argumentative, well motivated and well behaved, with appropriate exuberance: and outstandingly so'. There was no reference to any distinction between boarders and day girls which in the past had been a bone of contention for some day girls who felt swamped by a sea of boarders. In the 1990s, just as in the past, one of the attractions for day girls and their parents was the boarding ethos of the school with

Juniors in their dormitory and selecting cake at teatime.

Playing in the
'rough patch'.

Fun in the snow.

how can I solve it?' This sounds so very like the Badminton of Miss Baker.

In the way that staff perceived their head, Clifford Gould also appeared to share many of the characteristics of the school's most famous head – like Miss Baker, he was very clear about what he wanted, he was highly visible, he knew the girls, he was supportive of his staff, he had a sharp tongue at times and did not suffer fools gladly. Some considered him to be over controlling and unable to delegate. He saw himself as a benevolent autocrat, granting staff freedom within agreed parameters. The success of the school during the 1980s and 1990s he attributed to the fact that both staff and girls appreciated that they were valued, producing improved results all-round. With a content governing body, a happy staff and happy pupils, the school became successful because it was effectively governed by consent. All the machinations that had gone on in the 1970s became unnecessary and irrelevant.

its extensive range of after-school activities. The business of life at the school was reflected in the way many things, even among staff, were always done at the last minute – the name 'Badminton time' was coined for this phenomenon. One newcomer to the staff in 1992 found that the girls and staff took the approach, 'here is a problem,

School photo, 1994.

'There is a real sense in the school that people are valued for themselves'

Gould felt at one with the traditions of Badminton. He told parents that the school was defined by 'a wonderful absence of humbug. There is a real sense in the school that people are valued for themselves'. He continued that 'when you get unanimity of purpose and consistent attitudes, pupils know where they are and life can be relatively free of pettiness and hassle'. This created a fundamental honesty which he illustrated by the story of a 50p coin found in a corridor and taped to a notice board with a note asking anyone who had lost it to claim it – it was still there three days later and was added to the school's charity collections. He considered it irrelevant to be asked whether he believed in God or not, as one governor did; he was sure that the school's approach to spiritual matters encompassed, as it always had, those of every faith or none, and he fought hard to make sure that this remained the case. He appreciated the more personal way in which moral guidance was promoted at the school without being dogmatic or repressive; he was in fact describing the perpetuation at Badminton of the Quaker approach first adopted by Miss Baker. He recognised as Miss Baker had the dichotomy between educating 'like-minded, rather exclusive pupils living in a rarified atmosphere' while 'encouraging access to outside influences and the popular culture which can be so threatening to those very values we cherish'. So he too, like Miss Baker, urged girls to appreciate their position of privilege and reminded them that they had 'a duty to use their talents and skills to create economic and cultural prosperity for the benefit of *all* the people, not just their own narrow circle'.

Whether or not the head was autocratic, the staff believed that he was. And the unwitting result was that the head found that the staff came to believe that his way was the only one. He stumbled on this realisation after returning from a sabbatical in the early 1990s to find that absolutely nothing had been done differently in his absence. People were asking themselves, 'What would the head think?' Gould considered himself redundant, irretrievably stuck on a pedestal. He decided that in the interests of the school the time had come for a change at the top. With several key staff due to retire in the late 1990s, he felt that he should step down in time to give his successor a free hand in their appointment. He announced to the governors in March 1996 that he wished to go at the end of the next academic year. As it turned out, because of impending changes governing the early retirement scheme for teachers, he had to leave a term early, in the spring of 1997.

Clifford Gould in the Staff Revue, 1983.

THIS KIND OF MAGIC
1997 Onwards

Jan Scarrow took up her post as headmistress of Badminton in September 1997. Educated at a co-educational grammar school in the West Riding of Yorkshire, she had graduated in history from Manchester and taken her Post-Graduate Certificate of Education at Sheffield. She had not planned to teach but discovered, when coaching fellow undergraduates in Latin, that she had a natural talent for the profession. She taught in several large comprehensive schools in Yorkshire and Lancashire before moving south. Her first post in the independent sector was at Stonar School, a girls' day and boarding school, founded in Sandwich in 1895, which had relocated to Wiltshire in 1939. Here she was head of history and head of sixth form, which latter role she ultimately combined with being deputy head and later acting head. Stonar was the first all-girls' school in which she had taught and the experience converted her to the advantages of single-sex education. She also served on the executive of the Secondary Heads Association where she had the advantage of seeing many different styles of leadership.

Jan Scarrow was less extrovert than her predecessor, with a quiet sense of humour, but this masked a similar decisiveness and sense of purpose. She was more attuned to the way the world of education had developed since the late 1980s, not just in terms of the work needed to devise the necessary policies governing school life but also in her awareness of the increasingly competitive nature of independent education and the need to promote the school more effectively. This, together with her caring attitude towards those in her charge, helped her to develop a very clear view of the future of the school. She realised Badminton could not afford to stand still and she also realised that there was still undeveloped potential within the school.

Compared with her predecessor, she was much more *primus inter pares*, more open, more willing to delegate, happy for others to come forward with ideas. This was clear from one of the first decisions she made. In her second term she created the first effective senior management team in the school's history. This comprised the deputy head, the bursar and the head of the Junior School.

Jan Scarrow, headmistress.

Her first deputy was Stella Berkeley, who had succeeded Janet Hughes as deputy in 1984. She had served at the school since 1970, and was head of modern languages for more than 20 years. Her role as deputy had been limited under Clifford Gould and she found her time under Jan Scarrow to be much more fulfilling. When she retired in 2000, Caroline Bateson was appointed as her successor. She had joined the school in 1986 as a history teacher, later taking over the department, and eventually became head of year 11. On her departure in 2006 as headmistress of Redland High School, Valerie Drew took over the post. Jan Scarrow further strengthened the senior management of the school by establishing the posts of head of sixth form, head of boarding and, much later, director of studies. Judith Wakeham, who had been head of English since 1989, became the first head of sixth form, and Carole Stoker the first head of boarding. Dr Christopher Enos would be appointed director of studies in 2006. Spreading responsibility among staff also lay behind the head's decision in 2001 to give departmental heads the freedom of managing their own budgets. Staff also benefited from the pay scale specific to Badminton which was adopted in 2000.

One of the first priorities in the school development plan, another innovation for Badminton, which the head presented to the governors, was the redevelopment of facilities for the sixth form. This was even more important for the future of the school in such a competitive educational environment. Jan Scarrow wanted to bring all sixth formers under one roof again (several were living in an annexe at Cote Grange Cottage) as well as improve what was on offer for both boarders and day girls. As they would demonstrate constantly throughout the next decade, the governors were very supportive of the headmistress's initiative. Pat Stone, who had given such positive leadership as chairman from 1985 and had been responsible for appointing Jan Scarrow, stepped down in 1998 and her place was taken by Richard Hodder-Williams, professor of politics and pro-vice chancellor at Bristol University, the second professor from the University to hold the post. He proved to be equally supportive and the school would benefit from his wisdom, enthusiasm and experience over the next nine years. The support of the governors

Sixth formers playing chess.

The Junior School Hall.

first time in 2000 and translate into reality the head's vision of the centre as a bridge for girls between school life and university.

A whole series of improvements followed across the school in subsequent years as part of a rolling programme which was kept constantly under review. In 1998 Little Grange, the former home of 'The Powers', was updated and became an annexe for the music department while the Junior School hall was refurbished. A review of boarding was carried out which at first considered the creation of vertical boarding houses to establish better relationships among the girls but this proved impractical in the absence of any purpose-built boarding houses. Instead, the focus became how the boarding needs of particular age groups could be met. There was a more rational distribution of girls of different ages across the existing boarding accommodation which was upgraded during the summer of 2000. With the end of boarding at 15 Downs Road, all boarders were housed in buildings within the school grounds, where accommodation within

allowed the construction of the new £1.5 million sixth-form centre to proceed in November 1998. With more common rooms, study bedrooms, seminar rooms and improved residential accommodation for staff, the building was completed within a year. This helped the school to increase sixth-form numbers to over 100 for the

A high standard of art is achieved by many girls.

Northcote and School House was modernised. Junior boarders were transferred from the Junior School to Cote Grange Cottage which also became the boarding house for years 7 and 8. At the same time girls in their GCSE year were given dedicated study facilities and assigned to tutor groups to support them during their exam year. All these developments received the approval of those statutory bodies charged, under the recently passed Children's Act, with responsibility for assessing the suitability of accommodation and facilities in boarding schools. Other developments in pastoral care included the review and formalisation of a wide range of policies. The most recent enhancement of the school's boarding provision has been the completion during 2008 of Badminton's first purpose-built boarding house for girls other than sixth formers.

The improvement in conditions for staff continued in 2002 when more common-room space was provided, along with better IT facilities and expanded work areas. A generous parent had made a substantial donation for the purpose of improving the school's computer network and this developed further under Jan Scarrow who also appointed the school's first dedicated IT technician. The development plan had also identified the need for better sporting facilities,

The Creative Arts Centre.

something also favoured by staff. In particular a badly needed all-weather surface to overcome the constant problems of waterlogged pitches was completed in 2004. This is also available for community use when the school does not need it. In 2006 the Sanderson Room, named after the former headmistress, was extended to include a recording studio while the ceramics, textiles and jewellery areas within the art block were upgraded. Alongside all this ran a maintenance programme, overseen by the governors' property

A wide range of art on display at an Open Day.

Playing the flute.

Top: A singing rehearsal.

Bottom: *The Pied Piper of Hamelin*, 2005.

committee, which dealt with matters such as the refurbishment of the drawing room, fiction library and school hall and the improvement of the Junior School classrooms. The Junior School itself, under the continued leadership of Ann Lloyd, became almost entirely a day school and, with around a hundred pupils, took as its aim the provision of a similar all-round education for girls under 11 as enjoyed by their seniors.

While Jan Scarrow and her team were embarking on the modernisation of the school inside and out, Badminton continued to sustain outstanding academic results. This was helped through the recruitment of able and talented staff who are also hard working and committed to teaching in the demanding environment of a

boarding school. The curriculum was overhauled and extended (Mandarin, for instance, was offered), information technology was improved, and whiteboards and overhead projectors were added to classrooms. All these things have improved the quality of learning. The pass rate over the last decade for both GCSEs and 'A' levels has been almost 100 per cent, while more than half in 2007 achieved A* grades at GCSE and almost 80 per cent A grades at 'A' level, placing the school among the top 30 in the country. Yet as Jan Scarrow told parents in 2007, 'we avoid a frenzied and superficial tick-list approach to education'. This is apparent in many aspects of the school which would meet the approval of both Miss Baker and Miss Sanderson. So there is no honours board, there are few prizes, there are no form orders and results are never published within the school. All this complements the work of the staff who year in, year out, succeed in nurturing their pupils, allowing them the space to discover themselves during the most formative years of their lives. And, as the deputy head has pointed out, for Badminton girls, 'it's cool to work'.

Broadening the girls' horizons continues outside the classroom where they are engaged in just as wide a variety of activities as ever. Music, art and drama are all stronger at Badminton than they have ever been. There are almost innumerable opportunities for travel. In 2007 destinations included Berlin, Paris, Washington, New York and Iceland. Many of these opportunities relate to exchange visits, sustaining the international element in the school's make-up. So Badminton has links with Nanyang High School in Singapore, St Anne's College, Hilton in South Africa, and, from 2008, the Presbyterian Ladies' College in Sydney, Australia. This is also a feature of the curriculum, notably in history and politics, although the Marxist slant on world events is no longer fashionable. Religious education continues to foster tolerance of the views of others with girls visiting synagogues, hearing lectures on Islam and attending conferences on philosophy. Every year one week in March is dedicated to fund-raising, organised by the school houses, which in 2007 raised more than £1,000 to support a school in Malawi. The girls raise money for a wide number of charities, from Children in Need and the Operation Christmas Child Appeal to Dr Barnado's and UNICEF. Some of these activities are run in conjunction with boys from Queen Elizabeth Hospital (QEH), a leading independent boys' school in Bristol. The girls have also had joint trips with QEH boys, including skiing in Canada and a regular conference on student politics held in Paris. The head acknowledges that she is often asked whether the school would admit boys. The response she gave to parents in 2004 was clear: 'girls are our priority – their needs, their development, their aspirations are our concern. We are passionate about educating girls. Our skill, our strength, our purpose and our expertise is in developing confident and competent young women'. But senior girls enjoy an increasing degree of freedom and are able to lead independent social lives while the self-contained school site, situated so close to the heart of a thriving and cosmopolitan city yet well away from it, offers the assurance of security to parents. The latter are encouraged to allow their daughters to take responsibility for their own actions rather than intervene too readily on their behalf. The school believes that if parents have made the decision to send their daughters away to Badminton, then they should expect the school to take care of them.

School trip to Barbados, 2004.

School trip to Paris for a politics conference.

Sixth formers walking up the school drive.

All these factors have made Badminton highly attractive. The school made sure in a more and more competitive market that it capitalised on these qualities. Felicity Hazell, the school registrar, led the initial marketing of the school and, after her departure, a dedicated marketing director, Henrietta Lightwood, was appointed to the senior management team and the school was able to increase numbers even beyond the record achieved under Clifford Gould. In 2008 the school included more than 300 girls in the senior school and nearly 120 in the Junior School. Almost all the boarders are now within the senior school where they make up almost two-thirds of the girls and where boarding accommodation is full. Most boarders are drawn from areas within an easy drive of the school, which includes not only Gloucestershire, Wales and the West Country but also parts of London, straight down the M4 motorway. The school also has girls from 37 different countries, such as Mexico and Kenya, the Ukraine and Kazakhstan, Kenya and Nigeria, Thailand and China, Spain and Germany. The sixth form has now grown to 110 pupils. The school could be more academically selective but, says Jan Scarrow, Badminton prefers to admit a more diverse range of interesting girls. Rather than

exam results, Badminton is more interested in offering girls an all-round education aimed at making them, as Miss Baker intended, citizens of the world. To widen access, the school has recently reviewed its scholarships and bursaries and also offers some 100 per cent foundation awards.

The school values too its links with former pupils. One of Jan Scarrow's aims has been to strengthen the involvement of the Old Badmintonians' Association within the school. Old Badmintonians can now keep in touch with each other more easily through the 'webalumnus' system administered from school by the OBA membership secretary. All girls automatically become members of the OBA on leaving school. The head and the chairman of governors have hosted several receptions in London for former pupils and in 2000 a Millennium reception was held at the school. Similarly, a close relationship has been forged with parents who have been encouraged to take part in planning social and educational events at the school. At the beginning of 2008 the post of chairman of governors will be held for the first time in Badminton's history by an Old Badmintonian, Alison Bernays, who also perpetuates the links between the school and the

In the classroom.

Urquhart family as the daughter of Andrew Urquhart. The headmistress has also fostered parental support and commitment towards the school, reinvigorating the parents' association, now renamed 'Involved', working hard to bring parents together socially within the school, facilitating the dissemination of information not only between school and parents but also between parents themselves. All this work aimed at former pupils and parents is all part of the head's concept of an integrated school community, be it boarders or day girls, parents or former pupils, teaching and ancillary staff or governors.

Badminton, reflected Richard Hodder-Williams at one open day, has 'this kind of magic'. The Independent Schools Inspectorate was bowled over by it during a visit in February 2003. They had high praise for almost every aspect of the school, from relationships among pupils and between pupils and staff to pastoral care, boarding provision and academic performance. They concluded that 'this is a very good school with many strengths and very few weaknesses'. The school today still reflects many of the qualities which made it so distinctive in the past but it has succeeded in adapting those to meet the needs of pupils and parents in the 21st century. This is depicted in the experiences of recent leavers. One girl, who left in 2003, described an ethos Miss Baker would have recognised. Discipline was based on mutual respect. Staff were disappointed when girls misbehaved and girls were ashamed of letting staff down. She reflected that, as in the 1930s and 1950s, some rules might seem petty but if you can abide by the smaller rules, you are less likely to succumb to the temptation of making bigger mistakes. The small size of the school, she felt, helped to create a friendly and lively

'It made me feel I can express myself without worrying about what other people think, that I can speak my own mind without being shot down'

atmosphere and build good relationships between pupils and staff. Above all, she felt that the school gave her confidence. A shy girl, she was almost overwhelmed when she first joined because she found her peers so loud – 'every single one of them had their own personality'. 'It made me feel I can express myself without worrying about what other people think, that I can speak my own mind without being shot down.' Another senior member of staff also commented that in parallel with the encouragement to achieve, there is still a philosophy of 'almost self second' – as a member of a global community, you have a responsibility towards everyone else in it. A philosophy first established at Badminton in the early part of the 20th century is just as important one hundred years later. Perhaps Jan Scarrow found the key to the school's success in maintaining a distinctive character in an age when many schools seem so much like one another. In looking back at her predecessors she realised, she said, that above all 'the approach to educating girls at Badminton had always been driven by conviction'. And she, also like those who have gone before her, remains absolutely dedicated, along with governors and staff, to ensuring Badminton continues now as in the past to 'develop young women who in every sense are citizens of the world'.

Head girls.

Scenes from school life, 2008.

INDEX

Italics indicate pictures.